.45

The Living Body

CHARLES HERBERT BEST

C.B.E., M.A., M.D., D.SC. (LOND.), F.R.S., F.R.C.P. (CANADA)
Professor and Head of Department of Physiology,
Director of the Banting-Best Department of
Medical Research, University of Toronto

NORMAN BURKE TAYLOR

V.D., M.D., F.R.S. (CANADA), F.R.C.S. (EDIN.),
F.R.C.P. (CANADA), M.R.C.S. (ENG.), L.R.C.P. (LOND.)
Formerly Professor of Physiology, University of Toronto, and
Professor of the History of Medicine and Medical Literature,
University of Western Ontario, London, Canada

► *The Living Body*

A TEXT IN HUMAN PHYSIOLOGY

Fourth Edition

HOLT, RINEHART AND WINSTON
New York · Chicago · San Francisco · Toronto

PREFACE TO THE FOURTH EDITION

THIS EDITION has been given a new look. The broader and longer pages of the present format, giving the book a more convenient size and shape, make for easier reading and enable the illustrations to be shown to better advantage. A number of new figures have been added to this edition and many of the old ones redrawn. Line drawings have replaced most of the photographs of earlier editions, which in many instances had not lent themselves to clear reproduction.

Nearly six years have passed since the last revision. During that time a mountainous volume of technical articles has appeared in journals devoted to physiological subjects; but from this mass of scientific writings relatively little that is appropriate for inclusion in an elementary text can be drawn. Only matter whose truth has been well established and has passed from the field of controversy is within the horizon of a junior book such as this. Anything less firmly based would require rather lengthy discussion with weighing of the evidence, pro and con, which would be both irksome and confusing to the junior student. Apart from these reservations the book has been brought thoroughly up to date. Readers interested in more specialized aspects of the subject should consult advanced texts.

A rather comprehensive pronouncing glossary of over twenty pages has been appended to the text of this edition (pp. 681–704). For the benefit of those interested in the origins and the exact meanings of words—an engaging subject—classical derivations have been included. The glossary has also been used to give brief descriptions, mere thumb-nail sketches, of certain phases of the subject, which being a little above the general level of instruction in the book, have been omitted therefrom.

N. B. T.

21 Ardwold Gate
  Toronto
    March, 1958

PREFACE TO THE THIRD EDITION

THE DYNAMIC nature of physiological study, though burdensome to those who must revise its textbooks, is one of its chief fascinations. The subject is never static but forever changing, always flowing and restless with fresh discoveries and new conceptions which sweep away without regret many old ideas and theories. The rapid advances made by physiology and the contributory sciences since the last revision of this book have made necessary many changes and additions. Two new Chapters (1 and 5) have been written. Chapter 1 has been devoted to "Elementary Physical and Chemical Principles," and should be a help to those readers who have had no instruction in the basic sciences; the use of radioactive isotopes in physiological research, and in the treatment of disease has been lightly touched on. In Chapter 5, entitled "The Defensive Mechanisms of the Body against Disease and Injury," the processes of immunity and related questions, the use of the "sulfa" drugs and antibiotics, as well as the problems of shock, anaphylaxis, and allergy, have been outlined. Chapter 14, dealing with "The Physiology of Reproduction," has been enlarged in scope by the addition of several new sections and the expansion of some of the old ones. All this new material together with that required to bring the text up to date has led inevitably to an increase in the size of the book. But the increased size is due also, and in large measure, to new illustrations, the total number of figures having been raised from 283 in the last edition to 400 in the present one.

In writing upon a subject such as that of mammalian physiology, which is so largely a study of interactions and integrations of processes and systems, it is not always possible to avoid some anticipation of the reader's knowledge. An endeavor has been made to offset this tendency by providing many cross-references in the text. But this provision may sometimes be found inadequate, and readers are advised to make free use of the index which is rather comprehensive.

Much of the rewriting in this edition has been undertaken to meet the suggestions and kindly criticisms of many colleagues, to whom sincere thanks are extended. More than a few of the changes which are believed to have improved the book are due to suggestions made by Professor J. B. Stier of the University of Indiana. His interest and care in reading the second edition from cover to cover, and his comments from the view of an American teacher are gratefully acknowledged.

Recognition of the painstaking care with which Mrs. Dorothy Spicer has given her secretarial assistance in preparing the manuscript for the press is also warmly expressed.

N. B. T.

21 Ardwold Gate
    Toronto
        March, 1952

CONTENTS

Properties of Cardiac Muscle. Perfusion of the Excised Heart. The Origin and Conduction of the Heartbeat. The Action of the Heart, the Cardiac Cycle. The Opening and Closing of the Heart Valves. The Regulation of the Heart's Action. Nerve Control of the Blood Vessels. Special Features of the Circulation in Certain Parts

CHAPTER 1

Elementary Physical and Chemical Principles[1]

The elements. Substances such as pure iron, copper, gold, silver, sodium, potassium, chlorine, iodine, oxygen, hydrogen, and a great number of others which are composed entirely of but one type of particle or *atom* are called *elements*. A list of the more common elements is given in Table 1-1 (p. 2). Those composing the animal body are shown in percentages in Figure 1.1 (p. 3).

The conception of an indivisible particle of matter—the *atom* (literally that which cannot be cut or divided)—goes back to ancient Grecian times (Democritus, 600 B.C.), but its modern history starts with John Dalton (1766–1844), an English chemist.

Nevertheless, the atom is not, as was believed for so long, the ultimate particle of matter; it is composed of still more minute particles arranged within it according to a definite pattern. The simplest and lightest—the *hydrogen atom*—resembles a miniature solar system. It consists of a core or nucleus with a much smaller and lighter particle revolving around it (Fig. 1.2). All atoms of whatever kind, whether of oxygen, chlorine, iron, gold, silver, or any other element, are constructed upon an essentially similar pattern; but the particles in the central core as well as the lighter revolving particles vary in number

[1] This chapter has been written for those readers who have had no instruction in chemistry or physics. It may be omitted by others. It is offered merely as an introduction to and an aid in the understanding of subsequent chapters. Several chemical and physical principles such as hydrogen ion concentration (p. 108), osmosis (p. 64), kinetic theory and diffusion (pp. 244 and 245), the composition of the principal foodstuffs (Chaps. 8 and 9), and the actions of enzymes (p. 288), are described more appropriately in chapters dealing with subjects to which such principles are most directly applicable.

Table 1-1

Common Name of Element	Greek or Latin Name	Symbol	Atomic Weight	Atomic Number
Aluminium	Aluminium	Al	26.98	13
Antimony	Stibium	Sb	121.76	51
Arsenic	Arsenicum	As	74.91	33
Barium	Barium	Ba	137.36	56
Boron	Boron	B	10.82	5
Bromine	Bromum	Br	79.92	35
Cadmium	Cadmium	Cd	112.41	48
Calcium	Calcium	Ca	40.08	20
Carbon	Carbon	C	12.01	6
Chlorine	Chlorum	Cl	35.46	17
Cobalt	Cobaltum	Co	58.94	27
Copper	Cuprum	Cu	63.54	29
Fluorine	Fluorum	F	19.00	9
Gold	Aurum	Au	197.20	79
Helium	Helium	He	4.00	2
Hydrogen	Hydrogenium	H	1.00	1
Iodine	Iodum	I	126.91	53
Iron	Ferrum	Fe	55.85	26
Lead	Plumbum	Pb	207.21	82
Lithium	Lithium	Li	6.94	3
Magnesium	Magnesium	Mg	24.32	12
Manganese	Manganesium	Mn	54.93	25
Mercury	Hydrargyrum	Hg	200.61	80
Neon	Neon	Ne	20.18	10
Nickel	Niccolum	Ni	58.69	28
Nitrogen	Nitrogenum	N	14.00	7
Oxygen	Oxygenium	O	16.00	8
Phosphorus	Phosphoricum	P	30.97	15
Platinum	Platinum	Pt	195.23	78
Potassium	Kalium	K	39.10	19
Radium	Radium	Ra	226.05	88
Silicon	Silicon	Si	28.09	14
Silver	Argentum	Ag	107.88	47
Sodium	Natrium	Na	22.99	11
Strontium	Strontium	Sr	87.63	38
Sulfur	Sulfur	S	32.06	16
Tin	Stannum	Sn	118.70	50
Uranium	Uranum	U	238.07	92
Zinc	Zincum	Zn	65.38	30

with the different kinds of atom. The central core or nucleus of the atom contains one or more particles called *protons*. Each proton holds a positive charge of electricity, and, except in the case of the hydrogen atom, is paired with an electrically neutral particle called a *neutron*. The hydrogen atom is a single proton, unpaired with a neutron. The particle or particles revolving in one or more orbits around the nucleus of the atom are electrically negative and are called *electrons*. The chemical properties of the atom are dependent upon the

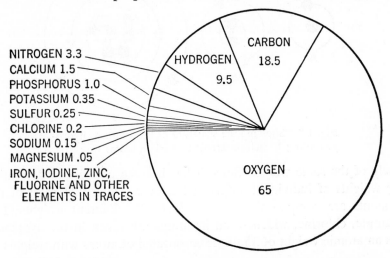

Fig. 1.1   Diagram to show the percentages of the elements composing the body.

electrons in the outer orbit. The number of protons, which as just mentioned varies with the kind of atom, is balanced by an equal number of electrons. Positive and negative charges being equal, the atom as a whole, so long as it loses none of its charges, is electrically neutral. The number of protons (or electrons) possessed by an atom is called the *atomic number*. The atomic numbers of the naturally occurring elements are from 1 (for *hydrogen*) to 92 for *uranium*. The atomic numbers for the other elements run in unbroken sequence between those two extremes.

Atomic weights. The atomic weight of an element is the weight of one of its atoms in relation to the weight of the hydrogen atom taken as 1.008. It is the weight of the smallest quantity of an element present in the molecule of a pure substance. It will be seen from Table 1-1 that the weights of the different kinds of naturally occurring atoms vary widely, *radium* (226.05) and *uranium* (238.07) being the heaviest in Table 1-1, but still heavier ones, such as *plutonium, ameri-*

cium, curium and *mendelevium,* etc., have been produced in the laboratory.

Isotopes. Until recent years it was universally believed that elements were atomically homogeneous—that its atoms were all pre-

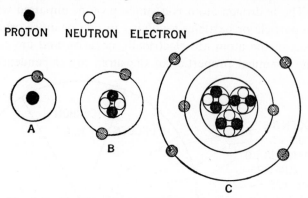

Fig. 1.2   Showing the structure of the atom. A, hydrogen atom; B, helium atom; C, carbon atom.

cisely of the same weight. Since it has become possible to determine the weights of individual atoms, it has been found that most of the elements are composed of atoms of slightly different weights. For example, chlorine, which when its atoms are taken in the aggregate has an atomic weight of 35.46, is constituted of atoms with weights of

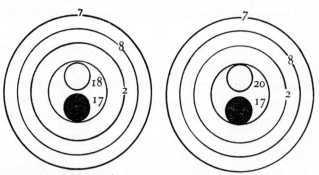

Fig. 1.3   The isotopes of chlorine. The figures refer to the numbers of protons and neutrons in the nucleus and to the electrons in the three orbits.

35 and 37, there being none having a weight of exactly 35.46. Atoms of the same element but of different atomic weights are called isotopes.

The disparity of the atomic weights of isotopes is due to their having different numbers of neutrons. Since neutrons do not carry an electric charge, the nuclear charges (protons) of isotopes are the same, or, in other words, their atomic numbers are identical. As a means of designating the different isotopes of a given element, the atomic weight is given in small figures above and to the right of the symbol for the element. Thus, the isotopes of chlorine are, Cl^{35} and Cl^{37} (Fig. 1.3). There are three isotopes of magnesium (Mg^{24}, Mg^{25}, and Mg^{26}), and three each of oxygen (O^{15}, O^{16}, O^{17}) and of hydrogen (H^1, H^2, H^3). Calcium has four isotopes (Ca^{40}, Ca^{42}, Ca^{43}, Ca^{44}). Iron also has four (Fe^{54}, Fe^{56}, Fe^{57}, Fe^{58}); zinc has five (Zn^{64}, Zn^{66}, Zn^{67}, Zn^{68}, Zn^{70}); and carbon has three (C^{12}, C^{13}, C^{14}). The proportions of the different isotopes in an element are not necessarily equal. In chlorine, for example, there is a greater proportion of the lighter isotopes (Cl^{35}) than of the heavier ones (Cl^{37}), which accounts for the atomic weight of 35.46. The proportion of each type of isotope in chlorine, however, as in other elements, remains fixed.

Radioactive isotopes. Many isotopes are radioactive like radium and uranium. That is to say, their nuclei are unstable and particles are shot out at very high velocities (20,000 to 100,000 miles per second).

Fig. 1.4   An alpha particle; it will be noted that it is of the same constitution as the helium nucleus.

The particles (see Fig. 1.4), usually referred to as "rays," consist of a group of two protons and two neutrons held together as a unit (*alpha particle* or *alpha "ray"*) and electrons (*beta "rays"*). A third type of ray with a high power of penetration is also emitted; rays of this type are known as *gamma rays* and are identical with or closely similar to hard *x-rays*.

Isotopes of various elements are now produced artificially by bombarding atoms with protons or neutrons produced by an apparatus called a *cyclotron*, developed by Dr. Lawrence of California. The high-speed projectiles penetrate the nuclei of some of the bombarded atoms; a nuclear reaction follows, and an isotope of the bombarded element, or of a newly created element, is produced. The production in this way of radioactive isotopes has been a great boon to those carrying out researches into biochemical and physiological problems. The radioactive isotope can be incorporated into a compound whose history in the body it is desired to follow. When such a compound is fed to an animal, it behaves chemically in the body as would the naturally occurring nonradioactive substance; but on account of its radioactivity it is "labeled" or "tagged" as it were, and can be detected in the body tissues or excreta by means of a Geiger counter, an instrument sensitive to the rays which the incorporated isotope emits.

Radium has long been used in the treatment of cancer and other malignant growths, the emitted rays having a destructive action upon the cancer cells, but they also destroy normal tissue and for this reason their action must be strictly localized to the diseased structure. Artificially produced radioactive isotopes are now employed for their therapeutic effects, and more especially those which have a selective action upon certain tissues, since they can be injected into the general circulation. The thyroid gland, for example, has a great affinity for iodine, and a radioactive isotope (I^{128}, I^{130}, or I^{131}) of this element concentrates its action upon thyroid tissue; it is, therefore, used in the treatment of certain types of goiter (Chap. 10). Radioactive phosphorus is attracted to and exerts its effect upon osseous tissue and is of value in the treatment of some types of bone disease.

Chemical symbols. The chemist employs a kind of shorthand language for the expression of the elemental composition of chemical substances and to indicate the character of chemical reactions. In this chemical language, the elements are designated by the first letter of their Latin names, or, when the initial letter of the names of more than one element is the same, a second letter of the name is added. Thus, F is the symbol for fluorine, but since there are a number of elements commencing with the letter C, the latter is used alone as the symbol for carbon, and copper (L. cuprum), calcium, chlorine, and cobalt are designated Cu, Ca, Cl, and Co, respectively. Similarly, while H is the symbol for hydrogen, mercury (Hydrargyrum) is represented by Hg, and helium by He (see Table 1-1).

A chemical *formula* indicates the atomic constitution of the molecules of a substance, the symbols of the elements being written in a certain conventional order (*empirical* or *molecular formula*) or according to a specific pattern which shows the spatial relationships of the atoms to one another in the molecule. The latter is called a *graphic* or *structural formula*.

An empirical formula indicates merely the number of the different kinds of atoms in the molecule. When there are more than one of the same kind of atom, a small figure is written below the symbol. Thus, sodium chloride is written NaCl, but water, which is formed by the union of two atoms of hydrogen and one of oxygen, is written H_2O. The two types of formula for the amino acid glycine are shown below:

$$C_2H_5NO_2$$

empirical formula

$$CH_2\!\!-\!\!NH_2$$
$$|$$
$$COOH$$

graphic formula

If we compare the symbols of the elements to the alphabet of ordinary language, then chemical formulas may be likened to words. Formulas written with appropriate signs $(+, -, =, \rightarrow)$ are known as equations; by this means, information is given with respect to the nature of the reactions taking place between the molecules (see below) of chemical substances when brought together. Thus, the formation of carbon dioxide by the action of hydrochloric acid on limestone (calcium carbonate) is expressed in the following equation:

$$CaCO_3 \ + \ 2HCl \ = \ CO_2 \ + \ CaCl_2 \ + \ H_2O$$

calcium   hydrochloric   carbon   calcium   water
carbonate   acid   dioxide   chloride

A molecule of calcium carbonate reacts with 2 molecules of hydrochloric acid to produce a molecule each of carbon dioxide, calcium chloride, and water. It will be noted that the two sides of the equation balance—that is, the number of calcium, carbon, hydrogen, chlorine, and oxygen atoms on the two sides are equal.

Chemical reactions–molecules. Certain atoms have an attraction or affinity for other kinds of atom, the two kinds uniting to form substances called *compounds,* which have properties quite different from those of the originally separate atoms. Common table salt, for example, which is known chemically as sodium chloride and has the formula NaCl, is formed by the union of one atom of sodium (Na) with one atom of chlorine (Cl). Sodium is a caustic solid element, highly destructive to animal and vegetable tissues; chlorine is a greenish, intensely irritating, poisonous gas; yet the compound, sodium chloride, which results from their union, is a mild harmless substance and, indeed, is indispensable for the well-being of the animal body. It is present in a concentration of about 0.6 percent in the body fluids. The particles of a compound such as sodium chloride, carbon dioxide, water, etc., are called *molecules.* Any pair or group of atoms which being united form a unit particle of a compound is so termed. The molecules of the compounds just mentioned are among the smallest and simplest known, but some molecules, such as those composing proteins, are relatively enormous, being constituted of hundreds of atoms of several different kinds. The *molecular weight* (which is arrived at by adding together the weights of the constituent atoms) of these large particles is thousands of times greater than the weight of a water molecule. The molecular weight of water (H_2O), for example, is only 18 (hydrogen 2 + oxygen 16), whereas that of certain proteins is in the neighborhood of 400,000 or more. The hydrogen molecule (H_2), for it is not only atoms of different kinds which form molecules, is the smallest and lightest of all. The atoms of nitrogen or of oxygen also combine molecules to form (N_2, O_2, and O_3).

If one wished to show graphically the great differences in size between the smallest and the largest molecules, one might represent a water molecule by a dot, then one of the largest protein molecules would require for its representation a space larger than this page. Molecules also vary in shape; some protein molecules, for example,

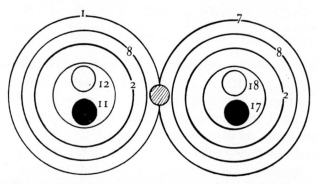

Fig. 1.5   Diagram showing the union of a sodium atom and a chlorine atom to form a molecule of sodium chloride. The figures indicate the number of protons and neutrons in the nuclei and of the electrons in the concentric orbits. The hatched circle represents the electron common to both types of atom in a molecule of sodium chloride.

such as serum albumin, are globular in form, while in others, such as muscle protein, the atoms are extended in chains to form long, elongated fiberlike molecules (see p. 362).

As implied at the beginning of this section, it is only some atoms which are capable of uniting with one another to form compounds. The attraction or affinity of one atom for another depends upon the instability of the outer orbit of electrons. For example, the number of electrons in the outer orbit of the sodium atom and of the chlorine atom render their outer orbits unstable. The former has one electron too many, the latter one too few, for stabilization. But there is always a tendency toward the stable state. This is achieved, when possible, by the sodium atom losing an electron and the chlorine atom gaining one. So then, when a sodium atom and a chlorine atom are brought together, an electron is transferred from the one (Na) to the other (Cl). When sodium chloride undergoes ionization (see p. 12) the sodium atom has one less electron than it had originally, and the chlorine atom one more. In the unionized state, the two atoms are held together, as it were, by the electron in question (Fig. 1.5).

Equivalent or combining weights. When the elements combine to form compounds, they do so in certain definite and unvarying proportions. The smallest amount in grams in which an element combines with 1 gram of hydrogen is called its *equivalent* or *combining weight.* An element also replaces 1 gram of hydrogen in a compound or combines with another element to form a compound by this same amount —its equivalent weight—or some simple *multiple* of it. The equiva-

Table 1-2

Element	Equivalent or combining weights (number of grams which combine with or replace 1 gram of hydrogen)
Calcium	20
Carbon	3
Chlorine	35.46
Magnesium	12
Nitrogen	4.67
Oxygen	8
Potassium	39.1

lent weights of a few of the commoner elements are given in Table 1-2. It will be seen by comparing Tables 1-1 and 1-2 that the atomic weight of an element is either equal to the combining weight or is a multiple of it. The equivalent weight of oxygen is 8, its atomic weight is $(8 \times 2 =) 16$; that of carbon is 3, its atomic weight is $(3 \times 4 =) 12$; the equivalent weight of nitrogen is 4.67, its atomic weight is $(4.67 \times 3 =) 14$, but the equivalent weight of chlorine and potassium are the same as their atomic weights—namely, 35.46 and 39.1 respectively.

Oxidation and reduction. When oxygen unites with another element, the compound so formed is called an *oxide,* and the process is referred to as *oxidation.* If the reverse action takes place—namely, a compound loses oxygen—the substance is said to be *reduced* and the process is known as *reduction.* But the *loss* of hydrogen from a compound is also called oxidation, and the *addition* of hydrogen to a compound is called reduction.

A compound of an element with hydrogen and oxygen is called a *hydroxide.* Iron rusts when exposed to moisture and air, the rust being a hydroxide of iron (ferric hydroxide). Many metals and other substances form oxides or hydroxides when exposed, the oxygen being derived from the atmosphere. The carbon in substances such as wool, coal, etc., undergoes oxidation during combustion, carbon dioxide (CO_2) being produced and given up to the atmosphere. The carbon of our food also undergoes oxidation in the body, the carbon dioxide so formed being exhaled in the breath. But many substances in the tissues undergo oxidation, not by the addition of oxygen, but by the loss of hydrogen brought about through the action of specific dehydrogenating enzymes (dehydrogenases).

Besides the combination of atoms with the formation of compounds, which so far has been chiefly dealt with, two other types of chemical reaction remain to be described: namely, the breakdown of molecules into smaller groups of atoms or into individual atoms—*decomposition* —and the disruption of the molecules of two or more compounds, followed by the union of the liberated atoms or groups of atoms in new combinations. This reaction is known as *double decomposition*.

The chemical reaction known as *double decomposition* can be illustrated by changes occurring when HCl is mixed with a solution of sodium bicarbonate. Upon the instant of mixing the two liquids, violent effervescence occurs, for the bicarbonate has been decomposed and carbon dioxide (a gas) is given up to the atmosphere. The hydrochloric acid also splits into its constituent atoms. Atoms of sodium unite with the chlorine atoms to form sodium chloride, carbon atoms with a molecule of oxygen to form carbon dioxide, and hydrogen molecules with oxygen atoms to form water, thus:

$$HCl + NaHCO_3 = NaCl + CO_2 + H_2O$$

hydrochloric   sodium   sodium   carbon   water
acid   bicarbonate   chloride   dioxide

The indestructible nature of the atom in ordinary reactions. Molecules disintegrate and fresh compounds are formed, but the atoms in the ordinary process of Nature are indestructible. Decay and disintegration of substances are occurring ceaselessly. Organic matter, animal and vegetable, is continually undergoing decomposition, its elements being returned to the earth and there reconstituted into new compounds. Even rocks become eroded and metals wear away, but the immortal atoms reappear in new forms. Though materials composing the world around us disappear and are lost to our senses, the sum total of matter undergoes no reduction in weight. When we watch a blazing log being consumed until nothing but the ash remains, we may doubt the general statement that matter is indestructible. But were it possible to collect the smoke and escaped gases and add them to the ash and weigh the whole, the total weight (less the oxygen used in the combustion) would be found to be equal to that of the original unburned piece of wood. Compounds composing the wood have been broken up; carbon has been combined with oxygen to form carbon monoxide (CO) and carbon dioxide (CO_2); hydrogen has

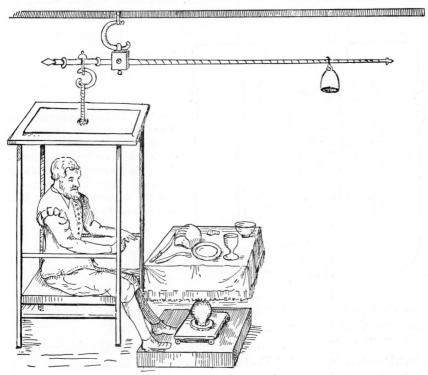

Fig. 1.6   Santorio Santorio carrying out an experiment upon himself seated in a large balance (steel arm).

been oxidized to water (H_2O); many other compounds have been decomposed and new compounds formed by the recombination of atoms momentarily freed. Did one know all the chemical reactions which had taken place, a balanced equation could be written (p. 7).

Nor is matter *created* in the sense that new atoms are formed. The growth of plants or of animal tissues is merely the accumulation of pre-existing atoms. A plant, for instance, acquires water, minerals, and nitrogen from the soil, and carbon from the carbon dioxide of the atmosphere; from these it builds its structure and gains in weight. The animal body takes in carbon, hydrogen, nitrogen, oxygen, and other elements in the food as well as oxygen from the atmosphere. Just as in the flaming wood, the carbon is oxidized to carbon dioxide and the hydrogen to water; part of the nitrogen of the food in combination with other elements (see amino acids, p. 360) is built into body tissue, and the remainder excreted. The carbon dioxide and part of the water is exhaled in the breath. If the adult body's intake of all the elemental materials were collected, their total weight would be found to balance the weight of the materials excreted in urine, feces,

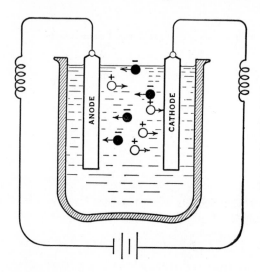

Fig. 1.7   Illustrating electrolysis. When an electric current is passed through a solution of an electrolyte (e.g., sodium chloride), the positively charged ions (cations) move to the cathode and the negatively charged ions (anions) to the anode.

skin (perspiration), and breath. The body's weight would be found to have remained unchanged.

An Italian physician (Santorio Santorio) living in the sixteenth and seventeenth centuries (1561–1636) was the first to demonstrate these facts. He spent most of his time in the latter part of his life in a large balance (Fig. 1.6); weighed all that he ate and drank and tried to balance the weight of these with the weight of his excreta (urine and feces), but found a discrepancy. The weight of that which he ate and drank was more than that of his excreta. He concluded that the difference was caused by the loss of water through the skin (i.e., evaporation) and in the expired air. This loss which was not revealed by his weighings he called *insensible perspiration* (see pp. 377–8).

Ionization or dissociation. Certain compounds, such as *hydrochloric acid* (HCl), *nitric acid* (HNO$_3$), *phosphoric acid* (H$_3$PO$_4$), *sulfuric acid* (H$_2$SO$_4$), *carbonic acid* (H$_2$CO$_3$), *sodium, potassium, calcium,* and *ammonium hydroxides* (NaOH, KOH, Ca(OH)$_2$, and NH$_4$OH, respectively), *sodium* and *potassium chlorides* (NaCl and KCl), copper sulfate ($CuSO_4$), and a great number of others when in aqueous solution, separate into their constituent atoms or groups of atoms. The separated atoms are electrically charged and are called *ions* (Gk. *ion*, going, traveling), because when an electric current is passed through an aqueous solution of one of these compounds they move at a certain definite velocity toward one or other pole of the battery (Fig. 1.7). This property of molecules to break up into electrically charged atoms is called *ionization* or *dissociation*.

Some ions, such as those of *calcium, hydrogen, sodium,* and *potassium,* are positively charged and move toward the negative pole or

Table 1-3

Name of Electrolyte	Percentage Ionized
Acetic acid	1.3
Carbonic acid	0.17
Hydrochloric acid	92.00
Hydrocyanic acid	0.01
Nitric acid	92.00
Sulfuric acid	61.00
Phosphoric acid	8.50
Potassium hydroxide	91.00
Sodium hydroxide	91.00
Sodium chloride	85.00

cathode; they are therefore called *cations*. Such atoms are positively charged because they have lost the electron that joined them to the other atom of the compound (see p. 8). Others, such as chlorine (chloride ion), having gained the electron lost by the other atom, are negatively charged; they move toward the positive pole or anode and therefore are known as *anions*. The anions are frequently *groups* of atoms and are given specific names, such as *nitrate* (NO_3), *phosphate* (HPO_4), *sulfate* (SO_4), *bicarbonate* (HCO_3), or *hydroxyl* (OH) ions. The nature of the charge carried by the atoms is indicated by a plus or a minus sign to the right and above the last symbol of the formula. Thus, the hydrogen ion is written H^+, and the chloride and nitrate ions Cl^- and $HNO_3{}^-$, respectively. If an atom carries two or more positive or negative charges, the respective sign is repeated; the calcium ion is written Ca^{++}, and the phosphate ion $HPO_4{}^{--}$.

The compounds mentioned above ionize to the greatest extent when dissolved in water, and to a much less degree in solvents such as alcohol or acetone, and do not dissociate at all in the great majority of solvents. Water itself is very slightly dissociated into H and OH ions.

Ionizable substances, since their solutions are capable of conducting an electric current, are called *electrolytes*. The movement of the two kinds of ion to the respective poles of an electric source whose terminals are immersed in a solution of an electrolyte is called *electrolysis*. Many compounds, such as cane sugar, do not undergo ionization, and are therefore called *nonelectrolytes*. A list of electrolytes and the percentages to which they undergo ionization in aqueous solution is given in Table 1-3. It will be observed that the percentages vary widely.

A few of the commoner electrolytes and the ions into which they separate are shown in the following equations:

$$CaSO_4 \rightarrow Ca^{++} + SO_4^{--}$$
calcium sulfate   calcium ion   sulfate ion

$$HCl \rightarrow H^+ + Cl^-$$
hydrochloric acid   hydrogen ion   chloride ion

$$HNO_3 \rightarrow H^+ + NO_3^-$$
nitric acid   hydrogen ion   nitrate ion

$$H_2SO_4 \rightarrow H^+ + H^+ + SO_4^{--}$$
sulfuric acid   hydrogen ions   sulfate ion

$$H_2CO_3 \rightarrow H^+ + HCO_3^-$$
carbonic acid   hydrogen ion   bicarbonate ion

$$NaOH \rightarrow Na^+ + OH^-$$
sodium hydroxide   sodium ion   hydroxyl ion

$$NaCl \rightarrow Na^+ + Cl^-$$
sodium chloride   sodium ion   chloride ion

$$H_3PO_4 \rightarrow 3H^+ + PO_4^{---}$$
phosphoric acid   hydrogen ions   phosphate ion

Acids, bases, and salts. Anyone even without a knowledge of chemistry knows, in a general way, the nature of an acid. A typical acid is sour or sharp to the taste, and unless very weak gives a burning sensation to the skin; if strong, it is highly destructive to animal and vegetable tissues; it also turns blue litmus paper pink or red. These properties are due to the hydrogen ion (H^+) (see p. 108). Every acid contains in its molecule at least one atom of hydrogen.

Lye, known chemically as sodium hydroxide ($NaOH$), and slaked lime ($Ca(OH)_2$) are bases. Typical bases in solution have a soapy feel, and most have a bitter taste; they turn red litmus paper blue. In strong solution, they also have a destructive action on animal and vegetable tissues. These properties are due to the hydroxyl ion (OH^-). Bases react with acids to form compounds called salts, a metal or other element of the base replacing one or more hydrogen atom of the acid. Two such reactions are shown below.

$$Ca(OH)_2 \; + \; 2HCl \; = \; CaCl_2 \; + \; 2H_2O$$

calcium   hydrochloric   calcium   water
hydroxide   acid   chloride

or

$$NaOH \; + \; HCl \; = \; NaCl \; + \; H_2O$$

sodium   hydrochloric   sodium   water
hydroxide   acid   chloride

Strong bases, such as sodium, potassium, or calcium hydroxides, are also known as *alkalis* (Arabian, *al,* the + *qaliy,* [*kali*], ashes, which are rich in sodium). They interact with fats or oils to form soaps. The adjectives corresponding to the nouns, acid, base, and alkali, are *acidic, basic,* and *alkaline.*

Solutions. When a substance such as sugar or salt is stirred in water, it "melts" away until the water is again quite clear. We say the sugar or salt has been *dissolved;* and the water and the dissolved substance are called a *solution* of sugar, in one instance, or of salt, in the other. The substance which goes into solution is called the *solute;* the liquid, whether water, alcohol, ether, oil, etc., in which the substance is dissolved, is called the *solvent.* When a crystalloid (see below) is dissolved and the solution well stirred, the solute becomes distributed uniformly throughout the solvent, the molecules being evenly intermingled. Once a substance composed of molecules having a size of the order comprising sugar or salt has been dissolved, it is not possible to separate the solute again from the solvent by mechanical means, as by filtering. The molecules of the solute pass as readily through the pores of the filter as do those of the solvent.

A *saturated solution* is one which, at a given temperature, holds the maximum quantity of the solute which it is capable of dissolving; it is said to be saturated at that particular temperature. If the solution, at a given temperature, contains less than the maximum amount of solute which it can dissolve at that temperature, it is said to be *unsaturated.*

Saturated solutions of certain substances when slowly and carefully cooled remain clear. The solution is then *supersaturated* at the lower temperature. But solid particles of the solute separate out if one of its crystals is dropped into the solution, or often if the solution is even slightly agitated. The substance continues to come out of solution until saturation at the lower temperature is reached.

Most substances increase in solubility with heating, but some are rendered more soluble by lowering the temperature. When the former class of substance go into solution, heat is absorbed—that is, the temperature falls. In the latter group, heat is given out, the temperature of the solution being higher than that of either the original solute or solvent.

A normal (N) solution is one which contains an equivalent (p. 9) in grams of solute per liter. Thus, a *normal calcium chloride* ($CaCl_2$) *solution* contains 55.5 grams of the salt (equivalent of calcium 20, and chlorine, 35.46). A solution containing a fraction ($\frac{1}{2}$, $\frac{1}{10}$, $\frac{1}{100}$) of the amount of the solute that is contained in a normal solution, or one in which twice the quantity is dissolved, is referred to, respectively, as half normal, one tenth normal (or decinormal), one hundredth normal, twice normal, and so on, and is abbreviated $N/2$, $N/10$, $N/100$, or $2N$.

A solution containing per liter an amount of a substance in grams equal to its molecular weight is called a *molar* or a *molecular solution*. Thus, a molar solution of calcium chloride ($CaCl_2$) contains $(40 + 71 =)$ 111 grams per liter. Solutions containing fractions or multiples of this quantity may be made up giving tenth molar, twice molar, etc., solutions.

A *physiological* saline solution contains about 0.9 percent of sodium chloride or about the concentration of the mineral salts of human blood plasma.

Suspensions and emulsions. *Solid* substances composed of relatively large particles of a diameter of 0.1 micron or more will remain suspended in water for a short time and then settle to the bottom of the container. But in suspensions of which the liquid medium is heavier and of a more viscous nature, such as mucilage, the particles settle very slowly, remaining suspended for long periods. Blood is a suspension of cells in a fluid called plasma (p. 57) which is some five times more viscous than water. The cells are about 7 microns in their largest diameters and remain suspended for a relatively short time after the blood has been drawn from a vessel and placed in a test tube. The size of the particles of any substance as well as the consistency of the liquid medium is a factor in the rate of settling, the larger particles settling more rapidly than the smaller ones. Particles of a size less than 0.1 micron remain suspended almost indefinitely, even in water (see suspensoids, p. 17).

Liquid particles or globules of about the same size as the solid particles in a suspension, when dispersed in another liquid, constitute an *emulsion*. The two liquids do not lose their chemical individuality. As with suspensions, the smaller the particles the longer they will remain dispersed in the medium. Fat, oil, resins, gums, and many other substances of both animal and vegetable origin form emulsions with variable size of particles. Milk is a familiar example of an emulsion of fat globules in an aqueous medium. Emulsification of the fatty substances of the food occurs with the aid of the bile in the small intestine (p. 334).

Crystalloids and colloids. Substances with molecules of relatively minute size—less than $1.0\mu\mu$ [2] in diameter—such as sodium chloride, sugar, copper sulfate, and the majority of chemical compounds, form true solutions, as described on page 15. They are called *crystalloids*. Materials composed of larger molecules—from $0.1\ \mu$ to $1.0\ \mu\mu$—or of smaller molecules clumped together to form particles of such a size, are called *colloids* (Gk. *kollae*, glue). Glue, gelatin, egg white and other proteins, starch, rubber, various enzymes (p. 288), many dyes, fine carbon particles as in smoke, or India ink, and a host of other substances, are colloidal in nature. The animal body—blood plasma and the protoplasm comprising the tissue cells—is composed largely of solutions of colloids. Solutions of colloids, also called *emulsoids* [3] or *suspensoids,* are frequently cloudy, turbid, or opalescent or, at any rate, not crystal-clear as are true solutions. But some colloid solutions are transparent, so the turbidity or clarity of a solution cannot be resorted to as a means of distinguishing a true from a colloidal solution. Colloid solutions have, nevertheless, certain unique characteristics: when, for example, a beam of light is thrown from one side into a colloidal solution, the diameter of the particles, being greater than the length of the waves of light, scatters the rays, and a bright opalescent cone is seen, known as *Tyndall's phenomenon.* The particles are also made dimly visible if a film of a colloidal solution is illuminated by a light directed upon it from one side and observed under the

[2] One micron (abbrev. μ) equals $\frac{1}{1000}$ millimeter. A millimicron (abbrev. mμ) equals $\frac{1}{1000}$ micron or $\frac{1}{1,000,000}$ of a millimeter. A micromicron (abbrev. $\mu\mu$) is $\frac{1}{1,000,000}$ of a micron or $\frac{1}{1,000,000,000}$ of a millimeter.

[3] Colloid solutions are divided into two main classes called *emulsoids* or *hydrophilic colloids* (Gk. *hudor,* water + *philo,* I love) and *suspensoids* or *hydrophobic colloids* (Gk. *phobos,* fear). The emulsoids have a strong affinity for water and for this reason are held more firmly in solution than are the suspensoids. The colloidal solutions of living matter—such as protein solutions—are for the most part emulsoids. The suspensoids have a tendency to come out of solution and are, in general, solutions of inorganic substances.

microscope. The ultramicroscope is based upon this fact; by means of this instrument the presence of particles, invisible through an ordinary microscope, is revealed.

We do not use the term *solute* in speaking of the particles of a colloid solution as we do of a substance which goes into true solution. The particles are called the *internal* or *dispersed phase* of the solution; the medium in which the particles are dispersed is known as the *external* or *dispersion phase*. A reversal of the two phases under certain conditions, such as a fall in temperature, is a characteristic of certain colloids (namely, glue, gelatin, and starch), the particles (internal phase) joining together and enclosing the medium (external phase).

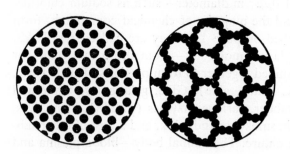

Fig. 1.8   Diagram to show the rearrangement of the particles when a sol changes to a gel.

(See Fig. 1.8.) The change is quite evident to the naked eye; the material no longer flows but has become firm or jellylike. The *hydrosol* (sol) has been converted to a *hydrogel* (or *gel*), as the colloid is now called. A change of this nature occurs in the conversion of the plasma protein fibrinogen to fibrin when the blood coagulates (p. 103).

Most colloids, owing to the relatively large size of their particles, can be separated from the dispersing medium and from crystalloids by means of a suitable filter. The procedure is called *ultrafiltration*. Such a process takes place in the body. The membrane forming the capillary walls, for example, serves as a filter which, while holding the plasma proteins to a large extent within the circulation, permits water and crystalloids to pass freely through to the surrounding tissue cells (see Fig. 3.10, p. 66). Nor do the plasma colloids normally enter the urine; they are prevented from escaping from the circulation by the interposition of a fine filter in the kidney, the water and crystalloids of the plasma alone passing into the renal tubules (p. 277).

Colloids, by means of *dialysis,* can also be separated from any crystalloids which may be associated with them. Colloid particles are unable to pass through certain membranes, such as sausage skin, frog's skin, cellophane, etc., which are permeable to the smaller molecules of water and crystalloids. If, therefore, a colloid solution containing salt is placed in a small sac made of sausage skin or cellophane and immersed in distilled water, the molecules of salt escape into the surrounding water and molecules of water pass into the colloid solution. This process continues until the concentration of salt is the same on the two sides of the membrane. If the distilled water is renewed repeatedly, the colloid solution is eventually completely freed of the crystalloid.

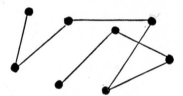

Fig. 1.9   Brownian movement. The successive positions of a particle of a colloid as observed by means of the ultramicroscope.

Brownian movements. This is an astonishing phenomenon first described about one hundred years ago by a British botanist, Robert Brown. When a colloid solution is observed with the ultramicroscope, random, erratic, zigzag movements of the particles are seen (Fig. 1.9). The movements occur ceaselessly and with great rapidity, the particles appearing to dart here and there like midges or a great number of rubber balls struck by invisible hands. The movements are not an inherent property of the colloid particles themselves, but are caused by the molecules of water and other molecules of the external phase coming repeatedly into near collision with them (see Kinetic theory, p. 243). It appears that actual contact of the smaller, rapidly moving molecules with the larger ones does not occur; it is prevented by mutual repulsion.

The particles of many colloids when in aqueous solution are electrically charged, carrying negative (OH^-) or positive (H^+) ions (depending upon the kind of colloid) adsorbed (see below) from the surrounding slightly ionized water (p. 109). Since like charges of electricity repel one another, the particles of a given colloid having the same sign of charge ($+$ or $-$) are prevented from gathering into large clumps; they are thus kept in a state of uniform dispersion. This fact, plus the Brownian movements just described, keeps the particles in a state of permanent suspension; they show little or no tendency to settle to the bottom of the containing vessel.

Adsorption. The property of any material to attract and hold molecules—solid, liquid, or gaseous—to its surface is called *adsorption*. The molecules or particles do not penetrate into the substance or structure of the adsorbing body; adsorption, therefore, is to be distinguished from *absorption*. Many colloids tend to be adsorbed on the surface of other bodies. They, in turn, exhibit the property of adsorbing smaller particles to a pronounced degree which, owing to the small size of the individual particles, offer in the aggregate an immense surface to still smaller particles in the dispersion phase. For this reason, finely ground charcoal and other colloids are most effective clarifying, decolorizing, or deodorizing agents, the molecules of the offending material being thus removed from solution or from air.

CHAPTER 2

Protoplasm. The Cell. The Tissues

Protoplasm is the material basis of all forms of life. The substance of the animal body—muscles, brain, kidney, liver, etc.—is composed largely of this "life stuff." Yet the exact chemical constitution of living protoplasm is unknown, for any of the means which might be employed to analyze it cause its death. Irreversible physical and chemical changes then occur, and we are no longer dealing with the substance whose composition we had set out to determine. The most that can be said with regard to the chemistry of protoplasm is that it consists of a watery solution of proteins, together with smaller amounts of carbohydrates (glycogen and glucose), lipids (fatlike materials), and inorganic salts (of potassium, calcium, sodium, magnesium, etc.). The word protoplasm (*literally*, the first thing formed) is itself no more than a generic term, for there are innumerable types of this material, its constitution varying in the different forms of life as well as in the different tissues of any individual. Furthermore, it is the seat of innumerable chemical reactions, oxidations and reductions, decompositions and syntheses; its chemical nature is therefore changing ceaselessly. Upon these changes the varied phenomena of life depend.

Physically, living protoplasm is a hydrosol or hydrogel belonging to the class of colloids already described as emulsoids. It is somewhat foamlike in appearance under powerful magnification; but it is questionable whether this is a natural property of protoplasm or merely caused by the technique used in preparing it for examination.

The Physiological Properties
of Protoplasm

The various physical and chemical processes of plant and animal life are simply the manifestations of the properties of protoplasm. It is these properties which we recognize as distinguishing the living from the nonliving world.

The protoplasm of animals possesses four fundamental properties: (1) irritability or excitability; (2) conductivity; (3) the power to convert the potential energy of food material into other forms of energy—thermal, mechanical, chemical, or electrical; and (4) growth.

Irritability or excitability. These terms refer to the ability to respond to a stimulus. A stimulus may be defined as some change in the environment occurring at a sufficiently rapid rate. The amoeba, for example, when stimulated, as by the touch of a stiff hair or by heating the water in which it is immersed, shows that it is alive by a movement

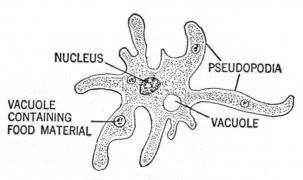

Fig. 2.1   An amoeba.

and a change in form of its minute body (Fig. 2.1). Also, the excised muscle of the frog shows its irritability, so long as it remains alive, by shortening (contracting) when stimulated in one or another of several ways (mechanically, thermally, chemically, or electrically).

Conductivity. The effect caused by a stimulus is not confined to the region in the immediate neighborhood of the stimulated point, but spreads throughout the mass of protoplasm. Thus, when one end of a muscle is stimulated, the contractile process travels to the other end. When the stimulus ceases, the part of the muscle to which the stimulus was applied is the first to resume the resting state; the opposite end of the muscle is the last to become inactive. This phenomenon of the stimulated muscle illustrates the property of conductivity. Conductivity reaches its highest development in nervous tissue. The disturbance set up in a nerve fiber by a stimulus is transmitted to the farthest end of the fiber, which in some instances is several feet long. In a warm-blooded animal, the disturbance or impulse, as it is called, is transmitted at the rate of some 300 feet per second—i.e., at about the velocity of a revolver bullet.

Metabolism. The ability which protoplasm possesses to liberate and convert to its own uses the energy stored in food material is referred to as metabolism (see also p. 351). The term embraces all those chemical reactions occurring in the tissues and from which energy is derived for the performance of muscular work or for sustaining the vital processes—e.g., the contractions of the heart, the activity of the nerve centers, the generation of body heat, and the manufacture of the digestive and other essential secretions (e.g., those of the ductless glands). Upon chemical reactions also depends the *growth* of the young animal. In the digestive tract, the food materials are broken down into simpler compounds which are absorbed by the blood and rebuilt to form body tissue.

The Cell

In very simple forms of life—e.g., the amoeba (Fig. 2.1)—a single small mass of protoplasm, called a cell, composes the organism's entire body. Such organisms are called *unicellular*. Other forms of life whose bodies are constituted of many such microscopic blocks of protoplasm are called *multicellular*. Higher animals are constructed of immense multitudes of cells grouped together into various patterns to form the different tissues of the body.

Though, as we shall soon see (p. 39), cells vary greatly in size and shape, the majority possess certain characteristics in common. Each possesses a smaller ovoid or globular body called the *nucleus* which in a typical cell lies near its center (Fig. 2.2). The protoplasm surrounding the nucleus and constituting, in most instances, the main bulk of the cell is called the *cytoplasm*.

The nucleus. The nuclear substance or *caryoplasm* is somewhat more viscous than the surrounding cytoplasm. The most important and essential nuclear material is in the form of granules [1] and is called *chromatin* (Gk. *chrōma*, color) which stains deeply with basic

[1] It is doubtful whether, in the living cell, the chromatin is in the form of granules. The latter are thought by some histologists to be the result of the reagents used in preparing the cell for microscopical examination. It is probable that in the untreated cell the chromatin is in the form of threads.

dyes such as hematoxylin. The granules appear to be disposed along a netlike framework in the spaces of which is an almost structureless viscous substance called the *nuclear sap*. Chromatin material is rich in *nucleoprotein,* which is a simple protein combined with nucleic acid (Chap. 9). The nuclei of most cells contain one or two small round bodies called *nucleoli* (sing. nucleolus) which stain with acid dyes such as eosin. Some of the masses of chromatin are conspicuous for their large size, and are known as *caryosomes*.

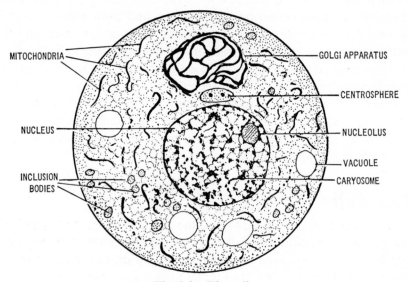

Fig. 2.2   The cell.

The function of the nucleus is closely related in some way to the metabolic activity of the cell, and the hereditary characters of the latter are bound up with the chromatin material, which breaks up into a definite number of separate pieces called *chromosomes* in the first stage of cell division (see Mitosis, p. 25).

The cytoplasm. The cytoplasm stains with acid dyes so that with double staining the cell nucleus and the surrounding cytoplasm are strongly contrasted. There are six types of structure within the cytoplasm which will now be described: (1) *mitochondria,* (2) the *centrosphere* with its *centriole*, (3) *Golgi apparatus* or *network*, (4) *fibrils,* (5) *vacuoles,* and (6) *inclusion bodies*. The first four of these are known collectively as organelles or organoids; they are living structures—integral parts of the cytoplasm.

(1) *Mitochondria* (Gk. *mitos,* a thread + *chondros,* a granule). These are short threadlike, rod-shaped or granular structures scat-

tered throughout the cytoplasm (Fig. 2.2). The function of the mito-chondria is uncertain but they appear to be associated with cellular metabolic processes.

(2) *The centrosphere* or *central body*. This is a small sphere or oval of protoplasm lying close to one pole of the nucleus. It contains two small, sharply staining granules called *centrioles*. These latter in the resting cell (i.e., a cell not undergoing mitosis) are closely asso-ciated with cell reproduction; during mitosis they are centers from which fine lines are seen to radiate, forming the so-called *asters*.

(3) *Golgi apparatus or network*. This was first described in 1898 by the celebrated Italian histologist Camillo Golgi. It consists of a meshwork of fibrils in the neighborhood of the centrosphere. Little is known of the function served by the Golgi apparatus, but in gland cells it appears to be closely associated with their secretory activity.

(4) *Fibrils*. Very fine filaments are to be found in most cells, in which they form an infinitely fine interlacement throughout the cyto-plasm. They are prominent elements in nerve and muscle cells, in which they run along more or less parallel lines. In some tissues they pass from cell to cell forming protoplasmic bridges.

(5) *Vacuoles*. In certain cells, round or oval and apparently empty spaces known as vacuoles are present. Sometimes they form part of a system of fine canals. The wall of the vacuole consists of a definite membrane which, in certain unicellular forms, is capable of rhythmic contraction, the vacuole absorbing fluid from the surrounding proto-plasm and discharging it to the exterior. Such a contracting vacuole serves in these forms as an excretory organ.

(6) *Inclusion bodies*. These, as their name implies, are not integral parts of the cytoplasm; they are such particulate matter as granules of carbohydrate, representing the food in storage form, pigment (in skin, retina, etc.), and secretory granules—e.g., the zymogens of the salivary and pancreatic cells (p. 325).

The cytoplasm at the circumference of the cell is condensed to form what is usually referred to as the *cell membrane*. This acts as a semi-permeable membrane (p. 65), and also serves to stiffen the contour of the cell and to give it definite shape. The view is widely held that the cell membrane is composed mainly of lipid (fatlike) material.

Multiplication of cells—mitosis and amitosis. The body cells of de-veloping and growing tissues multiply by a process called *mitosis* or *caryocinesis*. In this method of cell reproduction, complicated changes occur in the chromatin, preparatory to the division of the nucleus and cytoplasm and the formation of two new cells. The latter are called *daughter cells*.

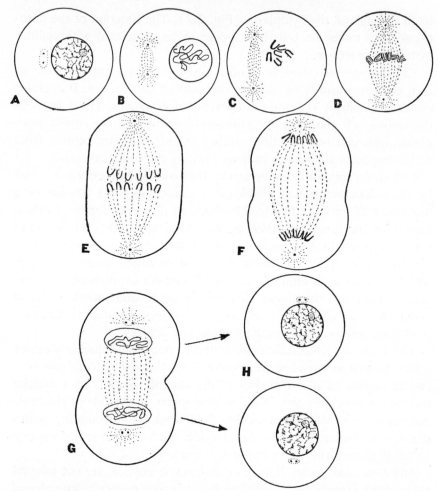

Fig. 2.3 Mitosis: A, B, C, prophase; D, metaphase; E and F, anaphase; G and H, telophase.

Though mitosis is a continuous process, it is customary to describe it in four stages: *prophase, metaphase, anaphase,* and *telophase.*

Prophase. In the *first stage or prophase,* the chromatin loses its granular appearance and forms a number of bent or twisted and somewhat tangled filaments called *spireme threads.* The centrosphere divides into two equal parts, each of which contains a centriole. The newly formed centrospheres move apart, but remain connected by delicate protoplasmic strands which stretch between them. These strands are known as the *mantle fibers* and the fusiform structure which they form is referred to as the *spindle.* Protoplasmic filaments also radiate into the cytoplasm from the centrioles giving a starlike

appearance to the latter, which are now called *asters;* the rays themselves are called *astral rays.* Toward the end of the prophase, the
spireme threads break up into shorter and thicker sections. These are
the *chromosomes* (Gk. *chroma,* color + *soma,* body). The nucleolus
and the nuclear membrane have disappeared. (A, B, and C, Fig. 2.3).

Metaphase. In the *second stage or metaphase,* the chromosomes
have migrated to occupy the *equatorial plane* of the cell where they
split lengthwise into two equal halves (D, Fig. 2.3). The asters have
by this time moved to opposite poles of the cell and the mantle fibers
stretch to the corresponding chromosome halves. The new-formed
chromosomes thus derived from those of the original cell are identical.
The doubling of the chromosomes is characteristic of the general
body cells, but does not occur in the mature sex cells (see Meiosis,
Chap. 14).

Anaphase. In the *third stage or anaphase,* the new chromosomes
are completely separated and, as though moving along the mantle
fibers, reach opposite poles of the cell. The cell has become elongated
(E and F, Fig. 2.3).

Telophase. In the *final stage or telophase,* changes follow which
are the reverse of those of the prophase. The chromosomes become
longer and thinner, resembling the threads of the spireme; they are
later joined by filaments to form a reticulum. Finally, nucleoli and
nuclear membranes appear, and two complete nuclei are formed. The
cytoplasm then divides and two daughter cells are produced (G and
H, Fig. 2.3).

It should be mentioned that the size, shape, and number of chromosomes vary with the species, but are always the same and characteristic for any given species of animal or plant. The chromosome number is 46 in man, 24 in the mouse, 4 in certain species of round worms,
and 16 in the onion. It is also clear that, through the splitting of each
chromosome into two, the nucleus of each daughter cell is assured of
receiving the exact number of chromosomes characteristic of the species (see also Chap. 14).

In certain very primitive forms of life and occasionally, though
usually under abnormal conditions, in the bodies of higher animals,
reproduction occurs without any preliminary changes having occurred
in the nucleus. This type of cell reproduction is called *direct* or *ami-
totic* division. In one type of amitosis, the cells divide into equal parts,
half of the nucleus going to each new cell. This is called *simple* or
binary fission (Fig. 2.4). In some forms (e.g., yeast cells), the cells
reproduce by "pinching off" a part of their protoplasm, the newly

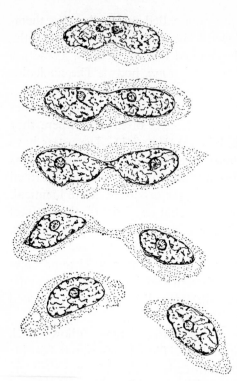

Fig. 2.4   Simple or binary fission.

formed cell being much smaller than the original. This form of division is called "budding." Certain animal forms such as sponges also reproduce in this way (Fig. 2.5).

Sexual reproduction—i.e., the reproduction of an entirely new organism composed of many different tissues by the union of sex cells (spermatozoon and ovum)—will be described in Chapter 14.

With a few exceptions the cells composing the tissues of the adult bodies of higher animals do not multiply. A nerve cell, or a cell of the liver, heart, or muscle, for example, once it has been destroyed is not replaced by a cell of its kind. Its place is filled by fibrous (scar) tissue. Blood cells, connective tissue cells, and the cells of the epidermis and the surface epithelium of the mucous membranes, on the other hand, are replaced when they die by their own type of cell. But the *adult* cells of even these tissues do not multiply; a red blood cell or an epidermal cell, for example, once formed does not divide. The production of new cells of these tissues is a function of younger more primitive cells in the bone marrow or in the deeper layers of the epidermis, respectively. Were it not for the inability of the cells of most adult tissues—nervous, hepatic, cardiac, muscular, etc.—to reproduce their kind, our bodies would, barring accidents, be immortal. Aging would be unknown; our organs and parts would be the seat of a ceaseless process of rejuvenation. But it is inevitable that

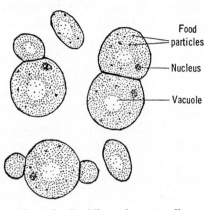

Fig. 2.5   Budding of yeast cells.

Food particles

Nucleus

Vacuole

with the passage of time the cells of vital structures show deterioration—undergo a progressive *degeneration*. This aging process commences at birth, and gradually, when the cells of some important structure are unable to perform their essential function, death occurs.

The Tissues

Each of the various parts and organs of the body of a higher animal is highly specialized for the particular function which it is called upon to perform. Since any organ is a mass of cells, its specialization must depend upon the character of the cells of which it is composed. The amoeba performs all the fundamental functions—respiration, digestion, excretion, etc.—within the compass of a single cell. Like a solitary pioneer on the frontiers of civilization, it must do all those things which are necessary for its existence. In the multicellular animal, the cells have undergone *differentiation* into various types and, like the classes of individuals making up the population of a civilized community, each type, though highly proficient in the execution of one or other particular function, has lost the versatility of the primitive organism. The tissues of the body are divisible into four main types—*epithelial, muscular, nervous,* and *connective*—according to the type of cell of which each is composed. The structure of nervous tissue is described in Chapters 11 and 12.

The epithelial tissues. Epithelial cells serve as a protective covering. They are arranged in a series of layers or strata to form the outer part of the skin (epidermis); they also line the digestive, respiratory, and urinary tracts. Other types of epithelial cell have acquired secretory functions. The various external secretory glands (digestive, mammary, sweat, etc.), as well as some of the glands of internal secretion (thyroid, parathyroid, anterior pituitary), are composed of epithelial cells (Chap. 10).

In many situations the cells rest upon a very thin sheet of delicate, rather indistinct fibrils embedded in a cement substance. This is known as the *basement membrane*. In certain other structures—e.g., the mucosa of the digestive tract—the cells lie upon a much thicker layer of connective tissue called the *membrana propria*.

Epithelial cells are of several varieties. Some, the *columnar* type, are relatively long and narrow, appearing under the microscope as slender columns set side by side like the stakes in a palisade (Fig. 2.6). In some situations, as in the linings of the nose, trachea (windpipe), and bronchi, the columnar cells are surmounted by fine hairlike

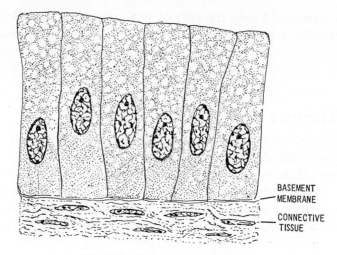

Fig. 2.6   Columnar epithelium.

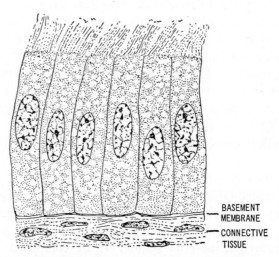

Fig. 2.7   Ciliated columnar epithelium.

structures called *cilia* (Fig. 2.7). Ciliated epithelium also lines the Fallopian tubes, epididymis, Eustachian (auditory) tubes, and the middle ear. The cilia, which are some 3 or 4 microns [2] in length, show an incessant motion. They bend quickly in one direction and then more slowly recover their original position. The movement is repeated at the rate of ten or more per second. The rate is slowed by cold and accelerated by warmth. Carbon dioxide, ether, chloroform, or alcohol vapor causes cessation of the movements. In the case of the respiratory

[2] A micron μ is $\frac{1}{1000}$ millimeter; a millimeter is about $\frac{1}{25}$ inch.

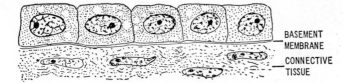

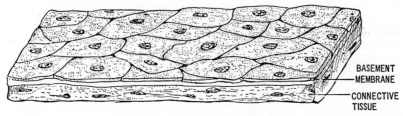

Fig. 2.8   Cuboidal epithelium.

Fig. 2.9   Squamous epithelium.

passages, the quick movement is toward the exterior—that is, from below toward the larynx or from above toward the nostrils. The cilia do not beat in unison; on the contrary, each beats a little time before its neighbor placed nearer the exterior. Thus, waves or ripples appear to pass over a ciliated surface like a field of standing wheat stirred by a breeze. The advantage of such a motion is obvious: it serves to sweep mucus and dust, or other small particles, from the respiratory passages. In the Fallopian tubes the cilia act to propel the ova to their destination (Chap. 14).

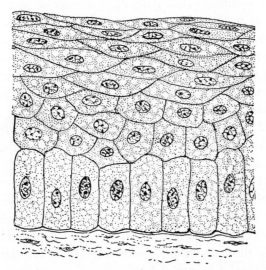

Fig. 2.10   Stratified squamous epithelium.

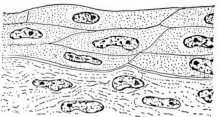

Fig. 2.12   Transitional epithelium, lining distended bladder.

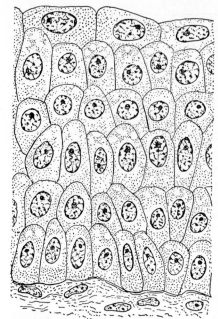

Fig. 2.11   Transitional epithelium, lining empty urinary bladder.

Epithelial cells, that are about as broad as they are long, are called *cuboidal* (Fig. 2.8). Another type of epithelium is composed of thin platelike or scalelike cells, and is therefore termed *squamous* (*squama = scale*) (Fig. 2.9). In some situations, as on the inner surface of the tympanic or drum membrane (Chap. 13), the epithelium consists of a *single* layer of squamous cells lying edge to edge as in a pavement. In other places, as in the skin, cornea, and lining of the mouth and vagina, there are several strata of cells. The deepest ones are cuboidal or columnar; those covering the surface are squamous. Between these two types is a series of layers whose cells decrease in thickness in each successive stratum nearer the surface. This type of epithelial tissue is termed *stratified squamous* epithelium (Fig. 2.10).

A modified type of stratified epithelium, called *transitional,* lines the pelvis of the kidney, ureter, bladder, and part of the urethra. Its surface cells are cuboidal rather than squamous. In the case of the bladder, this type of epithelium has the remarkable property of adjustment in relation to the state of the organ. In the distended bladder there are but three layers of cells, whereas in the empty viscus the number of layers is increased to six, the most superficial cells being rounded while the cells of the underlying layers are flask shaped or pear shaped (Figs. 2.11 and 2.12).

The skin. The skin consists of two main parts. The more superficial of these is called the *epidermis* or *cuticle;* the deeper portion is known as the *dermis, corium,* or *true skin (cutis vera).* The epidermis is composed of stratified epithelium; distinguishing microscopical features at different depths enable it to be described in four layers which

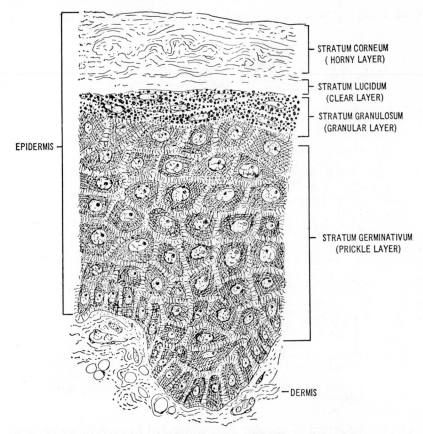

STRATUM CORNEUM
(HORNY LAYER)

STRATUM LUCIDUM
(CLEAR LAYER)

STRATUM GRANULOSUM
(GRANULAR LAYER)

EPIDERMIS

STRATUM GERMINATIVUM
(PRICKLE LAYER)

DERMIS

Fig. 2.13   A section of skin cut vertically to the surface.

have been given special names. These layers from the surface inward are: (1) the *stratum corneum* or *horny layer,* (2) the *stratum lucidum,* (3) the *stratum granulosum,* and (4) the *stratum germinativum* (see Fig. 2.13).

The *stratum corneum* consists of clear scalelike cells which are very thin near the surface but increase in thickness in successively deeper layers. The cells of the horny layer contain a protein called *keratin* (p. 361) and are without nuclei; the most superficial cells are being continually shed and replaced from below. The *stratum lucidum (clear layer)* is a narrow glistening band in which the cells are very indistinctly marked off, and contain, as a rule, no nuclei.

The *stratum granulosum* is made up of two or three, sometimes more, layers of triangular, rhomboid, or spindle-shaped cells; numerous coarse darkly staining granules are to be seen in the cytoplasm. The *stratum germinativum* (also known as the *stratum mucosum* or the *prickle layer*) consists of a layer of columnar or cuboidal cells lying upon and anchored to the corium, and some four to

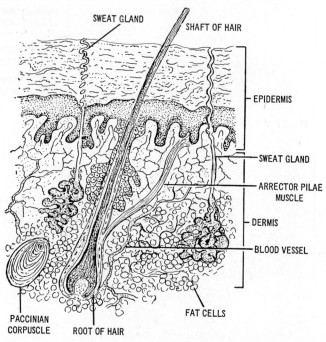

Fig. 2.14   Vertical section through the skin showing appendages.

six overlying layers of angular cells connected to each other by short protoplasmic spines or prickles. Multiplication of the cells of the skin takes place in this layer, especially in the most deeply situated cells; it is the only layer in which mitosis can be observed. It is from this fact that the layer derives its name. Most of the skin pigment is present in this layer (see below).

The *dermis* or *corium* is composed of loose connective tissue which contains the vessels and nerves of the skin. From its more superficial portion tonguelike processes—*papillae of the skin*—project into the overlying epidermis which appears to be molded over them.

The skin contains numerous small tubular glands (sweat glands and sebaceous glands) which arising in the dermis pass vertically outward through the epidermis to open upon the surface. These glands, together with the hairs and nails, are referred to as the *appendages* of the skin.

Beneath the dermis is a layer of connective tissue which usually contains much fat; it is called the *subcutaneous tissue.*

The *hairs* are developed from the epidermis but penetrate into the subcutaneous tissue. They are composed of an elastic horny material and have a definite structure. The *shaft* of the hair is that part projecting beyond the surface of the skin; the buried part is called the *root*. The lower end of the root shows a swelling known as the hair bulb. The elongated socket enclosing the root of the hair is called the *hair follicle;* it is composed of several layers of epithelial cells surrounded by a connective tissue coat. Delicate strands of smooth muscle —the erectors of the hairs (*arrectores pilorum;* sing., *arrector pilae*) —arise in the outer part of the dermis and run obliquely inward to be attached to the hair follicles near their middle. These muscles cause the erection of the hairs of animals

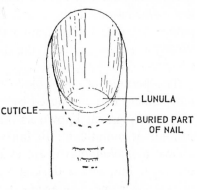

Fig. 2.15   The fingernail.

and the feathers of birds. They cause that roughening of the skin in man known as "goose flesh."

The nails. The human nails are horny curved plates firmly adherent to the dermis upon which they are molded. This part of the dermis is called the *nail bed.* The part of the nail embedded in the skin is called the *root.* The nails of man and the horns, claws, and hoofs of animals are modified epidermis (Fig. 2.15). The hard shiny exposed part of the nail is a thickened and greatly expanded stratum lucidum. The stratum corneum is represented only by the thin layer of cuticle at the base of the nail which tends to overlap the *lunula*— the half-moon-shaped pale area at the nail base. The nails grow in length by the multiplication of the cells composing the outer layers of the stratum germinativum.

The living *color and the temperature* of the skin depend upon the blood in a network of minute veins lying in the dermis immediately beneath the papillae, and called the *subpapillary venous plexus.* The blood in this plexus shows through the overlying epidermis. When the vessels are dilated, the skin is a deeper color and usually warmer than when they are constricted. However, changes in skin temperature are not due so much to the caliber of the cutaneous vessels as to the rate of blood flow through them; that is, to the volume of blood in a unit of time that is drawn from the deeper, warmer parts of the body to the superficial vessels.

The hue of the skin—that is, its tendency to take on either a pink or a bluish tint—is dependent upon the degree to which the blood in the superficial vessels is oxygenated. If the blood contains the normal proportion of oxyhemoglobin, the skin has a pink or a scarlet hue; if it contains an abnormally high concentration of reduced hemoglobin, the skin will have a bluish tint. Therefore, in states in which the oxygenation of the blood in the lungs is interfered with as in pulmonary disease or strangulation, or the peripheral circulation is slowed as in heart disease, the skin is bluish (see cyanosis and anoxia, Chap. 6).

The permanent skin color—that is, the shade or tint of the skin independent of that caused by its blood supply—is due to fine granules of a pigment known as *melanin* present in certain cells of the stratum germinativum. In fair-skinned races, these cells, which are known as *melanoblasts,* are to be found only in the deepest cells of this layer but, in the darkest skins, they are present throughout the prickle layer and may even extend into the stratum granulosum.

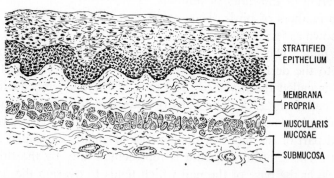

STRATIFIED EPITHELIUM

MEMBRANA PROPRIA

MUSCULARIS MUCOSAE

SUBMUCOSA

Fig. 2.16   Section of mucous membrane from the esophagus.

The skin carries out two essential functions: (1) to protect the underlying more delicate and sensitive tissues from mechanical, thermal, and chemical injuries, and from the inroads of bacteria (Chap. 5) or other pathogenic organisms; and (2) to aid in the regulation of the body temperature (p. 375). Small quantities of waste materials, especially urea, are excreted by the skin in the sweat.

This mode of elimination is probably of little importance in health, but is sometimes invoked in advanced kidney disease when the physician employs every means to promote the secretion of sweat.

The skin is also an important medium through which the body is supplied with vitamin D (Chap. 9).

Mucous membrane. The linings of the respiratory, digestive, and genitourinary tracts are called *mucous membranes.* They consist of a layer or several layers of epithelial cells laid upon a *basement membrane.* Beneath the latter lies a stratum of interlacing connective tissue fibers known as the *membrana* or *lamina propria,* which in many situations immediately overlies a relatively thick layer of loose connective tissue containing vessels and nerves, and small glands (Fig. 2.16); this is called the *submucosa.* In the esophagus,

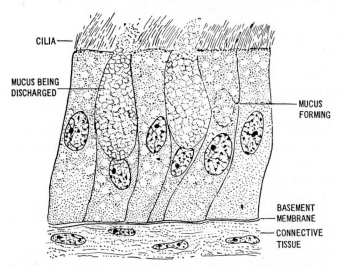

CILIA

MUCUS BEING DISCHARGED

MUCUS FORMING

BASEMENT MEMBRANE

CONNECTIVE TISSUE

Fig. 2.17 Ciliated columnar epithelium, showing goblet cells.

stomach, and intestines, but not in the respiratory and genitourinary tracts, a layer of smooth muscle known as the *muscularis mucosae* lies between the lamina propria and the submucosa. The epithelial cells of mucous membranes differ in kind according to their location. In the trachea and bronchi, for example, there are a number of cell layers, the most superficial being of the columnar ciliated type, but in the esophagus the cells are stratified squamous, and in the stomach and intestines they are simple columnar.

Mucous membranes secrete a slimy, tenacious material called *mucus.* This secretion, which contains a protein material (a glycoprotein, p. 361) known as *mucin,* is formed within the cytoplasm of the epithelial cells. As the material accumulates the cell becomes distended and, finally bursting, discharges its contents. The mucus coats the epithelial surface, serving as a protection against injurious substances or to trap small foreign particles. From their flasklike appearance when filled with mucus, cells of this type are referred

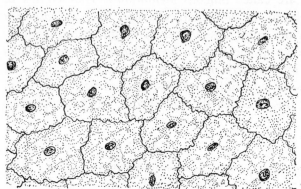

Fig. 2.18   Endothelial or mesothelial cells.

to as *goblet cells.* Though a certain proportion of the epithelial cells constantly secrete mucus, the number is greatly increased by mechanical stimulation, or by infection or other harmful action. We are all familiar with the running nose of the common cold, and with the expectoration of mucus which accompanies inflammation of the trachea or bronchi (Fig. 2.17).

Endothelium is usually classified as a type of epithelial tissue. It consists of extremely thin, waferlike cells with wavy or jagged edges (Fig. 2.18) which are laid edge to edge to form exquisitely delicate glistening membranes lining the chambers of the heart, the blood vessels, and the pericardial, pleural, and abdominal cavities.[3] The smallest lymphatics and blood vessels (capillaries) have transparent walls composed of a single layer of endothelial cells held together by a very thin layer of a cementing substance (see p. 50).

Glandular tissue. The epithelial cells composing glands are arranged in various patterns (Fig. 2.19). In one of the simplest types of gland, the secreting cells form a single tube which opens directly upon the surface (mucous membrane, skin, etc.). Such glands are called *simple tubular.* In other kinds of tubular glands, the deep part of the tube becomes branched. In other glands again, the cells sur-

[3] The term *mesothelium* is now usually applied to the linings of the body cavities (pleural, peritoneal, etc.), the word *endothelium* being reserved for the linings of the heart, blood vessels, and lymphatics. But mesothelium and endothelium are similar in structure and origin.

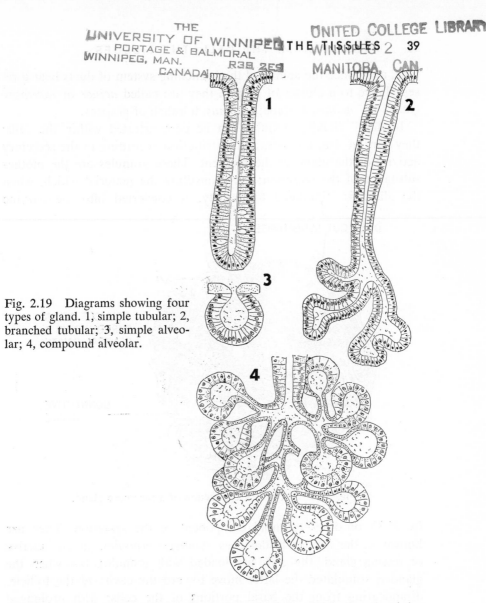

Fig. 2.19 Diagrams showing four types of gland. 1, simple tubular; 2, branched tubular; 3, simple alveolar; 4, compound alveolar.

round a central more or less spherical cavity into which the glandular secretion is received. The cavity with its wall of secreting cells is called an *acinus, follicle,* or *alveolus* (see Fig. 2.20). The channel or *duct* leading from the acinus may open directly upon the surface. But in large glands of this sort, the duct joins a similar one from a neighboring follicle to form a larger channel which unites in turn with others of the same size. Successive unions of this kind result in the formation of a rich rootlike system of ducts, the secretion being discharged to the surface ultimately through a single or a few large ducts. The salivary glands and the pancreas are glands of this latter type, and, since the acini and the branching system of ducts bear a re-semblance to a cluster of grapes, they are called *acinar* or *racemose glands* (L. *acinus,* a grape; *racemus,* a bunch of grapes).

In many glands, granules can be demonstrated within the cells; they vary in size, number, and distribution according to the secretory activity of the gland at the moment. These granules are the mother substance of the secretion; they constitute the material which, when the gland is stimulated to activity, is converted into the enzyme

DUCT CUT LENGTHWISE

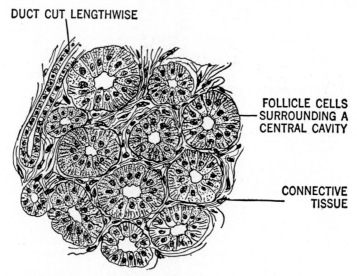

FOLLICLE CELLS
SURROUNDING A
CENTRAL CAVITY

CONNECTIVE
TISSUE

Fig. 2.20   Showing cross section of a racemose gland.

(p. 288) or other essential component of the secretion. They are known in the former instance as *zymogen granules.* In an inactive or resting gland, the cells are loaded with granules, but when the gland is stimulated the latter move toward the cavity of the follicle, disappearing from the basal portions of the cells; with prolonged activity the cells are completely cleared of granules, the gland being then exhausted (see Fig. 2.21).

Muscular tissue. There are two main types of muscular tissue: *striated* or *striped* and *unstriated* or *unstriped* (also called *plain* or *smooth*). Skeletal or voluntary muscle—e.g., the muscles of the limbs and of other parts that carry out movements under the control of the will—is striated. With the exception of that forming the heart, the involuntary muscle of the internal organs—e.g., stomach, intestines, bronchi and bronchioles, uterus, Fallopian tubes, etc.—is nonstriated. The muscle fibers in the skin attached to the hair follicles, in the walls of the blood vessels, and around the alveoli of various glands are also of the unstriated variety. The muscle of the heart though striated differs in important respects from voluntary muscle (p. 158).

Muscle cells are long and slender and for this reason are usually referred to as muscle fibers. They are usually tapered at their ends which are applied side by side to form longer or shorter chains. They vary very greatly in length, from a few microns—the length of cer-

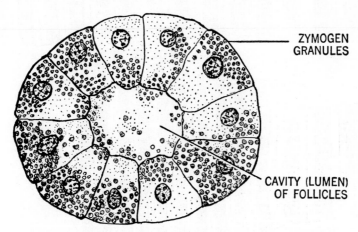

ZYMOGEN
GRANULES

CAVITY (LUMEN)
OF FOLLICLES

Fig. 2.21   Cross section of follicle of a racemose gland (e.g., salivary) showing zymogen granules being discharged into alveolus.

tain nonstriated fibers—to 35 or 40 mm as shown by the fibers of some skeletal muscles. In the large muscles of the skeleton, great numbers of such fibers are massed together into bundles. The bundles are bound together by connective tissue into larger masses. The contractile power of a muscle depends upon the combined effect of the innumerable fibers of which it is composed.

Upon close examination under the microscope a striated muscle fiber shows a series of alternating light and dark transverse bands. Each fiber is ensheathed by a delicate membrane called the *sarcolemma* (*Sarx, flesh* [*muscle*] + *lemma, husk*), and running through its entire length are a great number of fine parallel filaments—the *myofibrils*. The latter are embedded in the cytoplasm, which is usually referred to as the *sarcoplasm*. Each myofibril is constituted of a number of alternating light and dark sections. They are called the J and the Q discs, respectively (see Fig. 2.22). A narrow dark line, known as the Z line or Krause's membrane, divides each light or J disc transversely into halves. The discs in all the myofibrils lie

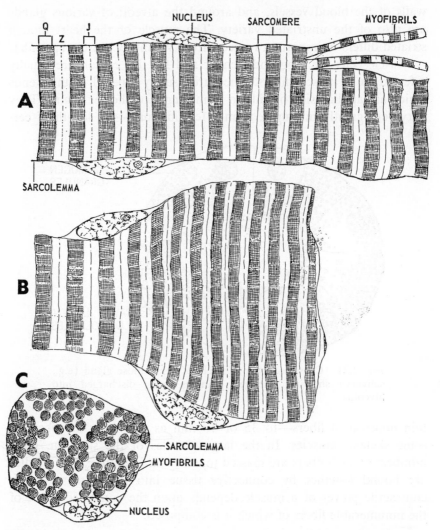

Fig. 2.22   A striated muscle fiber, highly magnified. A, resting muscle, two myofibrils teased out from end on right. B, contracting muscle. C, cross section of a single muscle fiber.

in line across the fibers—light to light and dark to dark. They are responsible for the crossbanding of the fiber mentioned above. The myofibrils are the most minute parts of the muscle which can be seen with the ordinary microscope, but even these, delicate as they are, can be shown by means of the electron microscope to consist of a large number of fine threads of protein material called *actomyosin* (see p. 497). These infinitely fine threads are called *micellae*. They are the essential contractile elements of muscle fiber.

The part of a myofibril lying between two Z lines is called a *sarcomere*.

The striated muscle fiber contains one or more nuclei just beneath the sarcolemma; in a long fiber several nuclei may be seen. In having its nuclei placed near its outer boundary, the striated muscle fiber differs from most other cells, in which the nuclei are centrally situated. Each muscle fiber is separated from its neighbors and com-

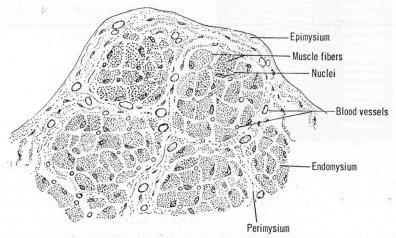

Fig. 2.23 Cross section of a portion of a muscle.

pletely enveloped by a thin investment of connective tissue. This sheath which lies outside of the sarcolemma is called the *endomysium*. A connective tissue layer, the *perimysium,* also encloses groups of muscle fibers holding them in bundles. The envelope of connective tissue surrounding the entire muscle is called the *epimysium* (Fig. 2.23). See also page 479.

The striated muscle fiber as viewed under polarized light. Light particles (photons) vibrate in all planes at right angles to the direction of the beam of light. Certain crystals, such as a Nicol prism, have the property of intercepting the particles in all planes but one. The light is then said to be polarized. If, therefore, two Nicol prisms are set up in the path of the beam and at right angles to one another all particles are intercepted, and no light whatever gets through to the eye. The field is completely dark. If, however, a muscle fiber is placed between two such "crossed" prisms, the field is no longer black, but shows alternate light and dark bands corresponding to the striations seen by ordinary light, except that the light or J band is now dark and the dark or Q band is light (Fig. 2.24). This is

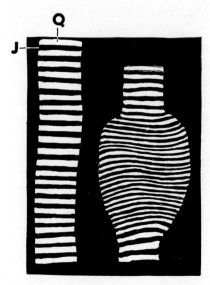

Fig. 2.24 Muscle fiber as seen by polarized light. Resting muscle on left; contracting muscle on right. Note that the Q and J discs become almost equal in thickness during contraction.

because the Q band contains some material, probably of a crystalline nature, that is able to bend or twist *part* of the light transmitted through the first Nicol in such a way as to allow it to get through the second. The Q band is therefore said to be *doubly refractive* or *anisotropic* (Gk. *an,* not + *isos,* equal + *tropos,* turning—i.e., unequal refraction). The J discs are said to be isotropic (equal refraction).

Generally speaking, *unstriated* or *smooth* muscle fibers are shorter than the striated variety, and are usually spindle shaped (i.e., thicker in the middle than at the ends); they do not possess a sarcolemma; the nucleus is more centrally situated; and the myofibrils are few and inconspicuous. They show no regular cross markings (Fig. 2.25).

The connective tissues. Connective tissue serves as a strengthening, connecting, and supporting material. It binds together masses of other types of cell, and forms a supporting framework for various organs. Thus, it holds bundles of muscle fibers together; forms fibrous investments (capsules) for the kidney, liver, etc.; and enters largely into the composition of the deeper layers of the skin. It also serves to fill in spaces between neighboring organs and parts, and

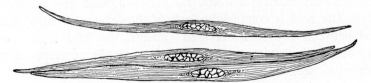

Fig. 2.25 Smooth (nonstriated) muscle fibers.

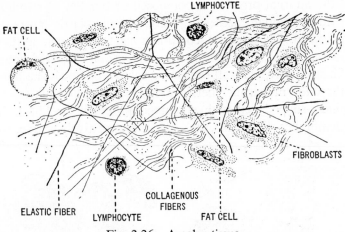

Fig. 2.26 Areolar tissue.

replaces tissue which has been destroyed by injury or disease (scar tissue). Connective tissue proper consists of a mass of long slender fibers embedded in a homogeneous jellylike matrix or ground substance. The ground substance predominates, cells being relatively few. The fibers are the elongated bodies or the long processes of the cells; nuclei are therefore sparsely scattered throughout the tissue. In many types of connective tissue, the fibers possess elastic properties, due to the presence of a protein known as elastin. The walls of the blood vessels are also well supplied with elastic fibers which are found in two layers. The larger arteries recoil after stretching almost as freely as a piece of rubber.

In some regions, such as in the walls of the trachea, bronchi and bronchioles, in the larynx, in the deeper layers of the skin, and in certain ligaments of the spinal column, the connective tissue is dense and composed largely of *elastic fibers*. The tendons of muscles, the ligaments of the majority of the joints, and the membranous cover-

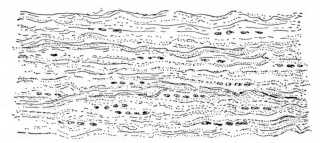

Fig. 2.27 Fibrous connective tissue.

ings of the internal organs are composed of bundles of strong, tough fibers which, though possessing little or no elastic property, are highly flexible. These fibers contain a protein known as *collagen,* and are therefore spoken of as the *collagenous* type of connective tissue fiber. The typical cell of the connective tissues is the *fibroblast.* From these the numerous fibers are derived. The fibroblast is a long, flat, spindle-shaped cell with elongated processes or fibers. In tendons, membranes, ligaments, etc., nuclei are relatively scarce, the sub-

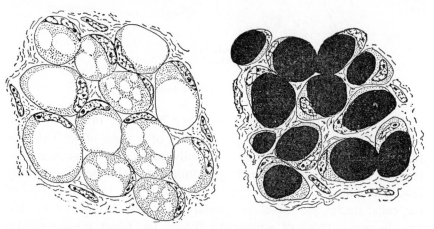

Fig. 2.28   Adipose (fatty) tissue. Clear spaces in the left-hand figure are fat droplets; in the figure on the right the fat has been stained black by osmic acid. The fat cells are shown in various stages of development.

stance of the tendon, membrane, or ligament being composed almost entirely, or at least predominantly, of fibers.

Areolar tissue is the most generalized and widely distributed form of connective tissue. It is loose in texture and composed of an interlacement of collagenous and elastic fibers running in all directions, a gelatinous ground substance, and a variable number of cells of different types scattered throughout. The meshes (areolae) between the fibers have suggested the name for this type of tissue. Areolar tissue is found beneath the skin (subcutaneous tissue), filling the spaces between muscles and the internal organs, and ensheathing the blood vessels.

Areolar tissue is much more cellular and contains leucocytes, fat cells, and various reticulo-endothelial elements (p. 94), as well as the fibroblasts just mentioned (Figs. 2.26 and 2.27).

Adipose or *fatty tissue* is a modified connective tissue. Certain cells of areolar tissue have the special ability to withdraw fat from the blood stream and deposit it within their bodies. The fat collects within the cytoplasm as droplets which gradually increase in size until they fill most of the cell, the original cytoplasm and the nucleus being displaced to the periphery and flattened against the cell membrane (Fig. 2.28). Adipose tissue consists of a mass of such fat-laden cells. Other cells of the areolar tissue have been crowded out while the fibers have largely disappeared. When the body loses weight, fatty tissue is one of the first to become reduced; it is drawn upon during starvation to furnish energy. The fat cells undergo a transformation. The fat droplets disappear; the cells shrink and, developing elongated processes, assume the appearance of fibroblasts. Adipose tissue is developed chiefly in subcutaneous situations and in the areolar tissue in relation to the abdominal organs.

Cartilage or *gristle* is also a modified connective tissue. There are three main types: *hyaline* (*glasslike*) *cartilage, elastic cartilage,* and *fibrocartilage.*

Hyaline cartilage is translucent and of a bluish-white color. It consists of large spherical or oval cells embedded in a nearly homogeneous ground substance. The cells are frequently found in pairs

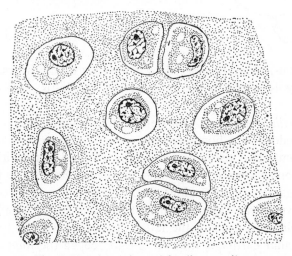

Fig. 2.29   A section of hyaline cartilage.

or groups and are then flattened where they are in contact with one another (Fig. 2.29). A narrow zone immediately surrounding the cartilage cells stains more deeply and is thus marked off, though not very sharply, from the rest of the ground substance. It is referred to as the *capsule.* Hyaline cartilage is found covering the ends of the bones inside joints (articular, cartilage); between the anterior ends of the ribs and the breast bone or sternum (costal cartilages); and in the nose, trachea, and bronchi. The greater part of the skeleton of the embryo is first laid down in cartilage which undergoes gradual conversion into bone (ossification) during the development of the embryo and throughout the growth period of the young animal after birth. The process of ossification is not complete in the human subject until adult life.

Elastic cartilage is yellow in color. It contains the same type of cell as that seen in hyaline cartilage, but the ground substance is not

Fig. 2.30   Thigh bone (femur) from which the minerals have been removed by acid; it is then able to be tied in a knot.

homogeneous, being reinforced by numerous elastic fibers. This type of cartilage is found in the external ear, epiglottis, and Eustachian tube.

Fibrocartilage is tough and dense. It is composed of collagenous fibers embedded in a homogeneous ground substance (matrix). This type of connective tissue is considered to hold a transitional position between hyaline cartilage and the dense connective tissue constituting ligaments and tendons. It is found in the form of discs between the vertebrae (intervertebral discs) and in the shoulder, knee, and hip joints. In each of the latter three situations, it forms a rim to the articular cartilage, thus serving to deepen the joint socket.

Bone or *osseous tissue,* another type of connective tissue, contains a large proportion of mineral matter, chiefly calcium and phosphorus (as tricalcium phosphate and calcium carbonate), but, also, smaller amounts of magnesium and traces of fluorine, chlorine, and iron. Some bones (e.g., those of the limbs) are developed by the deposition of minerals in cartilage. Others (e.g., the bones of the cranium) are formed by the mineralization of membraneous tissue.

But for the stiffening effect of these minerals, the bones would be no more rigid than many other tissues. Figure 2.30 shows a bone from which the minerals have been removed by treatment with acid.

Two types of osseous tissue enter into the construction of the long bones of the limbs. The *shaft* or *diaphysis* of a limb bone consists of a tube of hard *compact* bone, while the ends or *epiphyses* are composed of *cancellous* or *spongy* bone, covered by a shell of compact bone.

A section of compact bone from the shaft of the femur (thigh

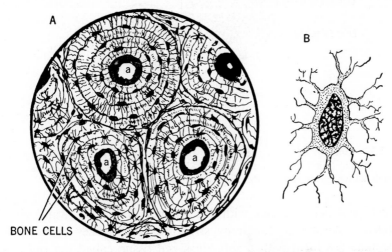

Fig. 2.31   A, section of osseous tissue from the shaft of a leg bone, showing Haversian canals with concentric lamellae; B, enlarged drawing of a bone cell.

bone) is shown in Figure 2.31. The heavily mineralized substance is laid down in a series of concentric plates or *lamellae* around narrow channels, called Haversian canals. The latter run for the most part parallel to the long axis of the bone; they contain blood vessels, nerves, and soft connective tissue. The bone cells or *osteocytes,* which have oval bodies and numerous fiberlike processes, lie in small cavities—*Howship's lacunae*—between the lamellae. Fine canals (canaliculi) leading from the lacunae lodge the processes of the osteocytes. The canals of neighboring lacunae communicate with one another. The bony lamellae are thus pierced in all directions by a system of fine interconnected channels. The hollow center of the shaft of the bone is filled with a soft, fatty material called the *yellow marrow.*

The osteocytes are of two types—*osteoblasts* and *osteoclasts.*

Through the activity of the former type of cell, bony tissue is laid down and molded in the growing bone. The osteoclasts are respon· sible for the absorption of bony tissue. Thus, by the properly balanced actions of these two types of bone cell the growing bone is sculptured into its characteristic structure and shape.

Cancellous bone is made up of slender bars of osseous tissue called

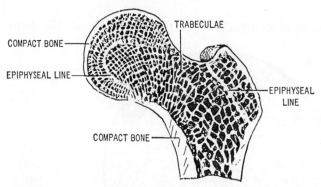

COMPACT BONE

TRABECULAE

EPIPHYSEAL LINE

EPIPHYSEAL LINE

COMPACT BONE

Fig. 2.32   Section of the upper end of the thigh bone (femur) showing cancellous bone. Note the heavier bars of bone along the lines of stress—i.e., through which the weight of the body is transmitted.

trabeculae which interlace with one another (Fig. 2.32), and give a spongelike pattern to the bony structure. The spaces between the trabeculae are filled with a soft, dark red tissue called the *red marrow* which is responsible for the manufacture of red blood cells, granular leucocytes, and probably also the blood platelets (Fig. 2.33). This substance consists of a mass of immature red blood cells and granular leucocytes in various stages of their development, as well as the forerunners of the platelets—the *megacaryocytes* (Chap. 3)— and a few mature erythrocytes and leucocytes. The ribs and bodies of the vertebrae as well as the ends of the long bones are composed of cancellous bone covered by a thin layer of compact bone. In the cranial bones, the spongy bone is also found sandwiched between two layers of dense bone.

Intercellular substances. Between the cells forming a solid tissue there is a semifluid viscous and structureless material resembling a soft jelly. In most tissues this gelatinous material is very scanty and serves as a glue or cement to hold the cells together and to permit water, dissolved substances, and even particulate matter to pass between the cells. Thus, material passes readily through the capillary wall from the blood into the surrounding fluid in the tissue spaces,

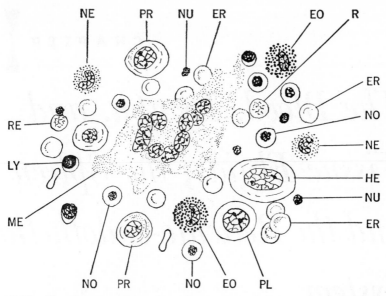

Fig. 2.33   Showing a section of red bone marrow. EO, eosinophil leucocyte; ER, erythrocyte; LY, lymphocyte; ME, megakaryocyte; NE, neutrophil leuco-cyte; NO, normoblast; NU, extruded nucleus from normoblast; PR, primitive erythrocyte; PL, primitive leucocyte; R, reticulocyte; RE, reticulocyte with ex-truded nucleus; HE, earliest stage in development of the blood cells—ancestor of both red cells and granulocytes (hemocytoblast).

or in the reverse direction from the extravascular fluid into the blood stream. This material between the cells is called *intercellular cement*. In other tissues—e.g., the connective tissues—the jellylike material is more abundant and forms a matrix in which cells and fibers are embedded. It is called *intercellular ground substance*. Chemically, it consists of *hyaluronic acid*. It is present as a homogeneous jellylike cell-free material in several situations, such as in the interior of the eyeball (the vitreous body), and as a thick covering for the umbilical cord, which has been known for many years as Wharton's jelly. Hyaluronic acid is liquified by an enzyme known as *hyaluronidase*. This enzyme is present in many tissues of the body. When injected subcutaneously, its liquifying action upon the ground substance of the subcutaneous tissues enables any injected fluid (e.g., physiolog-ical saline) to penetrate more widely from the point of injection. When certain tissue extracts (e.g., of testes) were observed to exert such an action, the factor responsible, whose chemical identity was then unknown, was referred to as the "spreading factor." Hyaluron-idase is also produced by certain bacteria which are thus aided in spreading through an infected tissue.

CHAPTER 3

The Blood, Lymph, and Tissue Fluids; the Spleen and the Reticulo-endothelial System

The blood and tissue fluids of multicellular animals perform those functions which in unicellular forms are carried out through the medium of their watery environment. Thus, the amoeba receives its oxygen through diffusion from the surrounding water. Carbon dioxide produced within the cell diffuses outward through the cell membrane. Respiration, the absorption of oxygen and the elimination of carbon dioxide, is therefore a relatively simple process for the amoeba. The processes of nutrition and excretion are accomplished in a manner equally primitive. Food materials pass through the cell membrane either in solution or as fine particles, and waste products pass into the surrounding medium. Other requirements of the unicellular organism, such as the maintenance of an optimum temperature and the proper degree of moisture, are dependent upon the immediate environment.

The elemental needs of each cell in a multicellular form, from the most primitive type to the highest vertebrate, are the same as those of the unicellular organism; yet in the evolution of higher forms, the cells constituting their bodies have become far removed from immediate contact with the outside world. No longer can the exchange of respiratory gases, the acquisition of nutriment, and the excretion of waste products be carried out in the direct and simple manner practiced by the unicellular forms. The more primitive of the multicellular types overcame the difficulty by the development of canal systems which opened upon their exteriors and through which the water flowed freely, in and out, bringing oxygen and nutriment to the more deeply lying cells and bearing carbon dioxide and other excretory products away. This, the first attempt at a circulation, was an open one. As higher forms evolved, the circulation became closed—the waters of the environment no longer flowed through the body. Yet, the vessels of this closed circulatory system were filled with a liquid which took the place of and fulfilled the duties of the watery environment of the more primitive types. The blood and other body fluids may be looked upon as that environment which has been enclosed within the bodies of the higher forms, but which has undergone certain modifications in composition to meet the requirements of the more specialized cells of various types of which their bodies are composed.

In health, the chemical constitutions of the blood, and body fluids generally, vary with respect to both gases and solids in solution, within but very narrow limits. The mechanisms maintaining this relative constancy—the chief of which are the lungs, kidneys, skin, bowels, and ductless (endocrine) glands—interact in the most complex manner and carry out their functions with the greatest precision. They respond with the utmost delicacy to any condition which might tend to cause any departure from the normal state. This relatively unvarying composition of the internal environment has been named *homeostasis* by the late Professor Cannon of Harvard.

Functions of blood and body fluids. The functions of the blood and body fluids are summarized as follows:

1. *Respiratory*. The transport of oxygen from the air in the lungs to the tissues, and of carbon dioxide from the tissues to the lungs.

2. *Nutritive*. The conveyance of food materials, glucose, amino acids, and fats from the alimentary canal to the tissues.

3. *Excretory*. The removal of the waste products of metabolism; e.g., urea, uric acid, creatinine, etc.

4. *Maintenance of the water content of the tissues*. Though the blood itself is contained within definite channels—arteries, capillaries, and veins (p. 121)—a constant interchange of fluid takes place across the walls of the finest vessels (p. 65). It is the fluid lying

outside the blood vessels—the *interstitial* or *tissue fluid*—and not the blood itself which comes into actual contact with the cells of the solid tissues. Such fluid is comparable to the watery environment of unicellular forms of life and may be rightly looked upon as the cellular or internal environment of higher forms or, as the great French physiologist of the nineteenth century, Claude Bernard, termed it, the *milieu interne*. Interstitial fluid closely resembles the blood plasma in composition and is identical in this respect to lymph (p. 98). Through the medium of the interstitial fluid, the final stage in the passage of oxygen and food material to the cells, and the first stage of the journey of carbon dioxide from the tissues to the lungs and of other waste products to the kidneys, is made.

5. *Regulation of the body temperature* (see p. 376).

6. *Protective and regulative.* The blood, tissue fluids, and lymph contain certain chemical substances of a complex nature, antitoxins, lysins, and other antibodies which are the basis of the body's defense against bacteria and injurious agents of various kinds. The blood is also the vehicle by which the hormones of the different ductless glands (Chap. 10) are carried to all parts of the body.

The distribution of the body water. The total quantity of water in the body is around 70 percent of the body's weight. Part of this water, about 20 percent of the body weight, lies outside cells and is therefore called *extracellular* water. It comprises the water of the blood plasma, of the lymph, of the interstitial or tissue fluid, and the small amounts of fluid in the pleural and abdominal cavities and in the pericardial sac (p. 115). The water within the tissue cells, the *intracellular* water, is much more abundant, amounting to about 50 percent of the weight of the body. The partitions of the body water are shown in Figure 3.1 and the water content of the several types of tissue

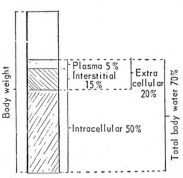

Fig. 3.1 Diagram showing the divisions of the body water.

are given in Table 3-1. It may cause some surprise that the water content of the blood is no greater than that of some of the so-called solid tissues.

In health, the volume of body water is kept remarkably constant. Any tendency toward a reduction in volume arouses the sensation of thirst, and a balance is struck between the intake and the output

Table 3-1

Percentage of water in several types of tissue

Adipose tissue 20
Blood (cells 65, plasma 92) 80
Bone (marrow free) 25–30
Connective tissue 60
Kidney 80
Liver 70
Muscle (striated) 75
Nervous tissue:
    Gray matter 85
    White matter 70

of water. The amount of water taken into the body daily, or over any considerable period, must equal the amount lost from the body (i.e., the water output). Otherwise the body would lose or gain weight, the tissues would contain less (i.e., become dehydrated) or more than the normal amount of water.

The water *intake* comprises water drunk as such or as other beverages, as well as the water in semisolid and solid food.[1] The *output* of water takes place through the skin, the expired air (which is saturated with water), and in the urine and feces.

A balance sheet of the intake and output of water for an average-sized man, at moderate air temperature and humidity, is given in Table 3-2.

Table 3-2

The water balance
(24-hour period in cc)

Intake		Output	
Solid and semisolid food ...	1200	Skin	350
Water of metabolism [1]	300	Expired air	500
Drinks (water, milk, coffee,		Urine	1500
tea, etc.)	1000	Feces	150
	2500		2500

[1] Meats, bread, and the so-called solid foods, other than those consisting largely of fat, actually contain a large proportion of water. Lean raw beef (muscle), for example, is 75 percent water before cooking. Even perfectly dry food furnishes water to the body during its metabolism; its hydrogen being oxidized to water (H_2O). This is called the *water of metabolism*.

The amount of water lost through the skin surface and lungs amounts to about one third of the total water output. Water is lost through the skin not only in sweat, but as a result of the diffusion outward of water from the moist tissues beneath the skin and its evaporation from the body surface. Even though no secretion of sweat occurs, as in the rare instances when sweat glands are lacking, water is continually being lost from the body in this way as from any moist object. The water lost through skin and lungs varies, of course, with the temperature and humidity of the air. The greatest loss occurs in a hot, dry atmosphere. A rise in air humidity reduces evaporation from the body surface and consequently the amount of water lost in this way is also reduced. A rise in body temperature increases water lost both by increasing the rate of respiration and by increasing the evaporation from the body surface. In fever, therefore, excessive water loss (dehydration), unless guarded against, is likely to occur.

The physiological mechanisms controlling the body's water balance are of the utmost complexity and delicacy; they can only be touched upon lightly here. The composition of the blood (its osmotic pressure), the antidiuretic hormone of the pituitary body (p. 438), the sense of thirst, and the activity of the kidneys are the chief factors concerned. Any tendency toward a reduction in body water is followed by a rise in the osmotic pressure of the blood which stimulates the output of the hormone of the pituitary body and reduces the output of urine; at the same time the sensation of thirst signals to consciousness the necessity for drinking and thus replenishing the body's store of water. Generally speaking, water can be retained in the body only as an isotonic solution (p. 67); that is, one with an osmotic pressure identical with that of the fluids within the tissue cells. Therefore, any dilution of the blood in electrolytes, or any undue concentration, is counteracted, as just indicated, by increasing the water output or intake, respectively.

Composition of the Blood

The blood is a highly complex fluid in which are suspended solid elements—the *blood cells* or *corpuscles*. Though blood is fluid, it must be classed as a tissue. As a matter of fact, the water content of blood is not greatly higher than that of most of the so-called solid tissues. If a tube is filled with blood and rotated rapidly in an instrument known as a centrifuge, the cells are thrown down to the bottom of the tube. The blood is thus separated into two portions—a packed mass of cells which constitute around 45 (44 to 47) percent of the volume of the specimen and an almost clear, faintly yellow fluid called the *plasma,* which makes up the remaining 55 (53 to 56) percent. To obtain a precise measurement of the proportion of red cells to plasma, an instrument called a *hematocrit* is employed (see Pl. 1 and Fig. 3.7). The plasma contains *proteins* as well as many organic and inorganic substances in solution—nutritive and waste materials, antibodies, hormones, and other compounds of an unknown or imperfectly known chemical constitution. The specific gravity of whole blood is about 1.055; that of plasma about 1.027. The cells of blood are of three types—the *red corpuscles* or *erythrocytes,* the *white corpuscles* or *leucocytes,* and the *platelets* or *thrombocytes.*

The composition of blood is summarized as follows:

Whole blood
   A. *Cells:*
      (1) Red corpuscles or erythrocytes
      (2) White corpuscles or leucocytes
      (3) Platelets or thombocytes
   B. *Plasma:*
      (1) Water 90 to 92 percent
      (2) Solids, 8 to 10 percent
         (a) *Proteins,* 7 percent. Serum albumin, serum globulin, and fibrinogen.
         (b) *Inorganic constituents,* 0.9 percent. Sodium, calcium, potassium, magnesium, phosphorus, etc.
         (c) *Organic constituents* (other than protein). Nonprotein nitrogenous substances (urea, uric acid, xanthine, hypoxanthine, creatine and creatinine, ammonia, and aminoacids), neutral fats, phospholipids, cholesterol, glucose.
      (3) *Respiratory gases,* oxygen and carbon dioxide.
      (4) *Internal secretions, antibodies,* and *various enzymes.*

The plasma proteins. The total protein concentration of the plasma is around 7 percent. The plasma proteins are of three types—*serum albumin* (4 percent), *serum globulin* (2.7 percent), and *fibrinogen* (0.3 percent).[2] The origin of the serum albumin is not known with certainty, but the experimental evidence points to the liver as the most probable source; there is little doubt that fibrinogen is produced in the liver. The serum globulin is derived from the lymphocytes. It was thought at one time that plasma protein was food protein

---

[2] Plasma from which the fibrinogen has been removed through clotting is called *serum.*

which was being transported from the digestive tract to the tissues. It is now known, however, the food protein is not absorbed as such, but must first be broken down into its constituent amino acids (p. 360).

By a special method (electrophoresis) the serum globulin can be split into three fractions, called *alpha, beta,* and *gamma* globulins.

The proteins of the plasma serve several important *functions:* (a) they exert an osmotic pressure amounting to from 25 to 30 mm of mercury, which is a factor of first importance in the regulation of the blood volume (p. 63), and in the excretion of urine (p. 276); (b) they give viscosity to the blood, and thus aid to some degree in the maintenance of the blood pressure (p. 147); (c) the fibrinogen, but not the other kinds, plays an essential role in the coagulation of the blood (p. 103); and (d) the gamma fraction of the serum globulin (gamma globulin) is associated with the production of immune bodies (pp. 101 and 215). The concentration of this protein is increased during the process of immunization.

Most of the organic constituents of the plasma other than protein represent waste products of metabolism (e.g., urea, uric acid, etc.) together with nutritive materials (e.g., amino acids, glucose, and fats) absorbed from the intestinal tract. Of the inorganic constituents of plasma, sodium chloride is in highest concentration. The plasma also contains potassium, calcium, magnesium, sodium bicarbonate, and minute amounts of iodine and iron. Phosphorus is present in both inorganic and organic forms. The concentration of inorganic phosphorus is about 3 mg and that of the organic form about 40 mg per 100 cc of blood. Potassium is in relatively high concentration in the cells of the blood and in the cells of the solid tissues, but is in low concentration in the plasma and the body fluids generally. Sodium has a reverse distribution, being relatively high in the blood plasma and the body fluids, but is in low concentration in the blood cells and in the cells of the solid tissues. In some species this mineral is absent from the erythrocytes (see Table 3-3).

Table 3-3

Inorganic constituents of plasma, red cells, and whole blood.
Milligrams per 100 cc, average values

	Sodium	Potassium	Calcium	Magnesium	Chlorine	Iodine	Iron
Plasma......	340	20	10	2.7	370	0.001	0.1
Cells........	0	420	0	6.0	190		100
Whole blood.	160	200	5	4.0	250		50

The proportions of the inorganic elements in plasma, blood cells, and whole blood are given in Table 3-3. The concentrations of minerals in blood cells and plasma may be taken as representative of their proportions in the cells and fluids of the body generally. Serious results follow if, as in adrenal insufficiency (p. 425), these relationships are disturbed.

The Red Blood Cells or Erythrocytes

The human erythrocytes of man and those of most higher animals are circular disc-shaped cells possessing no nucleus. They have a mean diameter of 7.2 microns (0.0072 millimeters), and a thickness of

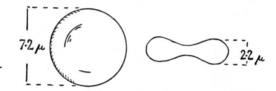

Fig. 3.2.   Showing the diameters of a red blood cell.

about 2.2 microns (Fig. 3.2). The central portion of the cell is much thinner than the circumference which, therefore, appears as a rim around a central depression. This construction gives the cell a biconcave contour or a roughly dumbbell outline when viewed edgewise. In shed blood, the red cells show a tendency to adhere to one another by their flat surfaces. This arrangement, which resembles a stack of

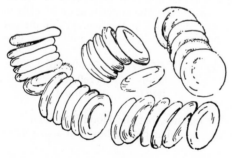

Fig. 3.3   Showing erythrocytes in rouleaux.

coins toppled over (Fig. 3.3), is spoken of as a *rouleau* and the process as *rouleaux formation*. The cell is bounded by a membrane composed of protein in association with the lipid materials, *lecithin* and *cholesterol*. The chief function of the red cells is respiratory; namely, to carry oxygen from the lungs to the capillaries (p. 249) of the various tissues, and mainly in an indirect way, to transport carbon diox-

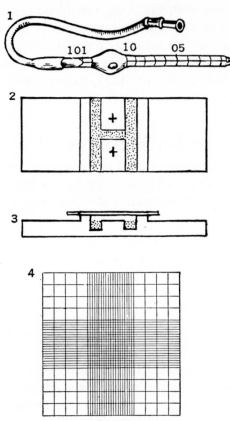

Fig. 3.4 Hemocytometer for counting the red blood cells. 1, pipette for diluting blood sample; 2, glass slide, provided with two platforms on each of which ruled squares marked by +, and shown highly magnified in 4, are engraved. Each square has an area of 1/400 sq mm; 3, slide in cross section with cover glass in position. The skin near the base of the thumb nail is pricked with a sterile needle or a fragment of glass, and blood drawn into the pipette as far as the mark 0.5. A suitable diluting fluid is then sucked up as far as the mark 101. The blood is thoroughly mixed with the diluting fluid (the glass bead in the dilated part of the pipette facilitates mixing). The fluid in the stem of the pipette is first expelled, a drop of the blood, diluted 1 part in 200, is then expressed on to the surface of each platform of the glass slide and a cover glass laid on. A trench bounding each platform on three sides provides for any overflow. The depth of the film of diluted blood between a platform and a cover glass is 1/10 mm. The volume of diluted blood marked off by one square is therefore 1/4000 cu mm. The blood cells in a number of squares are counted and the average taken. The concentration of cells in cubic millimeter of blood is then readily calculated. If the average number of cells in each square is 7, then the total number in a cubic millimeter is— $4000 \times 7 \times 200 = 5,600,000$.

4000	×	7	×	200	=	5,600,000
(cu mm fluid over 1 square)		(average cells per square)		(dilu- tion)		(cells per cu mm)

The white cells are counted in a similar manner, but the blood is diluted 1 in 20 by a fluid which destroys the red cells; a similar pipette but with appropriate graduation is employed.

ide from the tissues to the lungs (pp. 111 and 252). The ability of the cell to carry oxygen is dependent upon its containing a remarkable pigment called *hemoglobin* (p. 68). It is to this pigment that the characteristic color of blood is due.

The number of red cells in a cubic millimeter of blood is usually stated to be 4,500,000 for women and 5,000,000 for men. As a matter of fact the values in health are somewhat higher than these, and in a robust young male 6,000,000 is not an unusual figure. The number shows some slight variation during 24 hours, being lowest in the early morning, but increasing gradually throughout the day. The number of red cells is somewhat higher (by half a million or so per cubic millimeter) in newborn infants than in older children or adults.

The number of red cells in a cubic millimeter of a given specimen of blood is determined by counting the cells beneath the microscope. The instrument used for such a purpose is called a *hemocytometer* (see Fig. 3.4). The actual procedure followed in the enumeration of the red and white cells is described in the legend. By knowing the number of red cells per cubic millimeter (i.e., their concentration) as well as the quantity of blood in the body (p. 63), an approximate estimate of the total number of cells in the circulation may be arrived at. The figure is about thirty-five trillion (35,000,000,000,000).

Variations in the number of red cells. The red cell count (i.e., the number of red cells in each cubic millimeter of the blood) is increased: (a) during muscular exercise, (b) at high altitudes, and (c) as a result of a rise in environmental temperature. Also, a loss of water or of plasma from the blood (anhydremia, p. 83), although obviously not increasing the total number of circulating cells, will raise their concentration, and will therefore increase the red cell count.

The rise in the red cell concentration which occurs during muscular exercise, and at high environmental temperatures, is due mainly to contraction of the spleen which serves as a reservoir for red cells (p. 96). Contraction of the spleen also occurs when a person breathes

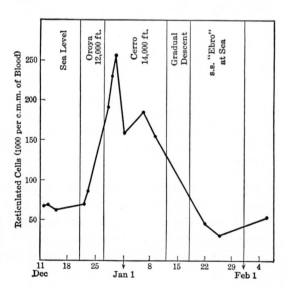

Fig. 3.5   A graph of the reticulocyte response to low tension of oxygen in the atmosphere (high altitude). (After Barcroft.)

rarefied air (i.e., air having a low pressure of oxygen) either in a closed chamber, in which the atmospheric pressure is reduced artificially, or in airplane or mountain ascents. An extra supply of red cells is thus discharged into the circulation. If the breathing of rarefied air is continued over a long period, as by those living in mountainous regions, the red bone marrow—the tissue wherein the red cells are manufactured (p. 50)—is stimulated, its bulk is considerably increased, and the red cell count is permanently raised. A count of 8,000,000 is not unusual in mountain dwellers. When the red bone marrow is *suddenly* stimulated by a low oxygen tension, as when a person who has been accustomed to live at a low altitude ascends to a great height (over 10,000 feet), the cells that are discharged into the general circulation are in a somewhat immature stage of their development. These cells, which normally are less than 1 percent of the red cells in the general blood stream, may increase to constitute 5 percent or more of the total number of red cells. These slightly immature cells are known as *reticulated cells* or *reticulocytes* (p. 70, see also Pl. 2 and Fig. 3.5).

Blood whose concentration in red cells has been raised either by contraction of the spleen or by the greater manufacture and discharge of corpuscles from the red bone marrow, is capable of carrying a greater load of oxygen from the lungs to the tissues. This is a distinct advantage during muscular exercise, or when the pressure of oxygen in the atmosphere is low. In the latter instance, the high red cell count helps to compensate for the low oxygen pressure of the atmosphere.

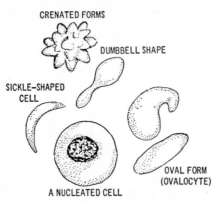

CRENATED FORMS

DUMBBELL SHAPE

SICKLE–SHAPED CELL

OVAL FORM (OVALOCYTE)

A NUCLEATED CELL

Fig. 3.6 Some abnormal types of erythrocyte found in the blood in anemia.

When the temperature of the environment is raised, the discharge of blood from the spleen serves the useful purpose, through augmenting the volume of circulating blood, of increasing the capacity of the body's heat radiating system and thus aiding in the regulation of the body temperature (Pl. 6A).

Abnormalities in the form and structure of the erythrocytes. Nucleated cells containing hemoglobin and of the same size as erythrocytes are known as *normoblasts* (see p. 70); they are normal constituents of the red bone marrow, but are only seen in the general circulation in anemia or other abnormality of the blood. Also, the presence in the circulation of reticulocytes persistently over 1 percent is abnormal, or at least unusual. In disorders of the blood, red cells in very early stages of their development and containing little or no hemoglobin appear in the circulation, as well as deformed erythrocytes known as *poikilocytes*. These latter include mulberry, shrunken, hourglass, and other bizarre shapes. Shrinkage of the erythrocytes with the production of eminences on their surfaces, like the mulberry forms just mentioned, can be induced by immersing the cells in a hypertonic saline solution (p. 68), when, as a result of the higher salt concentration in the surrounding fluid as compared with that inside the cell, osmotic force causes the transfer of fluid from the cell. Such shrinkage and deformation of the cell is called *crenation* (Fig. 3.6); the process whereby it is produced is the reverse of that causing hemolysis (see p. 84).

Cells below or above the normal size are characteristic of certain anemias (p. 72).

The Volume of the Blood

The total quantity of blood in the body of an average-sized man (70 kilograms) is around 6 liters (over 6 quarts), or about one eleventh of the total weight of the body. It can be measured in the living sub-

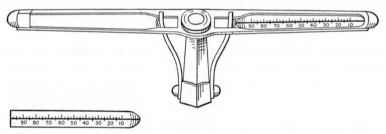

Fig. 3.7   Hematocrit. Blood to which sodium oxalate or other anticoagulant agent has been added is drawn into the graduated tubes which are then placed in the holder and rotated in a centrifuge at a rate of 3000 revolutions per minute. The blood is thus separated into a red (cells) and a straw-colored portion (plasma), the proportions of each being easily determined by means of the graduations on the tubes.

ject by injecting a solution of a harmless dye into a vein. *Vital red* is the dye most commonly used for this purpose. A few minutes after its injection the dye becomes thoroughly mixed with the circulating blood. A sample of blood is then withdrawn from a vein by means of a syringe, and the plasma separated from the cells by centrifuging. The plasma, which is now colored pink by the dye, is compared with a standard solution containing the dye in known dilution. The extent to which the sample of injected dye has been diluted in the blood stream is thus arrived at. From this the total volume of the *plasma* is calculated. But it is desired to know the volume of the *whole* blood—i.e., of cells and plasma. The next step is, therefore, to determine the proportion of cells to plasma in a sample of the subject's blood. This is done by centrifuging a sample of blood in an instrument known as an *hematocrit* (see Fig. 3.7). If the blood has the normal proportions of cells and plasma—namely, 45 percent and 55 percent, respectively—and the volume of the plasma as indicated by the dilution of the dye in the circulation is 3.4 liters (3400 cc), then the total blood volume is $\frac{34}{55} \times 100 = 6.1$ liters

Another method of more recent development in which the volume of the *whole* blood is measured employs a radioactive isotope of iron (Fe^{55}). Erythrocytes from a healthy donor belonging to a compatible blood group (p. 78) are "tagged" with the isotope by injecting the latter into the donor some 24 hours previously. A sample of his blood is withdrawn at the end of this period, its radioactivity is determined, and it is then injected into the subject whose blood volume is to be estimated. After time has been allowed for thorough mixing in the circulation, a sample of blood is drawn and a determination made by means of a Geiger counter of the quantity of radioactive iron that it contains; the dilution of the injected blood in the recipient's blood is then calculated and the blood volume estimated.

Regulation of the blood volume. The passage of materials through membranes. The volume of the blood in health remains remarkably constant. There are two main factors in its regulation: (a) the *osmotic pressure* of the proteins of the plasma and tissue fluids, and (b) the *hydraulic or hydrostatic pressure* of the blood in the capillaries and of the fluids surrounding them.

Osmotic pressure may be best explained by citing an example. If an aqueous solution of cane sugar or sodium chloride is placed in a small closed sac made of a suitable membrane and immersed in water, and if the membrance is permeable to water but impermeable to the molecules of the dissolved substance, then water will pass into the sac but the sugar or salt molecules will not pass out (that is, into the surrounding water). The pressure within the sac, therefore, rises; the walls of the sac become distended and may rupture. The force created in this way is spoken of as the *osmotic pressure*. The dissolved material appears to "attract" or "draw" the water through the membrane. A membrane which permits the passage of water, but bars the passage of some water-soluble substance is said to be *semipermeable* with respect to that substance (Fig. 3.8). Now, the membrane forming the walls of the capillaries (which connect the small vessels on the arterial side of the circulation with the small veins, see p. 124) is semipermeable only in so far as the plasma proteins are concerned. It permits the passage of water and the relatively small molecules of sugar, urea, sodium chloride, and other crystalloids, but hinders the passage of the relatively very large molecules of the plasma proteins. Only very small quantities of the latter pass through the capillary wall. The proteins of the plasma, therefore, exert a force which "draws" water from the surrounding tissue spaces, and tends to prevent the passage of water out of the vessels. The crystalloids (sugar, sodium chloride, etc.) on the contrary exert little or no osmotic pressure in so far as the plasma and the tissue fluids are concerned. The osmotic force exerted by the proteins of the plasma equals a pressure of from 25 to 30 mm of mercury (mm Hg).[3] In order to overcome this osmotic pressure and drive water and dissolved salts through the capillary wall, an opposing hydraulic pressure must be applied. This

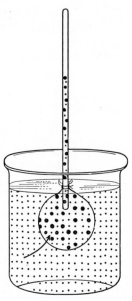

Fig. 3.8 Diagram illustrating osmotic pressure. A sac formed of a semipermeable membrane is fastened to one end of a tube. The large dots represent sugar molecules; the small ones, water molecules. Water passes through the pores of the membrane as indicated by the arrow. The pressure within the sac rises as shown by the height of the fluid column in the glass tube.

is provided by the pressure of blood in the capillaries. The capillary blood pressure must, of course, be greater than the protein osmotic pressure. Such a relationship between osmotic and hydraulic pressures exists at the arterial end of the capillary. But a gradual fall in blood pressure occurs from the arterial end where it amounts to a little over 30 mm Hg, to the venous end where it is around 12 mm Hg. In the

[3] The pressure exerted by the plasma proteins is very low as osmotic pressures go. A solution of cane sugar or a solution of an electrolyte, such as sodium chloride, when separated from water by a semipermeable membrane (impermeable to the sugar or salt but permeable to water) would exert an osmotic pressure hundreds of times greater than that exerted by the blood plasma.

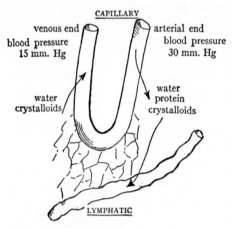

Fig. 3.9 Illustrating the exchange of fluid between blood capillary, tissue spaces, and lymph vessel.

venous end of the capillary, the osmotic pressure, therefore, exceeds the hydraulic pressure by several millimeters of mercury, and fluid is "drawn" back into the vessels (Fig. 3.9). Thus, through the passage of fluid from one part of the capillary and its return to the circulation at another part, oxygen and nutritive materials are conveyed from the blood to the tissue cells, and carbon dioxide and other waste products from the cells to the blood. The osmotic and hydrostatic pressures of the tissue fluids surrounding the capillaries are also factors which must be considered in the transference of fluid across the capillary membrane. The osmotic pressure of these fluids serves to counteract in part the osmotic pressure of the plasma. The tissue fluids also exert a certain, though small, hydrostatic pressure which offsets somewhat the driving force of the capillary blood pressure.

In order to visualize the passage of molecules or ions through a membrane, which appears to be a continuous sheet, it is supposed that the membrane is pierced by numberless "pores" or "channels," and, acting like a sieve, permits molecules below a certain size to pass but bars the escape of larger particles. Such a mechanical conception, though it may not express the precise truth, does, neverthe-

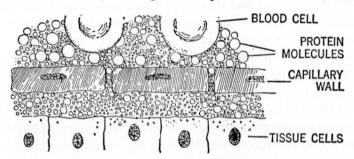

Fig. 3.10 Diagram to illustrate the retention of large molecules (plasma proteins) within the circulation, and the escape of smaller ones (sodium, chloride, glucose, urea, amino acids, etc.). The relative dimensions of the molecules and of the blood and tissue cells are represented only in a very general way.

less, explain why a membrane, such as that forming the capillary walls, permits the free escape of the small molecules of water, sugar, sodium chloride, etc., while barring the transmission of the much larger molecules of the plasma proteins (see Fig. 3.10). When, however, we come to consider other membranes, such as the one enveloping the erythrocyte, any structure of a sievelike nature fails to explain the free passage of some ions and the barring of other smaller ones. With the exception of the hydrogen ion the membrane of the red cell

Table 3-4

Blood		Tissue fluid
Hydrostatic pressure 30 mm Hg		Hydrostatic pressure 8 mm Hg
Net or effective hydrostatic pressure 22 mm Hg	Capillary wall	⟶
Osmotic pressure 25 mm Hg		Osmotic pressure 10 mm Hg
Net or effective osmotic pressure 15 mm	⟵	

Therefore, force driving fluid from capillaries = 7 mm Hg

is almost impermeable to cations, such as those of potassium (K^+), sodium Na^+), and calcium (Ca^{++}). As we have already seen, the interior of the blood cells and also the tissue cells are rich in potassium but poor or quite lacking in sodium, or calcium, or in both. The blood plasma, on the other hand, and the body fluids generally, have a relatively high concentration of sodium and a moderate content of calcium. Anions, such as HCO_3^- (of carbonic acid) and Cl^-, pass freely across the boundary of the red corpuscles. The membrane thus holds potassium within the cells while preventing the entrance of sodium and calcium. These facts cannot be explained on the basis of size, for the HCO_3 ion is larger presumably than the potassium, sodium, or calcium ion.

Except for small variations which occur from time to time as a result of ionic interchanges, the osmotic pressures of both the plasma and the fluid within the red cell are equal. The contents of the cell and the plasma are in osmotic equilibrium, or *isotonic,* which is the customary term. If distilled water be added to the plasma, or the cells be placed in a salt solution of lower osmotic pressure than that of the interior of the erythrocytes—that is, the cells are now surrounded by a *hypotonic* solution—water is "attracted" or "drawn" into the cells which then increase in volume and lose their hemoglobin (p. 84). On the other hand, when, as described elsewhere, the erythrocytes are immersed in a fluid having a higher salt concentration than the plasma—that is, in a *hypertonic* solution—water is lost from the cells which become shrunken or crenated (p. 63).

A homely illustration of osmotic effects is afforded by the behavior of an unskinned fruit such as a peach when it is placed in water (the water being hypotonic with respect to the fluids within the peach skin which acts as a semipermeable membrane) or when it is placed in a strong solution of sugar (which is hypertonic). In the first instance, water is absorbed by the peach which then swells and may burst its skin. In the second instance, the peach shrinks because water is "drawn" from it by the concentrated sugar solution in which it is immersed.

Hemoglobin

Hemoglobin, the coloring matter of the blood, belongs to the class of conjugated proteins, its molecule being composed of a pigment group called *heme* or *hematin* and a protein known as *globin*. The heme, in turn, is constituted of a pigment called *porphyrin* combined with iron.

Porphyrins are very widely distributed throughout animal and vegetable life. The green coloring matter of plants, known as *chlorophyll,* and pigments in the plumage of certain birds are porphyrin compounds. The brown pigment in the shell of the hen's egg is a porphyrin very closely allied to the porphyrin in hemoglobin. Porphyrins possess the property of combining with various metals—e.g., copper, cobalt, magnesium (in chlorophyll), silver, nickel, iron, etc. Such compounds are grouped as a class under the term *metalloporphyrins*. Heme is a member of this class, the metal in this instance being iron. Hemoglobin is therefore a *porphyrin-iron-globin compound*.

The constitution of the hemoglobin molecule may be shown concisely as follows:

porphyrin + iron = heme (or hematin)
heme (or hematin) + globin = hemoglobin

It has been mentioned that hemoglobin serves as a carrier of oxygen from the lungs to the tissues. This function is dependent upon the unique property, which the pigment possesses, of forming a very loose or unstable compound with oxygen. The hemoglobin molecule contains four atoms of iron, each of which can combine with a molecule of oxygen. But a true *oxide of iron is not formed;* the hemoglobin is therefore said to be *oxygenated,* not *oxidized.* The oxygenation of hemoglobin may be represented thus: $Hb_4 + 4O_2 = Hb_4O_8$.

The affinity of hemoglobin for oxygen is remarkable. When exposed to air it combines rapidly with oxygen—the compound being then called *oxyhemoglobin.* If the oxyhemoglobin is then exposed to an atmosphere in which the oxygen pressure is low, the compound readily decomposes, oxygen being liberated. That is, the oxyhemoglobin is reduced; the compound is then called *reduced hemoglobin.* The ease with which hemoglobin gives up its oxygen, as the oxygen pressure to which it is exposed is lowered, shows the loose way in which the oxygen and iron are combined. In a true iron oxide, as we know, oxygen is in firm combination with the metal and is *not* released when the oxide is exposed to a low pressure of oxygen.

The absorption of oxygen by the blood. The quantity of oxygen which blood will absorb is some sixty times greater than that which can be absorbed by an equivalent volume of water. For example, if 100 cc. of water are exposed to an atmosphere containing the same percentage of oxygen as is present in the air of the lungs, about $\frac{1}{3}$ cc of the gas will be absorbed. Yet 100 cc of blood exposed to the same atmosphere will absorb nearly 20 cc of oxygen. The difference is due entirely to the hemoglobin. The total amount of blood in the human body (5 to 6 liters) will hold from 1000 to 1200 cc of oxygen. This quantity of oxygen is used by the tissues in 5 minutes or so during rest, and in a fraction of a minute during strenuous muscular exercise. In the absence of hemoglobin, the entire duty for the carriage of oxygen would devolve upon the plasma (which is mostly water), and in order that this should be able to absorb and carry the quantity of gas necessary to satisfy the requirements of the tissues, its volume would have to be some sixty times greater than it is. The circulating fluid instead of being 5 or 6 liters, or about one eleventh of the body weight, would need to be more than 350 liters—over five times the bulk of the solid tissues!

The volume of oxygen which blood will take up when its hemoglobin is fully saturated is called the *oxygen capacity* of the blood. As just mentioned, this depends almost entirely upon the hemoglobin. The oxygen capacity of a sample of blood is therefore directly proportional to the quantity of hemoglobin which it contains. Each gram of hemoglobin takes up a maximum of 1.34 cc of oxygen. Now, each 100 cubic centimeters of normal human blood contains some 15 grams of hemoglobin. So then (15 $\times$ 1.34 $=$) 20 cc is the oxygen capacity of 100 cc of normal human blood. If, as in anemia, the hemoglobin content is below normal, the oxygen-carrying capacity of the blood is correspondingly reduced. Further details of the role played by hemoglobin in supplying oxygen to the tissues—i.e., its respiratory function—will be given in Chapter 6.

The Formation and History of the Red Cells

The red cells are manufactured in the red marrow of the bones—skull, ribs, vertebrae, and to much less extent except in children, in the ends of the long bones of the limbs. The term *hemopoiesis* is applied to the process of blood formation—i.e., to the production of all types of blood cell. When it is wished only to refer to the manufacture of red cells, the term *erythropoiesis* is employed. The red cells pass through several stages of development before they are discharged from the marrow into the general circulation. At one of the earliest stages leading to its maturation, the cell is quite large, has no hemoglobin, and possesses a nucleus. The cells of this stage are called *megaloblasts* (Gk. *megas, megal,* large + *blastos,* a germ or sprout). A little later, the cell acquires hemoglobin, becomes reduced in size, and is then called an *erythroblast*. The stage of the *normoblast* follows (Pl. 2). The cell at this stage is about the size of a mature red cell; it contains its full complement of hemoglobin, but still possesses a nucleus. In the final stage of maturation, the nucleus is expelled. The cell is now called a *reticulocyte* from the fact that when suitably stained its cytoplasm shows a fine reticulated or filigree pattern. Many cells at this stage of development, as well as normoblasts, may be seen in normal red marrow, but cells of the earliest stage, the megaloblasts, are very scarce, and erythroblasts are not plentiful. The reticulocytes are discharged into the general blood stream; normally, they constitute only about 0.5 percent of the total red cells in circulation (Fig. 3.5, p. 61). As mentioned earlier, when the bone marrow is stimulated, as by the low oxygen tension of the atmosphere which exists at high altitudes or by iron or liver administration in anemia (p. 74), large numbers of reticulocytes appear in the general circulation. They are also greatly increased in certain types of anemia.

Within a few hours after their arrival in the general blood stream, the reticulocytes lose their reticulated pattern and are then mature red cells or erythrocytes. In health, normoblasts, or any cells younger than these, do not leave the bone marrow. But in certain types of anemia, red cells in any stage of development may be found in the general circulation.

The life of the red cell. The average life of the erythrocyte is around 110 days (100 to 124 days according to various estimates). There are no special means provided for its destruction. It simply wears out as a result of the stresses and strains to which it is subjected, and breaks up in the blood stream. Small fragments, *hemoconia* or *blood dust* as they are called, may often be detected during the microscopic examination of a specimen of normal blood. The fragments are finally disposed of by the spleen, which contains large mobile cells which engulf them.

It has been estimated that in health something like a million cells per second disappear in this way and, of course, the same number must be formed afresh by the bone marrow. The number of red cells in the body at any moment, therefore, represents the balance struck between the red cell wastage and the production of new red cells by the bone marrow.

Factors in the regeneration of the blood. The red cell, as we have seen, consists of a framework (stroma) composed of protein and lipid materials, and a complex pigment—hemoglobin. The well-nourished body possesses adequate supplies of building materials for the manufacture of the cell stroma, and rarely is anemia due to any lack of the material required for the formation of this part of the cell. Not a great deal is known with regard to the mechanism of hemoglobin manufacture. It might be thought that green foods, since they are rich in the pigment chlorophyll (which, as mentioned on p. 68, is related chemically to heme), would supply elements necessary for hemoglobin synthesis. Yet it appears that chlorophyll is not utilized to any important extent for this purpose. Nor are the porphyrin and the iron in hemoglobin when taken in food utilized for the formation of hemoglobin. The heme cannot apparently be split into its constituents by the digestive enzymes (see p. 288); and neither heme nor hemoglobin can be used intact for the production of fresh hemoglobin. The globin part of the molecule can, however, be utilized, and the feeding of hemoglobin hastens the regeneration of blood pigment in certain forms of anemia. Not only is the iron in heme unavailable but the metal in other organic combinations is not utilized or is utilized very poorly. Iron in *inorganic* form (e.g., ferrous carbonate or ferrous sulphate) is absolutely necessary for normal erythropoiesis. A diet deficient in iron leads to anemia (p. 73), as does also the lack of first-class protein, the amino acids of which are required for the production of globin. The porphyrin part of the hemoglobin molecule (p. 68) can be synthesized by the body from substances furnished in the food, or from body tissues.

The ability of dogs on various diets to regenerate hemoglobin following hemorrhage was studied by Dr. Whipple and his associates of Rochester, N.Y. (see Table 3-5).

Table 3-5

The influence of diet upon hemoglobin production

Diet, grams daily	Hemoglobin produced, grams in 2-week period
Bread, 400	3
Milk, 450, bread, 400	3
Cream, 100, bread, 400	10
Spinach, 200, bread, 300	15
Raisins, 200, bread, 300	25
Eggs, 150, bread, 300	45
Chicken gizzard, 250, bread, 200	80
Chicken liver, 250, bread, 300	80
Kidney, 250, bread, 300	70
Beef liver, 450	95

Of all materials investigated, liver was found to cause the most rapid restoration of the hemoglobin. Kidney and chicken gizzard were also highly effective. As we shall see presently, these experiments led to the discovery of a highly effective means of treating a very grave type of anemia in the human subject.

It has been discovered within comparatively recent years that *copper* and *cobalt*, though not themselves constituents of the hemoglobin molecule, are also necessary, in some unexplained way, for the normal synthesis of the blood pigment.

Anemia

When the concentration of hemoglobin is below normal, the condition is called anemia. There are several varieties and grades of anemia. In very severe types, the hemoglobin may be as low as 10 percent of the normal quantity; i.e., it may be 1.5 grams per 100 cc of blood instead of 15 grams, as in health. The reduction in the hemoglobin may be the result either of there being fewer red cells, as in the most severe types of anemia, or of there being less hemoglobin in each cell, the total number of cells not being very greatly reduced. In some forms of anemia, both of these factors are present.

It has been mentioned that the number of red cells in the blood in health represents the balance struck between the loss of red cells through wear and tear in the circulation, and the production of new cells by the bone marrow. Anemia may result, therefore, from either increased destruction (or loss from the body) of red cells, or from diminished production. The anemias then may be divided into these two main categories.

A. Anemias due to blood loss or increased destruction of red cells.
1. *Posthemorrhagic.* In this type, a large amount of blood may be lost from the circulation either suddenly (*acute hemorrhage*) as a result of the opening of a large vessel—e.g., in accidental wounds, duodenal ulcer, etc.—or by repeated small hemorrhages (*chronic hemorrhage*).

2. *Hemolytic.* In this type, an abnormal number of red cells undergo destruction in the blood stream. Certain poisons—e.g., lead, arsenical preparations, etc.—cause destruction of the cells. In another type of hemolytic anemia, there appears to be some inherent defect in the erythrocytes themselves. They are more fragile and, in consequence, disintegrate more readily than usual.

B. Anemias due to defective blood formation. This group embraces anemias caused by:

1. *Iron deficiency.* Should the diet contain inadequate amounts of iron, anemia develops. In this type, the red cells, as a rule, are not greatly reduced in number, but they are smaller than the normal, and the concentration of hemoglobin in each cell is low. The pale color of the erythrocytes is usually quite evident upon microscopic examination. The qualifying terms *microcytic* (Gk. *micros,* small + *cytos,* a cell) and *hypochromic* (Gk. *hypo,* low + *chromos,* color) are frequently employed in referring to anemias of this class. Infants after the age of 6 months are likely to suffer from this type of anemia, because milk and other foods taken at this time are low in iron content, and the store of iron with which the baby came into the world has become exhausted.

2. *Protein deficiency.* A diet lacking in adequate amounts of protein of good quality is conducive to the development of anemia, for the amino acids necessary for the synthesis of the globin portion of

the hemoglobin molecule are absent or scarce. Food containing protein of high quality as in meat, liver, milk, eggs, etc., is just as important as iron for hemoglobin synthesis (see p. 71).

3. *Vitamin deficiency.* A severe dietary lack of vitamin C or of certain factors of the vitamin B complex, especially pteroylglutamic
(folic) acid, is sometimes a cause of anemia.

Anemias due to deficiencies in the diet are usually referred to as
nutritional anemias.

4. *Lack of the specific antianemic factor.* Anemia due to this cause
is commonly referred to as *pernicious anemia* because, until a cure
was discovered in 1926, it resisted all forms of treatment and invariably caused death. The hemoglobin may fall to a very low percentage
of the normal, due to the great reduction in the number of red cells.
Each cell actually contains a little more hemoglobin than does a
healthy cell. The cells are considerably larger than normal, and for
this reason are called *macrocytes* (Gk. *macros,* large + *cytos,* a cell).
In pernicious anemia, very large cells known as megaloblasts are also
seen, often in large numbers. They are very primitive cells, and resemble but are not identical with very immature erythrocytes of the
same name found in small numbers in normal bone marrow. This
normal bone marrow cell, as well as the megaloblasts of pernicious
anemia, contains no hemoglobin, and in appearance is not unlike the
large lymphocyte (p. 86).

The observations of Whipple and his associates, already mentioned (p. 72), suggested to two physicians of Boston—Drs. Minot
and Murphy—that liver might be of value in the treatment of pernicious anemia. The spectacular success which followed the feeding
of liver to victims of this disease is now well known. As a result of this
work of epochal importance, pernicious anemia was deleted, almost at
once, from the list of incurably fatal diseases.

It appeared that the liver normally discharged into the blood stream
a principle essential for the maintenance of the blood-forming function of the bone marrow. It was therefore concluded that the failure
of the liver to supply this essential principle was the cause of pernicious anemia. It has since been discovered that this essential substance is a vitamin of the vitamin B complex. It has been designated
vitamin B_{12} and is present in many foods as well as in liver. Extremely
minute doses of this material given by injection to a patient with
pernicious anemia arrest the disease almost immediately. But there
is more to this interesting story. If pernicious anemia is caused by a
lack of vitamin B_{12} and this vitamin is present in most foods of any

good diet, including food taken by those who develop pernicious anemia, it may well be asked, "Why then does the disease ever occur?" (See Fig. 3.11.)

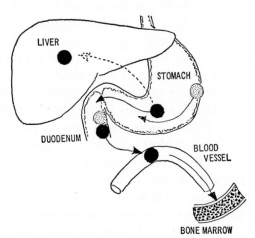

Fig. 3.11   Diagram to show the normal mechanism governing red cell production. *Black discs,* vitamin B$_{12}$ (extrinsic factor); *stippled discs,* enzyme (intrinsic factor).

The answer is that the primary cause of pernicious anemia is to be found in a defect in the mucosa of the stomach. The patient with pernicious anemia lacks an enzyme normally found in the gastric mucosa which is necessary for the absorption of adequate amounts of B$_{12}$. When relatively very large doses of the vitamin are given by mouth to the pernicious anemia patient, as in a potent liver extract, a small part passes through the intestinal wall into the circulation and is capable of arresting the disease. Ordinary foods, however, do not contain the vitamin in such large amounts. But, as mentioned before, only a very minute dose of pure vitamin B$_{12}$ (a mere fraction of a milligram) given parenterally is effective. Also, in the presence of a normal gastric mucosa, the amount of the vitamin in the diet is quite sufficient to prevent any lack of vitamin B$_{12}$. Pernicious anemia is, therefore, essentially a vitamin deficiency disease. Powdered hog's stomach, since it contains the enzyme essential for the absorption of vitamin B$_{12}$ from the food, also arrests the disease.[4]

[4] The gastric enzyme has not been identified but is not one of the known digestive enzymes, such as pepsin. The presence of such a principle was originally postulated by Dr. W. B. Castle of Boston and generally known as *Castle's intrinsic factor.* According to the theory which, until lately, was very generally accepted, the intrinsic factor acted upon an *extrinsic factor* in the food to produce a principle in the liver called the *hematinic principle.* The latter was the essential substance required for normal blood formation through an action exerted upon the bone marrow. There was much speculation as to the nature of the extrinsic factor, though some glimpse of the truth was gained, for it was thought to be a factor of the vitamin B complex or at least closely associated with the latter. The extrinsic factor is now identified as vitamin B$_{12}$, and as the so-called hematinic principle as well.

Another factor of the vitamin B complex, quite distinct from B_{12}, has been found within recent years to exert a curative effect in pernicious anemia. It is present in green vegetables, liver, kidney, and other foods. It was first named *folic acid,* but is now generally referred to by its chemical name *pteroylglutamic acid.* The action of this factor differs in certain respects from that of vitamin B_{12}. It has no power, for example, to prevent or arrest the degeneration of the nerve tracts in the spinal cord and the resulting paralysis, which is a very serious complication of pernicious anemia. The essential physiological relationship between this factor and vitamin B_{12} is not altogether clear.

5. *Toxic agents which depress the function of the bone marrow.* Certain chemical poisons (e.g., benzene compounds, radium salts, or toxic substances) produced in disease (e.g., nephritis and various infections) depress or destroy the function of the bone marrow. In some instances, the bone marrow is almost functionless, is much reduced in amount, and few red cells are produced to replace those which have been destroyed. Circulating red cells, as a consequence, fall to a very low level. The term *aplastic* is given to this type of anemia.

Hemorrhage

Hemorrhage may be defined as the loss of blood as a whole (i.e., of plasma and cells) from the blood vessels. The blood may escape from the body, as in accidents causing injury to an artery or vein—*external hemorrhage.* On the other hand, the blood may pass into the surrounding tissues, such as the brain or lungs, or into one of the hollow viscera, such as the stomach or intestine. This is called *internal hemorrhage.* However, the general effects are practically the same whether the hemorrhage is external or internal. If the quantity of blood lost is large, and especially if it occurs suddenly, the subject suffers severely from lack of oxygen as a consequence of the reduction in the number of erythrocytes. There is a fall in blood pressure, as a result of the reduction in volume of circulating fluid, and the heartbeat increases in rate.

Of the physiological adjustments which ensue to safeguard the body against the dangers of blood loss, some are effected almost immeditely after the hemorrhage; others not for some time. The first requisite, of course, is that the bleeding be staunched. This is accomplished through the clotting of the blood (p. 102), the contraction of the walls of the divided vessels, and the sticking together of the inner coat of the vessel. In this way the leak in the circulating system may be repaired. The *capacity of the circulating system* must also be reduced, in order to conform to the reduced volume of the blood. This is brought about through nervous reflexes. Nerve impulses are transmitted from centers in the brain and cord to the small blood vessels (arterioles, p. 122) in parts of the body, such as the skin, muscles, and intestines, whose functions are not immediately essential to life. The caliber of the vessels in these structures is narrowed. The blood pressure is therefore raised (p. 153), and an adequate supply of blood to the heart and the vital centers in the brain thus maintained. The spleen responds to hemorrhage (p. 96) by contraction and the discharge of a quantity of blood into the circulation; thus the blood volume is at once, in part at least, restored. The blood volume is also augmented by the passage of fluid—mainly water and salts—into the vessels from the tissue spaces. This process commences almost immediately after the blood has been shed and, provided that the hemorrhage is not very severe, restores the blood volume to normal within a remarkably short time. The withdrawal of fluid from the tissues causes the subject to suffer from thirst, and the administration of fluids at this time is of value in hastening the return of the blood volume to its normal value. A longer time is required for the replacement of the plasma proteins and a longer time still for the complete restoration of the blood cells by the bone marrow. The time following the hemorrhage, at which the blood cells are brought back to their normal number, varies with the nature of the diet (p. 72), the quantity of blood which has been lost, and the recuperative powers of the individual subject. After the withdrawal of a pint of blood from a healthy person for transfusion purposes, from 6 to 8 weeks elapse before the red cell count returns to normal.

Transfusion

When more than 40 percent of the blood is lost over a short period of time the body is usually unable to repair the loss unaided. Some artificial means of replacing the lost fluid must be resorted to. The intravenous injection of blood, plasma, or serum, or of some artificial solution with the object of restoring the blood volume is called *transfusion.*[5]

Transfusion with whole blood. Blood obtained from another person (usually referred to as the *donor*) is the ideal transfusion fluid,

[5] Strictly speaking, the word *transfusion* refers to the use of whole blood, serum, or plasma, and *infusion* to the use of other fluids.

for it is capable not only of restoring the blood volume but of furnishing erythrocytes as well. The transfused cells survive for a considerable length of time (probably for from 100 to 125 days). Blood may not be taken indiscriminately from any person and transfused into any other. Great care must be exercised in the choice of the person (the *donor*) from whom the blood is taken, for the blood of one person may result in the death of another into whose veins it is injected. The patient who receives the blood is called the *recipient*. Death may

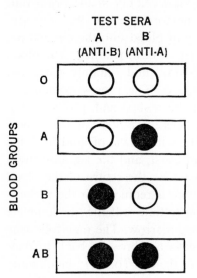

TEST SERA

A   B

(ANTI-B) (ANTI-A)

BLOOD GROUPS

O

A

B

AB

Fig. 3.12 Showing the method of determining the group to which a sample of blood belongs; black discs = agglutination, white = no agglutination. If neither test serum causes agglutination of the corpuscles of the blood being tested, the latter must belong to group O. If the corpuscles are agglutinated by B but not by A serum, the blood belongs to group A. If agglutination occurs with A but not with B serum, the blood is of group B. If both sera cause agglutination the unknown blood is placed in group AB.

occur even though donor and recipient are closely related. Such an untoward result is due to the patient's plasma containing a substance called an *agglutinin*, while the donor's erythrocytes contain a complementary substance called an *agglutinogen*. When unsuitable blood is transfused, the donor's erythrocytes become gathered together into clumps—*agglutination* (Pl. 3A, and Fig. 3.12). Such clumps of cells block the small vessels; later the cells disintegrate and liberate their hemoglobin. The pigment in the process of excretion by the kidneys obstructs and damages the urinary tubules, and the patient dies as a result of the suppression of urine. Types of blood which, when mixed, behave in this way are termed *incompatible*. It has been discovered that the entire human population of the earth—of no matter what race—can be divided into four groups according to the reactions of their bloods when mixed together. The groups are designated, respectively, by the capital letters, O, A, B, and AB, Table 3-6 shows the reactions between plasma (or serum) and the corpuscles of the various groups according to the classification worked out by Jansky.[6]

It will be noted that the *serum* of group AB (vertical row on extreme right) does not cause agglutination of the corpuscles of any group. That is, the red cells of any donor, it would be expected, could be injected with safety into a subject belonging to group AB. A person belonging to group AB has therefore been called the *"universal*

Table 3-6

Serum

		O.	A ..	B.	AB·
Corpuscles	O	–	–	–	–
	A	+	–·	+	–
	B	+	+	–	–
	AB	+	+	+	–

+ = agglutination; – = no agglutination

recipient." It is also evident from the table that the *corpuscles* of group O are not agglutinated by any serum (top horizontal row). A person of this group has therefore been called the *"universal donor."* Serious reactions and even death may result, however, when the donor belongs to group O or the recipient to group AB. The terms "universal donor" and "universal recipient" are therefore misleading. The donor should when possible be of the same group as that to which the recipient belongs; there is then no fear of incompatibility in so far as the main blood groups are concerned.[7] Or better still, the compatibility of the two samples of blood should be tested before the transfusion is made. The clumping of the corpuscles which occurs when they

[6] Previously, the blood groups were designated by Roman numerals I, II, III, and IV. The capital letters used today refer to the agglutinogen or agglutinogens present in the corpuscles. O means that the cells contain neither of the two main agglutinogens; A that they contain one (A); B that they contain the other (B), and AB that they contain both. In designating the two types of agglutinins (antibodies) in serum, the Greek letters o, α and β are employed. o means the absence of both. α, β and $\alpha\beta$ mean, respectively, that one or other or both are present. Therefore, to give the complete characteristic of a given type of blood in respect to its agglutinogens (corpuscles) and agglutinins (serum), we would write O $\alpha\beta$ (no agglutinogen, both agglutinins), Aβ (agglutinogen A, agglutinin β), Bα (agglutinogen B, agglutinin α), and ABo (both agglutinogens, no agglutinin). Thus the reaction shown in Table 3-6 can be understood. The cells of O group are not agglutinated because they contain no agglutinogen and the serum of AB group will not agglutinate any cells because it contains no agglutinin.

[7] This precaution will not, however, exclude the danger of incompatibility with respect to certain other factors, especially the Rh factor (see p. 80).

are mixed with an incompatible serum is clearly seen under the microscope. Even to the naked eye the masses of agglutinated corpuscles may be seen as minute particles, like grains of cayenne pepper, floating upon the surface of the clear serum.[8]

The agglutination of corpuscles when incompatible bloods are mixed is in the nature of an immune reaction (Chap. 5) resembling that whereby bacteria are agglutinated, and thus rendered innocuous by a specific substance (antibody) in the blood of a person infected with the same type of microorganism. However, an antibody active against bacteria is, as a rule, developed only after the blood has been invaded by the microorganisms, whereas the antibody to the agglutinogen in the corpuscles of an incompatible blood—that is, the agglutinin—is present naturally as an inherited characteristic. In this system the agglutinogen of the corpuscles is the antigen (Chap. 5).

The blood characteristics are inherited according to Mendelian laws, and just as the offspring of a brown-eyed and a blue-eyed parent may have either brown or blue eyes, so it is impossible to predict the blood characters of a child from those of its parents.

Transfusion of blood is employed in other conditions besides hemorrhage; namely, in surgical shock, extensive burns, in certain severe infections, and in extreme malnutrition of infants.

The Rh factor. Until a few years ago (1940), the four blood groups were believed to be the only ones that it was necessary to take into account when choosing a donor for transfusion, yet deaths following transfusion occurred from time to time for which no satisfactory explanation could be given. In so far as the O, A, B, and AB groups were concerned, the blood transfused in these fatal cases should have been compatible with that of the patient. When a survey was made of a number of these fatalities, it was discovered that they had all occurred either (1) in persons who had been transfused at some earlier time, that is, the fatality followed a *second* transfusion, or (2) in women who were pregnant or had given birth to a child. Research workers interested in the subject recalled that Landsteiner and Weiner of the Rockefeller Institute had discovered that the in-

---

[8] In order to determine to which of the four groups a particular blood sample belongs, the blood is tested with serum from blood groups A and B. Samples of sera from these groups are available in small sealed vials which in all large hospitals are kept in the refrigerator ready for use. If the corpuscles of the blood sample are agglutinated by A-test serum, but not by B, it belongs to group B. If agglutination occurs with B serum, but not with A, it belongs to group A. If agglutination follows mixing with both A and B sera, the sample belongs to group AB, and if neither A nor B serum causes agglutination the unknown serum belongs to group O (see Fig. 3.12).

jection of the blood of the Rhesus monkey into guinea pigs caused the formation in the blood of the latter of an agglutinin which caused the agglutination of the monkey's corpuscles and also of human corpuscles. The Rhesus corpuscles contain a substance—*an agglutinogen*—which, when injected into an animal such as the guinea pig whose blood does not itself contain it, stimulates the production in the recipient animal of an antibody—that is, of an *agglutinin.* Now, about 85 percent of members of the white race contain such an agglutinogen,

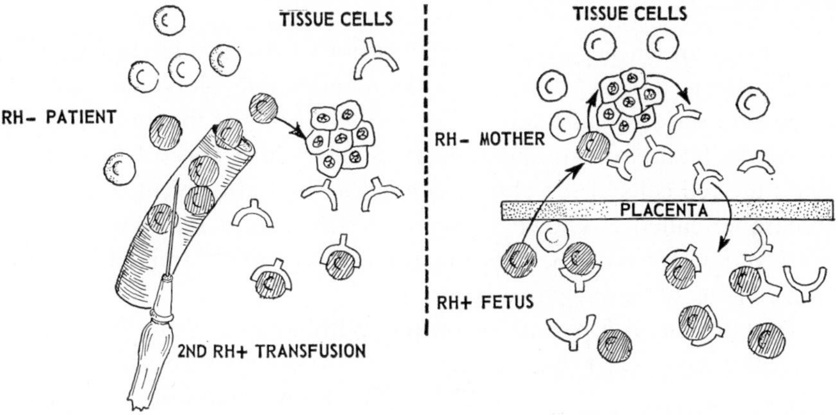

Fig. 3.13 Diagram showing reactions caused by the Rh factor. ○ = Rh−; ● = Rh+ (agglutinogen); Y = anti-Rh (agglutinin). A, reaction following a second injection of Rh+ blood into an Rh− patient. B, reaction caused by an Rh+ fetus in an Rh− mother.

or *Rh factor,* as it has been named (after the Rhesus monkey); the remaining 15 percent do not.[9] In other words, the corpuscles of 85 percent of persons of the white race, in that they contain the agglutinogen, resemble Rhesus corpuscles, the corpuscles of the remaining 15 percent, in that the agglutinogen is absent, resemble guinea pig corpuscles. Blood which contains the Rh factor is termed *Rh-positive;* blood which lacks it is called *Rh-negative.* When the blood of a person who is Rh-positive is injected into the circulation of one whose blood is Rh-negative, the antibody—agglutinin or *anti-Rh factor*—is produced. Such transfusion merely causes the production of the agglutinin; no reaction follows. But, if a second, similar transfusion is given, 10 days or more (even up to years) after the first, a severe, often fatal, reaction follows, due to the action of the accumulated agglutinin or anti-Rh factor. The fatal reactions following an initial

[9] Certain races—e.g., North American Indians, Japanese, Chinese, and Negroes of pure African stock—are 99 to 100 percent Rh-positive.

transfusion in women who had borne a child are explained on an essentially similar basis. But in such cases the blood of the unborn child contains the agglutinogen (inherited from the father). That is, in all cases in which such a reaction occurs, the blood of the fetus is Rh-positive while that of the mother is Rh-negative. Evidently red cells containing the agglutinogen, or fragments of such cells, have escaped from the fetal to the maternal blood through the delicate membranes of the placenta separating the two circulations, and have stimulated the tissue cells to produce the anti-Rh factor in the mother's blood (Fig. 3.13).

Though an Rh-negative mother bearing an Rh-positive fetus suffers no ill effects unless transfused with incompatible blood, the fetus is often very seriously affected by the anti-Rh factor of the mother which enters the fetal circulation and exerts a destructive (hemolytic) action upon the red cells of the child, both before and after birth. The blood disease so called is known as *hemolytic disease of the new born,* or *erythroblastosis foetalis;* it is invariably fatal unless treated by large transfusions of Rh-negative blood.

Transfusion with plasma or serum. Within recent years it has been generally recognized that in many cases of hemorrhage it is unnecessary to transfuse with whole blood. The body possesses an immense reserve store of red cells in spleen, liver, and skin which can be drawn upon in such an emergency. Death from hemorrhage is, as a rule, due not to the reduction in the oxygen-carrying capacity of the blood but to the loss of the bulk of circulating fluid and the resulting fall in blood pressure which this entails. Plasma or serum has therefore come into very wide use as a transfusion fluid. There are certain very definite and great advantages to be gained by the use of these blood derivatives. In the first place, plasma or serum when collected from a number of donors and mixed together (pooled) does not cause agglutination of the transfused patient's corpuscles. That is, it is universally compatible. Another great advantage of plasma or serum over whole blood is that either can be dried and stored in bottles, and thus be ready at hand for almost immediate use. All that is then required is the addition of sterile distilled water in an amount equal to that which had been removed by evaporation in the drying process. In the preparation of the dried product, the plasma or serum collected from a number of donors is separated from the cells by centrifuging and decanted off. The cells, as a rule, are discarded. The liquid part of the blood is frozen and then dried in the frozen state by subjecting it to a high vacuum (6 mm Hg or less). This method, the *desivac* *process,* is now employed in the preparation of dried serum (or plasma) on a large scale for the armed forces in Britain, Canada, the United States, and other countries.

The albumin of human plasma, dried and powdered, is also available. It is put up in sealed containers and ready for use after the addition of distilled water and the necessary blood salts.

Transfusion materials of nonhuman origin. The search for a suitable substitute for blood or its derivatives, plasma or serum, as a transfusion material has engaged the attention of scientists for a number of years. Provided that the material resembles plasma or serum in its *physical properties* and is capable of restoring and maintaining the blood volume for a reasonable length of time and thus of raising the blood pressure from a dangerously low level, the chemical composition of the transfusion fluid is of secondary importance. But the requirements of such an artificial transfusion material are many: (a) The molecule of the dissolved substance must be of such a size that the fluid will not leave the vessels too freely. (b) The solution must exert an osmotic pressure and possess a viscosity approaching as closely as possible that of whole blood; these qualifications depend upon molecular size and shape. (c) It should be as nearly as possible isotonic with the contents of the erythrocytes (see p. 68). (d) It must, of course, be innocuous in every respect. In addition, it should be readily available, preferably cheap, and capable of being quickly and easily prepared for intravenous administration. Provided it is suitable in the respects just listed, there appears to be no valid objection to the use of some fluid other than blood or serum to fill the vessels immediately after hemorrhage. Nevertheless, for some reason not altogether clear whole blood appears to be superior to any other transfusion fluid in the treatment of shock or severe hemorrhage.

Among the solutions of nonhuman origin which have been used in the past or are under investigation and trial at the present time are: (a) saline (0.9 percent solution of sodium chloride), (b) a 6 percent solution of gum acacia, and (c) a 6 percent solution of isinglass.

Saline solution (0.9 percent of sodium chloride) is of little value in hemorrhage or shock, for the simple reason that it is not held within the vessels. The molecule of sodium chloride is so small that it escapes freely through the capillary walls into the tissue spaces. When, however, the water of the blood alone is reduced (anhydremia), saline is of benefit.

Gum acacia was introduced during World War I for the treatment of hemorrhage resulting from wounds, and was highly successful. The reason for its success lay in the fact that its molecule is large and does not readily escape from the circulation. In the dilution used (6 percent of gum in 0.9 percent saline), this substance exerts an osmotic pressure about equal to that of the plasma proteins. The fluid is therefore retained within the vessels, the blood pressure is elevated, and the circulation to vital structures maintained. Gum acacia has come into disfavor, however, since the discovery that it damages the liver.

Isinglass is a protein very closely allied in its chemical and physical properties to gelatin. It is prepared from the swim bladders of fish (hake, cod, sturgeon, etc.). As a 6 percent solution in 0.9 percent

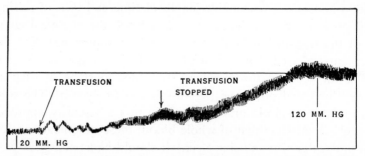

Fig. 3.14   Showing the effect on an animal's blood pressure of the transfusion of isinglass solution. The animal's blood pressure had been lowered by hemorrhage to the very low level of 20 mm Hg at the start of the transfusion. The animal survived but undoubtedly would have died had it not been transfused.

saline, it exerts an osmotic pressure comparable with that of the plasma proteins. It has proved successful in the treatment of acute hemorrhage in animals and in patients. It does not cause a foreign protein (antigenic) reaction or any other unfavorable effect (Fig. 3.14). As artificial blood substitutes, gelatin and dextran also have their advocates. The latter is a complex polysaccharide.

Hemolysis or the Laking of Blood

The plasma contain little or no hemoglobin. When normal blood is centrifuged, the red cells are thrown down and the supernatant plasma may then be seen to be almost colorless. But under the action of certain agents the hemoglobin is not retained by the erythrocytes, but escapes and colors the plasma. This process is termed *hemolysis* or the *laking* of the blood. The substance inducing the hemolysis is called a *hemolysin* or a *hemolytic agent*. Among the various agents which cause hemolysis are: (a) *hypotonic solutions;* (b) *chloroform, ether,* and *benzine,* and certain other *fat solvents;* (c) *bacterial poisons* (toxins); (d) the *venom of certain snakes;* and (e) *specific hemolysins.* The depth of color given to the plasma varies from a faint pink to a deep red, according to the degree to which the erythrocytes have been attacked by the particular hemolysin.

Hypotonic solutions (p. 68) act by disturbing the osmotic equilibrium between the interior of the red cell and the surrounding plasma. When, for example, distilled water is added to blood, the salts of the plasma are diluted and the osmotic pressure of the plasma is reduced below that within the cells. Water is therefore "attracted" into the cell which, as a consequence, increases in volume and, finally rupturing, liberates its coloring matter. When the cell is completely hemolyzed in this way, its colorless framework may still be seen. Such decolorized cells are referred to as "ghosts."

The fragility test. If normal red cells are immersed in a series of hypotonic solutions of sodium chloride graded in small differences of salt concentration, they commence to hemolyse when the percentage of salt is approximately 0.42. Hemolysis is complete when the salt concentration is approximately 0.36 percent. In hemolytic forms of anemia, the red cells are less resistant—that is, more fragile—than normal to hyoptonic solutions and commence to hemolyse at a salt concentration of about 0.5 percent, and are completely hemolysed at around 0.4 percent. In pernicious anemia, on the contrary, they show an increased resistance to hemolysis; the hemoglobin commences to escape from the cells at a salt concentration of 0.38 percent and is complete at 0.30 percent.

Chloroform, ether, etc., cause hemolysis, apparently, by dissolving the lipid materials composing the cell membrane and stroma. The manner in which bacterial and many other of the organic hemolytic agents act is not clear.

Specific hemolysins constitute a class of immune substances. For example, if an animal is given a series of daily injections of blood of another species, a substance is gradually developed in the serum of the recipient animal which has the power to hemolyse the erythrocytes of that species to which the donor animal belongs, but is not hemolytic for the erythrocytes of other species. (See Chap. 5.)

The White Cells or Leucocytes

The leucocytes, unlike the red cells, possess a nucleus but no hemoglobin or other coloring matter. They number only about 8000

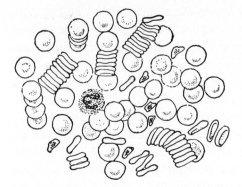

Fig. 3.15   A film of normal blood illustrating the relative numbers of red and white cells and platelets. A field as large again as that shown would probably contain no other white cell.

(6000 to 10,000) per cu mm. That is, the red cells outnumber the white by about 600 to 1 (Fig. 3.15). The white cells are of two main types: (a) Those without granules in the cytoplasm and with an unlobed nucleus; these are called *agranular leucocytes*. (b) Those with granules in the cytoplasm and a nucleus possessing two or more lobes; these are termed *granular leucocytes, granulocytes,* or *polymorphonuclear leucocytes* (see Pl. 2 and Fig. 3.16).

The agranular leucocytes are of three varieties—the *large* and *small lymphocytes* and the *monocytes.* The first two types closely resemble one another except in size; the small lymphocyte is about 8 microns in diameter, the large from 10 to 12 microns. The small lymphocytes constitute about 25 percent of the white cells, the large lymphocytes about 3 percent. The monocytes are larger than the large lymphocytes, measuring about 15 microns in diameter, and their nuclei, which are usually indented on one side or horseshoe shaped, do not stain so deeply as those of the large lymphocytes. Though there is some doubt as to the nature and origin of the mono-

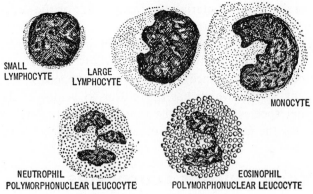

SMALL LYMPHOCYTE

LARGE LYMPHOCYTE

MONOCYTE

NEUTROPHIL POLYMORPHONUCLEAR LEUCOCYTE

EOSINOPHIL POLYMORPHONUCLEAR LEUCOCYTE

Fig. 3.16   Types of leucocyte.

cytes, most observers believe that they belong to the reticulo-endo-thelial system of cells (p. 94). They may become very actively phagocytic. As a rule, they constitute no more than from 2 to 4 per-cent of the white cells.

The granulocytes are also of three types—the *eosinophils,* the *basophils,* and the *neutrophils.* The cytoplasm of the eosinophils is packed with coarse granules which stain with acid dyes (e.g., the red dye, eosin); the nucleus has, as a rule, but two lobes. Normally, these cells constitute only 2 or 3 percent of the leucocyte population.

The granules of the basophils stain with basic dyes (e.g., meth-ylene blue). Their nuclei are also bilobed. Basophils are scarce (not more than 0.5 percent) in normal blood.

The neutrophils are about 10 microns in diameter, and contain numerous fine granules which stain with neutral dyes, or with a mix-ture of an acid and a basic dye (e.g., eosin and methylene blue). When so treated, the granules are colored violet. The majority of the neutrophil leucocytes possess nuclei which are divided into from

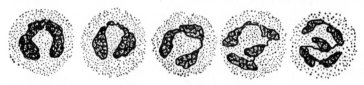

Fig. 3.17   Showing stages in the life of a polymorphonuclear leu-cocyte (see text).

two to five lobes (Fig. 3.17). The number of lobes depends upon the age of the cell, the oldest ones having five or more, while the youngest (which are very few in number) show only a suggestion of lobulation. The neutrophils are the most numerous type of white cell, constituting from 65 to 70 percent of the total count.

The granulocytes are formed in the red bone marrow, whereas the large and small lymphocytes are produced in the lymph nodes and lymphoid tissue, generally, throughout the body (see p. 98). The monocytes are generally believed to be elements of the reticulo-endothelial system. (See also p. 94.)

The functions of the leucocytes. The neutrophilic polymorpho-nuclear leucocytes, together with the monocytes and other reticulo-endothelial elements, constitute probably the most important means that the body possesses for its defense against invading micro-organisms. The ability of these cells to attack bacteria depends upon their motility, and a proclivity for the ingestion of solid particles

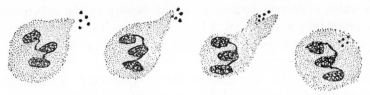

Fig. 3.18   Drawing of a neutrophil at half-minute intervals to show motility and phagocytosis. The dots represent a group of bacteria.

(Fig. 3.18). The latter action, which was first demonstrated by Metchnikoff, is termed *phagocytosis* (Gk. *phago,* I eat). These two varieties of white blood cell are free lances among the body cells; they wander from place to place through the tissues, for practically no part of the body is barred to them. They insinuate a process (*pseudopodium*), improvised at the moment from their cell protoplasm, through one of the joints in the endothelium of the capillary wall (Fig. 3.19). Then, by causing the semifluid substance of the cell body to stream into the protoplasmic protrusion, they pass out of the blood vessels. By this process of *diapedesis,* as it is called, myriads of the white corpuscles may pass out of the vessels in a remarkably

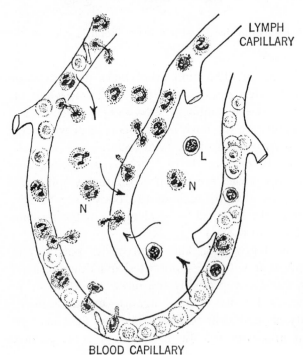

LYMPH CAPILLARY

N

L

N

BLOOD CAPILLARY

Fig. 3.19   Illustrating the passage of poly-morphonuclear leuco-cytes from the circulation by diapedesis: L, lymphocyte; N, neutrophil leucocyte.

short time. Reaching a point where the bacteria have entered the body and established a beach head, they surround the threatened area and proceed to destroy the invaders. If, for example, an actively inflamed region should be examined under the microscope, masses of neutrophils would be seen, and many of these would be observed to hold bacteria imprisoned within their bodies. As many as fifteen or twenty organisms may be seen at times within a single cell. It has been shown that the germs are ingested alive, and remain so for a time within the leucocyte.

When a tissue such as the mesentery or web of a frog, in which the capillaries are clearly visible beneath the microscope, is examined in the living state a short time after a suspension of bacteria has been injected into it, the small vessels leading to the site of inoculation are found swarming with neutrophils. In the tissues round about, the amoeboid cells are seen moving somewhat ponderously hither and thither to engulf the offending bacteria. The monocytes, though much less numerous, also join in the general attack and show their phago-cytic propensities to a marked degree. After the first flooding of the tissues with neutrophils and monocytes, numbers of the latter come to rest and together with other reticulo-endothelial elements of the tissues surround and isolate the infected area from the neighboring healthy tissues. Until this is accomplished the danger of the infection becoming more widely spread always exists. In their struggle against bacteria, equipped as these are with powerful toxins, many of the white cells are killed. These collect within the infected area together with exuded plasma, liquefied tissue cells, and a few red cells that have escaped through the injured walls of the capillaries. This mate-rial constitutes pus, and the so-called pus cells are dead leucocytes. The circumscribing wall and its semifluid contents constitute an *abscess*. A "boil" or *furuncle* is a small abscess of the skin and sub-cutaneous tissue which commences as an infection within a hair follicle. By the action of the phagocytes, aided by a protein-digesting ferment (*protease*) which they elaborate, the overlying structures whether connective tissue, mucosa, or skin are, in part, removed piecemeal. The wall of the abscess cavity over a small area of skin or mucous membrane becomes gradually eroded to the thinness of paper. The abscess is then said to "point"; it bursts soon afterward and dis-charges its content of pus.

Not only the bacteria themselves but any infected foreign mate-rial, such as a rose thorn, a wood splinter, bullet, or shell fragment, is loosened or eroded and, when possible, removed by the phagocytes (Fig. 3.20). Sterile foreign material—e.g., a catgut suture, or a blood clot—is broken down, and necrotic tissue is separated from the living by phagocytosis and by enzymes present in the blood tissues. Devitalized bone, though not removed in its entirety, unless it is of very small size, is, nevertheless, eroded and separated from the living tissue by the leucocytes. The disappearance of effete organs,

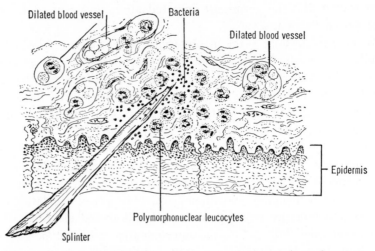

Fig. 3.20   Showing migration of leucocytes (polymorphonuclears) to an infected area in the skin.

such as the tail and gills of the metamorphosing tadpole or the creeping muscles of insect larvae, is effected in a similar manner.

Of the functions of the other varieties of granulocytes—the eosinophils and basophils—little is definitely known. They are not markedly motile, and are not phagocytic. The eosinophils are increased above the normal of 2 or 3 percent in certain affections, notably, asthma, infestations with various types of parasitic worms, and in allergic conditions. The number of eosinophils in the circulation is strongly influenced by the adrenocorticotrophic hormone of the hypophysis (Chap. 10), through its stimulating effect upon the production and liberation of adrenal cortical hormones. When the pituitary hormone or an extract of the adrenal cortex is injected into the body, a marked reduction in the number of circulating eosinophil leucocytes occurs. Indeed, the eosinopenic response constitutes the most sensitive test for the presence of ACTH in any biological fluid.

The lymphocytes are not amoeboid—that is, they do not progress by the protrusion of pseudopodia. They are capable of a certain slow progression, however, as a result of spasmodic movements of the cell nucleus. They have little phagocytic power and from all accounts possess no proteolytic ferment.

The role played by the lymphocytes has been a subject of speculation for a number of years. It has long been recognized that these blood cells were concerned in chronic inflammatory conditions, for a great migration of small lymphocytes to the chronically inflamed tissues (*small cell infiltration*) was a common observation, but, until recently, little was known definitely of the functions of these white cells. Modern research has revealed the important duty which they perform in the processes of immunity (p. 215). They give origin to one of the proteins—the globulin—of the blood plasma. The antibodies of paramount importance in establishing resistance to bacterial infections are closely associated with plasma gamma globulin. In experiments upon animals, it has been found that during an infective state the lymph nodes and other collections of lymphoid tissue show a great destruction of lymphocytes. They break down, their substance undergoing disintegration to furnish plasma globulin. The adrenal cortex and the pituitary gland, through its adrenocorticotrophic hormone (p. 435), exert a controlling influence upon lymphocyte dissolution and globulin production and, consequently, upon the production of immune substances (antibodies).

Variations in the number of leucocytes. A rise in the number of white cells of the blood is called *leucocytosis*. The increase may be due to any one of the various cell types. More specific terms are frequently employed, such as, *lymphocytosis, eosinophilia,* and *neutrophilia* for an increase in the number of lymphocytes, eosinophils, and neutrophils, respectively. The neutrophil count is raised markedly by acute septic infections. Among physiological conditions which cause a moderate increase in this type of white cell are muscular exercise, pregnancy, and injections of adrenaline. Lymphocytosis occurs in certain chronic infections; eosinophilia is seen in asthma, in some skin diseases, and in diseases caused by parasites (e.g., intestinal worms). In order to determine which type of white cell is responsible for the leucocytosis, it is necessary to perform a *differential count*. This consists in examining a stained smear of blood under the microscope and counting the numbers of the different types in a total of several hundred cells. The percentages of the various types are then calculated. In some instances the *proportions* of the different types are altered, though no change occurs in the *total* white cell count.

A grave disease of the blood marked by an enormous, one might call it a malignant, increase of leucocytes is called *leukemia*. There are several different forms of the disease depending upon which type —granulocyte, small or large lymphocyte, or monocyte—is increased in number. The white cell count in this condition may reach 250,000 or more per cu mm, and many cells in the earlier stages of development are seen in the circulation. The red cells are usually reduced in number; i.e., there is an associated anemia.

Leucopenia is the term applied to a reduction in the number of leucocytes below the normal; it occurs in certain infectious diseases, notably pneumonia and typhoid fever. Certain drugs (e.g., amidopyrine) used for the relief of headache, or pain in other parts of the body, are believed to be responsible for a fatal disease in which the granulocytes are reduced to a very low level. Resistance to infection is greatly lowered as a consequence. Scarcity of one or other type of leucocyte alone is called *lymphopenia, neutropenia,* or *eosinopenia,* respectively.

The production and maturation of the leucocytes. The granulocytes, like the red cells, pass through several stages of development in the bone marrow (see Pl. 2), and it is only cells in the final stage which normally reach the general circulation. The cells of the earliest stages are nongranular and show no division of the nucleus into lobes. These cells are called *myeloblasts*. Subsequent stages are marked by the appearance of granules which increase in number as maturation progresses and undergo differentiation into the three types, but the nucleus as yet shows no lobulation. These cells are called *myelocytes*. In the final stage—i.e., just before the cell is discharged from the marrow into the general circulation—constriction of the nucleus occurs at one point, but no definite division into lobes is evident. As already mentioned, the lobulation becomes pronounced and the number of lobes increases as the cell ages in the circulation. The life of a granulocyte is about 21 days.

The lymphocytes are produced not in the bone marrow, but in the lymphoid tissues (e.g., lymph nodes, spleen, etc.).

Physiological factors concerned in acute inflammation. It is evident from what has been said in the preceding section that the functions of the neutrophil leucocytes are closely bound up with the physiological processes associated with acute inflammation. A substance is to be found in pus or other inflammatory exudate, known as the *leucocytosis promoting factor* (Menkin), which attracts the neutrophils to the injured tissues. A second chemical factor discovered by Menkin and named *leucotaxin* increases the permeability of the walls of the smallest blood vessels (capillaries, p. 124); and a third, *histamine,* dilates the capillaries as well as increasing the permeability of their walls. In inflammatory reactions, the capillaries and the vessels next in size, namely, the arterioles, are dilated as well through axon reflexes (p. 520), the fine nerve endings being stimulated by the injurious agent, whether this is of a chemical (e.g., bacterial toxin) or a mechanical nature. These effects upon the minute blood vessels cause the passage of an excessive quantity of fluid (plasma) from the circulation into the surrounding tissues, which results in swelling of the inflamed part. The dilated vessels bring more blood to the affected region which causes reddening and a local rise in temperature. The *swelling, redness,* and *heat*—three of the *cardinal signs of inflammation*—are thus accounted for by the vascular reactions. The other signs of inflammation—namely, *pain* and *loss of function*—naturally follow, the former being due to the involvement of the sensory nerves in the inflammatory process as well as to the pressure upon the nerves by the accumulated fluid. The temporary loss of function of a movable part is due, in many instances, simply to the pain which results from any attempt at movement. This is nature's way of encouraging recovery, by enforcing rest. In other instances the loss of function—which may be permanent—is due to the inflammation having implicated the special structures upon which the particular function depends. (See also p. 233.)

The Blood Platelets or Thrombocytes

These are small bodies about a quarter of the diameter of a red blood corpuscle. They do not possess a nucleus but their protoplasm contains distinct granules (Fig. 3.21). Their origin is not known with certainty. The most widely held opinion concerning the origin of the platelets is that they are fragments of protoplasm broken or separated in some way from giant cells in the red bone marrow. These latter cells, known as *megacaryocytes,* are of relatively enormous size (Fig. 3.22) and contain several nuclei massed together near their centers. Some authorities have suggested that the platelets are the remnants of disintegrated erythrocytes.

The platelets number about 250,000 per cu cm. They play an important part in the coagulation of the blood (p. 102).

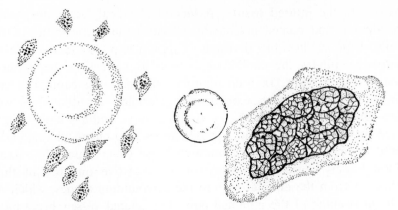

Fig. 3.21   Blood platelets. A red blood cell shown for size comparison.

Fig. 3.22   A megacaryocyte. Red cell shown for size comparison.

The Reticulo-Endothelial System

This is a system of primitive cells normally present in the general connective tissue, lungs, spleen, liver, lymph nodes, bone marrow, and other situations. Many varieties exist, several of which possess phagocytic properties, and some of very large size are actively motile. One type of reticulo-endothelial cell, namely, the monocyte, has al-

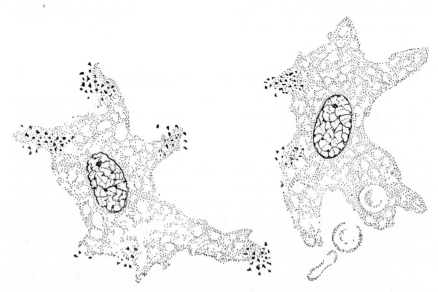

Fig. 3.23   Macrophages containing phagocytosed carbon grains (*left*) and a red blood corpuscle (*right*).

ready been mentioned as being present in blood. Reticulo-endothelial cells of the spleen are responsible for the final disposal of the fragments of red cells which they engulf, the hemoglobin being freed of iron and converted to bile pigment (p. 329). The reticulo-endothelial cells in the blood sinuses of the liver are known as Kupffer cells. These, as well as those in bone marrow and the general connective tissues, also possess the ability to convert into bile pigment the hemoglobin liberated from disintegrated red cells. The reticulo-endothelial cells of the general connective tissues are of exceptionally large size. They play a prominent role in the body's defense against invasion by microorganisms. These cells are actively motile and phagocytic, ingesting bacteria and any other foreign material which may be introduced into the tissues. For example, after the injection of India ink (which consists of a suspension of carbon grains) into an animal, these *macrophages,*[10] as they are called, gorge themselves with the foreign particles. They are thus made conspicuous beneath the microscope (Fig. 3.23). In inflammatory conditions, they gather in large numbers around and within the inflamed part. In the lung, macrophages are active in the removal of foreign particles (e.g., dust, carbon particles) which have been carried into the alveoli by the inspired air.

The reticulo-endothelial elements in the neuroglia of the central nervous system are called *microglia.* They differ little from those in the general connective tissues.

The Spleen

The spleen is an organ about the size of the fist situated in the abdomen behind the stomach and above, but to some extent overlapping, the left kidney. It contains, under ordinary circumstances, a relatively large amount of blood which is held in spaces (sinuses) lined by cells belonging to the reticulo-endothelial system. The blood is delivered into the substance of the spleen (splenic pulp) by small arteries. It then percolates into the sinuses through gaps between the cells forming the latter's walls (see Pl. 3B). The sinuses are drained by veins through which the blood is conveyed to the portal vein and thence to the liver. Dotted throughout the spleen, like islands, and surrounded by the pulp, are small lighter-colored areas composed of lymphoid tissue. These are the corpuscles of Malpighi (an Italian anatomist of

[10] The smaller phagocytic cells of the blood, namely, the neutrophils, are sometimes referred to as *microphages.*

the seventeenth century who first described them). Each of these areas is pierced near its center by a small blood vessel. The capsule of the spleen contains smooth muscle; smooth muscle also penetrates its substance.

The spleen is known to possess three important functions.

1. Blood reservoir. It serves as a *reservoir for blood* which can be drawn upon to augment the blood volume when the need arises.[11] The blood held by the spleen has a higher concentration of red cells than the blood of the general circulation, so that, when the organ contracts, not only is the total volume of circulating blood increased, but the

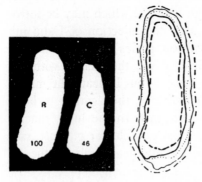

Fig. 3.24   Changes in volume of spleen as a result of emotional excitement (after Barcroft). Sketch on left, R, rest; C, dog sees cat. The numbers represent the relative sizes of the dog's spleen. Sketch on right, —.—.— rest; ———— smells cat; . . . . . . hears cat; — — — sees cat; ------ chases cat.

number of cells per cubic millimeter of blood is also raised. The several conditions which cause the spleen to contract are: a rise in environmental temperature, strenuous muscular exercise, emotional excitement (fright, rage, etc.), carbon monoxide poisoning, hemorrhage, and rarefied atmospheres. The immediate stimulus to splenic contraction in the last three conditions is a low oxygen tension in the blood, but its great sensitivity to nervous influence is illustrated by the observation that even a sudden sound (e.g., the slamming of a door) will cause it to contract (see Fig. 3.24). The spleen also shows *spontaneous* rhythmical contractions at the rate of about two per minute (Fig. 3.25). The small changes in blood volume which such movements induce cause corresponding variations in the blood pressure. The value of the organ in certain emergencies associated with a need for an additional supply of red cells is evident from an experiment performed by Professor Barcroft of Cambridge University upon guinea pigs. Two groups of animals were exposed to carbon monoxide gas. The concentration of gas in the atmosphere and the length of exposure were the same for both groups. The animals of one group,

[11] Experiments upon animals indicate that as much as 25 percent of the normal blood volume may be added to the circulation by contraction of the spleen.

however, had had their spleens removed; these animals died, whereas those of the other group which had not been operated upon survived.

2. Destruction of damaged red cells. This function depends upon the presence of the large phagocytic cells (macrophages) already mentioned under the section on the reticulo-endothelial system. Healthy red cells appear to be immune to attack from these scavenger cells, but cells which have outlived their usefulness, or those whose structure is in some way abnormal, are readily disposed of. Fragments of red cells which have broken up in the blood stream are also ingested by the macrophages of the spleen.

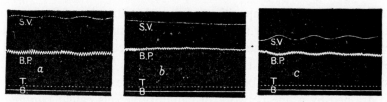

Fig. 3.25 Showing effect of splenic contractions on arterial blood pressure; S.V. = splenic volume. B.P. = general arterial blood pressure. T = time, 5 sec. B = baseline at 40 mm Hg. Spleen in plethysmograph; a, before clamping splenic vessels, b, after clamping vessels, c, after removal of clamp. (From Barcroft and Nisimaru.)

3. The formation of lymphocytes. The lymphoid tissue of the spleen, as does similar tissue in other situations, lymph nodes, etc., manfactures lymphocytes. In embryonic life, erythrocytes and granulocytes are also formed in the spleen, but its ability to produce these types of blood cells ceases a little time before birth.

The spleen probably possesses other functions which have not yet been discovered. It exercises certain functions (e.g., bile pigment production and antibody formation) by virtue of the large numbers of reticulo-endothelial elements which it contains. It has not been demonstrated to possess an endocrine function (p. 403). That it is an important organ and guards the welfare of its possessor in several ways is undoubted. Nevertheless, it is not essential to life under ordinary circumstances, for when excised it is scarcely missed. Excision of the spleen (splenectomy) is practiced for certain hemorrhagic diseases in which the platelets are reduced in number, presumably as a result of some abnormal action which it exerts upon these blood elements. Splenectomy is also performed for a type of hemolytic anemia in which the red cells are more fragile than normal. The spleen appears to be in some way responsible for the increased fragility of the cells, for, following its removal, the anemia is usually cured or greatly improved.

Although no ill effects have ever been observed in man following removal of the spleen, yet from the results of experiments upon animals it is probable that in certain emergencies (e.g., hemorrhage, gas poisoning, or surgical shock) a person deprived of his spleen would not have quite as good a chance of survival as would one with his spleen intact.

The Lymph and the Lymphatic System

The formation and composition of lymph. The tissue fluid, as explained elsewhere, is derived from the blood plasma. A large part of the fluid which leaves the arterial end of the capillary is returned to the circulation through the capillary near its venous end. But the tissue spaces, as well as being in relation to the blood capillaries, are also drained by a fine network of capillary vessels called *lymphatics*. Whereas the fluid reabsorbed by the blood capillaries is an aqueous solution of crystalloids (inorganic salts, sugar, urea, etc.), the fluid which passes into the lymph vessels contains some plasma protein as well. Small colloidal particles, such as those of India ink and other dyes which may have entered the tissue spaces from the blood, are also taken up by the lymphatics. Such particles do not return to the circulation through the walls of the blood capillaries. The fluid in the lymphatic vessels is called *lymph*, but it is almost identical in composition with the tissue fluid. Lymph contains the same constituents as are found in blood plasma, though in different concentrations. It contains the three plasma proteins, but the total protein concentration is between 3 and 4 percent as compared with around 7 percent for plasma. The calcium and total phosphorus are both lower than in the plasma; the other constituents (e.g., sodium, potassium, magnesium, chlorine, sugar, urea, etc.) are in about the same concentrations in the two fluids. Lymph contains numerous lymphocytes and an odd granulocyte, but very few or no red cells, under normal circumstances. The lymphocyte count varies considerably in different specimens of lymph from 1000 to 20,000 per cu mm.

The lymph vessels (lymphatics). The lymphatic system commences at the periphery in the network of fine vessels just mentioned. Such vessels are found in the skin (see Fig. 3.26) and subcutaneous tissues, in the fasciae of muscles, and in the connective tissue of the abdominal and thoracic viscera. Those in the villi of the small intestine are called *lacteals* (L. *lac,* milk). Through them a large proportion of the fat of the food is absorbed into the circulation, their name having been suggested by the milky appearance of their contents (usually referred to as the *chyle*) after a meal of fat. The lymph capillaries join to form larger vessels which ultimately form two main trunks— the *thoracic duct and the right lymphatic duct.* The former receives all the lymph of the body except that from the right side of the head, neck and thoracic wall, right arm, right lung, right side of the heart, and upper surface of the liver. Lymphatics of these parts drain into the right lymphatic duct. Each of these large vessels opens into the subclavian vein of the corresponding side of the body (see Fig. 3.26). A section of a lymph vessel is shown in Figure 3.27.

The lymph nodes (or glands). At certain strategic points in the course of the medium-sized lymph vessels are situated small ovoid or round structures composed of lymphoid tissue. These are the *lymph nodes* (Fig. 3.28). These bodies are com-

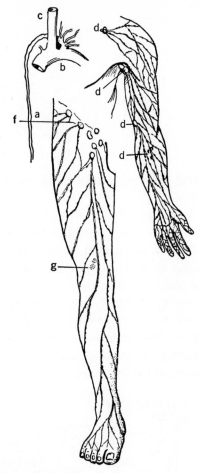

Fig. 3.26   *On left, above,* thoracic duct (*a*) opening into left subclavian vein (*b*); (*c*) internal jugular vein; *on right, above,* the main lymphatic vessels of the upper limb; (*d*) lymph nodes. *Below,* main lymphatics of the lower limb; (*f*) lymph nodes in the groin; (*g*) nodes (dotted outline) at the back of the knee.

posed of a network of delicate septa, the spaces between which are packed with masses of lymphocytes. Lymph vessels, usually four or five in number, enter the convexity of the node; they are called *afferent vessels.* The lymph leaves the node by a single efferent vessel which emerges from the concavity or *hilum* of the node. The lymph in its course from the tissue spaces to the point where it is returned to the

Valve   Endothelial cells

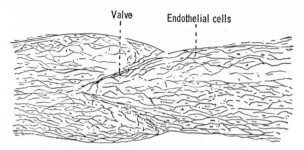

Fig. 3.27   A lymph vessel.

blood must pass through the lymph nodes, which act, in a sense, as filters.

In the upper part of the body, lymph nodes are situated in the sub-cutaneous tissue on the inside of the front of the elbow joint (Fig. 3.26), in the armpit, behind the ear, and running down either side of the neck. Those in the armpit and at the elbow drain lymph from the hand, those of the neck receive lymph from the head and throat. A group of lymph nodes can be felt as hard shotlike objects in the groin; they receive lymph from the external genital organs and lower limbs. Another group of lymph nodes, situated behind the knee, drain lymph from the foot and leg. Lymph nodes are also situated more deeply in the tissues of the neck and limbs, as well as along the course

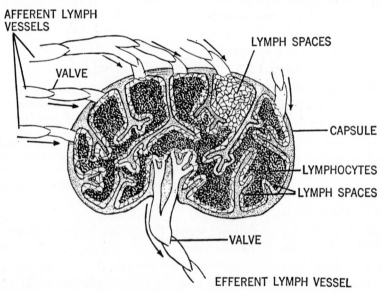

Fig. 3.28   Diagram of lymph node, sectioned to show internal structure; one area free of lymphocytes to show lymph spaces.

of the lymph vessels draining the viscera. When the hand or foot is infected, the lymph glands at the elbow and armpit in the one instance, and at the knee or in the groin in the other, may become inflamed and swollen as a result of bacteria or their products which have been carried upward by the lymph current. In septic conditions of the scalp, throat, or ear, the nodes receiving lymph from the infected area become similarly involved. Within the nodes, bacteria are attacked by leucocytes and other phagocytic cells. The lymph nodes must therefore be looked upon as important elements of defense against the invasion of the blood by microorganisms traveling along the lymphatic channels. They constitute a second defense line, the phagocytic cells at the primary site of infection bearing the first shock of the attack.

Other functions of the lymph nodes. Besides acting as filters and thus playing a prominent role in the defenses of the body against the inroads of bacteria, the lymph nodes exercise two other highly important functions: (a) the production of lymphocytes, and (b) the manufacture of plasma protein (globulin). The nodes form plasma globulin through the disintegration of the lymphocytes of which they are largely composed. This protein (gamma globulin) of the plasma is closely associated with the immune bodies (antibodies) through which bacteria and their toxic products are destroyed and antidoted. The disintegration of the lymphocytes within the lymph nodes and the production of antibodies appear to be controlled by the adrenocorticotrophic hormone of the pituitary body (Chap. 10). This immunizing function of the lymph nodes constitutes a third line of defense against infective agents.

These functions are not confined to the lymph nodes; the nodes possess such functions because they are composed of lymphoid tissue. The manufacture of plasma globulin and of lymphocytes are functions of lymphoid tissue in general—in the spleen, tonsils, thymus, Peyer's patches of the intestinal wall, etc.

Edema. An increase in the quantity of tissue fluid to the point where it causes a readily detectable increase in volume of a part is called *edema*. It is most frequently seen in the skin and subcutaneous tissues, about the ankles, or in the face below the eyes, as a symptom of heart or of kidney disease. When the edema is well marked, the skin appears "puffy," and, when one presses it with a finger, a dent or pit is left which takes a little time to level up again.

Edema is due to an imbalance of those factors regulating the interchange of fluids between the vessels and the tissue spaces (see p. 65). It may result, therefore, from any of the following causes: (a) increased capillary pressure, as in heart disease; (b) reduced plasma osmotic pressure, as in chronic kidney disease; (c) increased permeability of the capillary wall, as in acute kidney disease or as a result of certain poisons (e.g., histamine); (d) obstruction of the lymph channels (lymphatic edema).

Edema may be quite local and form small, well-defined, raised, pale areas in the skin. Such occur in susceptible persons after eating certain foods (e.g., shellfish, strawberries, celery, etc.). The condition is called *urticaria,* and known popularly as *hives.*

The Coagulation of Blood and Lymph

If blood is collected in a test tube it will be found after 5 or 6 minutes to have set into a jelly. The tube may be inverted, but the blood, which is now said to have *clotted* or *coagulated,* does not flow. When a section of this clot is examined under the microscope, it is found to be composed of a tangled mesh of very delicate fibrils among which are entrapped, as in a net, erythrocytes, leucocytes, and many fragmented platelets. The filaments are composed of *fibrin,* an insoluble gel (p. 18) form of *fibrinogen* produced during the clotting process.

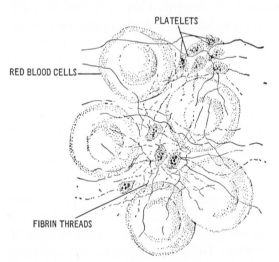

PLATELETS

RED BLOOD CELLS

FIBRIN THREADS

Fig. 3.29 Showing red cells, platelets, and fibrin threads in a blood clot.

They may be seen in many places to radiate from centers formed of platelets. If the clot is allowed to stand for a while, it undergoes shrinkage, and, as it shrinks, expresses from its meshes a clear, faintly straw-colored fluid. This clear fluid is the *serum* (Pl. 1). The serum remains fluid indefinitely; it is quite incapable of clotting, for it contains no fibrinogen. Plasma separated from the blood cells by centrifuging, clots in a way similar to that of whole blood and expresses the clear serum. The clot is white, since it contains no cells, but except for this difference it is identical with that formed in whole blood. The clotting process is essentially, therefore, a phenomenon of the plasma. Lymph also clots, though somewhat more slowly and less firmly than does blood or plasma.

The clotting mechanism. Four substances are necessary for the coagulation of blood: *prothrombin, thromboplastin, calcium,* and *fibrinogen.* Prothrombin gives rise to thrombin, an enzyme. Fibrinogen, prothrombin, and calcium are present in circulating blood. Thromboplastin (a lipid or fatlike compound containing phosphorus) is widely distributed throughout the tissues, the lung and brain being especially rich in this factor. It is absent or present in only small quantities in blood plasma. When blood is shed, thromboplastin is liberated from injured tissue and probably also from the leucocytes of the blood itself. The thromboplastin, acting upon the prothrombin in the presence of calcium, in an ionized form, converts it to the active thrombin. Thrombin acts in turn upon the soluble protein fibrinogen, converting it to insoluble fibrin which, as mentioned above, is deposited as fine threads to form the framework of the clot (Fig. 3.29).

The foregoing is a description of the clotting mechanism in the simplest possible terms. The chief factors are summarized in the following scheme.

$$\text{Prothrombin} + \text{calcium} + \text{thromboplastin} = \text{thrombin}$$
$$\text{(inactive)} \qquad\qquad\qquad\qquad\qquad\qquad \text{(active)}$$
$$\text{Thrombin} + \text{fibrinogen} = \text{fibrin}$$
$$\text{(soluble)} \quad\; \text{(threads)}$$

The mechanism of blood coagulation has been found to be most complex and several details have been omitted from the above scheme; one of the more important of these concerns a globulin in the plasma which accelerates the conversion of prothrombin to thrombin. This factor has been named *plasma accelerator globulin* or, briefly, *plasma AC globulin.*

Blood does not clot in the living body because there is not sufficient free thromboplastin to convert the inactive prothrombin into the active thrombin. Clotting within the vessels is further guarded against by the presence in the blood plasma of a substance which neutralizes the action of any thrombin which might be present. This antagonist to thrombin is called the *normal antithrombin* of plasma. When, however, blood escapes from a cut vessel and flows from a wound, thromboplastin is liberated from the damaged tissue cells and also from disintegrated platelets. Thus, the clotting process is immediately initiated.

Anticoagulants. Substances that prevent the coagulation of blood are called *anticoagulants*. Among such are *hirudin* and *heparin, dicoumarin, sodium* or *potassium oxalate, fluorides, citrates,* certain *neutral salts,* e.g., *sodium* and *magnesium sulphates.* The oxalates act by precipitating the calcium of the blood which, as mentioned above, is required for the formation of thrombin. Fluorides and citrates form soluble compounds with the calcium, but the latter, in so far as the clotting process is concerned, is in an inactive form (un-ionized). *Hirudin* is a material secreted by the mouth glands of the leech. It prevents the blood of the parasite's host from coagulating while it is being sucked. Hirudin is prepared commercially for use, chiefly in physiological experiments; heparin, however, has largely taken its place.

Heparin (Gk. *hepar,* liver) is an anticoagulant of special interest, since it is found in mammalian liver, lung, muscle, and other tissues. It is very powerfully anticoagulant, 1 mg of a highly purified preparation being capable of preventing for 24 hours the coagulation of 500 cc of blood, if kept at a temperature of about 50° F.

Dicoumarin is a poison formed in spoiled clover silage. This material has been responsible in the past for a fatal hemorrhage disease of farm animals that have been fed on spoiled clover. Dicoumarin acts by reducing the prothrombin concentration of the blood to such a low level that clotting cannot occur. Prothrombin is produced in the liver, and it is probable that the poison acts upon this organ and interferes in some way with prothrombin production. This anticoagulant is now widely used in the treatment of coronary thrombosis, and other forms of intravascular clotting, for the purpose of preventing the spread of the clotting process.

A low prothrombin concentration of the blood with a tendency to bleed is associated in some animal species with a dietary lack of a vitamin found in certain green foods (e.g., alfalfa, spinach, cabbage, etc.). This is known as vitamin K, or the antihemorrhagic vitamin (see p. 397).

The concentration of prothrombin in the blood of the newborn child is frequently much below the normal level, due apparently to a lack of vitamin K in the mother's diet. It is unusual, however, for this to be a cause of bleeding, because when the baby is fed, the bacteria introduced into the intestine with the food are capable of synthesizing the antihemorrhagic vitamin. Sometimes, however, the prothrombin level of the infant's blood is so low at birth that it does not rise to normal before a grave hemorrhagic state—*hemorrhagic disease of the new born*—supervenes. It is treated by the intravenous administration of synthetic vitamin K.

The essential importance of prothrombin in the clotting mechanism is clearly evident from the foregoing account of its presence in low concentration. We have also seen that after ionized calcium has been removed from the blood by oxalate, or other means, clotting is entirely prevented, since prothrombin cannot be activated to thrombin.

The indispensability of the two other primary factors in the clotting process, namely, thromboplastin and fibrinogen, may be illustrated by the following observations. Thromboplastin, as mentioned above, is derived from tissue cells and from damaged cells in the blood itself. If the blood is drawn by means of a syringe directly from a blood vessel into a clean glass container made smooth by a coating of liquid paraffin or of a solution of silicone, the cells remain largely intact. For this reason, and because the blood does not come into contact with the tissues, it receives a minimum quantity of thromboplastin and, as a consequence, clots much more slowly than usual. The experiment of the "living test tube" also demonstrates the indispensability of thromboplastin for the clotting of blood. When a short section of the jugular vein in the living animal is isolated by ligatures from the rest of the vessel and removed, the blood within it, since it remains undisturbed and in contact with the smooth and uninjured lining of the vein's wall, does not clot for many hours.

Defibrinated blood is blood from which the fibrinogen has been removed as fibrin; it is incapable of forming a clot. Defibrination is carried out by whipping the blood with a bundle of thin twigs or wires. As clotting occurs, the fibrin collects upon the twigs and can in this way be removed, leaving only the serum and cells.

The mechanism underlying the clotting of the blood is chemical in nature, and, like other chemical reactions, is slowed by lowering the temperature and hastened by warming. Blood placed in the refrigerator immediately after it has been shed may remain fluid for 2 or 3 hours.

Means used to hasten coagulation. The coagulation of blood as it issues from a wound can be accelerated by several measures. Heat, powder dusted on the wound, tissue extracts (containing thromboplastin), a preparation of thrombin, and various chemicals (known from their action in this regard as *styptics* or *hemostatics*) accelerate the clotting process. Among the latter are alum, ferric chloride, zinc chloride, and silver nitrate. Such substances arrest bleeding in two ways; they hasten clotting of the blood through the precipitation of the plasma proteins which, by forming a sticky mass, mechanically impede the flow of blood and thus favor platelet disintegration; they also cause constriction of the walls of the small bleeding vessels. Certain physiological conditions hasten coagulation. Blood shed after muscular exercise or emotional excitement clots more quickly than usual owing to the discharge of *adrenaline* into the circulation (p. 420). Adrenaline (epinephrine) injected into the body also causes a sample of blood, drawn shortly after the injection, to clot more quickly, but no such effect upon the clotting mechanism results from adding adrenaline to blood outside the body,[12] or by applying it to a bleeding vessel. In the latter instance, however, adrenaline tends to stop the bleeding by constricting the small vessels with which it comes into contact. Thus, superficial bleeding or slow oozing of blood is very quickly arrested. The arrest of bleeding either by hastening coagulation of the blood or by constriction of the bleeding vessels is called *hemostasis*.

Coagulation time and bleeding time. *The coagulation time* is defined as the length of time, in minutes, measured from the moment the blood sample is collected to the appearance of the first definite sign of clotting. Several methods for determining this interval have been devised. The simplest is that of Howell, which consists in collecting the blood in a small test tube coated inside with liquid paraffin, and gently tilting the tube every 20 seconds or so until the blood is no longer liquid—that is, when the line of its surface no longer changes freely with tilting.

The bleeding time is measured by pricking the base of the fingernail and when a drop of blood appears, dabbing it lightly from time to time with a small piece of filter paper. The time from the appearance of the drop of blood to when the filter paper is no longer stained is taken as the bleeding time.

---

[12] The fact that adrenaline hastens the coagulation of the blood if injected into the body, but not when added to blood in a test tube, strongly suggests that it acts not *directly* upon the clotting mechanism, but only through some other structure, possibly a ductless gland, causing it to secrete a principle which exerts a direct coagulant action.

Hemorrhagic States Due to Failure of the Clotting Mechanism

In rare instances a deficiency of *fibrinogen* is the cause of the blood failing to form a firm clot, with the result that severe hemorrhage may follow a wound which in a normal person would be of little concern. It is a very common practice to give *calcium* in the belief that it will promote coagulation of the blood in hemorrhagic states. It appears, however, that the blood is never so low in calcium that clotting fails. Contrary to what might be expected, a hemorrhagic tendency is never due to a low concentration of calcium in the blood. Certain serious effects (e.g., tetany) ensue before the blood calcium is reduced to the point where the clotting mechanism is interfered with. The common use of calcium to promote the coagulation of the blood in hemorrhagic states is, therefore, without any scientific foundation.

A depression of the prothrombin of the blood (*hypoprothrombinemia*) is one of the commonest defects of the clotting mechanism. The tendency to bleed in *obstructive jaundice* and, as mentioned on page 104, in the hemorrhagic state of cattle fed upon spoiled clover, as well as in the hemorrhagic disease of the new born, is due to this cause.

In obstructive jaundice, bile, which is an essential for the absorption of vitamin K, does not reach the intestine. The body fails, therefore, to secure the vitamin required for the manufacture of prothrombin.

Hemophilia. Hemophilia is a disease in which the blood takes an abnormally long time to clot. The blood of a normal person clots within 5 or 6 minutes after its withdrawal from the body. In hemophilia the blood may remain fluid for an hour or more. There is grave danger, therefore, of a person afflicted with this disease bleeding to death, even from a trivial wound. Hemophilia is hereditary but it occurs almost solely in males and is transmitted only by females. This sex-linked type of heredity is also seen in the case of color blindness.

The manner in which the disease is carried from generation to generation may be illustrated by an example. If a man suffering from hemophilia—commonly known as a *bleeder*—marries a normal woman, no offspring of the union will show the disease. Some of the daughters, nevertheless, but not the sons, will, when they marry, transmit the disease to some of *their* sons, but not to the daughters. The latter, however, can again transmit it. The disease, therefore, skips a generation, a bleeder inheriting it from his mother's male forebears. Thus:

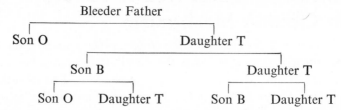

Bleeder Father

Son O   Daughter T

Son B   Daughter T

Son O   Daughter T   Son B   Daughter T

B means a bleeder; O means not a bleeder; T means a transmitter but not a bleeder.

What part of the clotting mechanism is at fault in this disease is uncertain, but there appears to be some defect in the production of an active thromboplastin in the plasma. The coagulation time in hemophilia is greatly prolonged. Bleeding due to this disease is treated most successfully by blood transfusions.

Purpura. Purpura is another hemorrhagic disease, in which blood leaks from the small vessels of the skin and mucous membranes. When the hemorrhages are from the cutaneous vessels, the skin is discolored by small purplish patches. Some defect in the capillary walls and a reduction in the number of platelets appear to be the chief factors concerned in the production of the disease. The coagulation time is within normal limits but the bleeding time is prolonged. One severe type of purpura is apparently due to some destructive action of the spleen upon the platelets. Removal of the spleen is followed in most instances by an increase in the platelet count and a cessation of the hemorrhages.

The Regulation of the Reaction of the Blood and Other Body Fluids

The acidity or alkalinity of a solution is dependent upon its concentrations in hydrogen ions (H^+) and hydroxyl ions (OH^-), that is, upon the degree to which the molecules in the solution are dissociated into their constituent ions. A tenth normal solution of hydrochloric acid (H^+Cl^-), for example, contains a high concentration of hydrogen ions, whereas the hydrogen ion concentration of a tenth normal solution of acetic acid is very much lower (see Table 1-3, p. 13). The acid properties of hydrochloric acid are, therefore, much greater than those of acetic acid. Similarly, a tenth normal solution of sodium hydroxide (Na^+OH^-) has a much higher concentration in hydroxyl ions than has a tenth normal solution of sodium bicarbonate. The former solution is therefore more alkaline. It must be emphasized that it is the concentration of the *hydrogen ion*—i.e., the extent to which the molecule is dissociated—and not the total number of *hydrogen atoms* which determines the acid reaction. Thus, HCl though it contains only one hydrogen atom in its molecule undergoes almost complete dissociation into H^+ and Cl^- and is, in consequence, a much stronger acid than acetic, whose molecules dissociate to a relatively small extent. Water undergoes dissociation to a very slight degree into H^+ and OH^-. The ionized hydrogen in a liter of water is 0.0000001 gram, or more conveniently expressed, 1×10^{-7} gram. We therefore say that the H ion concentration of water is 1×10^{-7} gram per liter. The symbol $^{-7}$ to the right of the figure 10 is termed the *negative exponent* or *index,* and means that to express the value in the form of a decimal fraction the figure 1 must be placed 7 places to the right of the decimal point (0.0000001). Expressed as a common fraction the 10^{-7} would be $\frac{1}{10000000}$ gram per liter.

Other examples of this system of notation are:

$$10^{-1} \text{ means } 0.1 \text{ or } \tfrac{1}{10}$$
$$10^{-2} \text{ `` } 0.01 \text{ or } \tfrac{1}{100}$$
$$10^{-3} \text{ `` } 0.001 \text{ or } \tfrac{1}{1000}, \text{ and so on}$$

The concentration of OH ions in water is also 1×10^{-7} gram per liter. That is, the H^+ ions and OH^- ions are in equal concentration; water is, therefore, neutral in reaction. Now the *product* of the concentrations of H ions and OH ions in water is 1×10^{-14} [(1×10^{-7}) $\times (1 \times 10^{-7}) = 1 \times 10^{-14}$]. Furthermore, in any aqueous solution, whether acid, neutral, or alkaline, the product of the concentrations of H^+ and OH^- ions is constant at 1×10^{-14}. This means that in an acid solution the H^+ ion concentration increases, whereas the OH^- ion concentration is reduced reciprocally. It is evident, then, that in order to express the reaction of a solution it is not necessary to give the concentrations of both H^+ and OH^- ions, but only of the H^+ ion. The reaction of water or any other neutral solution is indicated, therefore, by stating that it has an H^+ ion concentration (usually designated cH) of 1×10^{-7}. The hydrogen ion concentrations of alkaline solutions are less than 1×10^{-7}—that is, 1×10^{-8}, 1×10^{-9}, 1×10^{-10}, and so on, according to the degree of alkalinity. The hydrogen ion concentrations of acid solution are more than 1×10^{-7}; i.e., 1×10^{-6}, 1×10^{-5}, 1×10^{-4}, etc.

To summarize: neutral solutions have 0.0000001 gram of ionized hydrogen per liter—i.e., a cH of 1×10^{-7}.

Alkaline solutions have a lower H^+ ion concentration—i.e., from 1×10^{-7} to 1×10^{-14}.

Acid solutions have a higher H^+ ion concentration—i.e., from 1×10^{-7} to 1×10^{-1}.

Within recent times a more convenient method of expressing the hydrogen ion concentration has been introduced, in which the symbol pH, instead of cH, is used. Thus the expression $cH \times 10^{-7}$, indicating a neutral solution, becomes pH 7. Alkaline solutions have pH's ranging from pH 7 to pH 14; acid solutions from pH 7 to pH 1. It will be observed that the lower the pH number, the higher is the hydrogen ion concentration—i.e., the less alkaline or the more acid is

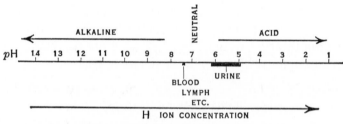

Fig. 3.30   (Explanation in text.)

the solution (Fig. 3.30). More advanced texts should be consulted if the reader wishes to understand the mathematical basis for this method of expressing the hydrogen ion concentration in terms of pH.

Arterial blood has a pH of between 7.39 and 7.45. Venous blood is very slightly *less* alkaline, having a pH between 7.37 and 7.42; the change is due to carbon dioxide and small quantities of lactic acid which the blood absorbs in passing through the tissues. Though large quantities of acid (carbonic, lactic, sulfuric, hydrochloric, etc.) are constantly being produced in the body as a result of various metabolic processes, the reaction of the blood and other body fluids remains remarkably constant around the figures just given. The three important mechanisms responsible for the maintenance of this constancy of reaction are:

1. The elimination of CO_2 by the lungs (p. 247).

2. The excretion of acid by the kidney [the urine is decidedly acid in reaction (p. 275)].

3. The buffer systems of the blood and other body fluids.

Buffers may be defined as chemical substances which when present in a solution permit no change, or only a slight one, to occur in that solution when acid (or alkali) is added to it. An amount of hydrochloric acid which if added to water would cause a pronounced increase in acidity would, when added to blood or any solution buffered against acid, produce no appreciable change in reaction. It is from this action in buffering the shock, one might say, of the added acid that these substances derive their name. For example, when hydrochloric acid is poured into a solution of sodium bicarbonate the very weak carbonic acid together with sodium chloride, a *neutral* salt, is produced. Furthermore, the carbonic acid is volatile; it escapes into the atmosphere. The result is that little change in the reaction of the solution occurs, even though it has received relatively large amounts of the strong acid. The sodium bicarbonate acts as a buffer. Thus:

$$\text{HCl} + \text{NaHCO}_3 = \text{NaCl} + \text{H}_2\text{CO}_3 \nearrow \text{CO}_2$$

hydrochloric acid	sodium bicarbonate	sodium chloride	carbonic acid

The chief buffer of the plasma and tissue fluids is sodium bicarbonate. A fixed acid such as lactic, formed during muscular activity, reacts with the bicarbonate as shown in the following equation.

$$\text{HLA} + \text{NaHCO}_3 = \text{NaLA} + \text{H}_2\text{CO}_3 \nearrow \text{CO}_2$$

lactic acid	sodium bicarbonate	sodium lactate	carbonic acid

The sodium bicarbonate of the plasma thus serves as a store of alkali available for the protection of the body against poisoning with the acid products of metabolism. It is therefore called the *alkali reserve*.

Other buffers of the blood are the plasma proteins (which form proteinates), phosphates, and the hemoglobin within the red cell. Hemoglobin is a weak acid; it is combined in the red blood cells with alkali (potassium) to form potassium hemoglobinate (KHb). This alkali acts to buffer carbonic acid entering the blood from the tissues. The contents of the erythrocytes, however, are separated from the plasma by a semipermeable membrane which will not permit the passage of K^+, Na^+, or Ca^{++} ions but allows the free passage of Cl^-, HCO_3^-, and other negative ions, as well as the H^+ ion and CO_2. When, therefore, the carbon dioxide produced in the tissues enters the plasma, the following interchange of ions occurs across the erythrocyte boundary. The carbon dioxide (CO_2) diffuses freely into the cell and, through the action of an enzyme called *carbonic anhydrase,* combines rapidly with H_2O to form carbonic acid (H_2CO_3). The carbonic acid, being a stronger acid than reduced hemoglobin, seizes the base combined with the pigment to form potassium bicar-

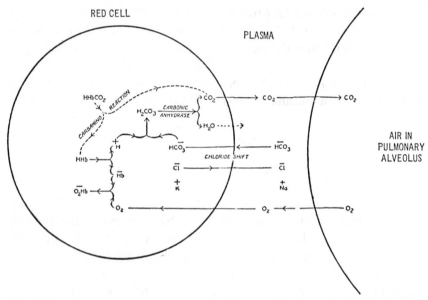

Fig. 3.31   Showing main processes occurring in the blood during the output of carbon dioxide and uptake of oxygen in the lung. (After Roughton, modified.)

bonate ($KHCO_3$) which dissociates into K^+ and HCO_3^- ions. The membrane of the cell, as just mentioned, is permeable to HCO_3^- ions but not to K^+ ions. HCO_3^- ions diffuse across the cell boundary into the plasma; the K^+ ions are retained. In order to maintain the balance between negative and positive ions on the two sides of the cell membrane, Cl^- ions derived from the Na^+Cl^- of the plasma pass into the cell in exchange for the HCO_3^- ions which pass out. In the plasma, the HCO_3^- ions unite with the Na^+ ions, which had been coupled with Cl^- ions, thus forming sodium bicarbonate ($Na^+HCO_3^-$). The mechanism just described is termed the *chloride shift* (see Fig. 3.31). This mechanism is responsible for the phenomenon, now well recognized, that an increase in the carbon dioxide of the plasma causes a rise in the alkali reserve (sodium bicarbonate). In the lungs, ionic interchanges in the reverse order occur. The hemoglobin when it becomes oxygenated is a very much stronger acid than is reduced hemoglobin or carbonic acid. It, therefore, recaptures the alkali (K^+) bound to carbonic acid. The carbonic anhydrase, whose action is now reversed,[13] decomposes the carbonic acid into carbon dioxide (CO_2) and water (H_2O). The carbon dioxide diffuses out of the cells, as they traverse the capillaries of the lungs, and is exhaled. The concentration of HCO_3^- ions within the cells is reduced as a result of these reactions. HCO_3^- ions pass from the plasma into the cells and Cl^- ions are transferred from the cells to the plasma. The sodium bicarbonate of the plasma is reduced, the sodium chloride increased, by the interchange.

Acidosis and alkalosis. The proportion of carbonic acid to sodium bicarbonate in the plasma is about 1 to 20, thus:

$$\frac{H_2CO_3}{NaHCO_3} = \frac{1}{20}$$

It is upon this ratio that the reaction of the blood largely depends. Any shift in the ratio causes a change in blood reaction. If, for example, the ratio should increase, say, to $\frac{1}{25}$, the blood would be more alkaline. If the ratio should be reduced to $\frac{1}{15}$, the blood would be less alkaline. In health, the ratio remains virtually constant. The several mechanisms mentioned above ensure this constancy. If, for example, there should be a tendency for the ratio to rise, as a result of an increased production of carbon dioxide, the bicarbonate of the plasma increases through the chloride shift mechanism. If, on the other hand, the bicarbonate is reduced owing to the accumulation of fixed acids (see equations, p. 111), more carbon dioxide is excreted by the lungs and the ratio thus maintained at its normal value.

In certain diseases, e.g., diabetes and kidney disease (nephritis), excessive acid production or reduced elimination of acid occurs, the bicarbonate of the plasma becomes markedly reduced, and a change in the ratio may result. The blood becomes less alkaline and the alkali reserve is diminished. The condition is then spoken of as *acidosis*. The term acidosis is also applied to the condition in which the plasma bicarbonate is reduced *but there is no change in the $H_2CO_3/NaHCO_3$ ratio and, consequently, no change in blood reaction*. This is spoken of as *compensated acidosis*. When, as in the first mentioned instance, the acidosis is accompanied by a change in blood reaction it is said to be *uncompensated*.

It should be emphasized that the $H_2CO_3/NaHCO_3$ ratio does not

[13] The action of most enzymes is reversible.

vary from its normal value of $\frac{1}{20}$ unless serious disease exists. There are two possible exceptions to this statement. First, in very strenuous muscular exercise the large quantities of carbon dioxide and lactic acid produced might result in a slight and *temporary* reduction in the alkalinity of the blood. Secondly, forced breathing (p. 255) if prolonged may, through the excessive loss of carbon dioxide, cause the blood to become temporarily slightly more alkaline.

It should be remembered, moreover, that the blood practically never, except in the last stages of some fatal disease, becomes *actually acid* in reaction—that is, with a pH less than 7, and rarely does it even approach the neutral point. The range of blood reaction compatible with life is from about pH 7.8 to 6.8. It is quite evident then, that the term acidosis is frequently used—especially by the advertisers of quack remedies—without any clear understanding of its meaning.

Alkalosis is the corresponding term used to denote an increase in sodium bicarbonate with or without a change in the $H_2CO_3/NaHCO_3$ ratio.[14] As in the case of acidosis it is called compensated or uncompensated, respectively, according to whether or not a change in the ratio and so, of course, in the blood reaction has occurred. Alkalosis may result from the ingestion of large quantities of sodium bicarbonate, from persistent vomiting, when hydrochloric acid is removed in the gastric juice, or from forced breathing when, as already mentioned, unusually large quantities of carbon dioxide are eliminated.

---

[14] It has been the custom to use the terms acidosis and alkalosis to denote changes in the alkali reserve regardless of whether or not an accompanying change occurred in pH. But with a view to more precise definitions, it has been suggested that the above terms be reserved for changes in alkali reserve in which the pH is normal, and that *acidemia* and *alkalemia* be used to denote changes in alkali reserve with a fall or a rise, respectively, in pH.

CHAPTER 4

The Circulation of the Blood

General Description of the Circulatory System

The blood circulates through the body in a completely closed system consisting of a pump—the *heart*—and a network of tubes—the *blood vessels*.

The heart. The heart is a hollow muscular organ, roughly cone shaped, situated near the center of the thoracic cavity, and in close relation to the lungs. About a third of its bulk lies to the right and two thirds to the left of the mid-line of the body. The heart is divided by partitions or septa into four chambers—the *right* and *left auricles* (or *atria*) and the *right* and *left ventricles*. The auricles [1] are situated above, posteriorly, and to the right; the ventricles are situated below, more anteriorly, and to the left. The broad upper part of the heart formed by the auricles is called the *base*. Its somewhat pointed lower part formed by the left ventricle is called the *apex;* this is directed downward, forward, and to the left (Fig. 4.1).

The heart is enclosed within a delicate two-layered membrane called the *serous pericardium;* each layer consists of a single stratum of endothelial cells. The inner layer, which is in contact with and adherent to the heart muscle, is called the *visceral layer* or *epicardium*. The outer layer is separated from the inner by a thin film of fluid and is known as the *parietal layer*. The potential space between the two layers is known as the *pericardial sac*. A tougher fibrous membrane—the *fibrous pericardium*—surrounds the serous pericardium and extends upward to blend with the coats of the great vessels; it is firmly

[1] *Auricle,* though an older anatomical term, is still most frequently used in physiology.

115

attached in front to the posterior aspect of the sternum and below to the central part of the upper surface of the diaphragm.

The right and left halves of the heart—the right auricle (or atrium) and ventricle, on the one hand, and the left auricle (or atrium) and ventricle, on the other—are not in communication. The partition interposed between the two auricles is called the *interauricular septum;*

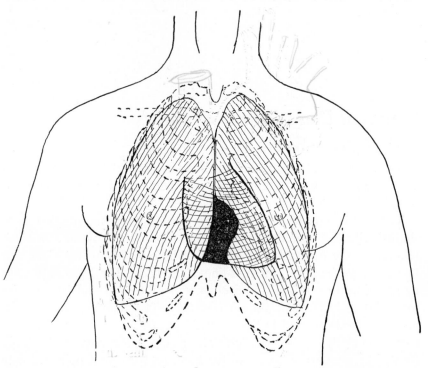

Fig. 4.1   Showing the position of the heart in relation to the chest wall and lungs. The black area indicates that part of the heart uncovered by the lungs.

that separating the two ventricles from one another is named the *interventricular septum.* The auricle of each side communicates with the corresponding ventricle through an opening, the *auriculo-* (or *atrio-*) *ventricular orifice,* guarded by the *auriculo-* (or *atrio-*) *ventricular valve.* These valves open toward the ventricles, permitting blood to enter from the auricles, but close the instant that the ventricle contracts; thus the passage of the blood backward into the auricles is prevented. The auriculo- (atrio-) ventricular valve on the left side is also known as the *mitral* valve, from its fancied resemblance to a bishop's miter or tall cap; that on the right side as the *tricuspid valve* (see also p. 174), because it consists of three triangular leaves or cusps.

The muscular walls of the auricles are thin compared with the muscle of the ventricles. The left ventricular wall has a wall about double the thickness of that of the right ventricle, since the work which it must perform is much greater than that performed by the

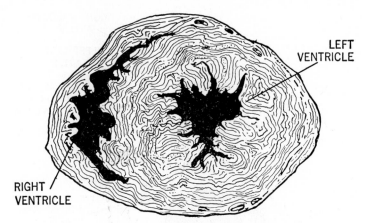

LEFT VENTRICLE

RIGHT VENTRICLE

Fig. 4.2   Cross section of heart through the ventricles.

right ventricle (Fig. 4.2). The heart chambers are lined by a delicate endothelial membrane called the *endocardium*. Springing from the wall of each ventricular cavity are two small muscular pillars, somewhat conical in shape and known as the *papillary muscles* (*musculi papillares*). From the apices of the latter, slender cords, the *chordae tendineae*, arise and are attached to the ventricular aspects of the auriculoventricular valves (Fig. 4.3). Acting like guy ropes, they support the delicate leaflets of the valves against the pressure developed in the ventricle during its contraction.

The arrangement of the fibers of the ventricles is very complex. They are disposed in a superficial and a deep series of layers. Of the superficial layers, some course from the upper and anterior part of the right ventricle downward and to the left, looping around the apex, in the form of a vortex (Fig. 4.4). Passing upward and inward they end in the papillary muscles of the left ventricle. Other superficial groups of fibers pass diagonally across the posterior surface of the heart from right to left. Of the deep layers, some pass from the papillary muscles of one ventricle to those of the other, encircling both ventricles in a scroll-like or S-shaped manner. Other groups encircle the left ventricle alone.

The right side of the heart contains venous blood; that is, blood which has passed through the tissues and given up a proportion of its load of oxygen (p. 247). The left side contains bright red (arterial) blood—blood which has been oxygenated in the lungs. The venous blood is delivered to the right auricle by two large veins—the *superior vena cava* which drains blood from the upper part of the body (head,

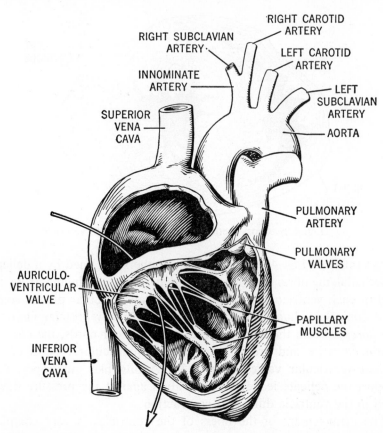

Fig. 4.3   Showing the heart and great blood vessels; interiors of right auricle and ventricle exposed. The right auriculoventricular valve (tricuspid) is shown.

neck, arms, and the interior of the thoracic wall), and the *inferior vena cava* which conveys blood from the lower part of the body (lower limbs and abdominal organs). The blood flows from the right auricle through the auriculoventricular orifice, into the right ventricle, from which it is discharged during ventricular contraction into the *pulmonary artery* and thence through the vessels of the lungs. After passing through the capillaries of the lungs, where it gives up carbon dioxide and absorbs oxygen, the oxygenated blood is conveyed by the four pulmonary veins (two from each lung) to the left auricle. It

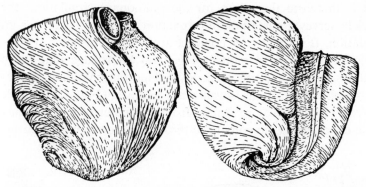

Fig. 4.4   Dissection of heart muscle to show the course of the fibers. (Redrawn, after Mall.)

then passes through the left auriculoventricular orifice into the left ventricle. When the ventricular muscle contracts, the blood is pumped into the *aorta*—the great artery which arises from the upper part of the left ventricle.

Thus, the blood circulates through the lungs from the right ventricle to the left auricle, and through the rest of the body from the left ventricle to the right auricle (Pl. 4). The course through the lungs is called the *pulmonary* or *lesser circulation;* that through all other parts of the body, the *systemic* or *greater circulation.* The right ven-

Fig. 4.5   William Harvey.

tricle is therefore the pump for the pulmonary circulation; the left ventricle serves a corresponding function for the systemic or greater circulation. Both ventricles contract at the same instant.

Though it is now a matter of general knowledge that the blood circulates in this way, the truth lay hidden until William Harvey, an English physician of the seventeenth century (Fig. 4.5), made the discovery. By his clear reasoning from a number of observations and simple experiments, he convinced those who were not blinded by pre-

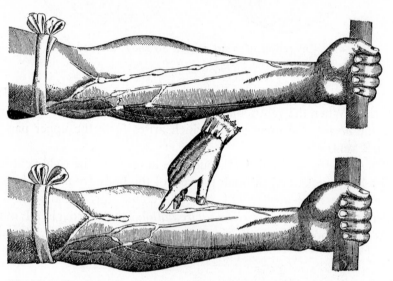

Fig. 4.6 From an engraving in Harvey's *Exercitatio anatomica de motu cordis et sanguinis in animalibus* illustrating one of his demonstrations. (See text.)

conceived notions that the blood must take the course outlined above. Harvey pointed out that, owing to the structure and arrangement of the valves of the heart, the blood must course through it only in one direction. He showed that when the veins of a limb were compressed the blood was dammed back on the side of the block farther from the heart (Fig. 4.6). These facts could mean only that the blood made a circuit of the body. An examination of the valves of the veins which were so placed that they would allow blood to flow toward the heart, but not in the reverse direction, supported this conclusion. In 1628, he published his great work *Exercitatio anatomica de motu cordis et sanguinis in animalibus* (*Anatomical Exercise on the Motion of the Heart and Blood in Animals*). Before Harvey's day the dogmas of Galen, a Greek physician who practiced medicine in Rome in the second century of the Christian era, dominated all medical thought. His views on physiology were accepted without question as the infallible pronouncements of a god. According to Galen, the food material absorbed from the intestines was conveyed by the portal vein to the liver where it was converted into blood. This newly formed and somewhat crude type of blood then passed to the right side of the heart where it was purified; the impurities, finding vent through the pulmonary artery and lungs, were exhaled in the breath. The blood formed in the liver did not circulate, but was conceived as simply ebbing and flowing in the veins; from it the tissues derived their nutriment. A small part of the blood in the right heart was believed, however, to find its way through invisible pores in the septum to the left side where, mixing with air received from the lungs through the pulmonary veins, it was transformed into a more refined type of blood. This arterial blood, as the result of the action upon it of a vital essence—the *pneuma*—received from the air, possessed a life-giving principle which Galen called the *vital spirit*.

This brief description of ancient and medieval physiology will give the reader an appreciation and idea of the fundamental nature and immense importance of Harvey's discovery. Galen was a great and wise physician and experimentalist of his time and it can be seen that in his theory of the pneuma, by which he sought to explain the difference between venous and arterial blood, he was groping for an essential life-sustaining principle in air which we now identify as oxygen. Indeed, with the clear vision of genius, he remarked, "When we know what supports a flame we shall know the cause of the body's heat." Oxygen was not discovered and its importance to living processes recognized until Lavoisier's work in the eighteenth century.

The blood vessels. There are four main types of blood vessel: *arteries, arterioles, capillaries,* and *veins.*

The arteries. These are of various sizes; the largest in the body are the *aorta*—which is the sole outlet for the blood from the left ventricle —and the *pulmonary artery,* which receives the contents of the right ventricle. In man, each of these vessels is a little over an inch in diameter. Traced peripherally, the channels of the arterial system divide and subdivide extensively like the limbs and twigs of a tree. The aorta ascends from its origin for a short distance and then, forming an arch, descends in front of the vertebral column through the thorax and abdomen. At the level of the fourth lumbar vertebra it divides into two vessels—the *right* and *left common iliac arteries.* Each common iliac divides into two branches—the *external* and *internal iliac* arter-

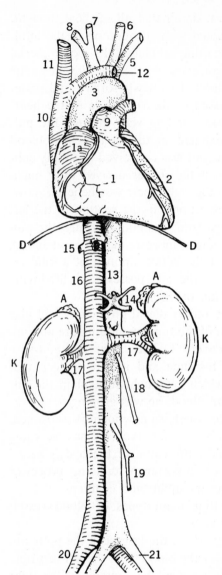

Fig. 4.7 Diagram of main vessels of the body. Veins and pulmonary artery in hatched shading; arteries stippled. 1, right ventricle; 1a, right auricle; 2, left ventricle; 3, arch of aorta; 4, innominate artery; 5, right subclavian artery; 6, left common carotid artery; 7, right common carotid artery; 8, right subclavian artery; 9, pulmonary artery; 10, superior vena cava; 11, jugular vein; 12, left subclavian vein; 13, abdominal aorta; 14, branches of celiac axis artery; 15, hepatic veins; 16, inferior vena cava; 17, renal arteries and veins; 18, superior mesenteric artery; 19, inferior mesenteric artery; 20, common iliac veins; 21, common iliac artery; A, A, adrenal glands; D, D, diaphragm; K, K, kidneys.

ies. The former carries blood to the lower limbs; after entering the thigh it is called the *femoral artery*. The internal iliac (or *hypogastric*) artery is distributed to the pelvis.

The thoracic and abdominal viscera are supplied by branches that spring from the aorta in its course through these cavities. Three large arteries spring from the arch of the aorta: the *left common carotid,* the *left subclavian,* and the *innominate arteries.* The last is a short trunk which divides into the *right common carotid* and the *right sub-*

clavian arteries. The common carotid arteries are the main arterial trunks to the head. They ascend on either side of the neck and at the upper border of the thyroid cartilage divide into the *external* and *internal carotid* arteries. The latter enters the cranial cavity where it divides into branches to supply the brain with blood. The subclavian artery conveys blood to the upper limb; at the root of the limb it is called the *axillary artery,* and in the arm the *brachial artery* (see Figs. 4.3 and 4.7). It will be noted that the common carotid and subclavian arteries on the right side spring from the innominate, whereas the left common carotid and subclavian arise directly from the aorta.

The foregoing is but the barest outline of the arterial system.

The walls of the arteries are thick and strong; they contain a large proportion of elastic tissue and a smaller amount of smooth muscle. They are lined by endothelium which is called the *internal coat* or

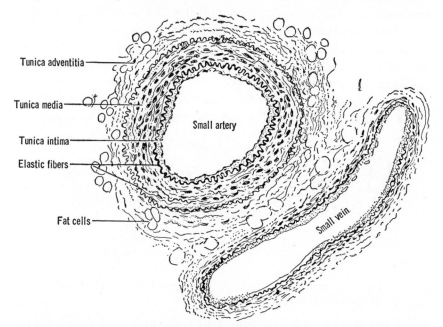

Fig. 4.8   Cross sections of a small artery and vein showing the three coats. Note that though the vein is larger it has a thinner wall.

tunica intima. The *middle coat* or *tunica media* is made up of elastic and muscular tissues. The *outer coat*, composed of connective tissue, is called the *tunica adventitia* (see Fig. 4.8). The proportions of smooth muscle and elastic tissue in the arterial wall vary with the size of the artery. Though elastic tissue enters largely into the construction of the largest vessels (e.g., the pulmonary artery and aorta) muscular tissue is relatively small in amount. In the medium and smallest arterial branches, especially in the latter, the smooth muscle is more abundant, the elastic tissue being correspondingly reduced. The walls of the arteries, except those of the smallest (1 mm or less in diameter), are themselves furnished with minute blood vessels. These vessels, called *vasa vasorum* (vessels of vessels), ramify in the tunica adventitia and outer layer of the tunica media. The small arteries, as well as the vasa vasorum, are supplied with nerves through which their calibers are controlled.

The arterioles. Each of the smallest arterial branches divides into a number of still finer vessels, called arterioles. The arterioles are about 0.2 mm in diameter, being just visible to the naked eye. Although they possess an endothelial lining and a thin layer of elastic tissue, their walls are composed mainly of smooth muscle whose fibers form encircling rings. The arterioles are supplied with nerves which, by bringing about contraction or relaxation of the rings of smooth muscle, control their calibers. Thus, the quantity of blood passing through this part of the circulatory system may be altered from time to time as occasion requires (see pp. 195–6).

The capillaries. An arteriole when traced peripherally is found to break up into a number of extremely narrow tubes, the capillaries.

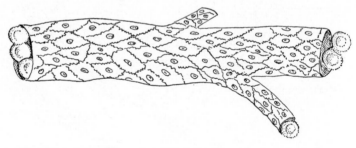

Fig. 4.9   A capillary; its wall is composed of a single layer of endothelial cells.

These vessels (Fig. 4.9) are from ½ to 1 mm long, and have a caliber which in many instances is no greater, and may be less, than the diameter of a red blood corpuscle (7 to 8 microns). The wall of a capillary is composed of *a single layer of endothelial cells*—a membrane of exquisite thinness which, as mentioned elsewhere (p. 66), permits the free passage of water and crystalloids between its cells, but is only slightly permeable to the plasma proteins. In amphibians, but not in mammals, there are to be seen, lying close to or in contact with the capillary wall, peculiar cells whose slender processes form a lattice-

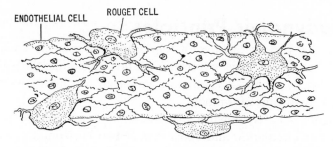

Fig. 4.10 Showing Rouget cells on the wall of an amphibian capillary.

work embracing the vessel (Fig. 4.10). They are called *Rouget cells*. The capillaries, though constituting such an inconspicuous part of the circulation, are nevertheless the *raison d'être* for the rest of the circulatory system. The heart is the pump and the relatively thick-walled arteries and veins simply conduits which carry blood to and from the capillaries; in the capillary region the object of the circulation—namely, to convey oxygen and nutritive materials to the tissues and to carry carbon dioxide and waste products away—is fulfilled. The walls of vessels larger than the capillaries are impervious to gases and liquids.

The veins. Like the arteries, the veins have walls composed of three coats, but the tunica media is poorly developed as compared with an artery of about the same size. The wall of a vein is, consequently, much thinner than that of its companion artery, but its caliber is considerably larger (see Fig. 4.8). The larger veins of the abdomen and lower limbs possess valves which open in the direction in which the blood is flowing—that is, toward the heart (Fig. 4.11). The very small veins succeeding the capillaries are generally referred to as *venules.*

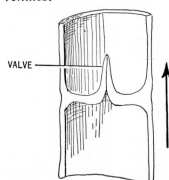

Fig. 4.11 A vein of the lower limb opened to show valve. The arrow indicates the direction of the blood flow.

Hemodynamic Principles

In order that certain features of the circulation may be understood, some of the physical laws governing the flow of liquids through tubes must be briefly reviewed. The more important of these laws may be illustrated by means of a model.

In Figure 4.12 is shown a piece of apparatus made to represent the systemic circulation and consisting of two horizontal glass tubes, AA and BB, from each of which a series of vertical side tubes of smaller caliber, T, T, T, and T′, T′, T′, are given off. The two systems of tubes are connected by finer tubes of elastic rubber. The hand bulb, H, is so valved as to direct a flow of fluid as indicated by the

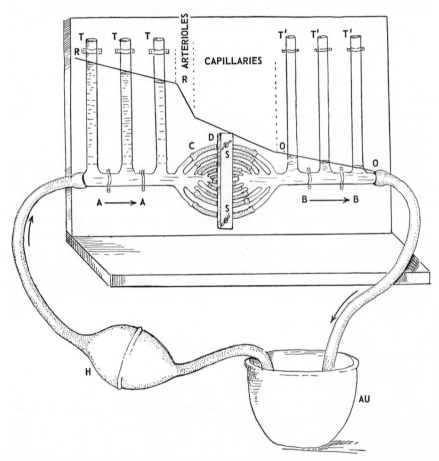

Fig. 4.12   Circulation scheme. A model composed of glass and rubber tubes, and a hand bulb, H, to illustrate certain facts in the circulation of the blood. (Description in text.)

arrows. It represents the left ventricle of the heart; the tube, AA, represents the aorta, and the vertical tubes, T, T, and T, represent some of its main branches. The system on the right corresponds to the venous system, in which BB are the larger veins (venae cavae) opening into the right auricle, Au, and the vertical tubes T', T', and T', their larger tributaries. The smaller rubber tubes, C, connecting the two systems represent the minute vessels, arterioles, capillaries, and venules. When the bulb, H, is alternately compressed and released at a suitable rate, it acts as a pump and, drawing fluid from the part of the system representing the auricle, Au, and the large veins, BB, forces it along AA. The fluid rises in the vertical side tubes, T, and its height in any tube indicates the pressure in centimeters of water at the point in the horizontal tube where that tube is given off. At every beat of the pump, the fluid in each side tube will be seen to fluctuate above, and then fall below, a certain mean level.[2] It will also be observed that the pressure (height) of the fluid in the side tubes falls progressively from tube to tube, as indicated by the slanting lines, R-R and O-O. This slope of pressure is due to the loss of energy caused by the frictional resistance offered to the flow of fluid along the horizontal tubes; for with a given amout of energy (transmitted to the fluid through the hand bulb), the greater the proportion of that energy which is expended in driving the fluid against resistance along the horizontal tubes, the smaller will be the proportion exhibited as pressure. The greater the area of the frictional surface over which the fluid flows—that is, the longer the distance along the horizontal tubes—the greater will be the energy expended in overcoming frictional resistance and dissipated as heat. Hence, the pressure in the second tube is less than in the first, and the pressure in the third tube is less, again, than in the second; and, if there were a long series of tubes given off from the horizontal tube, the pressure in each would be lower than that in the one before it to the end of the series.

The section of connecting tubes, C, beneath the bar, D, can be compressed or decompressed by tightening or loosening the thumb screws marked S, S; the calibers of these tubes are thus reduced or increased, respectively. When their calibers are reduced and the quantity of fluid passing through them is, in consequence, diminished, but the amount of fluid entering the system from the pump remains

[2] The model is not designed to illustrate the *action* of the heart, but only to show the physical principles governing the flow of liquid in narrow tubes. The ventricles, for example, *do not* "draw" blood from the auricles as the model indicates. On the contrary, the blood flows from the auricles into the ventricles under its own pressure.

approximately the same, then the pressure rises, as indicated by the heights of the fluid columns in the system on the left representing the arterial system. The pressure in the right-hand system, which represents the veins, falls, because less fluid now enters this system. Upon decompression of the rubber tubes, C—the quantity of fluid forced in by the pump again remaining unchanged—the pressure falls in the left-hand system and rises in the system on the right.

As the reader will learn later (pp. 195 and 196), the arterioles can be narrowed or enlarged in caliber by means of vasoconstrictor and vasodilator nerves supplying their muscular coat. The bar, D, in the model, by the tightening or loosening of which the small rubber tubes can be compressed or decompressed, represents these nerves.

Other hydrodynamic principles applicable to the circulation can be illustrated by means of the model. If, for example, the bulb, H, representing the left ventricle is compressed and decompressed more vigorously, more fluid will be pumped at each stroke into the system; the heights of the fluid in the side tubes, T, will show more pronounced fluctuations, and the mean pressure level will rise. More rapid strokes of the pump, with or without an increase of fluid forced into the system at each stroke, will also cause a rise in the mean level of the fluid in the side tubes. Changes of a similar nature in the action of the heart cause corresponding effects upon the arterial blood pressure.

If one of the small rubber tubes on the left of the bar, D, is loosened, punctured, or disconnected, so that a leak occurs in the system representing the arterial side of the circulation, a progressive

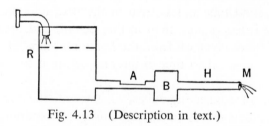

Fig. 4.13   (Description in text.)

or a sharp fall in the levels of the fluid in the side tubes will occur; if the leak is considerable, the pressure cannot be restored to its original level even though rapid and vigorous strokes are made with the pump. In a similar way, loss of blood by hemorrhage causes a progressive or a sudden fall in blood pressure, the rate of the fall depending upon the severity of the bleeding. A leak in the right-hand

(venous) system would likely have a slower and a much less pronounced effect.

Let us now turn from the consideration of fluid pressure to a study
of velocity of flow in a system of tubes. Physical principles governing the velocity of a fluid in a system of tubes comparable in size
to the blood vessels are best illustrated by means of the model shown
in Figure 4.13. The fluid in the reservoir, R, is kept at a steady level
by means of the flow from a faucet. Whatever quantity of fluid enters the reservoir by the faucet must leave by the mouth, M, of the
horizontal tube, H; otherwise the reservoir would overflow or be
gradually emptied. It follows then that equal quantities of fluid must
pass along equal lengths of the
tube, H, in any stated time. But
section A is narrower (i.e., its
capacity is less) than the sections of tube on either side. In
order then to transmit the same
volume of fluid, the velocity of
flow in the narrow section must

Fig. 4.14   (Description in text.)

increase. Section B is much broader; the flow in this section is, therefore, slower. It is immaterial to the general principle whether section B
is a single channel or is divided into a number of smaller ones as in Figure 4.14, for, provided that the *total* cross area—that is, the sum of the
cross areas of the small tubes in B—is greater than the cross area elsewhere along the horizontal tube, the flow through section B will be
slower. Though each individual tube may be extremely narrow, the velocity of flow in each of the constituent tubes of B will be less than in
any other part of the horizontal tube, H. Thus, with respect to velocity
of flow, one of these fine tubes, which constitutes but a small part of
the total cross area of the section which they occupy, differs from
the *single* narrow tube, A, since the latter offers the *sole channel* at
this point of tube H giving passage to the fluid. In the circulation of
the blood, the differences in velocity between, say, the aorta or large
veins on the one hand and the capillary region on the other *are due
entirely to variations in the total cross areas of the vascular channels
in the two situations* (see also pp. 134–5).

Though, in general, the physical principles of the circulation can
be demonstrated in a model, such a model differs from the vascular
system in certain important particulars. In the first place, the tubes in
the model, except those of the small rubber tubes in Figure 4.12,
have rigid walls; they lack the elasticity of the living vessels, and this

property of the vascular structures is essential for maintaining an adequate supply of blood to the tissues in the intervals between the beats of the heart (p. 148). Again, certain physiological factors come into play in the living body under varying conditions, so that it is not always possible to predict what will happen under a given set of circumstances. The complexity of these physiological factors, reactions and counterreactions, adjustments and compensations, preclude their being duplicated in any inanimate system.

The pressure of blood throughout the vascular system. In the model (Fig. 4.12), it will be observed that the oblique line R-R in the system on the left indicating the pressure levels at intervals along the

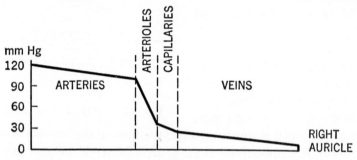

Fig. 4.15   Curve of blood pressure throughout the circulation— from left ventricle to right auricle.

horizontal tube, if continued to the right, would not meet the corresponding line O-O in the right-hand system, but would fall above it. This means that a fall in pressure more pronounced than elsewhere occurs in the region of the small rubber tubes representing the minute vessels of the vascular system. This relatively sharp drop in pressure is due to a greater amount of energy being expended in overcoming the frictional resistance offered by the small-calibered tubes, C; for the total surface over which the fluid flows is greatly increased by these subdivisions of the horizontal tube. Thus, in the vascular system, a large part of the ventricular contraction is expended in overcoming the resistance offered by the small-calibered arterioles; an abrupt fall in pressure, therefore, occurs in this region of the circulation. A more gradual fall in pressure occurs from this point on through the capillaries and veins to the right auricle, which is filled at a very low pressure—namely, about 5 centimeters of water (see Fig. 4.15). It will be seen (Fig. 4.18, p. 134) that when the *velocity* of the blood flow throughout the vascular system is plotted, the curve obtained is quite different.

The work of the heart–the cardiac output. The energy whereby the pressure is maintained in the vascular system and the blood driven through the systemic circulation is derived from the contraction of the left ventricle. The right ventricle drives the blood through the lungs. The work performed by these two cardiac chambers will now be considered. The work performed by a machine is expressed in foot-pounds or in kilogram-meters; that is, the vertical distance, in feet or meters, through which a given weight, in pounds or kilograms, is lifted. Thus, if a weight of 2 kilograms is raised to a height of 4 meters the work done is 8 kilogram-meters. The efficiency of the machine is the proportion of the total energy expended which appears as work. Thus

$$\frac{\text{work}}{\text{total energy expended}} = \text{efficiency}$$

The work performed by the heart when it contracts may be expressed in the same way, for it ejects a certain weight of blood at a mean pressure of about 1.25 meters of water (or blood), which is equivalent to saying that the heart raises the blood to a height of 1.3 meters. As we shall soon see, if a long glass tube be inserted into a large artery, and held vertically, the blood actually rises to a height of several feet.

Under ordinary conditions of bodily rest, by far the greater proportion (98 to 99 percent) of the work performed by the heart may be calculated from the following formula:

$$W = \tfrac{7}{6} QR$$

W = work in kilogram-meters
Q = quantity of blood ejected, in kilograms
R = mean blood pressure in the aorta, in meters of blood

To give an example: if the left ventricle discharges 60 grams of blood at each beat (contraction) against an aortic pressure of 125 mm Hg, that is equivalent to saying that the ventricular contraction raises 0.06 kilograms of blood to a height of 1.62 meters (mercury is approximately thirteen times heavier than blood). Then the work performed by the left ventricle at each beat is (1.62 × 0.06) 0.97 kilogram-meters, or (0.97 × 70) 68 kilogram-meters per minute, at a heart rate of 70 beats per minute.

The pressure in the pulmonary artery is only $\tfrac{1}{6}$ of that in the aorta. That is, the pressure developed by the right ventricle is only $\tfrac{1}{6}$ that developed by the left. The quantity of blood ejected by each ventricle is, however, the same. The fraction $\frac{7}{6}$, therefore, is used to obtain the work of the whole heart—that is, of both ventricles.

The cardiac output. The amount of blood ejected by one ventricle per minute is called the *minute volume* of the heart or the *cardiac output*. The minute volume of the human heart under ordinary conditions of mental and physical rest [3] amounts to from 4 to 5.5 liters, depending on the size of the individual.[4] It must be remembered, however, that, per minute, an equal volume of blood is ejected by the right ventricle, and that an equal volume passes through the lungs and through the systemic circulation. The minute volume of the heart is therefore also referred to as the *circulation rate*. In other words, it is the quantity of blood that passes per minute through the circulatory system. The quantity of blood ejected by one ventricle at each *beat* of the heart is called the *stroke volume;* it amounts to 60 or 70 cc under resting conditions. The cardiac output or minute volume is the product, therefore, of the stroke volume and the heart rate. Thus,

cardiac output (per minute) = stroke volume × heart rate.

The cardiac output is greatly increased during muscular exercise. In a robust healthy young man doing strenuous work, it may amount to over 20 liters. The minute volume of the heart is raised by increasing the output per beat (stroke volume) and usually by increasing the number of beats per minute (heart rate) as well. In persons of poor muscular development, the heart rate accelerates in response to exercise to a greater extent than in those of athletic build. That is, the former in order to increase their cardiac output, depend upon increase in heart rate to a greater extent than do the latter. In some athletes, for example, the minute volume may be increased several fold with little or no change in heart rate.

The minute volume of the heart is also increased during *digestion,* at *high environmental temperatures,* during *emotional excitement,* and in the *later months of pregnancy.* Among pathological conditions which increase the cardiac output are *hyperthyroidism* (p. 411), *fever*

---

[3] The cardiac output is affected by so many physiological conditions that, in order for the values obtained in different persons to be strictly comparable and have a definite meaning with respect to cardiac function, the determination must be carried out under uniform or *basal* conditions. The subject must have been without food for 12 hours and be at mental and physical rest in a room kept at an ordinary comfortable temperature—about 25° C.

[4] The cardiac output bears a closer relationship to the surface area of the body than to the body weight. The value is around 3 liters per square meter of body surface.

and *severe anemia*. It is reduced in *hypothyroidism* and in certain forms of *cardiac disease*.

The cardiac output in man can be measured only indirectly. The method of measurement is based upon what is generally known as the Fick principle. Fick pointed out that, if the quantity of carbon dioxide which was given off in the lungs (or of oxygen absorbed from the lungs) by each 100 cc of blood were known, and if the *total* quantity of CO_2 given off (or of oxygen absorbed) over a given period of time were also known, then the volume of blood which had passed through the lungs in that time could be calculated. For example, if the venous blood coming to the lungs contained 58 cc of carbon dioxide per 100 cc and the arterial blood leaving the lungs contained 52 volumes per 100 cc, then 6 cc of carbon dioxide per 100 cc must have been given off by the blood in its passage through the lungs. We must then first determine the gas content of the blood (either CO_2 or oxygen) in the arterial blood and in the venous blood. It is a comparatively simple matter to obtain a sample of arterial blood for analysis (by puncturing an artery with a hollow needle attached to a syringe). It is much more difficult to determine the gas content of the venous blood in the vessels of the lungs, or of the blood coming to the lungs (e.g., in the pulmonary artery). It can be obtained indirectly by a rather complicated procedure from the alveolar air, or by passing a slender rubber tube up the large vein of the arm into the right auricle of the heart and withdrawing a sample of blood. The oxygen or carbon dioxide content (that is, the load of either gas) of the blood in the auricle will, of course, be the same as that in the pulmonary artery.

The total quantity of carbon dioxide eliminated (or of oxygen consumed) over a period of a few minutes is next determined (pp. 356–7). Let us say that this amounts to 240 cc per minute. We now have all the data necessary for the calculation of the cardiac output. Thus:

$$\frac{\overset{\text{(Total } CO_2 \text{ eliminated per minute)}}{240 \text{ cc}}}{\underset{\substack{\text{(Difference between volumes of} \\ CO_2 \text{ in venous and arterial bloods)}}}{6 \text{ cc}}} \times 100 = \begin{array}{c} 4000 \text{ cc cardiac output} \\ \text{or minute volume} \end{array}$$

The Velocity of the Blood

The velocity of the blood varies in different parts of the vascular system. It does not, like the blood pressure, show a continuously progressive diminution from the aorta to the right auricle. The blood moves swiftly through the large arteries. In the human aorta, for example, its speed is around 0.4 meters per second when the body is at rest. The velocity decreases moderately throughout the arterial tree, but is greatly reduced in the capillaries, where it averages only 0.5 mm per second. The blood upon reaching the venous system speeds

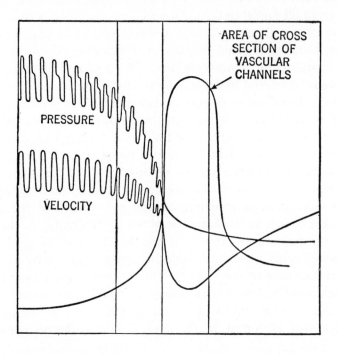

Fig. 4.16   Diagram showing the pressure and velocity of the blood in different parts of the vascular system. (Modified from Frederics.) Note the relation between blood velocity and vascular area, and the absence of rhythmical variations in pressure and velocity in the capillaries and veins.

up again, and, in the great veins feeding the heart (superior and inferior venae cavae), flows at a velocity not greatly less than that of the blood in the aorta.

The hydrodynamic principle stated on page 129 and illustrated by the models in Figures 4.13 and 4.14 is of such importance that it will be well to apply it more directly to the circulation. It should be emphasized that, except for very brief periods, the quantity of blood returned to the right side of the heart in any given time must equal that ejected by the left ventricle. *Variations in the velocity of the blood stream are due simply to differences in the dimensions of the total cross area of the vessels through which the blood flows.* The broader the passage for the blood, the slower will be its flow, and *vice versa.* It is quite immaterial to the principle whether the expansion of the bed of the stream is due to a single large channel, or to a division into a number of small, even minute, separate channels. Provided that the *total* cross area of a region of the vascular bed, which

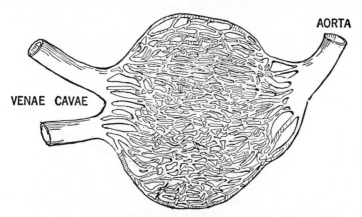

Fig. 4.17   Diagram illustrating the relative sectional areas of the aorta, capillary bed, and great veins. The area of the "capillary lake" is actually much greater relatively than is shown. (After Best and Taylor, *The Physiological Basis of Medical Practice.*)

constitutes the *only* passage for the blood from the left to the right side of the heart, is greater, the velocity of flow in the expanded part of the system will be reduced.

The human aorta is a little over an inch in diameter. All the blood ejected by the left ventricle must pass through this channel; the blood velocity must therefore be much greater here than in more peripheral parts of the vascular tree where, as a result of the numerous branchings and rebranchings, the total cross area of the vascular bed is increased. The flow in a carotid artery, for example, is slower than that in the aorta, for there are two carotids, as well as several other branches given off by the aorta, and the sum of their cross areas is considerably greater than that of the latter vessel. In the region of the capillaries where, as just mentioned, the flow is greatly slowed, the most pronounced widening of the bed is found. For this reason, the capillary area is frequently referred to as the *"capillary lake."* Though the cross area of each capillary is only a very small fraction of that of the aorta, the sum of all the cross areas of the capillaries is from 600 to 800 times greater (see Figs. 4.16 and 4.17).[5]

[5] The average diameter of a capillary is about 10 microns; the diameter of the human aorta is about 25 mm (approximately 1 inch).

In the venous system, the successive junctions of smaller veins to form larger trunks result in a progressive narrowing of the cross area of the vascular channels until, at the entrance to the right auricle, the two blood columns (in the superior and inferior venae cavae) have together a cross area only about double that of the aorta; and that is why the velocity of flow in these large veins is not so greatly less than the flow in the aorta. When the velocities throughout the vascular

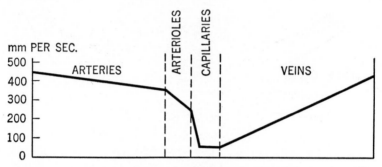

Fig. 4.18   Curve of velocity throughout the circulation—from left ventricle to right auricle. Compare with Figure 4.15.

system are plotted, it will be found that the second half of the curve is radically different from the curve of pressure. See Figure 4.18 and compare with Figure 4.15, page 130.

The velocity of the blood in the arteries, but not in the veins, varies with the heart beat above and below a mean value. During the ejection of blood from the ventricle, the velocity of the arterial blood rises to a maximum, but falls again when the heart pauses. The minimum value is reached just before the next heart beat.

The Arterial Blood Pressure

That the blood in the arteries is under a relatively high pressure was not demonstrated until about a century after Harvey's discovery of the circulation. In 1733, an English clergyman, the Rev. Stephen Hales, inserted a small brass tube (called a cannula) into the left carotid artery of a horse's thigh and connected it by means of the wind-pipe (trachea) of a goose with a glass tube 12 feet 9 inches long. The long glass tube was placed vertically. The flexible trachea served the purpose of a rubber tube which would be used today, but had not then been invented. When the clamp, previously placed upon the artery, was released, the blood rushed into the tubing and rose to a height of 9 feet 6 inches. The height of the blood column was observed to fluctuate several centimeters with each beat of the heart.

This method of measuring the blood pressure in animals has obvious disadvantages. In the first place, owing to the length of the tubing required, it is inconvenient. It is also inaccurate, since the blood which fills the long tube is out of circulation; the blood volume is correspondingly reduced, and the pressure as recorded is, in consequence, less than that which actually existed. Finally, the experiment is soon interrupted by coagulation of the blood in the tubing. It was not until nearly another century had passed that an advance on Hales' method was made. In 1828, the French physicist Poiseuille used a glass U tube filled with mercury for registering the pressure and an anticoagulant fluid to fill the tubing which connected the U tube (now usually referred to as a *manometer*) with the cannula in the artery. Since mercury is over thirteen times heavier than blood, the mercury rises only a few inches instead of several feet, as when the pressure was measured by the height of a column of blood itself. Before the clamp is released from the artery, the anticoagulant fluid is introduced under a pressure equivalent to what the blood pressure is expected to be. If the pressure of the fluid is adjusted so that it exactly equals the blood pressure, blood does not leave the artery, nor does an appreciable amount of anticoagulant enter the circulation. It has been customary ever since Poiseuille introduced the mercurial manometer to express the blood pressure in millimeters of mercury (mm Hg). Some years later Ludwig, a German physiologist, improved the method by placing a float, fastened to a wire bearing a writing point, upon the mercury column. The height of the column of mercury and its fluctuations could in this way be recorded upon a writing surface—a revolving drum covered with smoked paper—and permanent tracings of the blood pressure secured. The instrument bearing the writing surface is run by clockwork, and is known as a *kymograph*. Figures 4.19 and 4.20 illustrate the manner in which the measurement and calculation of the blood pressure are made.

The phases of the arterial blood pressure. The maximum blood pressure of warm-blooded animals has a value of from 110 to 150 mm of mercury. Unlike certain other physiological functions (e.g., heart rate, output of the heart, basal metabolism, etc.), no relationship exists between the height of the blood pressure and an animal's size. The blood pressure of the rat, for example, is about the same as that of man. The arterial blood pressure, like the velocity of the arterial blood, varies rhythmically with the beating of the heart, rising to a

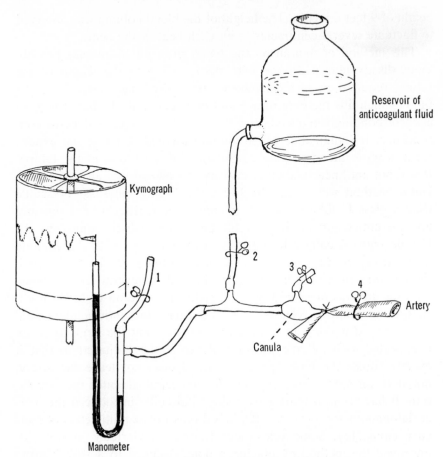

Fig. 4.19   Showing method of recording the blood pressure in animals.

maximum during the ventricular contraction (systole), when blood is pumped into the arteries, but falling again when the ventricle relaxes (diastole). The pressure reaches its lowest level just before the next beat. These variations are shown in Figure 4.21, which is a blood-pressure tracing obtained from the carotid artery of an animal by the method described above.

The maximum or *systolic pressure* in a young man has an average value under ordinary resting conditions of around 120 mm Hg. It may be a little above this value or 10 mm Hg or so below, and still be considered within the normal range. The minimum or *diastolic pressure* under similar conditions is around 80 mm Hg. The pulsation in the arteries is due to the difference between these two pressures, and is therefore called the *pulse pressure;* it amounts to

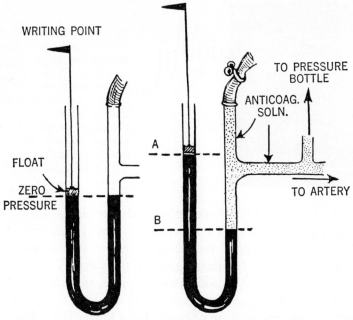

WRITING POINT

TO PRESSURE
BOTTLE

ANTICOAG.
SOLN.

A

FLOAT

ZERO
PRESSURE

TO ARTERY

B

Fig. 4.20   U-tube of mercury enlarged to show more clearly the manipulation of the manometer and the calculation of the blood pressure. The spring clamps 2 and 3, shown in Figure 4.19, are closed, and clamp 1 has not been applied. The mercury in both limbs of the U-tube are therefore open to the atmosphere, and at the same level, indicating zero pressure (left-hand sketch Fig. 4.20). A base line at this level is now inscribed on the rotating drum. Clamp 1 is applied (right-hand sketch Fig. 4.19); clamp 2 is opened and the tubing up to the mercury column filed with an anticoagulant fluid from the bottle set at a suitable height (to give a pressure approximately equal to that of the blood). Clamp 1 is released momentarily to permit the escape of air. The mercury, owing to the pressure of the anticoagulant fluid, is depressed in the right-hand limb and rises in the limb containing the float with the writing point. When clamp 3 on the artery is now released, the writing point may rise or fall a little depending upon how closely the animal's blood pressure has been predicted. Fluctuations due to the heart beat now appear in the tracing. The height of the blood pressure is indicated by the distance in millimeters between A and B— the levels of mercury in the two limbs of the U-tube—or, more conveniently, by measuring with a millimeter rule and multiplying by two, the distance from the base line (zero pressure) on the drum and the blood-pressure tracing.

(120 − 80 =) about 40 mm Hg. The value obtained by dividing the sum of the values for the systolic and diastolic pressures by two is called the *mean pressure*. Under resting conditions, therefore, the mean pressure amounts to

$$\left(\frac{120 + 80}{2}\right) = 100 \text{ mm Hg}$$

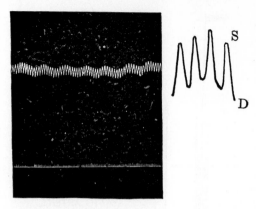

Fig. 4.21 Tracing of rabbit's blood pressure. Left-hand sketch, the larger fluctuations in blood pressure are due to the respirations, the smaller ones to the heart beats. The tracing near the bottom of the figure is made by a time marker. On the right, a section of the tracing is enlarged; S = systolic pressure; D = diastolic.

The fluctuations in the blood pressure due to the contractions and relaxations of the ventricle occur so rapidly that a mercurial manometer, owing to the inertia of the mercury, fails to follow them closely, always showing a lag. The thrust given to the mercury by the systolic rise in blood pressure is of such short duration that the heavy liquid does not reach the height which it would do were the pressure rise developed more gradually or sustained for a longer time. The systolic pressure as recorded by a mercury manometer is, in consequence, lower than the true value. In Figure 4.21, for example, the fluctuations due to the phases of the heart's action would be more pronounced if the recording apparatus were lighter in weight and, there-

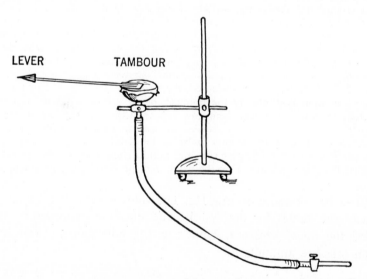

Fig. 4.22   Illustrating a nonmercurial type of apparatus for recording blood pressure which obviates the inertia due to mercury.

fore, showed less inertia. In animal experiments in which it is desired to show the true blood-pressure values or to reveal minor fluctuations on the main waves, apparatus of lighter weight is employed, the mercury being replaced by a lighter liquid; or tubing and a tambour as shown in Figure 4.22 is used. The method of recording the blood pressure in man (see below), in which the larger artery of the arm is compressed by air pressure which is measured by the height of a column of mercury, avoids the error due to the inertia of the mercury.

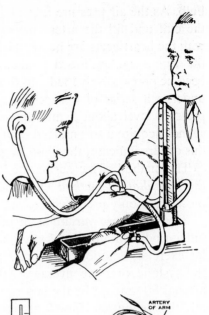

The clinical measurement of the arterial blood pressure. The blood pressure is measured indirectly in the human subject by means of an instrument called a *sphygmomanometer* (see Fig. 4.23). This comprises a flat rubber bag about 5 inches wide and 8 inches long, enclosed in an envelope of cotton cloth to prevent it from stretching under pressure. Two tubes, one connected to a manometer (mercurial or aneroid) and the other to a small hand pump provided with valves, communicate with the in-

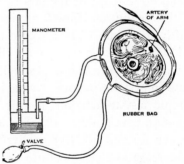

Fig. 4.23 Sketch illustrating the auscultatory method of determining the blood pressure in man. *Below,* drawing to illustrate the principle; cross section of the arm, with the armlet wrapped around it and connected with the manometer.

terior of the bag. The cloth-covered bag, which is usually referred to as the *cuff* or *armlet,* is wrapped snugly around the arm above the elbow, the tails of the cloth being wound bandage fashion to hold it in position. The pressure within the bag is raised by a few compressions of the hand bulb until the pulse at the wrist disappears—that is, until the air pressure overcomes the blood pressure and occludes the main artery (brachial) of the arm. The observer listens with a stethoscope placed over the artery in front of the elbow just below the armlet, while he gradually reduces the pressure by opening the valve close to the bulb. As the air pressure falls and allows the blood to escape beneath the cuff and fill the artery below, faint tapping sounds synchronous with the heart beats are heard. The reading of the manometer at which the sounds are first heard is taken as the systolic pressure. The sounds become progressively louder as the air pressure is reduced further, then undergo a series of changes in quality, and finally disappear. At a pressure level about 5 mm above that at which they disappear, the sounds acquire a soft muffled quality; the manometer reading at which this occurs indicates the diastolic pressure.

The method of measuring the blood pressure just outlined is called the *auscultatory method* (L. *auscultare,* to listen). It is the method most commonly practiced.

Blood pressure variations in health. The arterial blood pressure is influenced by a number of physiological conditions—age, sex, muscular exercise, emotion, digestion, and posture. In the newborn baby, the systolic pressure averages 40 mm Hg, but reaches a value of around 80 mm Hg by the end of the first month. It rises more gradually throughout childhood, attaining a level of about 100 mm by the twelfth year and 120 or so by the seventeenth. It remains around the latter level for a varying number of years. There is a tendency for the blood pressure to rise gradually after the twenty-fifth year, the increase in systolic pressure averaging about 0.5 mm Hg per year. For example, a systolic blood pressure of 135 mm Hg or so, though normal for a man between 50 and 60 years of age, would be too high for one between 20 and 30. But no fixed rule can be stated with respect to the increase in blood pressure with advancing years. It is questionable whether the tendency can be regarded as a physiological process, as is generally supposed; it is by no means of general occurrence. As compared with men of the same age, women usually have a somewhat lower blood pressure.

Muscular exercise causes a pronounced temporary rise in the blood pressure, the systolic pressure rising during strenuous exertion to 180 mm Hg or more; the diastolic pressure shows a smaller proportionate rise. The pulse pressure is, therefore, increased by exercise. A change from a lying down to a standing position causes a rise in the diastolic, but little change as a rule in the systolic pressure; the pulse pressure is therefore reduced.

Emotion (e.g., fear, worry, excitement, etc.) may cause a rise of several millimeters of mercury in the systolic pressure; the diastolic pressure is raised to a smaller extent. During digestion a moderate rise in the systolic pressure with little change in the diastolic occurs.

A reduction of from 20 to 30 mm Hg in the systolic pressure occurs during restful sleep, but if the sleep is disturbed by exciting or terrifying dreams, the systolic pressure may be elevated to 180 or 200 mm Hg.

Arterial hypertension. A persistent elevation of the arterial blood pressure above the normal range is called arterial hypertension. The abnormally high pressure is due to spasm of the arterioles (i.e., to an increase in the peripheral resistance, see p. 146). The systolic pressure, in the most severe cases of the disease, may amount to 300 mm Hg, and the diastolic pressure to 150 mm Hg. The condition leads to serious consequences; it throws extra work upon the heart and subjects the arterial system to undue strain. Enlargement of the heart, followed eventually by cardiac failure, and deterioration of the arterial tissue (arteriosclerosis, p. 144) result. Rupture of a diseased cerebral vessel may cause death; or death may result from the kidneys failing to perform their functions as a result of pathological changes in the renal vessels. There are two types of arterial hypertension. In one type, called *primary* or *essential hypertension,* the condition occurs unpreceded by kidney or any other disease. Essential hypertension, therefore, may cause, but is not itself the result of, kidney disease. In the other form, the hypertension is a consequence of chronic kidney disease (chronic Bright's disease, chronic nephritis).

A few years ago, Dr. Goldblatt and his associates in Cleveland carried out an interesting and highly important series of experiments upon dogs, which has shed a light on the origin of the type of arterial hypertension developing in the course of chronic renal disease. By means of a specially devised clamp, the renal artery to one kidney or to both was constricted and the renal blood flow thus reduced. When the renal artery of one side alone was narrowed in this manner, the blood pressure rose moderately but returned to normal again within a few weeks. When, however, the blood flow to both kidneys was reduced, or to one kidney only and the other kidney then removed, the blood pressure rose to a higher level and remained permanently elevated.

It has been shown that a reduction in the renal blood flow causes the production by the kidney of a chemical substance which, upon its discharge into the circulation, results in the constriction of the arterioles throughout the body. Such vascular constriction (see peripheral resistance, p. 146) is the direct and immediate cause of the hypertension in the experimental animals. The substance formed by the kidney is known as *renin;* it has been demonstrated in the blood of animals suffering from experimental hypertension, as well as in the blood of patients with the disease.

The constriction of the peripheral vessels in hypertension, resulting from clamping of the renal artery, is not caused *directly* by renin but by the production of another substance called *angiotonin* or

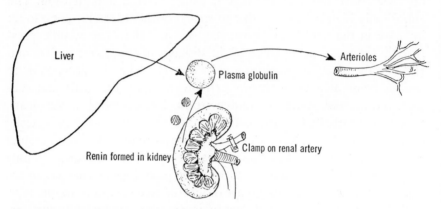

Fig. 4.24   Showing mechanism in experimental hypertension. The long arrow on right above represents the action of angiotonin.

hypertensin (Fig. 4.24). Renin is an enzyme which acts upon a globulin of the plasma to produce the latter material—which is the active vasoconstrictor agent.

It is strongly suspected that the hypertension occurring in renal disease is also due to the renin-angiotonin mechanism as a result of some interference with the renal blood flow.

The possibility that *essential* hypertension is also due to some abnormality in the renal circulation has been investigated by a number of research workers, but definite evidence for such a connection has not been secured.

Arterial disease. Almost from birth the fabric of the arteries starts to deteriorate, imperceptibly in the earlier years, but often quite rapidly from middle age on. Reduction of the elasticity of the arterial walls is the first physical change to be detected. The processes of degeneration vary, however, very greatly in different persons. "A man is as old as his arteries" a saying attributed to Osler, and which means that, generally speaking, the usual signs of old age and the deterioration of the arteries go hand in hand.

There are two principal types of arterial disease. In one form, the vessels become hard, stiff, and brittle (arteriosclerosis), owing to atrophy of the muscular and elastic tissues and their replacement by salts of lime. This change in the vascular wall permits the superficial vessels to be felt beneath the skin and to be rolled under an examiner's finger. Such "pipe-stem" arteries as they are called are met with most frequently in old age. In another much more serious type of arterial disease, the endothelium (tunica intima) is primarily attacked. Patches of the endothelial lining break down and are replaced by a soft fatty material in which lime salts are later deposited. The patches tend to spread and strip up the inner coat, and even to invade the muscular coat. This type of arterial degeneration is called *atheroma, atheromatosis,* or *atherosclerosis* (Gk. *athērē,* porridge + *scleros,* a hardening). It leads to weakening of the arterial wall, and is the cause of such vascular emergencies as *cerebral hemorrhage* (apoplexy) and *coronary thrombosis.* In the latter, the roughened inner surface by replacing the smooth endothelial lining has encouraged clotting within the vessel. This disease appears to be due to a disturbance in lipid metabolism. The atheromatous patches are composed of fats, cholesterol, phospholipids, and protein-lipid compounds (lipoproteins). Persons recovering from coronary thrombosis have an abnormally high concentration of plasma lipoproteins with a low density, and these, it is believed, are related to the atheromatous changes in the arterial walls. These lipids are also in high concentration in the blood of persons showing other clear evidence of atheromatous disease, and their concentration in the plasma tends to rise with age.

The cholesterol and other lipids of the blood are derived largely from the diet, and it would appear that in atheromatosis certain of these substances when in excess in the blood are deposited in the arterial wall. It is advised, therefore, that obese persons and those with a high concentration of lipids in the blood, or who have a family history of vascular disease should restrict their consumption of fatty materials—eggs, cream, butter and other animal fats.

The factors responsible for the maintenance of the normal arterial blood pressure. The arterial blood pressure is the result of the discharge by the heart into the arterial system of a volume of blood which cannot all escape through the peripheral arterial vessels (arterioles) into the venous system (through the capillaries and veins) before the next heart beat occurs. This means that the arterial system during life is at all times overfilled. The elastic arterial walls are therefore always more or less stretched. The height of the blood pressure is thus dependent upon two main factors—the output of the heart, and the caliber of the peripheral vessels. These and other factors concerned are listed below and will be considered in some detail:

1. *The cardiac output*—that is, the volume of blood discharged by the heart per minute;

2. *The peripheral resistance;*

3. *The total blood volume;*

4. *The viscosity of the blood;*

5. *The elasticity of the arterial walls.*

The cardiac output. It has been mentioned that the cardiac output is, as a rule, augmented by increasing both heart rate and the stroke volume, but that the extent to which each of these factors participates varies. The larger amount of blood discharged per minute into the arterial system can be accommodated within the arterial system only

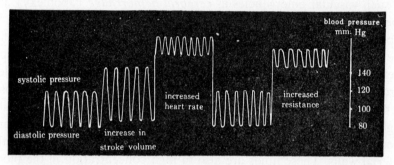

Fig. 4.25   Showing the effects upon systolic, diastolic, and pulse pressures of an increase in stroke volume, heart rate, and of peripheral resistance. (After Wiggers.)

by further stretching of the arterial walls. Both systolic and diastolic pressures rise, but both pressures are not necessarily raised to the same degree. When the increase in cardiac output is the result mainly of an increase in the stroke volume, the systolic pressure rises to a greater extent than the diastolic, with a consequent increase in pulse pressure (Fig. 4.25). If, on the other hand, the heart rate is markedly increased, the diastolic pressure tends to rise to a greater extent than the systolic because, since the time between beats is shortened, the decline in pressure during the diastole of the heart is arrested at a higher level by the arrival of the next beat. The pulse pressure is therefore reduced.

The peripheral resistance. This refers to the small vessels at the periphery—the arterioles and capillaries—but especially to the former, which, as already mentioned, offer resistance to the passage of blood from the arterial system into the veins. The arterioles and capillaries are furnished with nerves through which their calibers may be altered from time to time.

Constriction of the peripheral vessels reduces, temporarily, the outflow from the arterial system and, in accordance with the principle stated on page 127, a rise in arterial pressure occurs, provided the minute volume of the heart is not at the same time reduced. The arterial system must, therefore, contain more blood than formerly, and the arterial walls are more forcibly stretched. The pressure rises to the point at which the quantity of blood leaving the arterial system again equals that which is pumped into it by the heart; after that, no further rise in pressure occurs. Opposite effects are produced when the peripheral vessels dilate. The pressure falls until the outflow from the arterial system again just balances the inflow. The peripheral resistance may be compared to a dam in a river. If the dam is raised or lowered, the water continues to rise or fall, respectively (that is, its pressure increases or decreases), until it reaches the new level. From then on, the quantity of water which overflows in a given time is the same as it was at the original level.

Variations in the caliber of the arterioles of the abdominal (splanchnic) region are more effective than those of other vascular areas in causing changes in the blood pressure. The splanchnic vessels, when fully dilated, have a relatively immense capacity—sufficient to accommodate almost the entire blood volume. Some sudden and strong emotion may cause their dilatation, when a fall in arterial pressure and loss of consciousness (fainting or syncope) may result. On the other hand, stimulating the great splanchnic nerve (the large nerve of the abdomen through which nervous impulses reach the vessels, p. 195) in an anesthetized animal, as by the application of an electric shock, causes constriction of the abdominal vessels and, in consequence, a pronounced rise in blood pressure.

The blood volume. A sufficient volume of blood must be available to overfill the arterial system. That is to say, the arterial walls even at the lowest normal pressure (diastolic) are stretched. Any considerable reduction in blood volume, as by hemorrhage, causes the blood pressure to fall. Restoration of the blood volume by transfusion of blood or of a suitable blood substitute (p. 77) is followed by a rise in pressure.

The viscosity of the blood. Viscosity may be defined simply as the "thickness" of a liquid or the resistance which a liquid offers to its movement through a narrow tube. The viscosity of a particular liquid is determined by measuring the time which it takes, when acted upon by a constant force, to pass through a given length of a capillary tube. The viscosity of water is taken as unity, and that of various other liquids is expressed relatively to that of water. Thus, alcohol and ether are less viscous than water, while glycerine, oil, and syrup are much more viscous. Blood itself is some five times more viscous than water. We know that should two piston syringes be filled, one with a highly viscous liquid, such as syrup, the other with water, a greater effort would be required to drive out the syrup than to drive out the water, and a higher pressure would be created in the first syringe than in the second. The relatively high viscosity of blood increases the resistance in the vascular system; it tends to impede the flow through the arterioles, and so to enhance the effect which these narrow vessels themselves have in maintaining the arterial pressure. Variations in viscosity, therefore, have an effect upon the blood pressure similar to that caused by alterations in the caliber of the peripheral vessels. The relatively high viscosity of blood is due to the plasma proteins, and, to an even greater extent, to the corpuscles. The viscosity is lowered in conditions associated with low plasma protein concentration and in some anemias. It is increased in conditions associated with a high corpuscular concentration or when, as a result of the loss of blood water (anhydremia), the protein concentration of the blood is raised.

The elasticity of the arterial walls. If the arteries possessed rigid and not elastic walls, the systolic pressure would be higher, other things being equal, but there would be no diastolic pressure. That is to say, the arterial blood pressure would fall to zero between the beats of the heart. The absence of a rhythmical variation in the pressure— that is, of a pulse—in the capillaries and veins is due, in turn, to the existence of a pressure in the arteries during diastole. These facts are best illustrated by means of a model.

In Figure 4.26 is represented a bulb syringe, S, valved at A, and having a short tube, B, which dips into a basin of water. Leading from the opposite pole of the bulb is a longer tube, C. If the bulb is alternately compressed and released, water will be drawn from the basin, and discharged from the mouth of the tube (Fig. 4.26, 1). If the walls of the latter are composed of some rigid material (e.g., glass), it will be found that when the pump is worked the fluid issues from the tube in spurts or jets synchronous with each stroke, but no flow occurs between the strokes. An increase in the frequency or force of the strokes does not alter the intermittent character of the flow, nor does lengthening the tubing. If the peripheral resistance of the vascular system is imitated by attaching a nipple of small bore to the mouth of the delivery tube, thus increasing the resistance to the outflow of fluid, the issuing stream is finer and its velocity is increased, but it still remains intermittent (Fig. 4.26, 2). Now let the elasticity of the arterial wall be imitated by replacing the rigid tube, C, by one of rubber, but let the mouth of the tube be left free and not constricted in any way (Fig. 4.26, 3). The intermittent character of the flow from the tubing is unaffected. However, if the *small-bored nipple* representing the peripheral resistance be fixed into the mouth of the *elastic tubing,* the issuing stream will be found to have lost its pulsatile character and to have become continuous (Fig. 4.26, 4). Two factors are therefore necessary to produce a continuous outflow: (a) *elastic tubing*

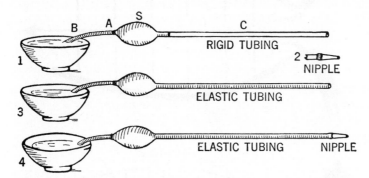

Fig. 4.26   Diagram illustrating the dependence of diastolic pressure upon the arterial elasticity and peripheral resistance. (Description in text.)

and (b) *resistance to the outflow*. The reasons for this are clear. If the tubing is made of elastic material, its wall is distended by the force of the pump and energy is thus stored up which is expended between beats as the elastic wall recoils. (See Fig. 4.27.) Thus, the fluid is driven along the tube during the pauses of the pump. Nevertheless, if the fluid can escape freely from the tube, the pressure does not rise to a sufficient height to distend the rubber wall—that is, elasticity is not called into play, overfilling of the tube does not occur, and, in consequence, the latter acts simply as though it were composed of rigid material.

The foregoing facts apply directly to the arterial system. The elasticity of the vascular walls and the peripheral resistance are both essential for the development of the diastolic pressure. As the contents of the ventricle are forced into the already overfilled arterial system during systole, the added pressure which is then exerted upon the vascular walls causes their further distension. After the completion of systole, the elastic walls rebound (recoil) and, pressing upon the blood within their embrace, force it onward through the peripheral vessels. In other words, the arterial lumen returns to its previous diameter and the energy that had been stored up during the stretching of the elastic tissue is in this way gradually expended during diastole (Fig. 4.27).

It may then be said that the *elastic recoil* of the arterial wall acts, in a sense, as a subsidiary pump to drive the blood onward in a con-

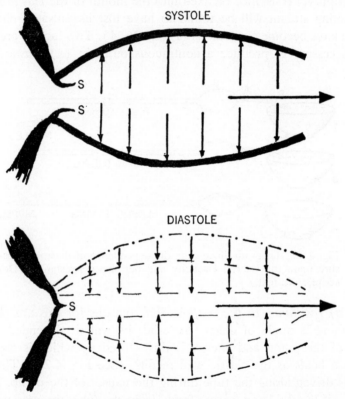

Fig. 4.27   Diagram to illustrate the storing of energy of the heart's contraction in the elastic arterial walls (at root of aorta) during systole and its release during diastole. Small arrows indicate the direction of movement of the arterial walls and of the force exerted during the two phases. Large arrows indicate the direction of the blood flow. S.S.S. semilunar (aortic) valves.

tinuous stream between the heart beats. Otherwise the pressure would fall to zero after each systole.

Interaction between the several factors maintaining the blood pressure. In health, the several factors mentioned in the foregoing paragraphs interact with one another to maintain the blood pressure at a fairly constant level. When a change occurs in one factor which, acting alone, would raise or lower the pressure, a compensating reaction of a reflex nature occurs which tends to offset its effects. For example, a moderate reduction in the cardiac output or in blood volume (as through hemorrhage) is not necessarily followed by a fall in blood pressure, since reflex narrowing of the calibers of the small vessels occurs: that is, the peripheral resistance is increased. Again, dilatation of the arterioles in one region, which of itself would lower the blood pressure, is balanced by constriction of the minute vessels in another (Lovén reflex). Also, increased blood volume or a rise in blood viscosity, which alone would cause an elevation of the blood pressure, is counteracted by vasodilatation. (See also pp. 196 and 197.)

Capillary and Venous Pressures

It has been mentioned that, except for the sharp drop which occurs in the region of the arterioles, the blood pressure falls in a gradual slope from the left to the right side of the heart (see Fig. 4.15, p. 130). The pressure is about 30 mm Hg at the arterial end of the capillary and about 12 mm at the venous end. The pressure of blood in the great veins is low (although the velocity is relatively high) and at the entrance of these vessels into the right auricle is only some 5 mm H_2O. In other words, the energy of the cardiac contraction has been almost entirely expended in overcoming the resistance offered to the flow of blood through the vascular system.

The venous pressure may be measured in man by an indirect method based upon the same principle as that employed for the measurement of the arterial blood pressure, but water or saline is used in the manometer for, owing to the low pressure to be measured, mercury, which is some thirteen times heavier than these liquids, would show a scarcely measurable change in level. A vein is selected upon the back of the hand and a small chamber with a transparent top is hermetically sealed by means of a special cement to the overlying skin (Fig. 4.28). The chamber is provided with two tubes, one of which is connected to a *water* manometer, the other to a hand bulb. The pressure within the chamber is raised by a few compressions of the bulb until the vein is seen to collapse. The pressure, which at this point just balances the pressure in the vein, is read from the manometer. While the measurement is being made, the vein under observation must be brought to the level of the right auricle; otherwise, the hydrostatic pressure of the venous blood—that is, the weight of the blood column extending from the vein level to the auricle—would be added to the pressure due to contraction of the left ventricle.

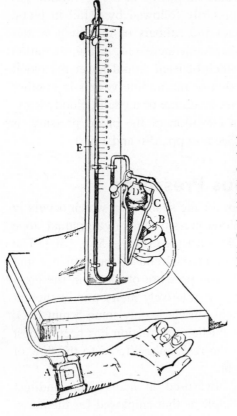

Fig. 4.28 Measurement of the venous blood pressure. The small chamber with transparent top (A) is cemented to the skin over a superficial vein. The pressure within the chamber is raised by means of the pressure-bulb arrangement B. C, D, until the vein collapses. E, manometer. (After Hooker and Eyster.)

The pressure of blood in the peripheral veins, such as those of the limbs, amounts to from 60 to 100 mm H_2O; it falls progressively through the larger veins to the right auricle. (See Fig. 4.15, p. 130.)

The Effect of Gravity upon the Circulation

When the human subject assumes the erect posture, the blood pressure in the arteries of the head and arms is not reduced; as stated on page 142, the diastolic pressure actually rises. This is so, even though the subject makes no effort, but is tilted on a moveable table from the horizontal to the upright position. If a fall in blood pressure of sufficient magnitude to deprive the brain of an adequate supply of blood occurred when the body changed from the recumbent to the standing position, fainting would result. Now, in order to maintain the blood pressure, the heart pump must receive an adequate supply of blood. The question then arises, "How, when the body is standing, is the blood conveyed against gravity up the great veins to the heart?" The factors concerned are four in number:

1. The contraction of the left ventricle. This *vis a tergo* (force from behind), as it is termed, drives the blood through the arterioles and capillaries and along the veins to the right side of the heart.

2. The respiratory movements. The pressure within the thorax (see intrathoracic pressure, p. 232) is always a little below that of the atmosphere. This "negative" pressure, which is exerted upon the blood through the thin-walled auricle and venae cavae, fluctuates with the respiratory movements, being increased (i.e., becoming more negative) during inspiration, when it amounts to about −6 mm Hg, and decreased during expiration to about −2.5 mm Hg. The intrathoracic pressure thus exerts a suction effect or pull (*vis a fronte*) upon the column of blood in the large veins of the abdomen.

The blood is also *forced* upward during inspiration, for when the diaphragm descends it increases the intra-abdominal pressure. The increased pressure is transmitted to the blood in the veins; since the blood is prevented by the presence of valves in the large veins of the lower limbs from passing downward, it is propelled upward. The respiratory movements thus act both as a force pump and as a suction pump to move the venous blood toward the heart.

The effect of the respiratory movements upon the flow of blood to the heart is especially important during muscular exercise when the excursions of the chest are deep and rapid.

3. The abdominal and limb muscles. When one is standing, the abdominal muscles contract and offer a firm support for the large veins of the abdomen. The venous walls are prevented from becoming overdistended under the weight of the blood which they contain. If the walls of the veins stretched and so increased their capacity, a larger mass of blood would be accommodated in the large veins of the abdomen, and the flow to the heart correspondingly reduced.

The muscles of the limbs perform a similar duty for the limb veins. Furthermore, they exert, during muscular movements, a varying pressure or massaging action upon the veins. By virtue of the valves in the veins (Fig. 4.11, p. 125), any pressure upon the column of venous blood is converted into an upward propulsive movement.

4. Constriction of the vessels of the splanchnic area. Through the action of the vascular nerves (p. 195), the small vessels—arterioles, capillaries, and small veins—in the abdomen undergo a reduction in caliber, and so in capacity. Thus, blood, which otherwise would collect in these areas when the erect posture is assumed, is directed upward into the large venous trunks.

In quadrupeds, the mechanisms for raising the blood against gravity are much less efficient than they are in man or in the apes. The dog, however, is able to compensate fairly well for the gravity effect, but the domestic rabbit may become unconscious or even die, if held up by the ears for any considerable length of time. This result is due to the heart being inadequately supplied with blood which, owing to the flabbiness of the abdominal muscles of the tame rabbit, collects in the large veins. Sheep also not infrequently become unconscious if held in a vertical position during shearing. Fainting (*syncope*) in the human subject is in most instances due, not to any affection of the heart itself, but to reduction of the venous flow to its chambers, for if the left ventricle does not receive an adequate supply of blood, the blood pressure in the vessels of the brain is not sustained, and the conscious centers suffer from lack of oxygen. Fatigue or some strong emotion such as fear or shock may, by inducing splanchnic vasodilatation and imperfect cardiac filling, cause loss of consciousness. But a factor probably of much greater importance than splanchnic vasodilatation is the widespread dilatation of the blood vessels in the muscles that occurs in most cases of fainting.

A person who stands quietly for some time—a soldier standing at attention on parade, for example—may fall in a faint because the venous flow is unaided by muscular movement. Such a result is the more likely to occur if he is fatigued, or if the day is hot and the vessels of the skin are therefore dilated. The treatment of a subject in a faint is simple; he is laid in the horizontal position, the effect of gravity upon the circulation being thus abolished. He should not be supported in the sitting position. As a matter of fact, the subject of a faint usually does the right thing himself—he falls to the ground. Pressure may be applied to the abdomen in order to force blood along the veins to the heart, but such a procedure is usually unnecessary.

The Effects of Acceleration upon the Circulation

A constant speed, however great, has in itself no effect upon the circulation, but acceleration—that is, a change in velocity either in the line of motion (*linear acceleration*) or in a change in direction, as when a body traveling along a straight course turns into a curvilinear one (*centripetal acceleration*)—may cause profound circulatory effects. Such effects not uncommonly result from the sudden and pronounced changes in direction entailed in military flying. For example, a pilot pulling out of a power dive—i.e., changing direction at high velocity from a downward to a horizontal and upward movement —has his head directed inward toward the center of a circular course and the lower part of his body directed outward. His blood, as a result of centrifugal force, is therefore "forced" away from the head into the lower part of the body. The high pressure of blood in the capillaries in the skin of the lower limbs may result in small cutaneous hemorrhages. The return of venous blood to the heart is reduced, with a consequent fall in the blood pressure in the cerebral and retinal vessels. Vision is temporarily lost and the pilot may become unconscious. Such effects are commonly referred to in the flier's parlance as "blackout." The abdominal organs may also be forced downward and drawing upon the diaphragm embarrass respiration. Any maneuver in which the head is directed outward—that is, toward the circumference of the circular movement—causes the reverse effect upon the circulation. The blood is now "forced" toward the head. The vessels of the head and neck become engorged and severe throbbing pain in the head is experienced. The eyes feel as if they were being forced from their sockets. There may be mental confusion. Rupture of a cerebral or retinal vessel may result.

The force exerted upon the body is expressed in units of gravitational force and designated $+G$ or $-G$, according to whether the acceleration is positive or negative; that is, according to whether the blood is driven away from or toward the head, respectively. A force twice that of gravity is referred to as 2 Gs; one three times gravity, as 3 Gs; and so on. Persons vary with respect to the centrifugal force which they can withstand before "blackout" occurs. The limit for most pilots is between 5 and 6 Gs ($+$). During World War II, double-walled suits were fashioned which were worn by fighting airmen in order to prevent "blackout" effects. Air under pressure, or water between the two layers of the suit, by affording support to the tissues of the lower part of the body, prevented the distension of the vessels and the pooling of blood in this region. Thus the vital centers of the brain were assured of an adequate supply of blood.

The Arterial Pulse

The pulse in the arteries is due, of course, to the beat of the heart. Though all arteries, large and small, pulsate, the pulse is felt most conveniently by placing the finger upon the radial artery, which lies near the outer border of the palmar aspect of the wrist. In health, the rate of the pulse, when the body is at rest or engaged in some light occupation, is around 70 per minute. The pulse is a *pressure change* transmitted as a wave through the arterial wall and blood column to the periphery. Though caused by the discharge of blood into the arterial system, it is in the nature of a transmitted impact, and *is not due to the passage of the ejected blood itself*. For example, when one

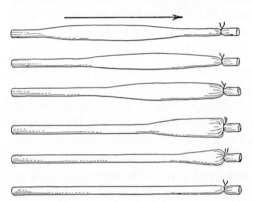

Fig. 4.29   Showing successive stages in the transmission of a pulse in a ligated artery.

places a finger upon the artery at the wrist, the pulse beat which is felt is not due to the arrival of blood which has been discharged an instant before from the left ventricle into the arterial system, but is due rather to the shock or impact given to the resilient arterial walls by the sudden entrance of that blood into the aorta. The wave thus set up in the wall of the aorta and in the column of blood therein travels from ten to fifteen times more rapidly than does the blood itself, and quite independently of it. The blood, as we have seen, has a velocity of around half a meter per second in the aorta, and less than that in the smaller arteries. The speed of the pulse wave is from 5 to 8 meters per second, and is practically the same throughout the arterial tree. That the pulse travels quite independently of the blood flow is evident from the observation that in an artery which has been tied across so that no blood flows through it, the pulse is not abolished, but travels in the usual manner up to the point of occlusion (Fig. 4.29).

The velocity of transmission of the pulse wave is dependent upon the character of the arterial wall. Were arteries made of unyielding material (e.g., glass), they and the incompressible blood within them would constitute a rigid system and, therefore, transmit an impact almost instantaneously from end to end. The arteries are, however, elastic and, in consequence, transmit a shock applied to their walls much more slowly.

The arteries become less resilient with age and the speed of the pulse wave therefore increases. At 5 years of age, for example, the velocity of the pulse wave is around 5 meters per second, whereas at the age of 80 it is in the neighborhood of 8 meters per second. In arteriosclerosis, in which condition the arteries are abnormally rigid, the pulse wave has a still higher velocity. The speed of the pulse wave can be measured by placing two levers, one upon an artery near the heart, the other near the periphery, and timing the arrival of the pulse at the two points. This distance between the two points is then measured. The distance (in millimeters) divided by the time (in seconds) which the pulse wave has taken to pass between the two points will give the velocity (in millimeters per second).

Thus, $\frac{D}{T} = V$, where D = distance in millimeters, T = time in seconds and V = velocity in millimeters per second.

The instrument employed for obtaining a graphic record (tracing) of the pulse wave is called a *sphygmograph* (see Figs. 4.30 and 4.31). The upstroke of the curve drawn by this instrument during the passage

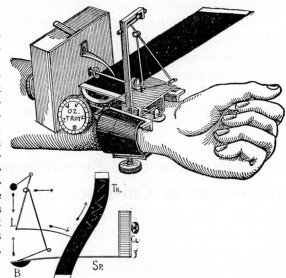

Fig. 4.30 *Upper drawing,* Dudgeon's sphygmograph in position. *Lower,* diagram of mechanism. Cl., clockwork driving the smoked paper, Tr., under the writing point of the level, L. Sp. is a steel spring with a button, B, which is applied over the radial artery. With each expansion of the artery, the button is moved upwards and causes a movement of the system of levers as indicated by the arrows.

of the pulse wave is abrupt and is called the *anacrotic* limb (Gk. *ana,* up + *crotos,* pulse). The downstroke has a more gradual inclination and is called the *catacrotic* limb (Gk. *cata,* down). The catacrotic limb shows, a short distance from the peak of the primary wave, a secondary elevation known as the *dicrotic* wave, which is immediately preceded by a slight negative fluctuation called the *dicrotic notch.* The latter is due to the slight backward movement (i.e., toward the heart) of the blood column in the artery, when the ventricle commences to relax. The dicrotic wave is caused by the checking of this backward movement of the blood column and its rebound from the aortic valves which, coming into accurate apposition at the end of ventricular systole (see p. 170), prevent the leakage of blood into the relaxing ventricle. When the aortic valves are removed, or hooked back with wires to prevent their closing, the dicrotic wave is not seen. In normal circumstances, dicrotic fluctuations can be revealed only by means of some graphic method of recording; they cannot be felt by the finger placed upon the pulse. In certain conditions, however, in which the blood pressure is abnormally low and the arterial wall, in consequence, less tense, the dicrotic wave may be felt as a distinct tap following the main wave. A pulse of this character—the so-called *dicrotic pulse* —is not uncommonly present in typhoid fever.

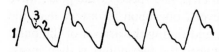

Fig. 4.31 Tracing of radial pulse. 1, anacrotic limb; 2, dicrotic wave; 3, dicrotic notch.

It should be mentioned that the height of the pulse tracing gives no indication of the height of the systolic blood pressure. Nor does the pulse wave as traced by the sphygmograph give any indication of the length of the pulse wave itself. The pulse wave in the arterial system is actually a long swell measuring from 5 to 6 meters (16 to 20 feet); that is, it is several times longer than the arterial system itself.

The Structure and Physiological Properties of Cardiac Muscle

The fibers of heart muscle possess cross striations, but these are less well marked than those of skeletal muscle. Unlike the cells of skeletal muscle, the cardiac fibers have no sarcolemma separating or insulating one fiber from another. On the contrary, they give rise to branched processes—slips or bridges—which join neighboring fibers and thus

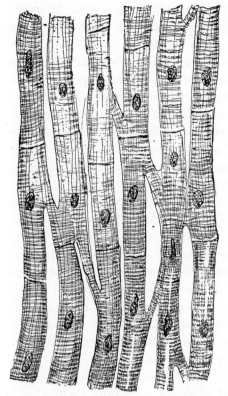

Fig. 4.32   Cardiac muscle fibers.

establish continuity between them. The heart muscle is therefore in reality a syncytium; that is, a large multinucleated mass of protoplasm rather than, like skeletal muscle, a number of separate units bound together (see Fig. 4.32).

The physiology of cardiac muscle will be taken up under the following heads: (1) *excitability and contractility*, (2) *rhythmicity*, (3) *conductivity*.

1. Excitability and contractility. Heart muscle responds by a contraction of its fibers to the various types of stimulus—thermal, chemical, mechanical, or electrical—which excite skeletal muscle. Its response follows the *"all-or-none" law* or *principle*. This law, which also applies to the conduction of the nerve impulse (p. 471) and to the contraction of an isolated fiber of skeletal muscle (p. 488), states that a stimulus, if it produces a response at all, will produce the maximum response of which the tissue is capable *under the conditions existing at the moment*. That is to say, increasing the strength of a stimulus above that which is just necessary to excite the heart muscle (threshold strength) does not increase the force of its contraction.

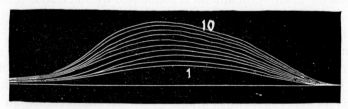

Fig. 4.33   Record of a series of contractions of frog's heart caused by electric stimulation of the ventricle. The ventricle was rendered quiescent by drawing a tight ligature (Stannius' ligature) between the auricles and the ventricles. Tracings taken on a rapidly moving surface. First contraction (1) the lowest, last contraction (10) the highest. (After Halliburton.)

Treppe. When the heart muscle is stimulated at regular intervals, the first few contractions increase progressively in amplitude. From the appearance given to the tracing by the initial contractions (Fig. 4.33), this behavior is referred to as *treppe* or the *staircase phenomenon.* It is probably due to the beneficial effect exerted upon one contraction by the rise in temperature and the acid metabolites (carbon dioxide and lactic acid) produced during the contraction or contractions which have preceded. The phenomenon of treppe does not, as may at first appear, contradict the "all-or-none" law, for the conditions in the muscle—that is, a rise in the temperature and acidity—have been altered by the initial contractions.

Refractory periods. Heart muscle will not respond to a stimulus while it is contracting; in this it differs from skeletal muscle (p. 488). This time, during which the cardiac muscle is unresponsive to stimulation, is called the *absolute refractory period.* The absolute refractory period of heart muscle is, therefore, of the same duration as the period of contraction. The absolute refractory period is followed by one in which the muscle gradually recovers its excitability. At the beginning of the latter—that is, at the commencement of cardiac relaxation— a stronger stimulus is required for excitation, and the force of the contraction which results is less than the normal. Excitability increases progressively and reaches its full value only when relaxation is complete. This phase of depressed but gradually increasing excitability is called the *relatively refractory period.*

2. Rhythmicity. This is an outstanding characteristic of the heart. The heart of the frog will contract spontaneously and rhythmically for a considerable length of time after its removal from the body, if simply kept moist with physiological saline (0.6 percent solution of sodium chloride). The rhythmicity is also an inherent property of the mammalian heart; it occurs quite independently of the central nervous system (see perfusion of the heart, p. 162).

When the heart of an animal is stimulated by an electric shock or a series of such shocks, the rhythm may be disturbed (made irregular or more rapid) but it will not, as will skeletal muscle (p. 489), give a sustained (tetanic) contraction. The cardiac contractions are always intermittent. Summation of contractions and tetanus cannot take place in heart muscle. This fact is dependent upon the absolute refractory period and ensures a pause between contractions, an essential requirement in order that the heart can perform its pumplike function. The heart muscle must first cease to contract and recover at least part of its excitability before another contraction can be evoked.

Extrasystoles or premature beats of the ventricle. If, when the heart is beating naturally, the ventricle is stimulated during its relaxation phase, a contraction occurs which varies directly in strength with the excitability of the muscle; this, as just mentioned, rises progressively throughout the relative refractory period. The maximal response is therefore obtained at the end of the latter. The response caused by the artificial stimulus is called a *premature beat* or *extrasystole*. Premature beats occur in the human heart as a result of some abnormal stimulation (p. 184), such as by some chemical agent carried in the

Fig. 4.34 Extrasystoles. Record of contractions of frog's ventricles. Upper row of arrows and dotted lines indicate the arrival of the auricular impulse in the ventricular muscle. Slanting arrows in this and succeeding tracings indicate the application of the artificial stimulus. In tracings 1, 2, and 3, the artificial stimulus is applied during the contraction of the muscle, and is therefore ineffective (absolute refractory period). In 4, 5, and 6, the stimulus falls in the relative refractory period and gives rise to an extrasystole, its amplitude being greater the later in the relaxation phase that the stimulus is applied. A long pause follows the extrasystole because the auricular impulse reaches the ventricular muscle during the refractory phase, and is therefore ineffective. E = extrasystole.

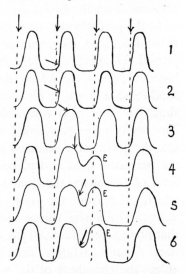

blood stream. The excessive use of tobacco is not infrequently a cause. An unusually long resting interval known as the *compensatory pause* follows the extrasystole (see Fig. 4.34). The pause is caused in the following way. The impulses causing the normal heart beat originate at regular intervals in the upper part of the right auricle and, spreading downward, excite the rest of the heart. When an extrasystole of the ventricle occurs, the next regular impulse from the auricle usually reaches the ventricle while it is absolutely refractory—that is, while it is still in the contracted state as a result of the abnormal stimulus. The muscle therefore fails to respond. Not until the next normal impulse arrives is the heart capable of contracting.

3. Conductivity. We have seen that, as a result of the fusion of branches or slips of one fiber with those of its neighbors, the heart muscle is a continuous protoplasmic mass. When, therefore, one part of the muscle is stimulated, the excitatory process spreads without interruption to all its parts. In the mammalian heart, the property of rapid conduction has been developed to a very high degree in a system of specialized tissue in the interior of the heart. This system will be dealt with shortly (p. 165).

Perfusion of the Excised Heart

Under appropriate conditions the excised mammalian heart will continue to beat for several hours. Even the human heart has been revived after death, and made to beat rhythmically for a time after its removal from the body.

In the perfusion of the excised heart, a fluid resembling the plasma, in so far as its inorganic constituents are concerned, must be employed. The perfusion fluid should be delivered under *pressure* to the blood vessels of the heart (coronary system, p. 204) in order that it shall reach all parts of the cardiac muscle; the *temperature* of the fluid should be that of a warm-blooded animal, namely, about 98.6° F. The perfusion is performed in the following way. A cannula is tied into the aorta and connected by rubber tubing to a reservoir filled with the perfusion fluid and placed at a height of about 5 feet above the level of the heart; the fluid is thus driven into the coronary arteries which arise from the root of the aorta just beyond the semilunar valves. The aortic valves are closed by the pressure of the fluid so that none enters the ventricle directly. After passing through the coronary system (arteries, arterioles, capillaries, and veins), the fluid enters the chambers of the heart from which it is allowed to escape through knife cuts made in the walls of the ventricles (see Fig. 4.35).

The heart muscle must be supplied with *oxygen*. This is accomplished by bubbling oxygen or simply air through the fluid in the reservoir.

It is of the utmost importance that the perfusion fluid contains the three inorganic cations Na^+, Ca^{++}, and K^+, in properly balanced proportions. This fundamental fact was first demonstrated many years ago by Sidney Ringer, an English physiologist (see Fig. 4.36). Experimenting with the excised frog's heart, he found that the heart beat could be maintained for a short time only, when physiological saline (0.6 percent sodium chloride solution) was used. The addition of a very small amount of calcium restored the beat, but the pauses between beats (diastolic periods) became shorter and shorter, and the heart came to a standstill in a firmly contracted state; this condition is called *calcium rigor*. When potassium instead of calcium was added to the physiological saline, the diastolic periods became progressively longer, and the heart ceased to beat in a fully relaxed state (diastole). This effect is referred to as *potassium inhibition*. A fluid prepared to contain sodium, calcium, and potassium chloride in suitable proportions (sodium chloride 0.6 percent for the frog heart or around 0.9 percent for the mammalian heart, with the other salts in the proportions shown in Table 4-1) will sustain the beat for long periods. This is known as *Ringer's solution*. If the perfusion fluid contains calcium in excess, the effect is the same as if it contained calcium in normal concentration but lacked potassium; calcium rigor ensues. On the other hand, when potassium is in excess the effect is the same as when calcium is lacking and potassium present in the correct concentration; potassium inhibition is induced. The effects of these two cations upon the action of the heart muscle are therefore antagonistic, one favoring contraction, the other relaxation. Only when they are present in balanced proportions, as in blood plasma, can the normal rhythm of the heart be sustained.

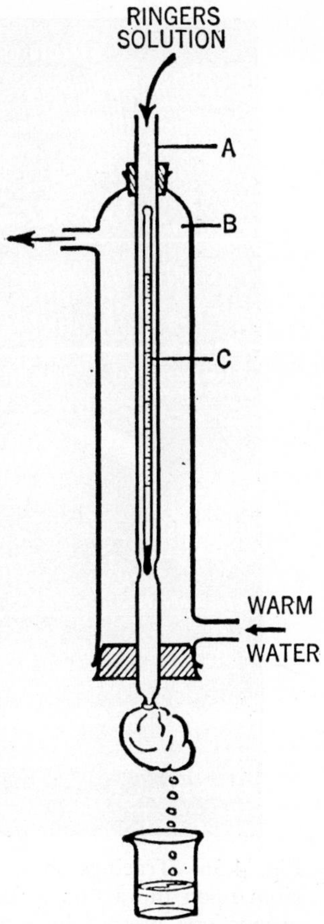

The reaction of the perfusion fluid is also of prime importance. The optimum reaction is around a pH of 7.4. If the fluid is too alkaline, an effect is produced upon the heart resembling that of an excess of calcium; if the hydrogen ion concentration is too high, it induces an effect similar to that caused by an excess of potassium.

Locke's solution and *Tyrode's solution* are modifications of Ringer's original fluid. They contain glucose, added for the purpose of furnishing fuel for the heart muscle, and sodium bicarbonate (0.02 percent) which maintains the fluid at optimum hydrogen ion concentration. Tyrode's solution contains,

Fig. 4.35 Showing apparatus for the perfusion of the isolated mammalian heart. A, tube conducting Ringer's solution to the heart. The lower end of this tube is tied into the aorta so that fluid is distributed through the coronary circulation to all parts of the cardiac muscle. B, waterjacket through which warm water (37.5° C) circulates; C, thermometer.

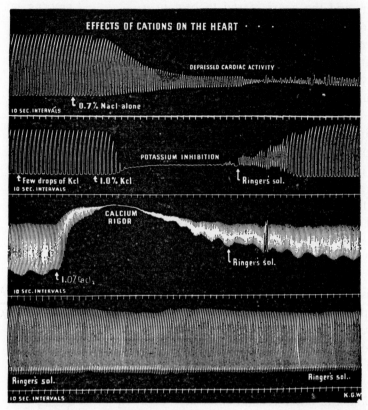

Fig. 4.36 Tracings showing the effects of sodium, potassium, and calcium upon the action of the heart. Not until all three cations are in the proportions present in Ringer's solution (lowest tracing) is cardiac behavior normal in character (kindness of Dr. K. G. Watkin).

as well as bicarbonate, the phosphate buffers—disodium and monosodium phosphates (Na_2HPO_4 and NaH_2PO_4). See Table 4-1.

Until quite recently it had been thought that glucose constituted the chief fuel of cardiac muscle. It now appears that the heart uses glucose to a minor extent; its main fuel is lactic acid. Lactic acid is formed during muscular contraction from the breakdown of glycogen (p. 368). It is also formed from glucose in the blood, and in the lungs at all times. The lactic acid so produced is utilized by the heart muscle to furnish energy for its contraction.

The hearts of lower orders, such as frog, are not provided with a special circulating system (coronary system) as is the heart of man or other mammals. The frog's heart will therefore continue to beat for

Table 4-1

Percentage composition of Ringer's, Locke's, and Tyrode's solutions, used in perfusion of the mammalian heart

	Ringer's solution	Locke's solution	Tyrode's solution
Sodium chloride	0.900	0.900	0.80
Potassium chloride	0.040	0.042	0.02
Calcium chloride	0.025	0.024	0.02
Magnesium chloride	—	—	0.01
Sodium bicarbonate	0.020	0.020	0.10
Monosodium phosphate	0.001	—	0.005
Glucose	—	0.10	0.10

some time if simply immersed in Ringer's or other physiological solution.

The Origin and Conduction of the Heartbeat

In the slowly beating heart of the frog, each beat may be seen to arise at the junction of the great veins with the *sinus venosus*—a chamber situated between these veins and the right auricle (see Fig. 4.37). The sinus venosus is present in the mammalian embryo but disappears during development. In the heart of the frog or the turtle, the beat spreads from the sinus venosus through the muscle of the auricles and ventricles. When a ligature is drawn tightly around the frog's heart at the junction of the sinus with the auricle (called the 1st Stannius ligature), or at any lower level, the impulse through the muscle is blocked and the heart below the block ceases for a time to beat. In the adult mammalian heart, a ring of fibrous tissue is interposed between the auricles and the ventricles; the beat therefore cannot be transmitted from the upper to the lower cardiac chambers by the ordinary muscular tissue of the heart. But a system of specialized tissue—the *junctional* or *nodal* tissues—has been developed in the mammalian heart, which possesses the property of rhythmical impulse formation and conductivity to a higher degree than does the muscle composing the auricular and ventricular walls. The beat is generated in a small mass of tissue belonging to this system, situated in the wall of the right auricle near its junction with the superior vena cava. This circumscribed

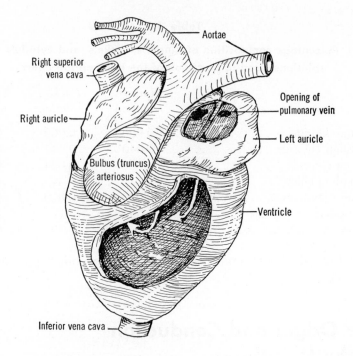

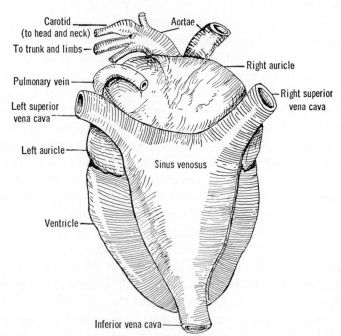

Fig. 4.37   The frog's heart; *upper drawing,* from in front; *lower drawing,* from behind.

knot of tissue differs in structure from the surrounding auricular muscle, being composed of muscle cells of a primitive type (Purkinje fibers), together with nerve fibers and a few nerve cells. It is called the *sinoauricular* or *sinoatrial* (S-A) *node* (Fig. 4.38), and is believed to be derived from the wall of the sinus venosus of the embryonic heart where this chamber joined the auricle. Heating or cooling the S-A

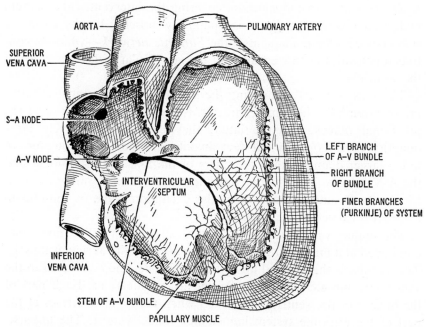

Fig. 4.38   The conducting (junctional) tissues of the heart. Wall of the right ventricle cut away exposing the septum.

node accelerates or slows, respectively, the rate of the heart. From such and other facts, it seems quite certain that the impulse which causes the beat of the heart is generated within this node of special tissue. The sinoauricular node is therefore commonly referred to as the *pacemaker* of the heart. The impulse spreads as a wave—the *excitation wave*—in all directions through the muscle of the auricles. The nature of the excitation wave cannot be defined precisely, but at any rate it is known to be accompanied by an electrical change, and is followed immediately (within 0.02 second) by contraction of the cardiac muscle.

The remainder of the specialized conducting system of the mammalian heart consists of the *auriculo- (atrio-) ventricular (A-V) node, the auriculo- (atrio-) ventricular bundle* and the *Purkinje net-work*.

The auriculoventricular node lies in the lower part of the inter-auricular system. It is composed of tissue similar to that of the sino-auricular node. The auriculoventricular bundle arises from the au-riculoventricular node and, after descending for a short distance, divides into two branches—one to each ventricle. Each branch de-scends beneath the endocardium covering the interventricular septum and, after giving off twigs to the papillary muscles, breaks up into a rich network of fine filaments—the *Purkinje network*—which is con-tinued beneath the endocardium of the ventricular wall to the base of the ventricles.

The muscle fibers composing the strands of the Purkinje network are of essentially the same character as those forming the rest of the junctional tissues; like the latter, they contain a relatively large quantity of sarcoplasm but few myofibrils. They are, however, of much larger diameter than the fibers of the S-A and A-V nodes and the A-V bundle. They merge with the muscle fibers forming the ven-tricular walls and through them the excitation wave or impulse to contract is carried to the latter.

The impulses are discharged rhythmically from the S-A node, and conducted at a uniform rate through the fibers of the auricular muscle. The impulse is then picked up by the A-V node, and conducted to the ventricular muscle by the bundle and its ramifications. Each part of the muscle of the ventricle is excited when the impulse arrives at the part of the Purkinje system immediately underlying it. The impulse, normally, is not conducted from point to point in the ventricle through muscular tissue, but follows this specialized pathway. Every muscle fiber of the ventricle is believed to receive a filament of the Purkinje network. The rate of conduction through ventricular muscle (which may in certain abnormal conditions conduct the impulses) is around 500 mm per second, whereas the rate through the specialized tissue is about 5000 mm per second.

The junctional or nodal tissues of the heart may be compared to a radio system, the S-A node to the broadcasting station, and the A-V node to a receiving center which, after picking up the message, trans-mits it by a telephonic system. In the heart, the bundle and its branches and the terminal network of Purkinje correspond to the telephone wires.

It should be noted that the S-A and A-V nodes are not connected by a tract of specialized tissue; the impulse in this part of its course is conducted solely through the ordinary auricular muscle. Also, *the A-V bundle is the only pathway along which the impulse can reach the ventricles,* for all other tissue in the mammalian heart joining the auricles and ventricles is of a fibrous nature and incapable of conducting an impulse. This slender strand of tissue is therefore a very important and vulnerable point in the conducting system of the heart. It is a "bottleneck" which the impulses must traverse. If interrupted, either experimentally in animals or by disease in man, the path of the impulse from auricle to ventricle is completely and permanently blocked.[6] The ventricle does not, however, cease to beat; for the specialized tissue below the block also possesses, though to a less degree than does the S-A node or the A-V node, the power of generating rhythmical impulses. The ventricular muscle excited by impulses arising below the block then beats at the relatively slow rate of about 35 per minute. The auricle being still under the control of the S-A node beats at the usual rate of 70 per minute. This dissociation of the rhythms of the auricles and ventricles, which follows interruption of the A-V bundle above its point of division into the two main branches, is called *complete heart block* or *auriculoventricular block* (see p. 183).

In other instances one or other *branch* of the A-V bundle may be interrupted by disease. The defect in conduction caused in this way is called *bundle branch block* or *intraventricular block*.

The Action of the Heart, the Cardiac Cycle

The action or beat of the heart consists of a succession of events which follow one another with great rapidity. It is therefore impossible, except by the use of special apparatus and improved methods, to analyze the beat into its different components. Starting with any given event in cardiac action (e.g., contraction of the auricle or of the ventricle), the series of changes which takes place in the heart until the first-noted event is repeated, is called a *cardiac cycle*. The cardiac cycle in the human subject, when the heart is beating at the usual rate of about 70 per minute, is $\frac{6}{7}$ (0.85) second. It is shorter than this, of course, when the heart rate is more rapid. Contraction of the auricular or of

---

[6] The most common condition affecting the A-V bundle is gradual hardening and narrowing of the coronary arteries which, by interfering with the blood supply to this vital tissue, convert it to a fibrous (nonconducting) structure.

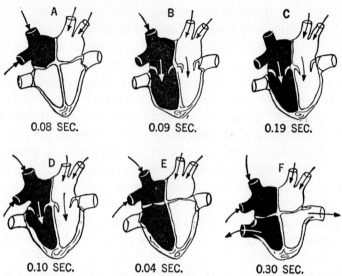

0.08 SEC.   0.09 SEC.   0.19 SEC.

0.10 SEC.   0.04 SEC.   0.30 SEC.

Fig. 4.39   Diagram to show the different phases of the cardiac cycle. A, auricles filling, valves between auricles and ventricles closed, ventricle relaxed, valves at arterial openings closed (*period of isometric relaxation*). B, the valves between the auricles and ventricles have opened, and blood is pouring into the ventricles which are still relaxed (*period of rapid inflow*). C, the auricles and ventricles are full; there is little or no movement of the blood (*period of diastasis*). D, the auricles contract (auricular systole) and empty into the ventricles which are over-filled with consequent further stretching of the ventricular muscle fibers; E, the ventricles immediately contract (*period of isometric contraction*) and close the openings into the auricles (auriculoventricular orifices guarded by the corresponding valves). The pressure then rises rapidly in the ventricles and, when sufficiently high to overcome the pressure in the pulmonary artery (and in the aorta), the valves guarding the orifices of the arteries open. In this sketch the valves are still closed; the ventricle is, therefore, a completely closed cavity. F, the arterial valves have been forced open, and the blood is now being driven into the pulmonary system (or aorta) (*period of ejection*). The left side of the heart is drawn as though empty in order to show more clearly the positions of the valves, but it must be remembered that whatever is occurring on the right side of the heart is occurring at the same instant on the left side. The figures refer to the duration of the periods at a heart rate of 70 beats per minute.

the ventricular muscle is called *systole;* so we speak of *auricular systole* or *ventricular systole,* respectively. *Auricular diastole* and *ventricular diastole* are corresponding terms which refer to the relaxation phase of the respective chambers. When the word systole or diastole is used alone, it is the systole or diastole of the ventricle that is meant.

The phases of the cardiac cycle are shown diagrammatically in Figures 4.39, 4.40, and 4.41. In animals, the cardiac cycle is most readily analyzed into its several phases by means of records, taken

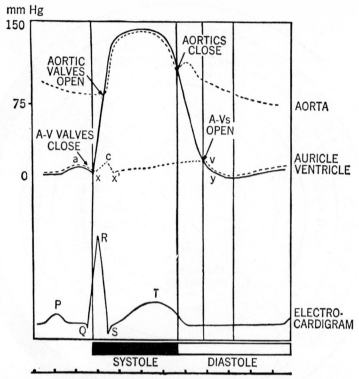

Fig. 4.40   Intraventricular, intra-aortic and intra-auricular pressure curves from heart of dog together with an electrocardiogram. The vertical lines pass through synchronous points in the four curves. Between the closure of the auriculoventricular valves and the opening of the aortic valves is the isometric period of contraction. From the opening of the aortic valves to the closure of these valves is the period of ejection, and from the latter event to the opening of the A-V valves is the period of isometric relaxation. The divisions in the line at the bottom of the diagram indicate $\frac{1}{20}$ second.

simultaneously, of the pressure changes occurring, respectively, in an auricle, a ventricle, and the aorta. Instruments specially designed to record rapid variations in pressure are placed in these situations. The records are taken simultaneously so that synchronous events in the curve can be compared.

We shall now describe in their proper sequence the several events in the cardiac cycle. The part of the cycle at which the description starts does not matter. The period immediately following the contraction (systole) of the ventricle will be chosen. (See Fig. 4.39.) At this time the ventricles are closed cavities. The valves guarding the orifices of the aorta and the pulmonary artery are closed, as are also those guarding the auriculoventricular orifices. The ventricular muscle is

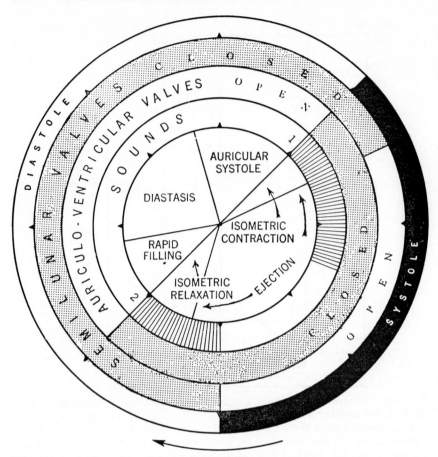

Fig. 4.41   Diagram of the cardiac cycle. The black part of the outer circle represents ventricular systole; the white part, ventricular diastole; division marks indicate $\frac{1}{10}$ second.

now relaxing but, since no blood can enter the ventricles from the auricles to stretch the muscle fibers, these are of the same length as during the preceding systole. This phase of the cardiac cycle at the commencement of ventricular diastole is therefore called the period of *isometric* (Gk. *isos,* same + *metron,* measure) *relaxation* (Figs. 4.40 and 4.41); it has a duration (at a heart rate of 70 per minute) of .06 to .08 second. At its termination, the auriculoventricular valves open and the blood flows rapidly into the ventricles from the auricles. This phase, which lasts for about 0.1 second, is called the period of *rapid filling* of the ventricles.

As the ventricles fill, the flow of venous blood becomes slower and then virtually ceases. This interval following the period of rapid filling is termed the *period of diastasis*. It varies considerably in length, being longer when the heart is beating slowly. During rapid action of the heart it may disappear entirely. *Auricular systole*—that is, auricular contraction—follows the period of diastasis; it gives an impetus to the blood flowing from the auricles into the ventricles. Auricular systole has a duration of about 0.1 second; at its termination the ventricles contract.

It should be emphasized that throughout all the phases of the cardiac cycle just described (vis., isometric relaxation, rapid filling, diastasis, and auricular systole) the ventricles are relaxing or are completely relaxed—that is, these events occur during the resting phase or *diastole of the ventricle*.

Ventricular systole which, as just mentioned, follows auricular systole is divided into two phases: the period of *isometric contraction* and the period of *ejection*. The rise in pressure within the ventricles when they contract firmly closes the auriculoventricular valves. The aortic and pulmonary valves, which were brought into apposition at the end of the preceding systole, have not yet opened; they are held closed by the higher pressure of blood in the aorta and pulmonary arteries. The ventricle being thus again a closed cavity but filled with blood which, of course, is incompressible, the muscle fibers obviously cannot shorten during this phase of systole. They contract isometrically. This phase, therefore, is appropriately called the period of *isometric contraction*. The pressure within the ventricles continues to rise rapidly, however, during this time. When it reaches a height sufficient to overcome the diastolic pressure in the aorta (about 80 mm Hg) and pulmonary arteries (about 15 mm Hg), the valves guarding these vessels are thrown wide open, and the ventricular contents ejected. The ejection period lasts for about 0.3 second (with heart rate of 70). It terminates with relaxation of the ventricular muscle. The pressure within the ventricles now falls below that in the large arteries, and the aortic and pulmonary valves close again as a result. The next phase of the heart's action is the period of isometric relaxation—the phase with which this description started. The cardiac cycle has been completed.

The *intra-auricular pressure curve*, it will be seen, consists of three positive waves, *a, c,* and *v,* and three depressions, *x, x,*[1] and *y*. The wave *a* is due to auricular systole, the depression *x* is due to auricular relaxation (auricular diastole). The wave *c* is caused by ventricular contraction which bulges the thin auriculoventricular valves into the auricle. The depression *x* [1] is dependent also on the ventricular systole.

When blood is ejected by the ventricle, the volume of the ventricle is of course reduced; the ventricular fibers shorten, and in doing so they draw upon and depress the floor of the auricle. This causes a negative fluctuation in auricular pressure. Furthermore, the ejection of blood from the thorax—a closed cavity—causes a temporary fall in intra-thoracic pressure which is transmitted through the thin wall of the auricle. There are, then, two factors—both dependent upon ventricular systole—concerned in the production of the depression x [1].

The next wave, v, is called a statis wave. Since the A-V valves are closed at this time, the blood cannot enter the ventricle but, accumulating in the auricle, causes a gradual rise in pressure. The depression y is due to the sudden opening of the valves and the consequent fall in auricular pressure as the blood flows rapidly into the ventricle (i.e., during the period of rapid filling).

The volume of the ventricles may be recorded by means of an instrument known as a *cardiometer*. This consists of a hermetically sealed chamber which is fitted to enclose the ventricles. It communicates by means of rubber tubing, through which changes in ventricular volume during the cardiac cycle are transmitted, with a recording apparatus. A marked reduction in volume occurs during the ejection period of systole but not during the period of isometric contraction. No increase in volume occurs during the period of isometric relaxation, but a marked increase occurs during the period of rapid filling when the ventricles are filling with blood.

The Opening and Closing of the Heart Valves

The heart is a pump, and its valves give direction to the movement of the blood. Those guarding the auriculoventricular orifices open toward the ventricles, thus allowing blood to pass from auricles to ventricles [7] (see Fig. 4.3, p. 118). They close at the commencement of the ventricular systole and remain closed until the end of the period of isometric relaxation; their closure during systole prevents the blood from being driven backward into the auricle when the intraventricular pressure rises. At the commencement of the ejection period, the valves surrounding the orifices of the aorta and pulmonary artery open outward—that is, toward the arterial lumen—but are closed during

[7] This arrangement of the valves of the heart was emphasized by William Harvey as important evidence for his thesis that the blood circulated.

diastole. They thus prevent the leakage of blood into the ventricles when the intraventricular pressure falls below the arterial pressure.

The valves are composed of delicate membranes formed of a double layer of endothelium continuous with that lining the chambers of the heart. They form two or three somewhat triangular leaves or *cusps* which are attached by their bases to the fibrous rings surrounding the auriculoventricular and arterial orifices. Near the bases of the valves, the two layers of endothelium are separated by a small amount of connective tissue and smooth muscle. The *auriculoventricular valve* of the right side (also known as the *tricuspid valve*) has three cusps

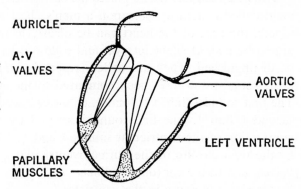

Fig. 4.42 Diagram of the left auriculoventricular (mitral) and aortic valves during the ejection period.

AURICLE

A-V VALVES

AORTIC VALVES

LEFT VENTRICLE

PAPILLARY MUSCLES

which fit neatly together by their free margins when the valve closes. The corresponding valve of the left side (also known as the *mitral* or *bicuspid valve*) has only two leaves. Both auriculoventricular valves receive support from a number of tendinous cords—the *chordae tendineae* (p. 117)—which pass from the papillary muscles to be attached to the ventricular surfaces of the cusps near their free margins. The chordae tendineae act as guy ropes which prevent the valves from being inverted into the auricles by the pressure developed within the ventricles. The fleshy columns—the papillary muscles—contract at the very commencement of ventricular systole and exert a pull upon the chordae tendineae, thus holding the valves firm (Fig. 4.42 and Fig. 4.3, p. 118). The *pulmonary and aortic valves* (also called the *semilunar valves*) have each three leaves or cusps. They possess no chordae tendineae.

The opening and closing of the heart valves are not due to any active movement of the valves themselves. Though, as just mentioned, the valves contain a few strands of smooth muscle, these are not responsible for their movements. The blood current and the difference between the pressures on their two surfaces are the only operating factors. During auricular systole, the A-V valves and, during the ventricular systole, the pulmonary and aortic valves are held open by the blood flowing through the respective openings. When auricular systole comes to an end, eddy currents arising in the ventricle bring the leaflets of the A-V valves gently into position. The pressure created immediately thereafter by ventricular systole closes them firmly. The closure of the aortic and pulmonary valves is caused in a similar manner; namely, by the higher pressure in the arteries (aorta and pulmonary artery) than in the ventricle when the ventricular muscle commences to relax.

The heart sounds. If one places his ear, or the receiver of an instrument called a *stethoscope,* upon a man's chest a little below the left nipple, the beat of the heart can be clearly heard. Two sounds, separated by a short silent interval and followed by a longer pause, can be distinguished. They are called, respectively, the first and second heart sounds, and have been compared to the syllables *"lub" "dup."* The first sound ("lub") is louder, of lower pitch, and longer than the second ("dup"). The first sound is caused by two factors: (a) the contraction of the ventricular muscle [8] and (b) the vibrations set up by the tight closure of the auriculoventricular (tricuspid and mitral) valves, and of the chordae tendineae as they are put upon the stretch by the rising pressure in the ventricles.

The second sound is caused by the closure of the aortic and pulmonary valves.

Valvular disease. The function of one or other valve of the heart may be interfered with as a result of some inflammatory disease (e.g., acute rheumatic fever or septicemia). The affected valve becomes deformed or partially destroyed so that its cusps do not come accurately into apposition to prevent leakage. The valve is then called *incompetent* and the leakage of blood is referred to as *regurgitation.* For example, when the aortic valves fail to close properly at the end of ventricular systole, blood flows from the aorta into the left ventricle during diastole, since the pressure in the aorta is higher than that in the relaxing ventricle; when the mitral valve is incompetent, blood is driven into the left auricle during ventricular systole. Now, these reverse movements of the blood cause abnormal sounds or *murmurs* to be heard. In aortic incompetence, the clear *second* sound of the normal heart is replaced by a murmur, and this is often continued through

---

[8] Any skeletal muscle causes a faint sound when it contracts as a result of the vibration of its fibers. This can be verified by listening over the contracting biceps of the arm with a stethoscope.

a part of, and sometimes throughout, the diastolic period; that is, a blowing or rushing sound is heard during the silent period which normally follows the second sound and separates it from the first sound of the next heart cycle. In mitral or tricuspid incompetence, the abnormal sound is heard during ventricular systole, and alters or replaces the normal *first* sound.

In other instances the diseased valve loses its resilient character, becoming stiff and its surface roughened. The cusps are not brushed aside by the current of blood but, projecting into the stream, offer an impediment. The orifice is therefore narrowed. This valvular condition is called *stenosis*. Thus, according to which valve is affected, *mitral, aortic, pulmonary, or tricuspid stenosis* is spoken of. Owing to the narrowing of the orifice, the blood passes through it at a higher velocity than usual. The blood flowing at high velocity over the roughened and irregular cusps causes a murmur. When an auriculoventricular valve is affected, the murmur is heard during those times when the blood normally enters the ventricle at highest velocity, namely, during the period of rapid filling—i.e., early in diastole, or during auricular systole which is just before ventricular systole (presystolic murmur). In aortic stenosis the murmur is heard during the ejection of blood from the ventricle.

It must be evident that the rigidity and deformation of a stenosed valve is likely to render it incompetent as well. Two sounds will then be present, one being due to the stenosis, the other to regurgitation.

A diseased valve increases the work of the heart. The heart is at a mechanical disadvantage. In aortic regurgitation, for example, the blood must eject not only the blood that it receives from the auricles but also that which leaks back from the aorta. Moreover, the disease which attacked the valve may have also injured the heart muscle. In order to carry on its work efficiently, the cardiac muscle fibers must become larger—longer and thicker—the chambers of the heart thus become enlarged and the ventricular walls much thicker. Dilation of the heart and increased bulk of the heart muscle (hypertrophy) is, therefore, a consequence of valvular disease. Such adjustments, or *compensation,* as they are called, may enable a person with valvular disease of the heart to enjoy good health for years and suffer little inconvenience from the mechanical defect.

Electrical changes in the heart. Contracting muscle is relatively negative (electrically) to resting muscle. The electrical changes in skeletal muscles are described on page 494. The same principles apply, in general, to heart muscle. When the excitation wave spreads through the heart, changes in electrical potential are created which may be recorded in animals by placing electrodes directly on the surface of the heart and connecting them through wires to a galvanometer. It is, of course, impossible to take records (*electrograms,* as they are called) in this way of the changes in electrical potential occurring

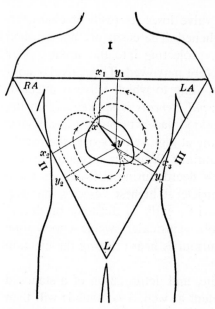

in the human heart. Nevertheless, the blood and tissues of the body have a relatively high electrical conductivity (Fig. 4.43); the beating heart may, therefore, be looked upon as an electric generator immersed in a conducting medium, and the electric currents (action currents) produced during the cardiac cycle may be "tapped," as it were, by connecting two parts of the body with a sensitive galvanometer. Einthoven, a Dutch physiologist, was the first to devise a galvanometer for this purpose. The moving part or indicator of the galvanometer consists of a very fine fiber of quartz glass through which the cardiac action currents are transmitted. In order to render it conductive, the fiber is coated with a silver

Fig. 4.43   Diagram illustrating the electric field surrounding the heart and the relation of the three standard electrocardiographic leads. (After Pardee.)

deposit (as in the backing of a mirror), and suspended between the poles of an electromagnet. The fiber moves outward (away from the arch of the magnet) or inward according to whether the cardiac current at the moment is being transmitted in an upward or a downward direction. By means of a projection system and a camera of special design, the movements are photographed. The record thus obtained is called an *electrocardiogram* (abbreviated: ECG), and the recording instrument—that is, the galvanometer together with the projecting and photographing apparatus—is known as the *electrocardiograph* (see Fig. 4.44). The parts of the body most usually connected to the instrument are the two hands (or arms) or the right hand (or arm) and left foot (or leg). In order to obtain a record of the electrical changes occurring in the heart, these members are joined through the

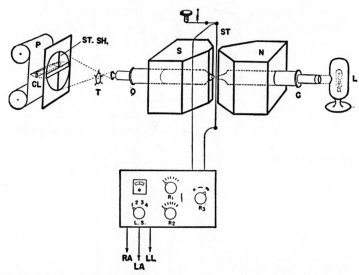

Fig. 4.44 Diagram of the principal parts of the electrocardiograph. P, roll of photographic paper moving behind the lens, Cl, which narrows the shadow, ST.SH, of the string ST. to a thin vertical line and focuses it upon the sensitive paper. By means of ruled etchings upon the lens, horizontal lines 1 and $\frac{1}{5}$ mm apart are thrown upon the record; the heights of the waves in the electrocardiogram can thus be measured and the electromotive force in each wave calculated. T is a rotating toothed disc which breaks the light beam at regular intervals of $\frac{1}{50}$ or $\frac{1}{25}$ seconds and by throwing vertical shadow lines upon the record serves as a time marker. O and C indicate the positions of the lenses in the projection system; S and N are the poles of the electromagnet; L is the source of light. The current from the subject passes through the control box below. Switches on the dial enable a record from any lead to be taken. RH, LH, and LL represent the three standard leads—right hand, left hand, and left leg. (Kindness of Dr. L. N. Katz.)

instrument in any one of the following combinations (see Figs. 4.43 and 4.45). Each combination is referred to as a *lead*. Thus:

Right hand (or arm) and left hand (or arm) is called lead I.
Right hand (or arm) and left foot (or leg) is called lead II.
Left hand (or arm) and left foot (or leg) is called lead III.

A switch on the instrument board enables records to be taken in succession from each of the three leads.

A fourth lead (lead IV or chest lead), in which one electrode is placed on the chest over the heart and the other on the left foot or ankle, has been introduced more recently, and is usually taken in series with the other (so-called *standard*) leads.

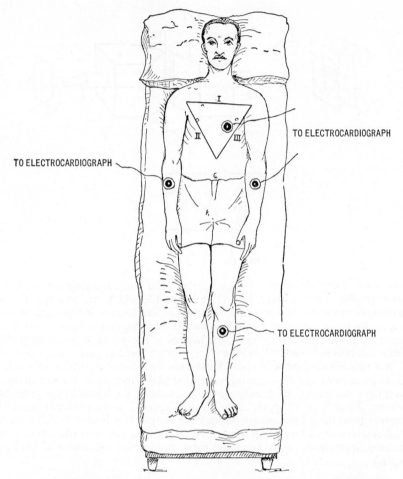

TO ELECTROCARDIOGRAPH

TO ELECTROCARDIOGRAPH

TO ELECTROCARDIOGRAPH

Fig. 4.45   Showing the three standard leads of the electrocardiograph and a chest lead. Contacts are made with the skin by means of suction cups—small rubber bulb and metal bell—the skin being first smeared with a paste containing electrolyte in order to ensure good conduction between the skin and the metal.

The normal electrocardiogram shows five *waves* or *deflections,* known simply by the letters P, Q, R, S, and T (Figs. 4.46 and 4.47). The P, R, and T waves are positive—that is, above the base line of the record; the Q and S waves are negative. P and T are blunt waves of relatively low amplitude. The R wave is a tall spike; it is the most conspicuous wave in the tracing and represents the highest voltage developed by the contracting ventricular muscle. The P wave is caused by the spread of the excitation wave over the auricle—that is, it precedes auricular systole by a fraction of a second. The Q, R, and S

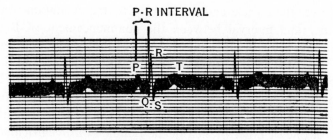

Fig. 4.46   Normal electrocardiogram taken in lead I. (Courtesy of Dr. John Hepburn.)

deflections are produced during the transmission of the excitation wave or impulse through the junctional tissues—auriculoventricular bundle and its branches, and the Purkinje network. The actual contraction of the ventricular muscle commences a fraction of a second after the beginning of the R wave. The T wave is recorded while the ventricle is relaxing (see also Fig. 4.40, p. 171).

The electrocardiograph is one of the most valuable instruments that the physician possesses for the investigation of the various abnormal heart conditions. It is now possible with its help to study diseases of the heart with a precision which hitherto was impossible. An electrocardiogram is now taken as a matter of routine, being almost as commonplace a procedure as the determination of the blood pressure. Important information is given by the electrocardiogram concerning the state of the conducting system of the heart and of the coronary system. Since the P wave is caused by the excitation wave

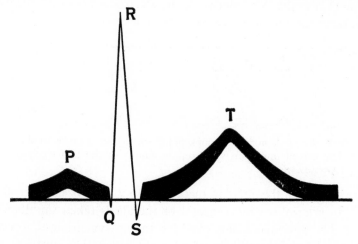

Fig. 4.47   The waves of the electrocardiogram enlarged and represented diagrammatically.

passing over the auricle and the R wave by the excitation of the ventricle, the time interval between the commencement of P and the commencement of R (P-R interval) gives the conduction time from auricle to ventricle—i.e., over the A-V bundle. The normal time does not exceed $\frac{1}{5}$ (0.2) second. It is usually around 0.12 second. Lengthening of the interval indicates depression of conductivity through the auriculoventricular connections—i.e., incipient or partial heart block. Disease of one or other branch of the bundle (*intraventricular block*) is also readily detected by means of the electrocardiograph. Marked distortion of the record occurs in this condition.

The venous pulse. The arterial pulse is not transmitted through the capillaries to the venous system (p. 148). The peripheral veins, therefore, do not pulsate, but the *jugular vein* is in direct communication with the right auricle, and any change in intra-auricular pressure causes a reflux of blood and volume changes in the blood within this vein which can be recorded clinically by means of suitable apparatus the receiver of which is placed over the vein at the root of the neck just above the clavicle (collar bone).

The jugular tracing shows a series of waves resembling, and having the same significance as, those already described for the intra-auricular pressure curve (p. 173). Since the *a* wave is due to auricular systole and the *c* wave to the commencement of ventricular systole (which causes the bulging into the auricle of the closed auriculoventricular valve), the length of the *a-c* interval gives the time of conduction of the impulse from auricle to ventricle. This interval, therefore, corresponds to the P-R interval of the electrocardiogram and, like the latter, does not normally exceed $\frac{1}{5}$ (0.2) second.

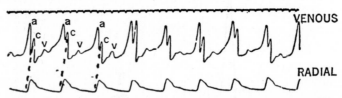

Fig. 4.48   A normal venous pulse and a radial pulse tracing. The dotted lines join synchronous points in the two tracings. (After Lewis.)

The waves of the jugular record are not always easy to identify unless an arterial tracing (carotid or radial) is taken simultaneously with it. The instrument employed for taking synchronous records of jugular and arterial pulses is called a *polygraph*. The upstroke of the carotid tracing occurs simultaneously with the jugular *c* wave, which can thus readily be identified. The positive wave immediately preceding the *c* wave must therefore be the *a* wave, and the positive wave immediately following *c* is the *v* or stasis wave caused by the filling of the auricle (see p. 173 and Fig. 4.48).

The apex beat. The contraction of the heart causes a slight impact upon the chest wall which can be felt by placing the fingers on the skin between the fifth and sixth ribs, and in a line with the center of the left collar bone—that is, about an inch below the left nipple (in the male). This impact is called the *apex beat*. The slight outward movement of this area of the chest wall can also be seen if the bare chest is looked at from one side, in a good light. The movement is caused by the pressure exerted by the left ventricle during its contraction. All dimensions of the ventricles are reduced when they contract, but no change in the level of the apex of the heart occurs. The base of the heart, therefore, must move toward the apex. The auricles and great vessels are thus elongated; they cannot move downward as a whole, for they are fixed above. At the same time, the heart rotates to the right, bringing the wall of the left ventricle and particularly that part forming the apex, against the chest wall. During ventricular diastole the base of the heart moves upward again. The up and down movement of the auriculoventricular groove (the junction between the auricles and ventricles) during the cardiac cycle can be seen quite plainly in the exposed heart of an animal.

Disorders of the heart beat. Certain abnormalities of cardiac rhythm in the human subject, e.g., heart block and extrasystoles, have already been mentioned. These, and some of the other cardiac irregularities, will now be briefly described.

Heart block or auriculoventricular block. This results from disease, usually a degenerative nature, affecting the auriculoventricular bundle. Interference with the blood supply to the heart, including the specialized tissue, as a result of "hardening" (sclerosis) with narrowing of the coronary vessels is a common cause of defective conduction through the bundle. The disease may completely interrupt the passage of impulses from auricles to ventricles; the auricles and ventricles then beat quite independently. In such an event, the radial pulse is around 35 per minute while the *a* waves (due to auricular contractions) in the venous pulse occur at the rate of 70 per minute. There is no regular time relationship between the auricular and ventricular waves of the venous pulse; corresponding abnormalities are seen in the electrocardiogram, there being about two P (auricular) deflections to each R (ventricular) deflection.

In less severe grades of the disease, the conduction time is length-ened, but no actual block exists. The P-R intervals of the electrocardi-ogram and the *a-c* intervals of the jugular tracing are prolonged. In other instances, block occurs intermittently. That is, after every two, three, or four auricular beats the impulse fails to get through to the ventricle which, in consequence, misses a beat. Three stages in disease

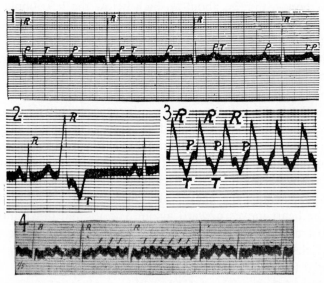

Fig. 4.49   1, heart block. Note absence of the normal relationship between the auricular (*P*) and the ventricular waves (*Q, R,* and *S*). 2, a ventricular extra-systole. Note the long pause following it. 3, ventricular paroxysmal tachycardia, actually a series of extrasystoles. 4, auricular fibrillation. Waves marked *f* re-place the normal *P* waves. (1, 2, and 3 by the courtesy of Dr. John Hepburn, 4 from Lewis.)

of the A-V bundle are therefore recognized, namely: (a) delayed conduction, (b) missed beats or incomplete heart block, and (c) com-plete heart block (Fig. 4.49, 1).

Extrasystoles or premature beats (see also p. 161). The abnormal impulse which excites the heart may arise in the auricle, the A-V node, or in the special conducting tissue of the ventricle. Thus, three types of extrasystole occur: *auricular, nodal,* and *ventricular.* In the auricular type, the impulses arise in some part of the auricle other than the S-A node; each of these impulses spreads to the ventricle, ex-cites it in the usual way, and causes a premature beat of the whole heart. There is, as a rule, no compensatory pause (p. 161). In the nodal type, the impulse arising in the A-V node passes upward through the auricular muscle and downward to the ventricle. Both chambers, therefore, beat almost or quite simultaneously. In the ventricular type, which has already been described on page 161, the premature beat is followed by a compensatory pause. In this variety, the abnormal impulse, since it excites one ventricle before the other, disturbs the electrical balance of the heart. The QRS group of waves of the electrocardiogram is therefore distorted (Fig. 4.49, 2).

Paroxysmal tachycardia. This name is given to a cardiac affection in which the heart suddenly commences to beat at an extraordinarily rapid rate and continues to do so for a period which varies in length in different instances from a few seconds to several hours or even days. The heart rate is from 150 to 250 per minute. The rapid beating is caused by impulses arising in some part of the heart other than the S-A node. They may be generated in the auricle, the A-V node, or in the ventricular part of the special conducting system. The condition therefore consists, actually, of a series of rapidly recurring extrasystoles (Fig. 4.49, 3).

Auricular flutter. In this heart condition the auricle beats more rapidly than in paroxysmal tachycardia—namely, from 250 to 300 per minute. Attacks of flutter are also usually of longer duration than those of paroxysmal tachycardia. Furthermore, the A-V bundle, even though healthy itself, is unable to transmit impulses at as high a frequency as they are produced by the fluttering auricle. Only a proportion of the impulses gets through; the ventricle, therefore, beats at a slower rate than the auricle. In other words, there is a *relative* or *functional* heart block. The ratio of auricular to ventricular beats is usually 3:1 or 2:1.

Auricular fibrillation. The auricle in this disorder does not contract as a whole, nor in an effective manner. Its walls twitch rapidly and incessantly at a rate of from 400 to 600 per minute. The auricle is never emptied by any effective contraction of its walls; the blood flows into the ventricle unaided by auricular systole. The *a* waves are therefore absent from the venous pulse, and the P waves from the electrocardiogram; they are replaced in either record by numerous small fluctuations called *f* waves (Fig. 4.49, 4). The auriculoventricular connections (A-V bundle) are capable of transmitting only a fraction of the impulses arising in the auricular muscle. Those that do reach the ventricle are irregular in time, and induce contractions of the ventricle of variable strength. The pulse is, therefore, very irregular and usually rapid. Auricular fibrillation is seen very frequently when the heart, as a result of disease of the heart muscle, is weakening and performing its work with difficulty. The serious nature of the condition is not due to any direct effect upon the dynamics of the circulation resulting from the absence of auricular systole, but rather to the irregular and rapid excitation of the ventricular muscle. The drug most commonly used in the treatment of auricular fibrillation is digitalis, which acts chiefly by depressing the conductivity of the A-V bundle. The ventricle is therefore shielded from many of the impulses arising in the fibrillating auricles; the pulse usually becomes slower and more regular in consequence; the general circulation is greatly improved.

The Regulation of the Heart's Action

The heart rate. The heart rate is more rapid in small animals than in large. The heart of the canary, for example, beats 1000 times per minute, whereas the average heart rate of the elephant is 25 per minute. In adult man, at rest, the usual rate is about 70 per minute, but a rate of 75 or of 60 per minute is not unusual in perfectly healthy persons. Athletes have, as a rule, a slower resting heart rate than have persons leading a sedentary life; the pulse rate of some famous runners is from 50 to 60 per minute, and it may show little increase in frequency during physical exercise. The heart rate diminishes progressively from birth, when it is around 130 per minute, to adolescence. The heart is accelerated in *muscular exercise,* by *emotional excitement,* at high *environmental temperatures,* and during *digestion.* Among abnormal conditions which cause an increase in cardiac rate are *hemorrhage, surgical shock, fever, hyperthyroidism,* and certain *cardiac disorders* (p. 185).

Tachycardia is a general term meaning increased heart rate. *Bradycardia* means an unusually slow rate of the heart.

The cardiac nerves. Although the heart will continue to beat rhythmically after all nervous connections have been cut, in the ordinary conditions of life, it is under the constant influence of nervous impulses, discharged from centers in the brain. These centers are influenced in turn by impulses conveyed to them from various parts of the body along *afferent nerves* (p. 460), as well as by impulses received from the higher centers (psychic, emotional) of the brain. It is common knowledge that emotional disturbances—anger, fear, excitement, etc.—exert a profound influence upon the pulse rate. The *efferent cardiac nerves*—i.e., the nerves which transmit impulses from the nervous centers to the heart—are the *vagus* and the *accelerator* (or *augmentor*) nerves (Pl. 5A). Thus, through its nervous connections, the heart may undergo slowing or acceleration as a result of the stimulation of nerve endings situated in regions remote from the heart itself. These reflex mechanisms are dealt with in greater detail on page 190.

The **vagus nerves** arise, one on each side, from the medulla oblongata (p. 546). The great majority of the fibers of which they are composed belong to the parasympathetic division of the involuntary or autonomic nervous system. The vagus branches are very widely distributed, passing to the bronchi, lungs, stomach, and small intestine, as well as to the heart. The fibers going to the heart separate from the main trunk of the nerve in the upper and lower parts of the neck. They terminate around nerve cells (ganglion cells) situ-

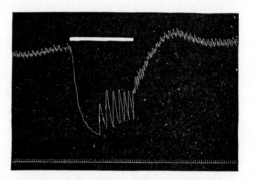

Fig. 4.50 showing the effect of an electric stimulus applied to the right vagus nerve. Heavy white line indicates the commencement and duration of the stimulus. Note the escape of the heart from the vagal stimulation.

ated in the auricular muscle. The impulses are relayed by the axons of the ganglion cells to the sinoauricular and auriculoventricular nodes. The fibers in the first link of the nerve path—that is, from the center in the medulla (generally known as the *cardioinhibitory center*) to the ganglion cells—are called preganglionic fibers. The axons of the ganglion cells, which constitute the second link, are called postganglionic fibers. The right vagus is distributed mainly to the S-A node; it affects the *rate* of the heart to a somewhat greater extent than does the left nerve. The left vagus is distributed chiefly to the A-V node; its effect upon auriculoventricular conduction is greater than that exerted by the nerve of the right side. (See below.) The distributions of the two nerves overlap to a considerable extent, however, since both the S-A node and the A-V node receive fibers from both.

Action of the vagus nerves. The vagus is the inhibitory nerve of the heart. When it is stimulated, slowing or stoppage of the heart results. Diminished force of the beat usually accompanies the reduction in rate. These effects result in a fall in the arterial blood pressure (Fig. 4.50). The vagus exerts no direct effect upon the ventricular muscle. Its action is upon the auricle, and the auriculoventricular bundle; stimulation of the vagus after section of the A-V bundle does not affect the ventricular rate. During vagal stimulation excitability of the auricular muscle is reduced, and its refractory period shortened; the rate of conduction from auricle to ventricles—that is, through the auriculoventricular bundle—is depressed. The slowing of the heart following vagal stimulation is due mainly to lengthening of the diastolic period and, when the heart stops, it does so in the diastolic phase. For this reason, the vagus is sometimes called the diastolic nerve of the heart. The action of the vagus upon the heart closely resembles that caused by an excess of potassium (p. 162).

When the heart is arrested by vagal stimulation, it very often commences to beat, though the stimulus is still being applied. That is to say, the heart breaks away from the vagal restraint. This is spoken of as the *"escape of the heart"* from vagal inhibition. The first few beats of the heart after it has escaped from vagal control are usually of exceptional force (Fig. 4.50). This is due most probably to the fact that the muscle fibers of the ventricle which, since the latter is fully distended by the venous blood during the period of inhibition, are very strongly stretched, and, therefore, cause an unusually powerful contraction (see Starling's law, p. 193).

The tone of the vagus. When the physiologist says a nerve or muscle possesses tone, he means that it exerts a continuous action. In this sense, the cardiac vagus (or rather its center in the medulla) has tone; it exerts a ceaseless restraint upon the action of the heart, sending a continuous stream of impulses along the vagus nerves which holds the heart in check. When this restraint is removed, as by cutting both vagus nerves, the rate of the heart increases very greatly. This method of demonstrating vagal tone cannot, of course, be used in man. Atropine, a drug which temporarily paralyzes the vagus, can, however, be given without danger. When a full dose of this drug is given, the heart rate is more than doubled (150 to 180 beats per minute).

The accelerator or augmentor nerves. These are nerves belonging to the sympathetic division of the involuntary or autonomic nervous system (p. 561). Like other pathways of the autonomic nervous system, the pathway for the accelerator impulses to the heart consists of preganglionic and postganglionic fibers. The preganglionic fibers are the axons of cells situated in the lateral horns of spinal gray matter in the upper five thoracic segments. The postganglionic fibers arise from the stellate ganglion, and the inferior, middle, and superior cervical ganglia of the sympathetic cord; they pass to the heart by the inferior, middle, and superior cardiac nerves (Pl. 5A). Fibers also pass to the heart from the upper two thoracic ganglia.

Stimulation of the accelerator nerves increases the rate of both auricles and ventricles and increases the force of their contractions. The nerves exert a direct action upon the ventricular muscle. They also enhance A-V conduction. Like the vagus, the accelerators exert a continuous effect upon the cardiac rate—that is, they exercise a tonic action. Consequently, when their influence is removed by excision of the sympathetic ganglia from which they arise, the heart rate slows.

Cardiac reflexes. The stimulation of almost any sensory (afferent) nerve in the body may cause a change in cardiac rate. In the frog, merely tapping the abdomen results in slowing of the heart, and it has been shown that in man, the stimulation of abdominal organs by manipulations during surgical operations causes changes in the heart rate. Depending upon the nature of the stimulus and the nerves stimulated, the heart may increase or reduce its rate during an operation. Again, irregularities in the action of the heart may result due to the production, reflexly, of extrasystoles (p. 184). Afferent impulses arising in a diseased organ may also influence the rate of the heart. Cardiac inhibition may be caused by stimulation of the endings of the fifth nerve in the nose, as by some pungent odor, or of afferent fibers in the lungs by irritant vapors. A similar effect may follow pressure upon the outer angle of the eye (*oculocardiac reflex*). In animals, stimulation of a spinal sensory nerve, such as the sciatic, is not infrequently followed by cardiac acceleration.

Among the afferent fibers which are most effective in bringing about reflex changes in heart rate are those contained within the vagus nerves themselves, for these nerves are made up of fibers which convey impulses *to* as well as *away from* the cardioinhibitory center. The afferent vagal fibers end in the heart and in the arch of the aorta (see cardiac depressor nerve, p. 199). The endings in the aortic arch and in the left side of the heart are stimulated by a rise in arterial blood pressure; the impulses increase the tone of the cardioinhibitory center; and cardiac slowing results. Those on the right side of the heart are stimulated by a rise in the pressure of venous blood in the great veins and auricle; they cause acceleration of the heart by depressing the tone of the cardioinhibitory center.

The sinus nerve. Another afferent nerve which, when stimulated, causes reflex slowing of the heart is the sinus nerve. Its endings are situated in the walls of the carotid sinus (p. 199). The normal stimulus to these nerve endings is a rise in arterial blood pressure.

Two well-known circulatory phenomena will now be described. The first is known as *Marey's law,* after a French physiologist; the other is called *Bainbridge's reflex,* after an English physiologist.

Marey's law. Marey's law states that the heart rate is inversely related to the arterial blood pressure—that is, a rise or a fall in the arterial blood pressure causes, respectively, slowing or acceleration of the heart. These effects are brought about through (1) the afferent fibers of the vagus ending in the aorta and the left side of the heart, and (2) the sinus nerves. Since reflex changes in the caliber of the peripheral vessels are also brought about through these nerves, any further description of their effects will be postponed until we come to deal with the control of the blood vessels (p. 199).

Bainbridge's reflex. This is the name given to the increase in heart rate which, as stated above, results from a rise in venous pressure. The rise in venous pressure that occurs when the heart becomes filled acts as a stimulus to the afferent vagal endings in the right auricle. Impulses are set up that depress the tone of the cardioinhibitory center. The heart rate is, in this way, automatically adjusted to the quantity of venous blood flowing into its chambers. This reflex comes into effect to produce increased heart rate during muscular exercise, cardiac action being thus adjusted to pump the increased quantity of blood brought to it from the contracting muscles.

The sensory pathways from the heart. The heart, like other internal organs, is insensitive to the ordinary types of stimulus. Those stimuli, for example, which arouse the sensation of touch, heat, cold, or pain, when applied to the skin, cause no sensation when applied to the heart. The heart may be touched, pinched, or cut without any sensation being aroused. In disease, however (e.g., angina pectoris) severe pain may be experienced. The pain is felt over the front of the chest and down the left arm. The pain impulses travel by afferent sympathetic fibers in the middle and inferior cardiac nerves. None apparently are conveyed by the vagus. They enter the cord via the posterior roots of the upper four or five thoracic segments. Removal of the upper sympathetic ganglia, or the injection of alcohol around these ganglia, interrupts the pain fibers or abolishes their conductivity, and is sometimes resorted to for the relief of the severe, intractable pain of angina pectoris.

The action of certain drugs upon the heart. *Atropine,* as mentioned on page 188, causes an increase in the heart rate by abolishing vagal tone. It acts by antagonizing the action of acetylcholine—the vagus substance (see below). *Muscarine,* a principle in poisonous mushrooms (amanita) slows or arrests the heart; thus, its action is similar to that following stimulation of the vagus. The effects of atropine and muscarine are, therefore, antagonistic. *Pilocarpine, physo-*

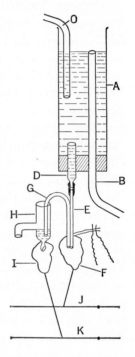

Fig. 4.51 The perfusion apparatus A is furnished with an overflow tube B, the height of which can be varied to allow alterations in the perfusion pressure. Fluid is delivered through the tube C. The fluid from A passes through the tube D to the inflow limb E of the double cannula which supplies the donor heart F. After irrigating the inside of the donor heart, the fluid passes by the outflow limb G to the glass cannulated tube H to which is attached the recipient heart I. This cannulated tube is provided with a lateral overflow, so that the hydrostatic pressure of the fluid supplied to the recipient heart remains constant. J and K are the levers to which the hearts F and I are respectively attached. (After Bain.)

stigmine (also called *eserine*), *choline,* and its ester, *acetylcholine,* have the same effect upon the heart as that of muscarine. *Nicotine* acts upon the ganglion (vagal) cells in the heart, first stimulating, and later paralyzing them; slowing of the heart followed by acceleration results. *Digitalis* depresses conduction in the auriculoventricular bundle, thus causing ventricular slowing. It also exerts a beneficial effect upon the heart muscle, and is probably the most valuable drug which the physician possesses for the treatment of a failing heart. Excessively large doses of digitalis may cause complete functional dissociation of the auricles and ventricles—heart block.

The chemical (humoral) transmission of vagus and accelerator effects. About 35 years ago, the astonishing and important discovery was made by Loewi, a German pharmacologist, that the vagus and accelerator nerves exert their actions upon the heart, not through the *direct* effect of nerve impulses, but through the intermediary of chemical substances. At the terminals of the vagus in the heart, *acetylcholine* is produced, and the cardiac slowing or arrest, which results from vagal stimulation, is the result of the direct action of this substance upon the heart muscle. The production of this vagal substance or *Vagusstoff*, as Loewi called it, was demonstrated by the following experiment. Two frog hearts were set up as shown in Figure 4.51. The perfusion fluid, after passing through the heart on the right (*donor heart*), then passed through the heart on the left (*recipient heart*). Now, when the vagus of the donor heart was stimulated for a time, inhibition of the recipient heart followed. The latter effect must have been due to a chemical substance passing into the fluid, perfusing the donor heart during the period of vagal stimulation, and then being conveyed to the recipient heart. Subsequent experiments have left little doubt that the chemical mediator of the vagal effects is an ester of choline, namely, acetylcholine. Experiments of a similar nature have proved that *adrenaline* (Chap. 10) is produced during stimulation of the accelerator nerves.

The vagal substance is quickly destroyed after its production. In order that a chemical shall serve as a mediator of vagal effects, it is absolutely necessary that it be removed rapidly after it is produced. Otherwise it would continue to exert its effect and so cause prolonged slowing or even arrest of the heart. The destruction of acetylcholine is brought about by the action of an enzyme present in the heart muscle as well as in the blood and other tissues. The enzyme is called *cholinesterase.* The action of physostigmine (eserine) upon the heart is, as mentioned above, similar to that of the vagus, or of acetylcholine itself. It has been shown that eserine acts simply by antagonizing the action of the cholinesterase. In other words, it prevents the destruction of acetylcholine which is being liberated constantly from the vagal endings and, as a consequence, enhances the tonic action of the vagus.

More recent work has shown that the conception of a chemical or humoral mechanism in the transmission of nervous effects has a much wider application. Not only the effects of the *vague and sympathetic* upon the heart, but also those of other parasympathetic and sympathetic nerves (e.g., of the stomach, intestine, blood vessels, etc.) are mediated by chemical materials (see p. 566).

The control of the action of the heart by chemical substances carried in the blood stream. The importance of the minerals *sodium, potassium,* and *calcium* upon the action of the heart has been described (see p. 162). *Adrenaline,* the hormone of the medulla of the adrenal glands, acts upon the heart in a manner similar to that of sympathetic stimulation (see p. 420). The *carbon dioxide* and *oxygen* pressures in the blood exert a powerful influence upon cardiac action. Excess of carbon dioxide (e.g., in asphyxia) increases the tone of the cardio-inhibitory center, reduces the rate of impulse formation in the S-A node, and depresses conduction in the auriculoventricular bundle; the heart is therefore slowed. When the pressure of carbon dioxide is such that a marked change in blood reaction toward the acid side occurs (e.g., to pH 7.0), heart block results. Reduction in the carbon dioxide pressure in the blood (as may be produced by prolonged forced breathing, p. 255) causes the reverse effects—namely, decrease in the tone of the cardioinhibitory center, increased rate of impulse formation in the S-A node, and enhanced conduction in the A-V bundle.

A low *oxygen* pressure in the blood causes an increase in heart rate. If the oxygen lack is severe or prolonged, slowing of the beat occurs, irregularities appear, and the heart fails. The heart muscle is unable to contract for long unless the oxygen supply is adequate; it is much more susceptible to oxygen lack (anoxia) than is skeletal muscle.

The length of the muscle fiber in relation to the force of the cardiac contraction. It has been demonstrated experimentally that the well-nourished heart possesses great reserves of energy. For example, when, as in muscular exercise, the quantity of blood entering the ventricles during their period of filling (diastole) is increased several fold, the heart ejects without difficulty the greater quantity of blood during the succeeding systole. Again, when the arterial blood pressure is raised to double the normal value, the left ventricle readily overcomes the great resistance and discharges its contents as easily, apparently, as it did at the lower pressure. Starling found that the dog's heart was capable of discharging, per minute, a weight of blood nearly sixty times that of the heart itself. We have already seen that the minute volume of a large robust man, whose heart weighs about 300 grams, may amount to over 35 liters (approximately 35 kilo-grams).

How does the heart gain the required energy for the performance of the extra work? Now, it is well known that a skeletal muscle contracts more forcibly if it is stretched by a weight, than if it is permitted to contract unweighted. The degree of stretch to which the muscle is subjected—that is, the length of the muscle fibers before excitation—determines the force of the ensuing contraction. The cardiac muscle fiber behaves in a similar manner. The greater the weight, within physiological limits, which is applied to the muscle during diastole and, consequently, the longer the fiber, the more powerful will be the following systole. In the case of the heart, the weight which stretches the muscle during diastole is, of course, the mass of blood entering the ventricles. Thus, automatically, the heart finds the necessary energy to perform the extra work entailed by an increased venous return. In order to gain power to eject blood against a raised arterial pressure, the heart does not completely empty itself for the first few beats after the pressure has been raised. The residual blood thus increases the diastolic volume of the heart—that is, increases the length of the muscle fibers. From then on, the heart empties its chambers completely during systole.

The ability of the heart to do work above the ordinary requirements of the resting state of the body is called its *reserve power*. One might therefore, in a sense, compare the cardiac muscle fiber to an elastic band which, as we know, rebounds most powerfully when it is fully stretched. The behavior of the heart in this regard has been expressed by Starling in the following words, "The energy liberated by a cardiac contraction is a simple function of the length of the muscle fibers of the ventricle at the end of diastole." This is known as *Starling's law of the heart*.

When, as a result of disease, the contractile power of the heart is reduced, it must dilate. In other words, it must increase the length of its fibers to a greater degree than does a healthy heart in order to perform the same amount of work. Thickening—*hypertrophy*—of the muscle fiber also occurs. Enlargement of the heart is therefore a sign of heart disease. Nevertheless, the enlargement in itself is beneficial, and may be looked upon as a compensatory process which enables a heart which is at a mechanical disadvantage (e.g., one with a valvular lesion) to discharge its functions. Indeed, the hypertrophied heart may have a reserve power almost as great as that of the normal heart. When the heart muscle itself is diseased, it may be so greatly weakened that it cannot even, at maximal dilatation, contract forcibly enough to maintain an efficient circulation. The signs of heart failure then ensue —breathlessness (dyspnea, p. 260), edema (p. 101), and the appearance of a bluish tint of the skin, especially of the lips, ears, and fingertips (cyanosis, p. 263).

It is now generally accepted that a healthy heart cannot be "strained" by overwork. Athletics, even though of a strenuous nature, do not injure a normal heart. In other words, the volume of blood brought to the heart from the contracting muscles is not great enough to tax the *normal healthy heart* beyond its reserve powers; the muscles will fatigue or come to the limit of their capability before the heart is injured. On the other hand, if a person with valvular, coronary, or other organic cardiac disease indulges in strenuous muscular exercise, serious injury may be inflicted upon the heart, for the work demanded of the heart may then exceed its reserve power, which has been reduced as a result of deterioration of the heart muscle caused by the existing disease.

Nerve Control of the Blood Vessels

As already mentioned on page 124, the walls of the arterioles are composed largely of smooth muscle fibers arranged in such a fashion that when they contract the vascular lumen is narrowed. This muscle, in so far as its nerve supply is concerned, may be compared to the muscle of the heart. One set of nerve fibers—*vasoconstrictors*—excite the muscle—that is, cause constriction of the arterioles. The other set—*vasodilators*—in-hibit the muscle, causing it to relax and so cause vascular dilatation.

The vasoconstrictor nerves. The vasoconstrictor nerves belong to the sympathetic division of the involuntary nervous system. They arise, in common with other sympathetic fibers (p. 563), from cells in the lateral horns of the gray matter of the spinal cord lying between the levels of the first thoracic and the third lumbar segments. The vasoconstrictor fibers to the vessels of the limbs, for the most part, are carried in the mixed spinal nerves (e.g., ulnar, sciatic, etc.). Those to the head and neck pass from the cervical ganglia of the sympathetic to the carotid arteries which they surround in a netlike (plexi-form) manner. These nerve nets or *plexuses*

Fig. 4.52 Showing effect upon arterial blood pressure of stimulating the right splanchnic nerve. (After Macleod.)

invest the vessels to their smallest branches, ultimately furnishing filaments to the arterioles. The vasoconstrictor fibers to the abdomen pass to the vessels in three well-defined strands—the *greater*, the *lesser*, and the *least splanchnic* nerves. The greater splanchnic nerve supplies the larger proportion of the arterioles of the abdomen; when stimulated, the wide-spread vasoconstriction which results causes a very pronounced rise in blood pressure (Fig. 4.52).

The vasodilator nerves. We may group the vasodilator nerves into three categories: (a) those which belong to the *sympathetic division* of the sympathetic nervous system, (b) those belonging to the *parasympathetic division,* and (c) those that leave the central nervous system in the *posterior spinal nerve roots.* The sympathetic vasodilators arise from the thoracic and lumbar segments of the spinal cord and follow the same general course as the vasconstrictors. They appear to be distributed almost exclusively to the vessels of the muscles and viscera.

Of the parasympathetic vasodilators, some leave the brain in the facial, glossopharyngeal, and vagus nerves; others arise in the sacral part of the cord and are carried in the pelvic nerve (p. 563) to the vessels of the bladder, rectum, and external genital organs. The vasodilators which leave the brain in the facial nerve enter its chorda tympani branch, and are ultimately distributed to the vessels of the tongue and salivary glands.

Vasodilator impulses conveyed along the pelvic nerve to the vessels of the penis or of the corresponding organ of the female—the clitoris—are responsible for the phenomenon of *erection* (Ch. 14).

The vasodilator fibers of the posterior spinal nerve roots appear to be distributed, mainly at any rate, to the skin of the limbs. There has been much discussion as to the nature of these nerves. When the posterior nerve roots supplying fibers to a limb are stimulated, the vessels may dilate. Many believe that the ordinary sensory fibers, of which the posterior roots are mainly if not entirely composed, must transmit the vasodilator impulses. That is to say, impulses pass to the vessels, apparently, over fibers which have been thought to be capable only of conveying impulses *to* the spinal cord—i.e., sensory impulses. According to this conception, the vasodilator impulses travel over the nerve in a direction opposite to that of the ordinary sensory impulses. For this reason, they have been termed *antidromic* (Gk. *anti,* against + *dromos,* a running) vasodilator impulses. Other physiologists offer another explanation of the vasodilatation which follows stimulation of the posterior roots, claiming that *efferent* fibers are contained in the posterior roots, and that these alone are the transmitters of vasodilator impulses. The question remains unsettled.

The vasoconstrictor and vasodilator centers. The vasoconstrictor and vasodilator centers are situated in the medulla oblongata, in the floor of the fourth ventricle (see p. 559). The vasoconstrictor center is connected by tracts of fibers with the nerve cells in the lateral horns of the spinal cord which, as mentioned above, give rise to the vaso-constrictor fibers. These cells may be looked upon as constituting a spinal vasoconstrictor center. Centers controlling the vessels also prob-ably exist at higher levels than the medulla—for example, in the hy-pothalamus and even in the cerebral cortex.

The vasoconstrictor center in the medulla and, though to a much less degree, the vasodilator center as well, possess tone. That is to say,

Fig. 4.53 Showing the vessels of rabbit's ear. The sympathetic (vaso-constrictor) nerves sup-plying the right ear have been cut. The nerves to the left ear are intact. Note the dilata-tion of the vessels of the right ear as com-pared with those of the left. The difference in caliber of the vessels on the two sides would be still more pronounced if the sympathetic nerves of the left ear had been stimulated.

impulses are constantly passing from the centers along the vasocon-strictor and vasodilator nerves. Under ordinary circumstances, vaso-constrictor tone predominates—the vessels being always slightly con-stricted. This tonic vasoconstrictor action is at once abolished if the spinal cord is cut across in the lower cervical region—the stream of impulses from the medullary center to the minute blood vessels being thus interrupted. The blood vessels then dilate, the peripheral resistance, which is such an important factor in maintaining the ar-terial blood pressure, is greatly reduced, and a profound fall in pres-sure results. The low blood pressure persists for a time, which varies with the animal species, being longer in mammals than in lower forms, and then gradually returns to normal. The restoration of the blood pressure to the normal level is due to the centers in the spinal cord assuming the functions of the isolated centers in the brain. Sectioning the splanchnic nerves, by depriving the abdominal vessels of tonic vasoconstrictor impulses, acts in a similar way to cause a fall in blood pressure.

That dilatation of vessels occurs when the vasoconstrictor fibers to a part are cut, can be very simply demonstrated upon a rabbit. The vessels of the rabbit's ear are plainly visible when the ear is held up in front of a bright light. If the sympathetic nerve in the neck (cervical sympathetic) is cut while the ear is being observed in this way, the ear becomes flushed and warm, and the individual vessels are seen to dilate; see Figure 4.53. The effect is still more striking if the opposite ear (with nerve uncut) is compared with the ear on the operated side. This experiment, first performed by Claude Bernard, the great French physiologist of the nineteenth century, is taken to mean that a constant stream of (tonic) vasoconstrictor impulses is carried along the intact nerve which thus maintains the vessels in a state of partial constriction. These impulses are interrupted when the nerve is cut.

Vascular reflexes. Variations in the caliber of the arterioles can be brought about by stimulating certain afferent nerves—i.e., through reflex action. The impulses set up in the afferent nerve pass to the nervous centers and are reflected along efferent nerves, vasoconstrictor or vasodilator, to the blood vessels. A rise or a fall in blood pressure, depending upon the afferent nerve that has been stimulated and the type of stimulus, may thus be induced. A reflex rise in blood pressure is called a *pressor* reflex; a reflex fall is called a *depressor* reflex. Stimulation of practically any afferent nerve in the body may cause a change in the calibers of the peripheral vessels. It is not always possible, however, to predict whether a pressor or a depressor reflex will result. A strong stimulus applied to an ordinary spinal sensory nerve is more likely to produce a rise in blood pressure. As a general rule, painful stimuli of various sorts result in a pressor, and mild pleasant types of stimulus, in a depressor response. In man, stimulation by cold (e.g., a draft) applied to a cutaneous area causes constriction of the vessels of the skin over parts of the body remote from the area to which the cold is applied, as well as of the vessels in the mucous membranes of the nose, throat, and bronchi. Gentle stimulation of the skin (e.g., massage) causes, as a rule, vasodilatation. Warming the skin usually causes vasodilatation in areas of skin some distance from the warmed part, but if the temperature is raised to the point where a painful sensation is aroused, reflex vasoconstriction is more likely to result.

The aortic and sinus nerves. There are two sets of afferent fibers which exert a very special controlling influence upon the circulation. When stimulated, they cause reflex slowing of the heart together with vasodilatation, especially of the abdominal (splanchnic) region of the vascular system. As a consequence of these effects, the blood pressure falls. One set of such afferent fibers is contained in the vagus nerve. They terminate peripherally in the wall of the aorta and base of the heart. An increase in the blood pressure, by stretching the aorta, stimulates the nerve terminals embedded in the arterial walls; impulses ascend to the cardiac and vasomotor centers in the medulla; impulses are discharged, in turn, down the efferent fibers of the vagus and the vasodilator nerves. The tonic vasoconstrictor impulses are, at the same time, reduced in frequency. The vasodilation is therefore due to reduced vasoconstrictor tone as well as to increased tone of the vasodilators. Although, in man, these afferent (depressor) fibers are bound up in the vagus trunk with the efferent fibers, in certain animals (e.g., the rabbit) they are contained in a separate branch of the vagus, known as the *cardiac depressor* or *aortic nerve*, shown in Figure 4.54.

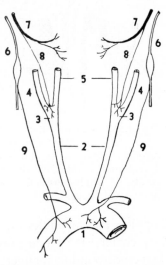

Fig. 4.54 Showing the carotid sinus and arch of aorta with the sinus and aortic nerves. 1, arch of aorta; 2, common carotid; 3, carotid sinus; 4, internal carotid; 5, external carotid; 6, vagus nerve; 7, glossopharyngeal nerve; 8, sinus nerve, branch of the glossopharyngeal nerve.

The other set of afferent fibers are contained in the *sinus nerve*, a small branch of the glossopharyngeal nerve. The filaments of this nerve terminate in receptors situated in the wall of the *carotid sinus*, the name given to a slight enlargement of the common carotid artery where it divides into the internal and external carotids (Fig. 4.55). These receptors, since they respond to a pressure or stretch stimulus, are called *pressoreceptors*. When stimulated in this way, as by a rise in blood pressure, nerve impulses are transmitted along the sinus nerve to the cardiac and vasomotor centers in the medulla oblongata. Reflex slowing of the heart, vasodilatation, and a fall in blood pressure follow. Mere compression of the sinus between the finger and thumb in an animal, or even pressure through the skin of the neck in a proportion of normal human subjects, will stimulate the nerve endings in the sinus wall and evoke the reflex. In certain rare instances, the human carotid sinus is abnormally sensitive. In such persons the lightest pressure in the neighbor-

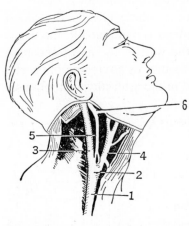

hood of the sinus (as during shaving, or buttoning a collar) may cause pronounced slowing of the heart, and a sharp fall in blood pressure. The fall in blood pressure may, by depriving the brain of an adequate supply of blood, cause syncope (fainting) or convulsions.

The maintenance of the arterial blood pressure within the normal limits is dependent to a large extent upon the activity of the sinus and aortic nerves. These nerves transmit at all times a stream of impulses to the cardiac and vasomotor centers, and thus exert continuously a depressing effect upon the blood pressure. Any marked rise in blood pressure increases the frequency of the afferent

Fig. 4.55 Showing the carotid sinus region in man. 1, common carotid artery; 2, carotid sinus; 3, internal carotid; 4, external carotid; 5, sinus nerve; 6, glossopharyngeal nerve.

impulses and magnifies the constant depressor effect upon the medullary centers; the blood pressure is thus automatically reduced again. In a corresponding manner, any tendency for the blood pressure to fall is countered by an opposite effect, namely, reduction of the frequency of the impulses going to the center and, in consequence, reflex cardiac acceleration and vasoconstriction (Fig. 4.56). The sinus and aortic nerves thus exert a governing or buffering effect upon the blood pressure, preventing it from fluctuating greatly in either direction. For this reason they are sometimes referred to as the "buffer nerves" of the circulation.

In hemorrhage, for example, the fall in blood pressure occasioned by the reduction in blood volume, diminishes the intensity of the pressure stimulus normally applied to the sinus and aortic nerves, thus lowering the frequency of the afferent impulses impinging upon the centers. Reflex vasoconstriction and cardiac acceleration follow, which tend to restore the blood pressure to its normal level. The vasoconstriction seen in surgical shock, and the ability of the circulation to compensate for the effect of gravity and maintain the blood pressure when the erect posture is assumed, are mainly dependent upon the activity of the sinus and aortic nerves.

Filaments of the sinus nerve also end in the *carotid body,* a collection of specialized cells in the neighborhood of the carotid sinus; but since this body is concerned with the control of respiration rather than with the circulation, its structure and function will be deferred.

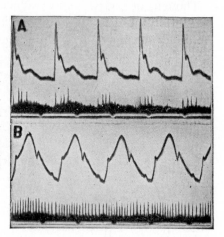

Fig. 4.56 *Record A, upper tracing,* blood pressure. *Lower,* record of impulses from a single isolated fiber of the sinus nerve. *Record B, upper tracing,* blood pressure at a higher level than in A: note that the impulses recorded in lower tracing from the sinus nerve are at a higher frequency and persist even throughout the diastolic phase.

A similar structure, known as the *aortic body,* is to be found on a small artery arising from the arch of the aorta; its receptors are innervated by terminals of the aortic nerve, and stimulated by a low oxygen tension of the arterial blood. When so stimulated, impulses travel along the aortic nerve, and reflex vasoconstrictor results. Thus, while the carotid body is concerned, chiefly at any rate, with the regulation of respiration, the aortic body is part of the mechanism controlling the circulation.

The reflex control of the heart and blood vessels is shown diagrammatically in Plate 5B.

Special Features of the Circulation in Certain Parts

The capillary circulation. The capillaries are the smallest vessels of the circulatory system, measuring about 1 mm in length, and having an average diameter of 8 to 15 microns. Their walls are composed of a single layer of endothelial cells cemented together at their edges, and are of such delicate construction that they are seen with the greatest difficulty, even under careful microscopic examination. The blood within the capillaries (the corpuscles being clearly seen through their walls) enables one to locate the position of these vessels. In amphibians, here and there, peculiar spiderlike cells are to be seen in close relation to the capillary. The bodies of these cells possess several long slender processes which embrace the endothelial wall. They are called *Rouget cells* (see Fig. 4.10, p. 125).

Though, of course, the existence of small vessels between the arterial and venous systems was implicit in Harvey's theory of the circulation of the blood, it was not until some years after Harvey propounded his theory that the capillaries were actually demonstrated by the Italian anatomist, Malpighi. It has been mentioned elsewhere (p. 125) that the whole purpose of the elaborate circulatory system is to drive blood through the capillaries, for it is through the walls of these vessels alone that oxygen and nutritive materials pass from the blood to the cells of the tissues, and carbon dioxide and waste materials from the tissue to the blood.

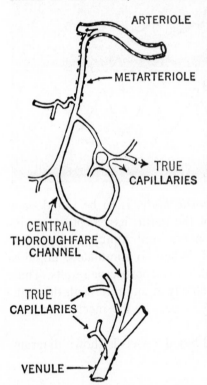

Fig. 4.57 Vessels in a capillary area. (After Chambers and Zweifach, modified.)

Each arteriole is continued into a vessel of about the size of a capillary but differing from the latter in that its walls contain a small quantity of smooth muscle; it is called a *metarteriole* (Fig. 4.57). Such vessels run centrally through a capillary area. This central or *thoroughfare channel* gives off a number of true capillaries —that is, simple endothelial tubes which, after forming a network of loops, return the blood to the central channel nearer its venous end. The metarteriole, by virtue of its smooth muscle and of its possessing a vasoconstrictor and vasodilator nerve supply, is capable of altering its caliber and thus of decreasing or increasing the quantity of blood flowing through the capillary area which it serves. The capillaries themselves, in opposition to older accounts given of these vessels, are not able actively to alter their calibers. They are merely dilated passively by an increased volume of blood entering them when the metarterioles dilate. Changes in the blood flow within the capillaries occur frequently in accordance with the state of activity of the surrounding tissues (Fig. 4.58). In a resting muscle, for example, a large proportion of the capillaries are closed, the channels being completely obliterated. When the muscle contracts, large num-

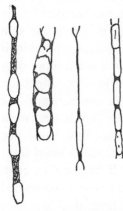

Fig. 4.58 The muscle capillaries of guinea pig injected during life with India ink, showing different degrees of constriction. Blank oval and circular areas indicate red corpuscles. (After Krogh.)

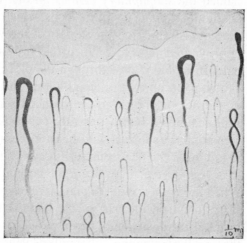

Fig. 4.59 Showing capillary loops in the human skin at the base of the fingernail, as seen under low power of the microscope. The divisions in the scale at the bottom of the illustration represent tenths of millimeters. (After Lewis.)

bers are opened up, thus increasing the blood flow through the tissue several fold, and assuring an adequate oxygen supply for the contraction process.

A number of chemical materials exert an influence upon the diameter of the metarterioles and so, indirectly, upon the caliber of the capillaries. Carbon dioxide and lactic acid, produced during tissue activity, cause dilatation of the metarterioles. Iodine, urethane, silver nitrate, and histamine have a similar effect. Adrenaline and pituitrin cause constriction.

The capillaries of the human skin. The most superficially placed capillaries of the human skin are in the form of hairpinlike loops situated in the papillae of the dermis, and running more or less at right angles to the skin surface with their convexities directed outward. They lie just beneath the papillae of the skin. These loops may be seen when the skin at the base of the fingernail is examined with a strong light beneath the microscope (Pl. 6A and Fig. 4.59). One limb of a capillary loop receives blood from the arterial side; the blood in the other limb, having given up a part of its oxygen load, is more venous in character. The venous limb drains into a plexus of capillary vessels lying beneath the bases of the papillae of the skin, and named the *subpapillary venous plexus*. It is the blood in this plexus, and not that in the capillary loops, which gives color to the skin. When the flow is rapid and the vessels of the venous plexus dilate, the skin is bright red in color. When the vessels are constricted, the skin is pale. If the blood flow through the plexus becomes slowed, more oxygen is given up by the blood within the vessels, a greater proportion of the hemoglobin is in the reduced state, and, in consequence, the skin acquires a bluish tint (see cyanosis, p. 263). This is seen most commonly in subjects with heart disease, the slowing then being due to failure of the heart pump. But slowing of the cutaneous blood flow, to a less degree, may occur in normal persons if exposed to cold. When the body is chilled, the arterioles of the skin become constricted (an attempt on the part of the body to conserve heat, p. 376); as a result of the diversion of blood to deeper parts, the blood flow through the capillaries of the subpapillary venous plexus may be slowed to such an extent that a definitely blue tint is given to the skin, especially of the finger tips, ears, and nose. (See also pp. 376–7.)

The blood supply to the heart muscle, or coronary circulation. The heart of mammals possesses a well-developed system of vessels—arteries, arterioles, capillaries, and veins. The blood is delivered to the heart muscle by the *right* and *left coronary arteries* (Pl. 7A) and, after passing through the small vessels, is drained into the right auricle by a large vein known as the *coronary sinus* (which receives blood from the *great, middle,* and *small* cardiac veins) and by the two *anterior cardiac veins*. A number of smaller and more deeply situated veins known as the *veins of Thebesius,* after an eighteenth-century anatomist who first described them, empty directly into the auricular and ventricular cavities. About 60 per cent of the blood escapes from the coronary system by the coronary sinus, the remainder by the anterior cardiac veins and the veins of Thebesius. The coronary arteries arise from the aorta just beyond the attachments of the aortic valves.

Unlike any other organ or tissue of the body, the greatest flow of blood through the heart muscle takes place during the diastolic phase of the heart. During the ejection phase of ventricular systole, the coronary blood flow is greatly reduced, for the cardiac muscle fibers when they contract compress the coronary vessels; the flow of blood is then reduced through some vessels and completely arrested through others.

The mean blood pressure during the diastolic phase of the cardiac cycle is, therefore, the important factor in filling the coronary vessels and determining the magnitude of the coronary blood flow.

The coronary vessels receive fibers from both the vagus and the sympathetic nerves. The vagus causes vasoconstriction; the sympathetic nerves cause vasodilatation. Adrenaline also causes dilatation of the coronary vessels; in animal experiments, a threefold increase in coronary blood flow has been obtained by the use of this substance.

Angina pectoris and coronary occlusion. The term *angina pectoris* means breast pain, and is used to denote an attack of pain, usually severe, felt beneath the breast bone (sternum), and in many cases in the left shoulder and arm. It is due to the heart muscle being inadequately supplied with oxygen. The commonest cause is disease (arteriosclerosis) of the coronary vessels. The disease causes narrowing of the caliber of the arteries and, as a consequence, reduces the blood supply to the heart muscle. The attack most frequently follows some muscular effort or emotional excitement which increases the cardiac output—that is, the work of the heart. In other words, the heart is called upon to do work for the performance of which it is unable to obtain an adequate supply of oxygen. A drug such as amylnitrite, or nitroglycerine, both of which are dilators of the coronary arteries, is commonly given to arrest an attack.

The severe pain associated with angina pectoris is believed to be due to the action of a chemical upon the nerve endings. This substance, when the oxygen supply to the heart is adequate, as in health, is removed or destroyed about as quickly as it is formed, but when the supply of oxygen is deficient its accumulation within the heart muscle gives rise to anginal pain.

Complete occlusion of a large branch of a coronary artery is not an uncommon event. The occlusion is usually the result of the clotting of blood within a vessel (*thrombosis*) that is the seat of arteriosclerosis. Coronary thrombosis, or occlusion of a large coronary branch from whatever cause, is accompanied by intense pain, nausea and vomiting, breathlessness, and collapse. Death may occur almost instantly. If recovery takes place, the area of heart muscle deprived of its blood supply dies (necrosis), and is replaced by scar tissue. Rupture of the diseased area may, however, occur before healing has taken place. The electrocardiogram taken shortly after an attack shows certain special features which are of the greatest value in diagnosis.

The pulmonary circulation. The blood passes from the right to the left side of the heart through the lungs. The same quantity of blood as is discharged in a given time by the right side of the heart is received and discharged by the left. In other words, the quantity of blood passing through the lungs per minute is the same as that passing through the systemic circulation. The vessels of the pulmonary circuit, as of any other part, consist of arteries, arterioles, capillaries, and veins. The main arterial vessel is called the *pulmonary artery*. It arises from the right ventricle and carries *venous blood*—that is, blood in which the hemoglobin is in the reduced state. The main veins are four in number (two from each lung); they contain *arterial* (oxygenated) blood, which they deliver into the left auricle.[7]

The capillaries of the lung differ from those of any other tissue in that they are separated from air only by the very delicate and incomplete membrane composing the walls of the pulmonary alveoli. The pulmonary capillaries can increase their capacity to a relatively great extent. Ordinarily the lungs contain from 6 to 10 percent of the total amount of blood in the body, but under certain conditions they may contain 20 percent of the total blood volume. If, for example, there is some resistance on the left side of the heart (e.g., mitral stenosis or weakness of the left ventricle) while the right ventricle continues to contract forcibly, the pressure in the pulmonary circuit rises; the capillary bed becomes distended, and a much greater volume of blood is contained in the lungs. This is likely to cause breathlessness—a common symptom of heart disease—because the dilated vessels encroach upon the pulmonary alveoli (p. 230). The greater amount of blood in the lungs also reduces the distensibility of the pulmonary tissue. The lungs are "stiffer" and do not distend and deflate during respiration with their normal resiliency. This tends to impair the exchange of the respiratory gases between the lungs and the atmosphere.

The pressure in the pulmonary circulation is about one sixth of that in the systemic circulation. In the dog, the mean pressure in the pulmonary artery is around 25 mm Hg as compared with 130 to 150 in the aorta.

Variations in intrathoracic pressure occur during ordinary quiet

[7] The blood carried to the lungs by the pulmonary artery does not serve to supply the pulmonary tissue itself with oxygen and nutriment. This function devolves upon the systemic circulation. The bronchial tree and pulmonary tissue are supplied by branches of the aorta.

respiration. The intrathoracic pressure amounts to about −6 mm Hg during inspiration, and about −2.5 mm Hg during expiration. More blood, therefore, is "sucked" into the great veins of the thorax and right auricle during inspiration than during expiration; more blood is discharged from the right heart into the pulmonary system during inspiration. The quantity of blood received and given out by the left side of the heart must, of course, vary with the quantity discharged by the right side. The variations in output of the left ventricle cause

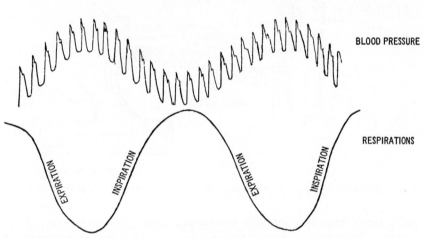

Fig. 4.60   Illustrating the effect of the respirations upon the blood pressure.

corresponding fluctuations in the systemic blood pressure. The increased discharge of the left ventricle and the rise in systemic blood pressure are not, however, synchronous with inspiration, but owing to the increased vascular capacity of the lungs themselves, caused by the inspiratory movement, are somewhat delayed. The rise in systemic blood pressure caused by inspiration, therefore, does not commence until near the end of this movement, and reaches its maximum toward the end of expiration (see Fig. 4.60).

The pulmonary vessels are supplied with fibers from the sympathetic and the vagus. The former are mainly vasoconstrictor in action, the latter mainly vasodilator.

The hepatic circulation. The blood from the gastrointestinal tract and spleen is collected by the portal vein and conveyed to the liver. The blood from the small intestine contains materials derived from the food—that is, glucose, amino acids, as well as a proportion of the fat. The portal vein breaks up within the liver into numerous branches; its smallest subdivisions run between the lobules of the liver, and are called *interlobular veins*. These open into capillarylike (but relatively wide) vessels called *sinusoids,* lying between rows of liver cells (the *liver cords*). All the sinusoids of a liver lobule converge toward the center of the lobule where they drain into a *central vein.* The central veins drain in turn into a system of larger (*sublobular*) veins which ultimately join to form vessels called the *hepatic veins;*

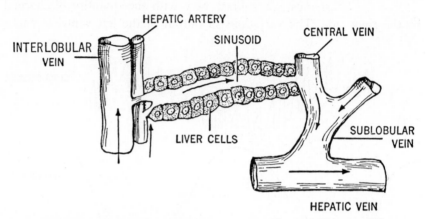

Fig. 4.61   The hepatic circulation; see also Figure 8.27, page 329.

these open into the inferior vena cava (see Figs. 4.61 and 8.28, p. 330). Thus the portal vein resembles an artery in that it breaks up into branches which lead into capillary vessels. It, therefore, lies between two capillary beds, one in the gastrointestinal tract and spleen which it drains, the other in the liver to which it is distributed. The blood of the portal vein has a pressure of only from 10 to 12 mm Hg; it has a relatively low content of oxygen and a relatively high content of carbon dioxide. But the liver cells must receive well-oxygenated blood under high pressure. This is delivered through the hepatic artery —a branch of the celiac artery. The latter vessel arises directly from the abdominal aorta. The blood of the hepatic artery is delivered into the sinusoids of the liver where it mixes with the blood of the portal vein (see Fig. 4.61). Thus, whereas the portal blood carries blood loaded with digestive products which are subjected to various changes by the liver cells, the latter cannot survive if they receive only the small quantity of oxygen which this blood can supply. The function of supplying the hepatic tissue with adequate quantities of oxygen devolves upon the blood of the hepatic artery.

The cerebral circulation. Blood is delivered to the brain through two pairs of arteries—the internal carotids and the vertebrals—and is drained away by the internal jugular veins. The vertebral artery is a branch of the subclavian artery. It must be remembered that the brain is enclosed in a rigid case—the skull. Since the contents of the skull—brain, blood, and cerebrospinal fluid—are incompressible, their volume can alter very little from time to time. More blood can be accommodated in the cranial cavity only through the displacement of an equal quantity of cerebrospinal fluid into the spinal canal, where room is made for it by the stretching of membranes situated between the joints of the vertebrae. Though the quantity of blood within the skull changes comparatively little from time to time, the *velocity* of the blood flow through the cerebral vessels varies considerably. The flow is determined largely by the blood pressure in the rest of the body, a rise in pressure in the aorta increasing the cerebral blood flow, and vice versa. For example, when a person assumes the standing position, the carotid sinus and aortic nerve mechanisms come into play and prevent a fall in the pressure of blood in the arteries going to the head, which otherwise would result from the effect of gravity upon the circulation. The brain is thus assured of an adequate blood supply.

The flow through the brain is dependent also upon the pressure gradient—that is, upon the difference between the pressures in the cerebral arteries and the cerebral veins. An increase in the pressure in the internal jugular veins (the pressure in the cerebral arteries being unchanged) will therefore tend to diminish the cerebral blood flow.

Variations in the blood flow through the cerebral vessels can occur, however, quite independently of the general blood pressure for, though denied for years it is now accepted that these vessels are supplied with nerves, which can bring about active changes in vascular calibers. Though the systemic blood pressure remains unchanged, an increased cerebral blood flood can therefore be effected through intracranial vasodilatation. Constriction of the cerebral vessels, with a constant systemic pressure, will cause the opposite effect—namely, a reduction in the blood supply to the brain. The vasodilator fibers to the cerebral vessels are derived from the facial nerve; the vasoconstrictors, from the sympathetic.

The Defensive Mechanisms of the Body against Disease and Injury; Shock, Anaphylaxis, Allergy

Infecting agents. Man, animals, and plants are constantly liable to attack by many lower forms of life—namely, *bacteria, fungi* or *molds* (which cause ringworm and other affections of the skin), and *protozoans.* These latter are the infecting organisms in some of the most virulent of human diseases, such as *malaria, amebic dysentery, African sleeping sickness,* etc. Bacteria and fungi belong to lower orders of the vegetable kingdom. Protozoa are unicellular animal forms (Fig. 5.1).

The viruses, another large group of infecting agents, are the cause of a number of well-known diseases, such as: *measles, mumps, chickenpox, smallpox, influenza,* one type of *pneumonia, anterior poliomyelitis (infantile paralysis), rabies, psittacosis* (a disease of parrots and allied species transmissible to man), and the *common cold.* They are also responsible for several diseases of plants and even attack bacteria.[1] It is the general opinion that viruses are living organisms,

---

[1] Viruses that infect bacteria are called *bacteriophages.* There are several varieties, each of which attacks a specific type of bacterium—e.g., staphylococci, colon bacilli, etc.

or relatively large molecules of nucleoprotein (p. 366) on the border line between the living and the nonliving. They are of minute size, as compared with bacteria; most are invisible under the ordinary microscope and pass readily through a fine filter (*filtrable viruses*). Unlike bacteria, they cannot be grown apart from living cells. The intensely infective nature of these agents is evident from the fact that, in the case of one at least, the particular disease of which it is the cause can be transmitted by as small an amount as 1 cc of a solution containing it in a dilution of only 1 part in 10 billion.

It had been suggested by various medical scientists from time to time throughout the centuries, even in Roman days, that disease was caused by minute invisible particles carried in the air. But it remained for the French chemist, Louis Pasteur (1822–95) to demonstrate that many diseases were caused by living organisms which we now know as bacteria. Joseph Lister (later, Lord Lister, 1827–1912), an English surgeon, brought Pasteur's discoveries to bear upon the practice of surgery. He showed that if strict antiseptic methods were applied, wounds would remain surgically clean—that is, free from infection. The work of these pioneers has made possible the great advances in surgery that have marked the last 90 years or so.

But even before this, Ignaz Semmelweis (1818–65) of Vienna and Oliver Wendell Holmes in America showed clearly to unprejudiced minds, (of which there were few at that time) that puerperal fever (blood poisoning following childbirth) was caused by an invisible something carried to the patient on the hands and instruments of the attending physician; and that death from this disease, which in hospitals sometimes reached almost the proportions of a plague, could be greatly reduced by the use of antiseptics. See Figures 5.2, 5.3, 5.4, and 5.5.

Bacterial forms. The types of bacteria are innumerable, but fortunately only a small proportion cause disease. Also, only a relatively few kinds of fungi and Protozoa threaten man or animals. Several bacterial forms are actually beneficial to man and some are even essential for human welfare. Those, for example, which inhabit the intestinal tract effect the final breakdown of food material with the formation of gas which, together with the bulk by which the bacteria

---

This calls to mind Dean Swift's amusing little rhyme which was written at least 100 years before bacteria were discovered.

"So, naturalists observe, a flea
Hath smaller fleas that on him prey;
And these have smaller still to bite 'em;
And so proceed *ad infinitum*."

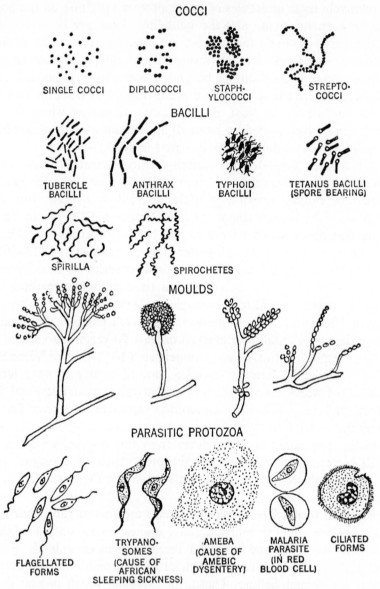

Fig. 5.1   Some pathogenic microorganisms.

themselves add to the feces, stimulate the bowel movements. Other bacterial types present in the intestine are capable of synthesizing several factors of the vitamin B complex, as well as vitamins C and K.[2]

[2] It sometimes happens that a patient receiving an antibacterial agent ("sulfa" drug or antibiotic, p. 221), especially when given by mouth, develops a deficiency in certain vitamin or vitamins as a result of the destruction of intestinal bacteria.

From others again, and from molds, anti-infective substances of various kinds have been isolated (see p. 221).

The commoner types of disease-producing (pathogenic) bacteria can be classified, on a basis of their microscopical appearances, into four main groups, *cocci* (*sing. coccus*), *bacilli* (sing. *bacillus*), *spirilla* (sing. *spirillum*), and *spirochetes* (see Fig. 5.1).

Fig. 5.2   Louis Pasteur.   Fig. 5.3   Joseph Lister.

The cocci are dotlike bodies (Gk. *kokkos,* a berry) which appear singly, in pairs (*Diplococci,* a species of which causes lobar pneumonia), in clumps like grapes (*Staphylococci*), or in chains (*Streptococci*). These last two types are the cause of acute pyogenic inflammatory conditions. One strain of streptococcus is the cause of scarlet fever.

The bacilli are rod-shaped organisms; examples of which are the *typhoid, tetanus,* and *diphtheria* bacilli and the *tubercle bacillus.*

Spirilla are slender organisms possessing a shape like the shaft of a corkscrew.

The spirochetes, one genus of which is the cause of syphilis, have a slender spiral structure.

The reactions of the tissues to infecting agents. A pathogenic organism or virus shows, as a rule, a highly selective action with respect to the tissue which it or its toxin injures, and the symptoms characteristic of the disease which it causes are the manifestations or the results of such injury, or represent the reaction of the tissue cells to invasion by the particular type of microorganism or virus. The toxin of the tetanus bacillus, for example, singles out nervous structures, lowering the "resistance" at synaptic junctions, so that a relatively

Fig. 5.4   Ignaz Semmelweis.   Fig. 5.5   Oliver Wendell Holmes.

mild stimulus—a mere touch, a faint sound, or a light—may cause widespread muscular responses. The viruses of rabies and anterior poliomyelitis also direct their attack to the central nervous system, the former injuring nerve centers in the brain, the latter destroying chiefly the motor cells of the spinal cord. The typhoid bacillus causes ulceration of the mucous membrane of the small intestine; the tubercle bacillus has a predilection chiefly for pulmonary, bone, and joint tissues (though almost any tissue may be attacked). The bacteria of general septic infections, the staphylococci and streptococci, show much less selectivity of action, for they may cause an inflammatory condition in any tissue (see also p. 92). The spirochete of syphilis is also devoid of selective action; skin, bone, nervous, or any other tissue may be attacked. The reactions of the tissues that it infects are, however, as are also those of the tubercle bacillus, quite characteristic. The infected tissues react to both of these types by attracting small round cells, mostly lymphocytes, which form masses around the invading organism. Thus a *tubercle* is formed in the case of tuber-culosis, or a tumorlike structure called a *gumma* if spirochetes of syph-ilis are the invading organisms.

The processes of immunity. The body is capable of putting up a de-fense which is, in part or entirely, successful against the inroads of most of the bacteria and viruses. The protection when it develops fully is called *immunity*. One who has suffered from an attack of small-pox, for example, cannot (except, perhaps, in the rarest instance) contract the disease again. With respect to that particular disease he is immune. Vaccination also confers immunity against smallpox.

The defenses of the body against the various disease-producing (pathogenic) organisms depend upon the activity of living cells. Cells, such as the neutrophil polymorphonuclear leucocytes and certain wan-dering cells of the reticulo-endothelial system, exert their protective action in an obvious, overt or, one might say, in a mechanical way; they ingest the bacteria. The phagocytic property of the neutrophil leucocytes has been already described in Chapter 3. The immunity which the leucocytes confer is not specific, for they attack various types of bacteria indiscriminately, though they are particularly active against the pus-producing (*pyogenic*) forms. Other cells of the body, espe-cially the lymphocytes in the lymphoid tissue, generally, through-out the body, produce and liberate chemical substances closely asso-ciated with the globulin of the plasma, which have a *specific* neutral-izing or destructive action upon the agent causing the disease. These substances, which go under the generic term of *antibodies,* are, as it were, made to order, each for protection against only one pathogenic agent. Thus the antibody which is responsible for immunity against smallpox is inactive against measles or any other infectious disease. There are several types of antibody—namely, *antitoxins*—which combine with and neutralize the bacterial poison, a substance gen-erally called a *toxin*. Others called *cytolysins* or *bacteriolysins* destroy the foreign cell itself; to this group belong the *specific hemolysins* (p. 84) which cause the destruction of the red cells of one species when injected into the blood of another. *Agglutinins* with which we are familiar (they were referred to in connection with the blood groups, p. 78) render bacteria innocuous by clumping them together in a mass. Agglutinins are produced in the blood of a patient suffering from typhoid fever. A test for the diagnosis of typhoid fever is based upon this fact; the serum of a patient with typhoid fever alone is cap-able of agglutinating a suspension of typhoid bacilli. Other antibodies, known as *precipitins,* form an insoluble compound with the bacterial toxin and with foreign proteins.[3]

The foreign agent—whether a red cell in incompatible blood, a tissue cell of another species, a bacterial cell, or a virus, which stimulates the tissue cells of the *host* (i.e., of the infected person or animal) to produce the antibody—is called an *antigen* (*anti* [body] + Gk. root *gen,* to form or produce). The response of the tissues of the host to the antigen and the production of the antibody, together with the reaction between the two, is called the *antibody-antigen reaction.* Paul

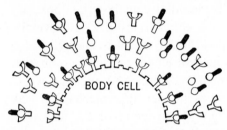

Fig. 5.6   Diagram illustrating the production of antitoxin according to Ehrlich's side-chain theory. ♀ = toxin, *black,* toxophore group; *blank circle,* haptophore group; ⋎ = receptors or haptins of body cell which join with the haptophore group of the toxin and through which the latter exerts its harmful effect upon the cell. Under the stimulus of the toxin (antigen), receptors are produced in excess and, escaping into the general blood stream, constitute the antitoxin.

Ehrlich of Berlin (1854–1915) many years ago sought to explain this reaction and the immunity which it conferred by what has come to be known as Ehrlich's *side-chain theory* of immunity (see Figs. 5.6 and 5.7). Thus, in the case of immunity due to an antitoxin, he conceived that the protoplasm of the tissue cells, stimulated by the antigen, formed and put forth active chemical groups, or side-chains, called *receptors* or *haptins;* these combined with the bacterial toxin, and, being thus linked to the tissue cells, brought about the injury characteristic of the disease. But the tissue cells produced an excess of such receptors which, becoming detached, passed into the general circulation where they combined with toxin before it could reach and damage the cells. These free receptors constituted the antitoxin. The same conception could be made to embrace other types of antibody. Ehrlich suggested that the toxin molecule possessed two active chemical groups; one, known as the *toxophore* group, was responsible for its injurious action. The other, called the *haptophore* group, united

[3] A delicate and specific test for human blood in medico-legal (murder) cases is based on the precipitin reaction. A rabbit is given a series of injections of a solution of human blood or serum. When the serum of the rabbit, which as a result of the injections has developed a precipitin active against human serum, is added to a specimen of the suspected blood (e.g., from stains on clothing, a presumed weapon, etc.) dissolved in a test tube, a slight cloudy precipitate appears if the material in question is human blood. If it is the blood of an animal, the solution remains clear.

with the cell receptor or haptin, and thus enabled the toxin to bring its action to bear upon the tissue cell.

Three types of immunity are recognized: *natural, active,* and *passive. Natural immunity,* also called inborn or innate, is that which has not been acquired by a previous attack of the disease, or in any other way. Thus, we are naturally immune to some diseases which afflict animals, and they possess a natural immunity to a great many human

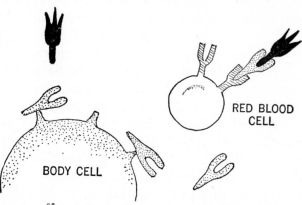

Fig. 5.7 Diagram illustrating the production and action of specific cytolysins, hemolysins, bacteriolysins, etc. According to Ehrlich's theory a substance destroyed by heat and called the *complement* (Ψ) is present in nearly all normal sera. It becomes joined to the receptor (Ψ) of the foreign cell by means of another substance called the *amboceptor* (Ψ), *intermediary,* or *immune body.* When this union takes place the foreign cell is destroyed. The amboceptor, which is not destroyed by heat, is produced by the body cells of the animal receiving the injection of antigen—e.g., foreign cells bacteria, blood cells, or tissue cells of another species; it is specific, having a destructive action only upon the kind of cells which were injected. The complement is nonspecific; its nonspecificity can be demonstrated in the following way. When the immune serum is heated, the complement but not the amboceptor is destroyed and the serum loses its cytolytic action; this is immediately restored, however, by adding *any* normal serum.

diseases—for example, measles and typhoid fever, to mention only two. Many persons appear to be naturally immune to anterior poliomyelitis, and to some other human diseases.

Active immunity is that which has been developed as a result of the activity of the body's own cells, as when a person has recovered from an attack of an infectious disease, or has had the antigen administered by injection as explained below.

Immunity produced by the injection of an antibody—e.g., diphtheria antitoxin—formed in the body of an animal or of another person is called *passive.* Diphtheria antitoxin, for example, is produced by the horse into which the toxin (antigen) of diphtheria has been injected. Serum from such animals is employed in treating diphtheria in patients suffering from this disease. In a similar way, serum from patients who have recently recovered from a disease—such as measles, scarlet fever, or anterior poliomyelitis—is used to immunize passively another person suffering from the same disease.

It is not always easy to say whether a person who has been exposed to some infection or other, but does not "catch" it, is *naturally* immune to the disease or has been actively immunized against it by having at some time previously contracted it in such a mild form that it was not recognized. An apparently natural immunity probably occurs in this way to the virus of anterior poliomyelitis and to the typhoid bacillus.

Active immunity may be conferred artificially in order to prevent persons from contracting a disease should they be exposed to it. They are injected (*inoculated*) with an emulsion of bacteria which have been killed by heat or chemical means. The toxin is not destroyed, and it is the essential antigenic substance. Such preparations of dead bacteria are called *vaccines*. This method of immunization is employed against typhoid fever and infections with pyogenic organisms. Other methods of vaccination are practiced for protection against the viruses of smallpox, anterior poliomyelitis, and rabies. Immunization against smallpox is carried out by infecting the subject with a mild form of the disease known as cowpox.[4] The lymph of calves which have been inoculated with the disease is pricked or lightly scratched into the subject's skin. In the case of rabies (hydrophobia), the victim of the disease is inoculated with a solution of the virus which has been weakened by drying and aging. Finally, the toxin of the causative organism—e.g., that of diphtheria or of tetanus (lockjaw)—may be rendered nontoxic by chemical treatment without destroying its antigenic properties—that is, its ability to stimulate anti-

[4] Vaccination against smallpox has a long history; it was practiced in Eastern countries, especially China and India, many hundreds of years ago. The method employed before Jenner was a rather dangerous procedure. But considering the terrible ravages of smallpox, it was justified. In this old method, the person whom it was desired to protect against smallpox was inoculated with a little material (usually first dried) from a pustule of a patient recovering from the disease. The virus, being in a weakened state, caused, except rarely, a mild form of the disease in the inoculated person. This method was introduced into England in the eighteenth century. Edward Jenner, an English physician, originated the modern method of vaccination against smallpox in 1796. The idea came to him from the remark of a milkmaid, " I cannot take the smallpox for I have already had the cowpox." The truth of this statement was known generally among the country people of the district. Jenner accordingly inoculated a boy of 8 years, named James Phipps, with pus from the hand of a dairymaid infected with cowpox. Cowpox, though allied to smallpox, is a quite mild disease. Two months later Jenner inoculated the boy with virulent smallpox virus. This, the crucial test, proved the efficacy of vaccination; Phipps did not contract smallpox. An outstanding example of the value of vaccination against smallpox is afforded by the statistics of the Franco-Prussian War (1870). In the Prussian Army but not in the French, vaccination was practiced. Only a few Prussian soldiers died of smallpox, but several thousand French soldiers succumbed to the disease.

body production. In other words, according to Ehrlich's theory, the toxophore groups but not the haptaphore groups of the toxin are destroyed. Immunizing agents prepared in this way are called *toxoids*. By the administration of diphtheria toxoid of young children, deaths from diphtheria, which used to run into high figures annually, have been reduced almost to the vanishing point.

Another immunizing procedure, especially against measles and infectious hepatitis, is the administration of gamma globulin (pp. 58 and 101).

Pain and rest. The pain and temporary loss of function of an inflamed or injured part are definitely protective provisions. Though we may think that pain has been imposed upon us by a malicious nature and could be dispensed with, we would soon be destroyed were it not for the warning which it gives of injury or of a threat of injury. In a certain nervous disease affecting the sensory fibers in the spinal cord which carry impulses giving rise to the sensation of pain and temperature from the hands, the patient is continually damaging his fingers; sores develop from such injuries, which are neglected because they cause no discomfort. It is also true that the most potent stimulus for evoking a protective reflex, such as jerking the hand away from a hot object, is a painful one. In the case of the eye, the winking reflex which shields the eye is extremely sensitive. Even the sight of an approaching object which might injure the eye will elicit the reflex; a stimulus applied to the cornea, the anterior surface of the eye which, if directed to any other part of the body surface would result in nothing more than a mild sensation of touch, when applied to the eye instantly causes a reflex closure of the eyelid. The cornea is richly supplied with pain fibers which have a very low threshold; almost any stimulus, except the very blandest such as a gentle jet of warm water, if it gives rise to any sensation at all, causes pain.

Of an importance as a protective device, nearly as great as that of pain, is the suspension of function in an injured structure. Rest, whether of a broken bone or a lung, enables the *healing power of nature* (*vis medicatrix naturae*) to exert most effectively its beneficent action. In some instances, such as in pulmonary tuberculosis where one lung is solely or predominantly affected, man, by artifice, does what nature cannot or fails to do. The severely damaged lung is immobilized—that is, put at rest by collapsing it (as by the injection of air into the pleural cavity of that side) or by cutting one phrenic nerve, and thus paralyzing the corresponding half of the diaphragm. So, also, a broken bone is immobilized by putting it in splints, and inflamed eyes are protected by a bandage or dark glasses (though some natural protection is afforded by contraction of the pupil and closure of the eyelids). Pain, of course, not only serves to warn and protect, but forces a part to be put at rest.

A recapitulation of protective mechanisms described elsewhere. There are a number of other defensive measures which the body can take against the variety of adverse conditions and dangers occurring in an ever-changing environment. Among such provisions of nature, most of which have been or will be dealt with elsewhere in this book, are: the coagulation of the blood and the other reactions which tend to ensure against fatal hemorrhage (pp. 102 and 76); the protection against a general blood infection afforded by the lymph nodes; the cilia and mucus of the upper respiratory passages as well as the cough reflex which serves to prevent the entrance of foreign material into the finer airways of the lungs (p. 258); and the reactions of the sympatho-adrenal system (pp. 424 and 564).

Finally, it should be mentioned that in order for the various safeguards to serve their purposes most effectively, since they are manifestations of living cells, all physiological processes must be maintained in states of prime efficiency. Unless this is so, the normal biochemical balance of the internal environment (Homeostasis, p. 53) is not secured. When the general health is undermined, a way is opened for invasion by pathogenic microorganisms. Diabetic patients, for example, are especially susceptible to infection; victims of this malady, and of nephritis and other general diseases, are often carried off, not directly by the disease itself, but by some "intercurrent infection" such as pneumonia or a septic condition.

Chemotherapy. This is the treatment of disease by the administration of a chemical compound, in many instances synthetic, by means of which the causative microorganisms are destroyed within the body of the patient, or their multiplication arrested. The science of chemotherapy has made enormous strides within the last 15 or 20 years. The aim of the investigator in this field is to prepare a chemical compound that acts selectively against one or more types of pathogenic organism, but, in the dosage used, exerts little or no toxic action upon the patient.

Paul Ehrlich, the founder of the science of chemotherapy, introduced some forty years ago an arsenical compound having a destructive action upon the spirochetes of syphilis. It was named *Salvarsan* or arsphenamine. It was also commonly known as "606" (six-o-six) because it was the last of a long series of compounds (presumably

606) which had been experimented with in the search of a cure for syphilis. Several compounds of arsenic and antimony have since been synthesized which are active against the protozoan organisms of malaria, African sleeping sickness, and other tropical diseases.

The "sulfa" drugs. In 1928, it was discovered by Dr. Domagk, a German scientist, that *prontosil,* a red dye, when administered to mice enabled them to withstand an injection of patheogenic bacteria that was ordinarily lethal. It was found later that a chemical group containing sulfur was the active antibacterial agent. This compound was prepared separately; it is colorless and known as sulfanilamide. The use of this drug and its derivatives—the so-called *"sulfa"* or *sulfonamide drugs*—has opened up a fresh vista in chemotherapy. Several bacterial diseases from which the death rate was extremely high have been treated with these compounds with spectacular success. A large number of derivatives of sulfanilamide have been synthesized, such as *sulfapyridine, sulfathiazole, sulfacetamide,* and *sulfadiazine,* to mention those in most common use. The sulfonamides are not equally active against different bacterial forms. One drug may be active against one group of bacteria but may fail against another group.

Antibacterial agents such as the "sulfa" drugs do not kill the bacteria, like antiseptics or other chemicals such as the arsenical compounds. *They prevent the bacteria from multiplying.* They are *bacteriostatic* [5] (L. *statos,* standing) rather than *bacteriocidal* (L. *caedo,* I kill).

Antibiotics. An entirely new class of highly effective antibacterial agents has been discovered within recent years. These substances, known as *antibiotics,* are obtained from other living organisms, especially fungi, molds, and bacteria. It was through a happy accident and alert observation that the first of these principles was discovered. In 1929, Dr. (later Sir) Alexander Fleming, an English bacteriologist, noticed that the growth of a culture of staphylococci, which had been exposed to the air of the room, was arrested in the neighborhood of the growth of a mold that had fallen upon the same culture plate. He suggested that the mold had produced a substance inimical to the bacteria. Dr. (later Sir) H. Florey and his associates at Oxford instituted a series of experiments during World War II which re-

[5] The mode of action of sulfanilamide is believed to be as follows. A factor of the vitamin B complex, para-aminobenzoic acid, is an essential requirement for some enzyme system in the bacterial cell. Owing to the similarity of their chemical structures, the "sulfa" drug and the vitamin compete for inclusion in the enzyme system. When the drug is taken up by the latter, the entrance of the vitamin into the system is "blocked." The enzyme is thus rendered inactive, and the bacteria are unable to multiply.

sulted in the isolation of the antibacterial principle from the mold. The mold had previously been identified as *Penicillium notatum;* the active principle was, therefore, called *penicillin.* Both Fleming and Florey received the Nobel Prize in 1945.

A number of antibiotic principles have since then been isolated from various molds and bacteria. The most valuable of these agents are *streptomycin, terramycin,*[6] *aureomycin,* and *tyrothricin.* Streptomycin is obtained from the funguslike bacteria, *Streptomyces;* it is active against the tubercle bacillus and a number of other pathogenic bacteria. Aureomycin is furnished by another species of *Streptomyces;* it is active against some virus infections and several types of bacteria. Tyrothricin is derived from a bacterial form found in milk and soil; it is especially valuable for local application in staphylococcic and streptococcic infections of the skin. Most of the antibiotics are bacteriostatic in their action, but some are also bacteriocidal. Others are active against pathogenic fungi.

Pathogenic organisms show a remarkable adaptability to the action of various agents employed against them. They tend to become gradually resistant and can then tolerate larger doses of the antibacterial substance. When this occurs, the physician's strategy, when feasible, is to attack with some other antibacterial substance. Another person may become infected with the resistant bacteria. When, for example, infection is derived from a patient with tuberculosis treated with streptomycin, the effectiveness of this valuable drug, in so far as the second infected person is concerned, is greatly reduced.

Shock

Shock is a term which has been given to a number of different conditions associated with a state of prostration or collapse. A variety of qualifying words is used to distinguish the several, often unrelated, states to which the term shock has been applied. *Primary* or *nervous shock, secondary* or *traumatic shock, anaphylactic shock, hemorrhagic shock, shell shock, spinal shock,* and *insulin shock* are a partial list of such states. Two severe types of shock—secondary or traumatic shock and anaphylactic shock—will be described.

[6] Terramycin and aureomycin are also known as *oxytetracycline* and *chlortetracycline,* respectively. Since the isolation and great success of penicillin, the most intensive search for other antibiotics has been instituted; besides the four mentioned above, a host of new ones have been isolated. Some of these have proved of great value—e.g., *erythromycin, chloromycetin, bacitracin, carbomycin,* etc.—while others are not very active or are too toxic for use.

Secondary or traumatic shock. Immediately following a severe wound, the subject is weak and feels faint and may pass into a state of collapse as a result of pain, fright, apprehension, or other emotion. This state immediately following an injury is known as *primary* or *nervous* shock. It is of comparatively small physiological interest and does not end fatally in a previously healthy person. If the wound is of moderate severity, the subject's condition improves after a period of rest and appropriate treatment. If, on the other hand, the injury is very severe—especially if much blood has been lost—the wounded person gradually sinks into a condition of great weakness with falling blood pressure. This state of extreme prostration which becomes most profound in from 3 to 5 hours following the injury is known as *secondary* or *traumatic* shock. It is also known as *deferred, wound,* or *surgical* shock. The chief features of traumatic shock are associated with failure of the peripheral circulation—very low blood pressure, constriction of the arterioles with dilatation of the capillaries. There is usually also a loss of plasma from the circulation into the tissues, with a resulting concentration of the blood in red cells, and a reduction of the total volume of blood in the circulation. The patient usually remains conscious but is extremely weak and listless, with a cold clammy skin and a thin faint pulse. Shock has been the subject of intensive research, especially during the two world wars, but the underlying cause leading to its development has not been entirely revealed. Many believe that it is due simply to a reduction in blood volume, either as a result of the loss of plasma into the tissues at the site of the injury or to hemorrhage. Others maintain that some other factor, as well—probably a blood-pressure lowering principle produced by the liver and discharged into the circulation—is responsible for the profound fall in blood pressure.

The only treatment which is of any avail in shock is the transfusion of plasma or of blood, but all too frequently even this fails to save the patient.

Anaphylaxis, anaphylactic shock. If an animal is given an injection of a foreign protein—such as serum albumin of another species—and after a period of 10 days or more is given a second injection of the same protein, a sudden and great fall in the injected animal's blood pressure results. Death usually occurs within a few minutes. The first injection of protein is said to "sensitize" the animal to the second injection which may be only a very minute quantity. The foreign protein acts as an antigen (sometimes called specifically the *anaphylactogen*) causing the body cells, in the interval between the two injections, to produce an antibody (p. 215), which reacts in some way with the second dose of protein. The precise nature of this antigen-antibody reaction and its relation to anaphylactic shock are not altogether clear, but it is generally believed that it is associated with the liberation of histamine (an amine derived by the loss of carbon dioxide from the amino acid histidine) and that this amine or a closely similar substance is responsible for the effects. The anaphylactic reaction shows pronounced species differences with respect to the tissues upon which the effects are manifested. In the dog, for example, the chief anaphylactic effects, apart from the fall in blood pressure, are upon the liver and alimentary tract; there are vomiting, diarrhea, and engorgement of the vessels of the liver, stomach, and intestines. In the guinea pig, spasm of the smooth muscle of the bronchioles occurs, and the animal dies in asphyxia. The subcutaneous injection of antigen into a rabbit causes a severe tissue reaction at the site of the injection where an abscess forms and death of tissue ultimately occurs. If this animal receives the second dose of protein intravenously, circulatory failure results and the animal passes into a state resembling traumatic shock. Most of the effects enumerated, as well as the species differences, can be induced by injections of histamine, which strengthens the belief, though does not absolutely prove, that histamine liberation is the cause of the anaphylactic manifestations. Histamine can be extracted from normal tissues, but it exists apparently in some innocuous form. Large amounts are found in the blood of the dog when anaphylactic shock supervenes, and in the blood and lungs of the guinea pig. The mechanism which causes the liberation or accumulation of histamine in these tissues in anaphylactic shock is unknown.

In man, death from anaphylactic shock has occurred on several occasions as a result of the injection of foreign serum (horse or bovine) for therapeutic purposes, as in the treatment of diphtheria or tetanus, the patient having been sensitized by the injection of serum at some time previously. Milder reactions of an anaphylactoid nature, such as skin rashes, vomiting, or circulatory disturbances, are not very uncommon following the injection of foreign serum and are spoken of as "serum sickness."

Allergic conditions—such as hay fever (from the inhalation of pollen dust), gastrointestinal upsets, rashes, etc., caused by eating certain foods by susceptible persons—are anaphylactoid in nature. Essentially similar mechanisms are involved.

CHAPTER 6

Respiration

All living things, with a few exceptions, absorb oxygen. The oxygen combines with the carbon and hydrogen furnished by food material. Carbon dioxide (CO_2) and water (H_2O) are produced. These oxidations take place in the cells of the tissues; they generate heat and furnish the organism with energy for the performance of work (see Chap. 9). The carbon dioxide, so formed, is eliminated; the oxidation of the hydrogen constitutes an important source of body water (the water of metabolism). The exchange of gases (O_2 and CO_2) between an organism and its environment is termed *respiration*.

In unicellular organisms and many multicellular forms of lower orders, the gaseous exchange takes place directly between the cells and their surroundings (see Fig. 6.1). Higher forms of animal life are composed of cells of which the great mass are removed from direct contact with the external environment. But the cells of such higher forms, like those of the most primitive, are bathed in fluid. This tissue fluid we

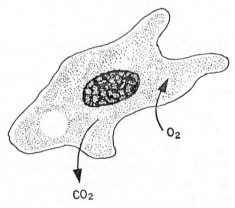

Fig. 6.1 Respiration of a unicellular organism (e.g., an amoeba).

may speak of as the *internal environment;* from it the cells absorb oxygen (as well as nutriment) and into it the cells discharge their waste materials, including carbon dioxide (Fig. 6.2). Through the medium of the blood-vascular system, oxygen is transported from the external to the internal environment; thus a steady supply of oxygen to

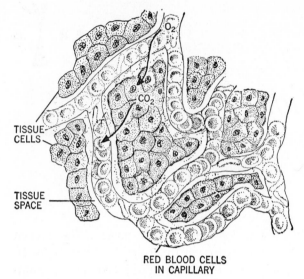

TISSUE CELLS

TISSUE SPACE

RED BLOOD CELLS
IN CAPILLARY

Fig. 6.2   Illustrating internal respiration. Capillary shown filled with red cells.

the cells is secured. By the same means, carbon dioxide is carried from the tissue fluids. In air-breathing animals, the exchange of gases between the blood and the external environment takes place in the lungs. This is called *external respiration*. In fish, it is a function of the gills. The exchange of gases between the tissue cells and their fluid environment is termed *internal respiration*.

An Outline of the Structure of the Respiratory Organs

The air passages. These are the *nasal cavities,* the *pharynx, larynx, trachea, bronchi,* and *bronchioles* (see Figs. 6.3 and 6.4). The interior of the nose is divided into two lateral halves by the nasal septum. From the lateral wall of each nasal cavity spring three spurs of bone called, respectively, the *inferior, middle,* and *superior turbinates* (or *conchae*). These incompletely divide each side of the nose into three passages (the meatuses of the nose). Situated between the superior turbinate bone and the floor of the skull is a small recess containing the olfactory epithelium (Chap. 13). The main air currents do not enter this recess, the meatuses of the nose alone serving as airways. The meatuses are lined with ciliated epithelium; the movements of the cilia are toward the exterior; thus mucus and dust, or any other foreign particles that may enter the nasal passages in the inspired air, are carried to the nostrils.

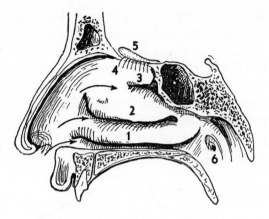

Fig. 6.3   The inner surface of the outer wall of the nose. 1, inferior concha (turbinate); 2, middle concha; 3, superior concha; 4, olfactory nerves; 5, olfactory bulb; 6, opening of auditory (Eustachian) tube. The arrows indicate the course taken by the air in breathing.

The nasal cavities open posteriorly into the *pharynx* which, therefore, serves as a common passage for the transmission of air to the larynx, and of food from the mouth to the esophagus. During swallowing, the food has the right of way, the respirations being then for a moment arrested.

The larynx. The larynx is situated in the neck in front of the lower part of the pharynx and at the commencement of the trachea or windpipe. It contains the vocal cords, and will be described more fully later.

The trachea and bronchi. The human trachea is a tube about $\frac{3}{5}$ inch in diameter and 4 inches long, extending from the larynx to a little

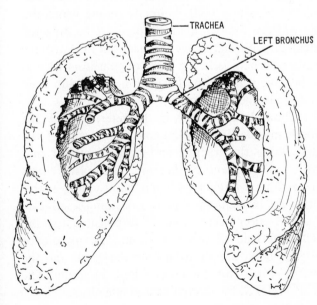

Fig. 6.4   Showing trachea and bronchi. Portion of the lung tissue removed to show branchings of the bronchial tree.

below the upper boundary of the chest; here it divides into two branches—the *right* and *left bronchi*. Each bronchus enters the corresponding lung and divides, like the limbs of a tree, into a number of smaller branches. The larger of these are also called bronchi, but the finer terminal twigs are referred to as *bronchioles*. It is, of course, imperative that this important airway always be kept open. The patency of the trachea is ensured by the presence of a series of C-shaped rings of cartilage which support its wall in front and at the sides. The gaps in the cartilages posteriorly, as well as the intervals

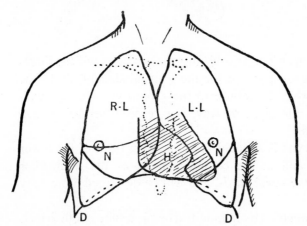

Fig. 6.5 Showing the lungs in relation to the heart and chest wall. R.L, right lung; L.L, left lung; H, heart; N, nipple; D, dome of the dia-phragm.

between them, are bridged by a strong fibroelastic membrane. The trachea is lined by ciliated columnar epithelial cells among which are many goblet cells. The walls of the two main bronchi are constructed upon a plan almost identical with that of the trachea, but the cartilage in the walls of the smaller bronchi is in the form of thin isolated and irregular plates which become smaller and fewer in number with each successive branching of the bronchial tree.

The bronchioles are about 1 mm or less in diameter. Their walls are composed of smooth muscle lined by mucous membrane of the same character as that lining the trachea and bronchi except that goblet cells are absent. Cartilage is entirely lacking. The muscle fibers of the bronchioles are arranged circularly. Their contraction, therefore, causes narrowing of the bronchiolar lumen. In asthmatic attacks, marked bronchiolar constriction occurs and is responsible for the respiratory distress characteristic of this condition. The muscle of the bronchioles receives its nerve supply from both the vagus and the sympathetic; the former is constrictor, the latter dilator in action. The bronchiolar muscle is also relaxed by adrenaline and ephedrine.

The lungs. The left lung is divided by a fissure into two lobes, an upper and a lower (see Fig. 6.5). Two fissures divide the right lung into three lobes. The bronchi and all but the very finest bronchioles possess no truly respiratory function; no interchange of gases can

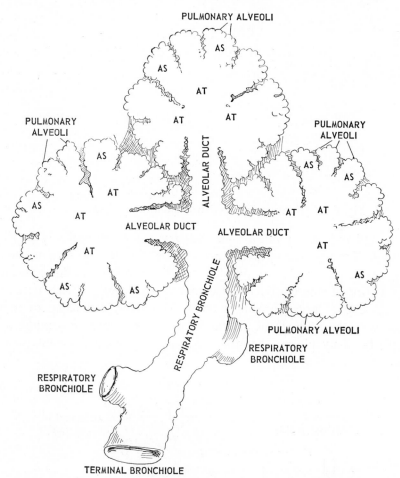

Fig. 6.6   Diagram of a lung unit. AT, atrium; AS, air sac.

occur across their relatively thick walls. They serve merely as airways.

The lung tissue proper consists of an immense number of *air spaces* arranged in clusters. Each cluster is called a *lung unit.* Each of the terminal twigs of the nonrespiratory part of the bronchial tree (*terminal bronchioles*) opens into a lung unit. One of the latter with its several named parts—*respiratory bronchiole, alveolar ducts, air*

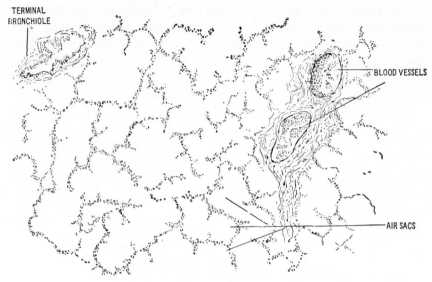

Fig. 6.7   Microscopical section of pulmonary tissue.

sacs, and *pulmonary alveoli*—is illustrated diagrammatically in Figure 6.6. The pulmonary alveoli are seen as from four to six outpouchings of the cavity of each alveolar sac. A single layer of flat cells and a network of fine elastic fibers compose their walls; a rich network of blood capillaries surrounds them. Moreover, according to most observers, the walls of the alveoli are incomplete and show numerous gaps. In many places, therefore, the capillary wall alone intervenes

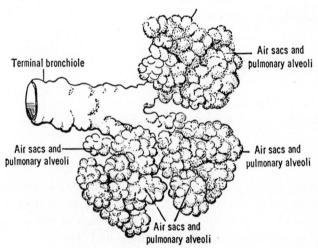

Fig. 6.8   Model of a lung unit.

between the blood and the alveolar air. Thus the blood as it flows through the lungs is separated from the air in the alveoli by, at the most, two membranes—the alveolar and capillary walls—so extremely thin that little hindrance is offered to the free exchange of the respiratory gases. The number of pulmonary alveoli in both lungs has been estimated to be about 750,000,000.

A microscopical section of pulmonary tissue is shown in Figure 6.7, and a model of three lung units in Figure 6.8.

The Mechanics of Respiration

The chest or thorax is a closed cavity, bounded *laterally* and *behind* by the ribs and the vertebral column; *in front* by the ribs and sternum (breast bone); *below* by a dome-shaped sheet of muscle (the diaphragm), which separates it from the abdominal cavity; and *above* by the upper ribs and the tissues of the neck. The lungs, heart, and great blood vessels almost completely fill the thorax.

The lungs are covered by a thin membrane called the *pleura,* which passes from each lung at its root (i.e., at the point where the main bronchus and pulmonary vessels enter it) on to the interior of the chest wall and upper surface of the diaphragm. Thus, two membranous sacs, called the *pleural cavities,* are produced, one on each side of the chest, between the lungs and the thoracic boundaries. Since the pleura covering the lung and that lining the chest are in contact under all conditions of health, no actual space exists; these so-called cavities are potential ones only. In disease, however, air, fluid, or blood may collect and separate the pleural layers to produce an actual space.

The part of the pleural membrane lining the thoracic wall is called the *parietal* pleura (L. *paries,* gen. *parietis,* a wall), while that portion covering and firmly adherent to the surface of the lungs themselves is called the *pulmonary* or *visceral* pleura. Inflammation of the pleura is called *pleurisy*. The inflammatory process may cause the production of little or no fluid—*dry pleurisy*—or may be accompanied by the exudation of a considerable amount of clear fluid— *pleurisy with effusion*. If the fluid becomes purulent, the condition is called *empyema*.

The central part of the thoracic cavity lying between the lungs, and bounded in front by the sternum and behind by the vertebral column, is known as the *mediastinum*. It is divided for the purpose of description into an upper and a lower part, called the *superior* and the *in-*

ferior mediastinum, respectively. The latter consists of three parts—
anterior, middle, and *posterior mediastina.* The middle mediastinum
contains the heart, enclosed in the pericardium, and the commencement of the aorta. The division of the trachea into the right and left
bronchi is contained in the posterior mediastinum. The anterior mediastinum, in front of the heart, is almost obliterated by the approximation of the two pleural sacs. It contains only a little areolar tissue
and two or three lymph nodes.

The intrapleural pressure. The pressure between the layers of the
pleura (*intrapleural pressure*), and indeed throughout the thorax

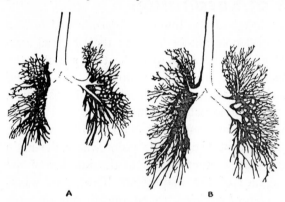

Fig. 6.9 Tracing from
x-ray photograph demon-
strating the elasticity of
the bronchial tree. A, full
expiration; B, full inspiration. (After Macklin.)

A   B

generally (*intrathoracic pressure*), is below that of the atmosphere.
This subatmospheric or so-called negative pressure is due to the elasticity of the lungs. Before birth the lungs are airless, the air sacs are
of small size and contain a little fluid. The thoracic cavity is filled by
the almost solid lungs, the heart, and great vessels. The pressures
within the pleural cavities and in the interior of the lungs are equal.
With the first breath after birth, the thorax is expanded in all its diameters. This reduces the pressure within the thorax—that is, on the
pleural aspects of the lungs—and tends to reduce the pressure within
the air sacs (*intrapulmonary pressure*). The air sacs, however, are in
communication with the outside air through the air passages. Atmospheric air, therefore, enters the lungs to equalize the pressure, and,
were the lung tissue inelastic, equalization of pressure between the
atmosphere and the pleural cavities would also result. But the bronchial tree and the lung substance itself are richly supplied with elastic
tissue. When the lungs expand and fill the enlarged thoracic cavity,
the elastic tissue is stretched. The lungs in postnatal life are, therefore, constantly under tension with a tendency to recoil to their original dimensions. This pull of the elastic lungs away from the thoracic

walls, though it cannot separate the layers of the pleura, creates a "negative" pressure.

Throughout life the intrapleural pressure undergoes rhythmical variations with the respiratory movements as a result of changes in the thoracic dimensions and the consequent variations in the degree of stretching to which the lungs are subjected (see Fig. 6.9). The intrapleural (or intrathoracic) pressure is around −6 mm Hg during inspiration and −2.5 mm during expiration. The importance of the

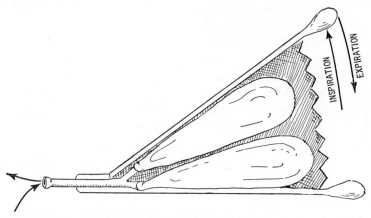

Fig. 6.10   (Description in text.)

subatmospheric pressure within the thorax in aiding the return of venous blood to the heart has been pointed out (p. 153).

The respiratory movements–the intake and expulsion of air. The drawing of air into the lungs is called *inspiration,* and its expulsion *expiration.* The capacity of the thorax is enlarged during inspiration and reduced during expiration. These two movements alternate rhythmically at a frequency, in the adult, of from 18 to 20 per minute. The rate is more rapid in infants and young children.

At the end of expiration, the pressure of air within the lungs (*intrapulmonary pressure*) equals or nearly equals the atmospheric pressure. The inspiratory movement, as mentioned above, reduces the pressure upon the pleural surfaces of the lung. The air sacs are dilated thereby and the air within them is rarefied—i.e., reduced below that of the atmosphere. Air, therefore, flows into the lungs until the intrapulmonary pressure again almost equals that of the atmosphere. During expiration the intrapleural "negative" pressure is reduced, the air sacs return to their previous dimensions, and the intrapulmonary pressure rises above that of the atmosphere; air is therefore expelled from the lungs.

It should be emphasized that the lungs play a purely passive role in the respiratory movements. The changes in volume which they undergo, and to which the intake and expulsion of air are directly due, are brought about solely through changes in the capacity of the thoracic cavity. The inspiratory and expiratory movements of the thorax may be compared to the opening and closing of a fire bellows. A pair of bellows, which may be taken to represent the thorax, is shown in Figure 6.10. Two elastic bags, contained within it and communicating with the outside air through the nozzle, correspond to the lungs and air passages. The space surrounding the bags is hermetically sealed and corresponds to the pleural cavities. Opening the bellows ("inspiration") causes the bags to expand and fill with air; closure of the bellows ("expiration") to the stop S causes their partial deflation. Since the bags, like the lungs, are made of elastic material, they are always tending to recoil against the distending force. This "pull," as between the layers of the pleura (i.e., in the pleural cavity), produces a "negative" pressure between the bags and the walls of the bellows.

Having outlined the general principles underlying the ventilation of the lungs, the muscular mechanisms whereby the changes in thoracic capacity are brought about will now be described.

The enlargement of the thorax during inspiration. All diameters— vertical, anteroposterior, and transverse—are increased during the

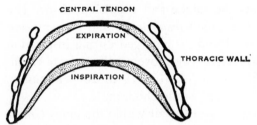

CENTRAL TENDON

EXPIRATION

THORACIC WALL

INSPIRATION

Fig. 6.11   Showing position of the diaphragm at the end of a full inspiration and a full expiration, respectively.

inspiratory phase. Increase in the vertical diameter of the thorax is brought about by the descent of the *diaphragm*. This is an arched tendomuscular sheet which separates the thorax from the abdominal cavity. The muscle fibers arise from the spinal column and lower ribs and, arching upward and inward, are inserted into a central leaf-shaped tendon. This tendon forms the highest part or dome of the diaphragm and is called the *central tendon of the diaphragm* (Fig.

6.11). The central tendon of the diaphragm blends with the under surface of the pericardium; on either side of the pericardium the diaphragm is in contact with the bases of the lungs. When the muscular fibers of the diaphragm contract, the structure shows little change in shape, but is seen under the x-rays to move downward as a whole very much like the stroke of a piston (Fig. 6.11). The diaphragm is the most important muscle of respiration, about 60 percent of the volume of the air respired being due to its action.

During inspiration the thorax is enlarged in its anteroposterior diameter by the movement, into a more horizontal position, of the third, fourth, fifth, and sixth pairs of ribs, which at the end of ex-

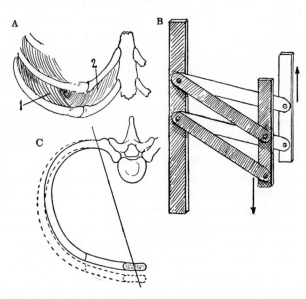

Fig. 6.12   A, fourth and fifth ribs and section of sternum. 1, external intercostal muscles; 2, internal intercostals; B, diagram illustrating the action of the external intercostals. C, showing axis of rotation of ribs in bucket-handle movement.

piration slope obliquely downward and forward (Fig. 6.12 A and B.) This movement is brought about by the contraction of the external intercostal muscles. The fibers of the latter take a slanting direction across the intercostal space from the lower border of one rib downward and forward to the upper border of the next rib below. When the external intercostal muscles contract, the anterior ends of the four pairs of ribs are elevated and the sternum thrust forward and upward. Any downward pull which the contracting external intercostal muscles exert upon the upper of two adjacent ribs is antagonized by the upward pull of certain muscles of the neck (*scalenus muscles*) which are inserted into the first and second ribs. Thus the upper of any two adjacent ribs serves as a fixed point for the intercostal fibers, so that, when they contract, the lower rib of each pair is raised anteriorly and assumes a more horizontal position.

The part of the thorax bounded by the seventh, eighth, ninth, and tenth ribs is increased in its transverse diameter by rotation of these ribs around an axis directed from the sternum obliquely backward and a little outward (Fig. 6.12 C). At the end of expiration these ribs are bowed outward and downward, and their movement during inspiration has been compared to raising a bucket handle from its position of rest toward the horizontal plane (Fig. 6.13).

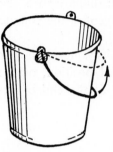

Fig. 6.13   Illustrating   bucket-handle movement of lower ribs.

Expiration. This phase is effected mainly in a passive manner in quiet normal breathing. At the end of the inspiratory phase, the external intercostal muscles and the diaphragm relax. The walls of the thorax, by virtue of their own weight and their inherent elasticity, together with the pull exerted by the recoil of the elastic lungs and bronchi (see Fig. 6.9), return to their original (preinspiratory) position. The relaxed diaphram ascends, being drawn up by the "negative" intrathoracic pressure and also by the elastic recoil of the lungs.

Accessory muscles of respiration. In forced or difficult breathing, certain muscles come into play to facilitate the respiratory movements; in *inspiration,* the nostrils and the opening between the vocal cords (glottis) are enlarged by muscular action, thus permitting a freer entrance of air into the lungs. The muscles of the neck (*anterior* and *middle scalenus* muscles and the *sternomastoids*) contract and raise the first rib, lifting the sternum upward and forward, and increasing the inspiratory movement of the succeeding ribs. Thus the capacity of the thorax is materially increased. During a forced or difficult *expiration,* the abdominal muscles contract and, increasing the intra-abdominal pressure, aid in the ascent of the diaphragm. The internal intercostal muscles exert a weak expiratory action; their fibers run in a direction the reverse of that of the external intercostals; their contraction depresses the ribs. Thus, expiration becomes a more active movement than normal.

Artificial respiration. When the respiratory mechanism has failed, as in the apparently drowned or as a result of carbon monoxide poisoning, electrocution, or other cause, some artificial means must be employed to bring air into the lungs until natural breathing is resumed or until all hope of this occurring has been abandoned.

In any method of artificial respiration, promptness in starting the treatment is of first importance. So long as the heart beats, the tissues for a time are able to gain a small amount of oxygen from the circulating blood. But the heart is peculiarly susceptible to oxygen deprivation and, unless the air in the lungs can be renewed and the blood oxygenated, it will soon cease to beat. Nervous tissue also, especially the higher centers of the brain, does not survive for more

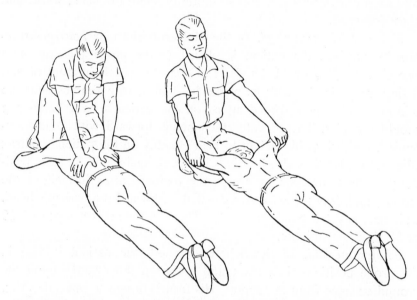

Fig. 6.14   Holger Nielsen method of artificial respiration. (From First Aid, Metropolitan Life Insurance Co.)

than a few minutes after its oxygen supply has been arrested. When the heart ceases to beat and can no longer maintain the circulation, methods of resuscitation are usually of no avail. However, it is often impossible for one who is not medically qualified to detect the beat of the heart when it is very weak. For this reason artificial respiration should be continued until natural breathing has been restored or until a physician has pronounced the death of the patient. Not until then should hope be abandoned.[1]

Most methods of artificial respiration are designed to increase and reduce alternately the capacity of the thorax in such a way as to *draw* air into the lungs and expel it again. Thus the blood is oxy-

---

[1] If a physician is not available, efforts at resuscitation should be persisted in until *rigor mortis* (stiffness of the muscles after death) is clearly evident.

genated and carbon dioxide removed. Several methods have been devised for this purpose.

Until recently the *Schafer method* of artificial respiration has been most widely used, but the *Holger Nielsen* method, for which a greater efficiency in ventilating the lungs is claimed, is now recommended. Whichever method is used, water, mucus, or other obstruction to the free passage of air, is first removed from the mouth and throat; the tongue is drawn forward, and all clothing about the neck, waist, and chest loosened.

Holger Nielsen method. In the Holger Nielsen or *back-pressure-arm-lift method,* the patient is placed in the prone position, with one cheek resting on his hands. The operator kneels in front of and facing the patient's head; he places his hands, with thumbs near the mid-line and fingers spread apart, on the patient's back below the shoulder blades. The operator then bends forward with elbows extended, and brings his weight to bear steadily on the patient's thorax (Fig. 6.14). He then slowly brings his trunk again into the erect position; at the same time he grasps the patient's arms just above the elbows, and draws them forward—that is, toward the patient's head. This movement expands the chest. The movements are repeated 10 or 12 times per minute.

Schafer method. In the Schafer method, the patient is also in the prone position—i.e., chest and abdomen downward—upon the ground or some form of support. His face is turned to one side (Fig. 6.14) and one arm is extended in front along the ground while the other is bent at the elbow providing a rest for the side of the head. The operator, with trunk erect, kneels astride the patient a little below the level of the hips and facing his back. The operator places the palms of his hands over the subject's lower ribs on either side so that his fingers pointing downward curve around this part of the chest. Then, with his arms held straight and rigid, he swings forward slowly until his shoulders are in a vertical line with his hands, and brings his weight to bear upon the patient's ribs. Thus air is expelled from the chest.[2] This movement should take about 2 seconds. The operator then releases the pressure and resumes his original position; the chest recoils and expands, air is drawn into the lungs. In about 2 seconds the operator swings forward again. The double movement is repeated 12 or 15 times per minute.

---

[2] Not only is the lower part of the patient's chest compressed, but the diaphragm is pushed up as well.

Care should be taken to keep the patient warm throughout the entire procedure. When consciousness returns a hot drink may be given.

Eve's rocking method. This method, invented by Dr. Eve, an English physician, makes use of the weight of the abdominal viscera to lower and raise the diaphragm in imitation of its normal inspiratory and expiratory movements. The subject is placed prone upon a stretcher or board which is balanced in the center upon a trestle or other support and rocked around his transverse axis. Each tilt of the body, either in the head down or feet down position, is to an angle of from 45 to 50 degrees with the horizontal. In the feet down position, the abdominal viscera drag the diaphragm down; in the head down position, the diaphragm is pushed up. Ten double movements are made per minute.

Artificial respiration should be continued until natural breathing returns or until a physician has examined the patient and pronounced him dead. Before artificial respiration has been started all possible obstructions to the entrance of air into the air passages should be quickly removed: mucus or water should be clear from the throat, and all clothing about the neck, chest, or abdomen loosened.

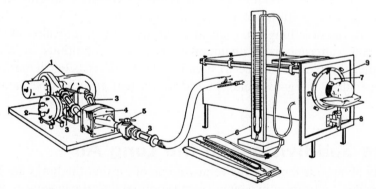

Fig. 6.15   Drinker's mechanical "iron lung" method of artificial respiration. 1, pumps; 2, motor for rhythmically alternating the pressure within the chamber; 3, vents; 4, alternate; 5, valve; 6, manometers; 7, external shutters; 8, adjustment for head rest; 9, adjustable ring to hold collar in place. (After Shaw and Drinker.)

The Drinker mechanical method. This method is used when artificial respiration must be carried out for long periods—days, weeks, or even months—owing to paralysis of the respiratory muscles. Such an emergency is most likely to arise as a result of infantile paralysis (anterior poliomyelitis). The patient lies upon a bed within a hermetically closed steel cabinet, only his head appearing outside the apparatus. A flexible collar is fitted around his neck, so as to prevent the leakage of air (Fig. 6.15). A motor-driven pump causes alternate variations in the air pressure within the chamber. Reduction in air pressure from 3 to 4 mm below that of the atmosphere causes expansion of the chest (inspiration). The next moment the pressure within the chamber becomes atmospheric, the chest returns to the resting position, and expiration occurs. Portholes for tending the patient are provided in the walls of the apparatus. The patient is kept continuously in the chamber until respiratory muscles which have not been paralyzed, or unparalyzed fibers within the affected muscles (e.g., diaphragm or intercostals), have developed sufficient strength to carry out, unaided, the movements required for adequate ventilation of the lungs.

A rocking bed, operated by a motor, has recently been designed to carry out artificial respiration by the Eve method over long periods. It is claimed to induce better ventilation of the lungs than the Drinker method.

In cases of apparent drowning or gas poisoning, it is usually of great benefit to add oxygen to the inspired air. Carbon dioxide in a concentration of about 7 percent is also frequently employed, the object being to stimulate the respiratory center (p. 253) and bring on natural breathing. Oxygen and carbon dioxide are also used in patients suffering from pneumonia and other conditions in which, though the patient is able to breathe, the blood is being imperfectly oxygenated, the gases being passed into a tent covering the patient's head and trunk.

The Subdivisions of the Lung Air

Only about one tenth of the total volume of air that the lungs are able to inspire and expire in a single respiration (see vital capacity, p. 242) moves into and out of the lungs during ordinary quiet breathing; this, which amounts to about 500 cc, is called the *tidal volume*. In an inspiration of maximum depth, six times this amount (namely, 3000 cc) can be inhaled. This is termed the *inspiratory capacity* (it includes tidal volume). If one empties his lungs as completely as possible (forced expiration) after an ordinary expiration, about 1000 cc of air can be expelled from the lungs. This air, which can be expelled by an extra effort, is called the *expiratory reserve volume*. The lungs cannot, of course, be emptied completely for they are kept in the partially expanded state by the subatmospheric pressure within the pleural cavities. Even after the most forcible expiration, from 1000 to 1500 cc of air remain in the lungs. This large volume of air can be expelled only after death by opening the thoracic cavity, thus establishing communication between the pleural cavities and the

Table 6-1

Tidal volume	500 cc
Inspiratory capacity (which includes	
tidal volume)[3]	3000 cc
Expiratory reserve volume	1000 cc
Vital capacity	4000 cc ✓
Residual volume	1200 cc ᵥ
Total lung capacity	5200 cc

atmosphere; it is called the *residual volume* (see Table 6-1 and Fig. 6.16). But, the lungs, after the chest has been opened or even after they have been removed from the body, contain air entrapped within the air sacs. This part of the residual air is termed the *minimal air*. To it the lung tissue owes its buoyancy when put into water. The lungs of a stillborn child, since they have not been expanded by

[3] If the tidal volume is not included, it is called the *inspiratory reserve volume*.

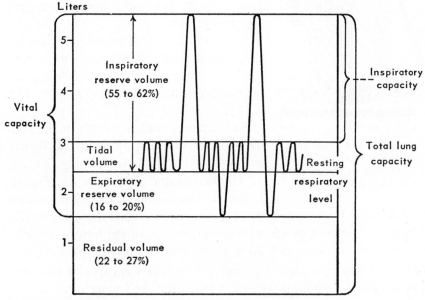

Fig. 6.16   Showing subdivisions of the lung air.

breathing and contain no air, sink in water. This fact is the basis of an important medicolegal test in cases of suspected infanticide, by means of which it is possible to determine whether or not an infant had been born alive.

The maximum quantity of air which can be expired after the deepest possible inspiration—that is, the sum of the inspiratory capacity— and the expiratory reserve volume is called the *vital capacity*. Athletes and other persons in good physical condition have, in general, greater vital capacities than those of the same size who lead a sedentary life or are debilitated. The vital capacity is therefore used as one of the criteria of physical fitness. In health it bears a relationship to the surface area of the body, amounting to 2500 cc per square meter of body surface for the average man, 2000 cc for women, and 2800 cc for athletes. For a man of average build (1.7 square meters of body surface), it amounts, therefore, to (1.7 × 2500 =) 4250 cc. Certain diseases of the lungs, chest, and heart reduce the vital capacity below the normal standard for the individual.

The vital capacity is measured by having the subject inspire fully, and then empty his lungs as completely as possible into an instrument called a *spirometer* (see Fig. 6.17).

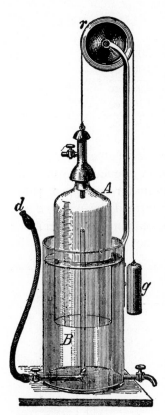

Fig. 6.17   Spirometer. *A,* graduated glass bell; *B,* water; *d,* mouthpiece; *g,* counter weight; *r,* pulley. (After Reichert.)

The average values of the main subdivisions of the lung air in round figures are tabulated in Table 6-1 on page 241.

Alveolar air and dead space air. The air in the air sacs,—that is, the air in contact with the true respiratory part of the lungs—is called the *alveolar air.* The space enclosed by the nonrespiratory part of the lungs—namely, the bronchi and muscular bronchioles, trachea, larynx, pharynx and nasal cavities—is called the *dead space;* it has a capacity of about 150 cc. The air within this space is called the *dead space air.*

The Chemistry of Respiration

The exchange of the respiratory gases (oxygen and carbon dioxide) between the blood and the air in the lungs, and between the tissue cells and the blood, follows those physical laws which govern the behavior of gases in general. Some space will be devoted, therefore, to an account of the properties of gases.

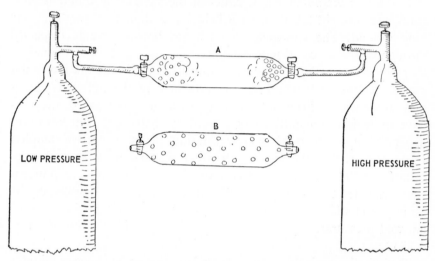

Fig. 6.18   Illustrating the diffusion of gases. The two gas storage cylinders contain the same kind of gas at unequal pressures. In the cylinder on the left, the gas is at the lower pressure. When samples of gas from each cylinder are allowed to enter the glass chamber A, the molecules, as indicated by the small circles, intermingle freely and become evenly distributed (as in B) with consequent equalization of pressure throughout.

The kinetic theory. The behavior of a gas is explained upon the theory that its molecules are in ceaseless motion. They move at high velocity and if unobstructed in any way become separated from one another by immeasurably great distances. A gas, therefore, is capable of expanding to infinite dimensions, its molecular concentration diminishing proportionately as it expands. When confined, the gas molecules strike numberless blows upon the walls of the container. The pressure exerted by a gas is attributed to this ceaseless molecular bombardment. It follows, therefore, that the greater the number of molecules within a given space (i.e., the higher their concentration), the higher will be the gas pressure.

If two samples of the same gas but of different molecular concentrations be brought together, rapid and even distribution of the molecules takes place between the two samples, with consequent equalization of the pressure throughout any space in which the gas is confined (see Fig. 6.18). The final pressure has a value somewhere between the pressures of the separate samples. *Gas molecules are therefore said to move from a point of higher to one of lower pressure.*

When two *dissimilar* gases, either at the same or at different pressures, are brought together, each behaves as though it were the only kind present. The molecules of each gas become evenly dispersed throughout the space, its molecular concentration and, in consequence, its pressure becoming everywhere equal. After mixing, the molecular concentrations and, therefore, the pressures of the individual gases may differ widely from one another for, as just mentioned, they behave quite independently of one another, their final concentrations depending upon the original concentrations of the respective samples. In order to realize the speed with which dispersion of the molecules occurs, one has only to recall how quickly some odorous or pungent gas permeates the atmosphere. The process whereby samples of the same gas at different pressures, or of different gases at the same or unequal pressures, become uniformly mixed is called *diffusion* (Fig. 6.18).

Though the molecular movements are very much slower, liquids and solids in solution behave in the same way. For example, a basin of water in which a bottle of red ink is opened carefully, so as to avoid mechanical mixing, becomes, after a time, of a uniform color throughout. Molecules of gases also diffuse into liquids which are in contact with them until the gas pressures within and without the liquid are equal.

The properties of gases are stated more specifically in the following laws.

The gas laws. *Boyle's law.* The temperature remaining constant, reduction in the dimensions of the space in which a gas is confined increases the pressure of the gas and vice versa. In other words, at constant temperature the pressure of a gas varies inversely with its volume—the product of the pressure and the volume is constant; i.e., doubling the pressure reduces the volume by half; or conversely, doubling the volume of the container reduces the pressure by half.

Charles' (or Gay-Lussac's) law. For each rise in temperature of 1° C a gas expands by approximately $\frac{1}{273}$ of its volume at 0° C provided that the pressure is kept constant; or, its volume remaining constand, the pressure of a gas increases by $\frac{1}{273}$ for each degree (Centigrade) rise in temperature.

Dalton's law of partial pressures. A quantity of gas when mixed with other gases exerts the same pressure as it would exert were the other gases not present. The total pressure of a mixture of gases is, therefore, the sum of the pressures of the individual gases in the mixture, each gas exerting a pressure proportional to its percentage in the mixture. For example, the atmosphere (dry) at sea level has a pressure of 760 mm Hg; it contains 20.96 percent of oxygen. The *partial pressure* exerted by oxygen, in the air at sea level is, therefore,

$$\frac{20.96}{100} \times 760 = 159.2 \text{ mm Hg}$$

or approximately $\frac{1}{5}$ the pressure of the atmosphere at sea level.

Henry's law of the solution of gases. The temperature remaining constant, the quantity of gas which goes into solution in any given liquid is proportional to the partial pressure of the gas. For example, water when exposed to the atmosphere absorbs the constituent gases—oxygen, nitrogen, and carbon dioxide—in quantities proportional to the pressure which each exerts in the air mixture. The partial pressure or tension of each gas in the water will be the same as its partial pressure in the atmosphere. The liquid is then said to be equilibrated with the gas.

The compositions and partial pressures of the gases in atmospheric, expired, and alveolar airs. Atmospheric air contains 20.96 volumes percent of oxygen, 79.00 percent of nitrogen, and 0.04 percent of carbon dioxide. It also contains minute amounts of argon and other rare gases. The approximate partial pressures of these gases in the atmosphere (that is, in inspired air) are, therefore, 158, 596 and 0.30 mm Hg, respectively. In expired air the pressure (tension) of oxygen is lower (since its percentage is lower) and that of carbon dioxide higher, than in inspired (atmospheric) air. In the air of the pulmonary alveoli (alveolar air), the oxygen pressure is lower again, and the carbon dioxide pressure higher than in the inspired air (see Tables 6-2 and 6-3, p. 246). Thus, the pressure of oxygen declines from inspired air to alveolar air, and that of carbon dioxide from alveolar air to inspired air. Nitrogen is an inert gas so far as respiration is concerned—that is, it is neither used in the body (like oxygen) nor produced (like carbon dioxide). The difference between the pressure of nitrogen in the expired and alveolar airs, on the one hand, and in the inspired air, on the other (see Table 6-3), is due simply to changes

Table 6-2

Volumes percent of gases in dry, inspired, expired,
and alveolar airs (average figures)

	Volumes percent		
	Inspired (atmospheric) air	Expired air	Alveolar air
Oxygen	20.96	16.3	14.2
Carbon dioxide	0.04	4.0	5.5
Nitrogen (with argon and other rare gases in minute quantities)	78.00	79.7	80.3
Totals	100.00	100.0	100.0

Table 6-3

Partial pressures of gases in inspired, expired, and
alveolar airs (average figures). Barometer
reading 760 mm Hg.

	Partial pressures		
	Inspired air mm Hg	Expired air mm Hg	Alveolar air mm Hg
Oxygen	158.2	116.2	101.0
Carbon dioxide	0.3	28.5	40.0
Nitrogen	596.5	760.0	760.0
Water vapor	5.0	47.0	47.0
Totals	760.0	760.0	760.0

in the pressures of the other gases and to the water vapor added to
the air in the lungs, for it should be remembered that the *total* pressure of expired air or of alveolar air must be the same as that of the
atmosphere.

The partial pressure of water vapor in the air of the lungs amounts
to about 47 mm Hg. The value for the barometric pressure, less 47,
must therefore be used in calculating the partial pressure of one or
other gas in the expired or the alveolar air from its percentage. For
example, if the expired air contains 16.3 percent of oxygen and the
barometer registers 760 mm, then the partial pressure of oxygen is

$$\frac{16.3 \times (760 - 47)}{100} = 116.2 \text{ mm Hg}$$

The diffusion of gases between the atmosphere and the air in the alveoli. As has been pointed out, the lungs are not filled with fresh air during inspiration nor completely emptied during expiration (p. 240). The tidal air amounts to only about one sixth of the total quantity of air contained in the lungs, under ordinary circumstances. The ventilation of the air sacs is brought about largely through diffusion—that is, the movement of gas molecules from a point of higher to one of lower pressure. Diffusion is very materially aided by mechanical mixing caused by the respiratory movements, especially during the elastic recoil of the lungs at the end of inspiration. Oxygen diffuses into the alveolar air from the fresh air drawn into the respiratory passages (dead space) during inspiration, and carbon dioxide diffuses from the alveolar air into the air of the dead space. (See Table 6-3 and compare figures for partial pressures of oxygen and carbon dioxide in inspired, expired, and alveolar airs.) During expiration a part of the air (about 500 cc of the total 2500 or 3000 cc in the lungs) is forced from the air sacs. About 350 cc of this is expelled to the outside together with about 150 cc which had filled the respiratory passages. The last 150 cc of alveolar air replaces that which has been swept from the dead space. At the next inspiration the column of air which was in the dead space is drawn back again into the air sacs, together with 350 cc or so of atmospheric air. Another 150 cc of atmospheric air fills the dead space.

The depth to which fresh air is drawn into the air sacs varies, of course, with the quantity of air inspired. In very shallow breathing, pure atmospheric air may not fill the dead space, whereas in deep breathing it penetrates beyond the respiratory bronchioles (p. 229).

The exchange of gases between the alveolar air and the blood. Each minute during bodily rest from 4 to 6 liters of blood are delivered to the lungs by the pulmonary artery. In traversing the capillaries of the lungs, the red blood corpuscles are separated from the alveolar air by the exquisitely thin and highly permeable membranes forming the alveolar and capillary walls. In their passage through the capillaries which surround the alveoli, the red cells are for the most part in single file. Thus, a thin film of blood, having an area calculated at about 1000 square feet, is exposed to the alveolar air. The blood coming to the lungs (i.e., the mixed venous blood from all parts of the body), having given up a part of its oxygen load to the tissues and having received therefrom a somewhat smaller volume of carbon dioxide, has therefore a relatively low pressure of the former gas and a relatively high pressure of the latter. The capillary blood and the alveolar air (which at the end of inspiration has a relatively high pressure of oxygen and a low pressure of carbon dioxide) come rapidly into gaseous equilibrium, oxygen diffusing from alveolar air to blood and carbon dioxide from blood to alveolar air. The blood leaving the lungs (arterial blood) therefore contains more oxygen and less carbon dioxide than does venous blood; the oxygen and carbon dioxide pressures show corresponding differences, the oxygen pressure being around 100 mm Hg in arterial and 40 mm in venous blood; the carbon dioxide pressures are about 40 to 46 mm Hg, respectively (see Pl. 6B).

The *volumes percent* (i.e., the number of cubic centimeters of gas in 100 cc of blood) and the pressures of oxygen and carbon dioxide in arterial and in mixed venous blood are given in Tables 6-4 and 6-5.

Table 6-4

Pressures of oxygen and carbon dioxide in arterial and in mixed venous blood (averages). Compare with Table 6-3.

	Pressures		
	Arterial blood	*Mixed venous blood*	*Difference* [4]
Oxygen	100	40	60
Carbon dioxide	40	46	6

Table 6-5

Volumes percent of oxygen and carbon dioxide in arterial and in mixed venous blood (averages)

	Volumes percent		
	Arterial blood	*Mixed venous blood*	*Difference*
Oxygen	19	12.5	6.5
Carbon dioxide	50	56	6.0

[4] Carbon dioxide is much more diffusible (30 times) than oxygen, so that rapid diffusion of the former gas takes place at a smaller pressure difference.

The gaseous exchanges in the tissues. The gaseous exchanges taking place in the tissues (internal respiration) are the reverse of those in the lungs (external respiration). The oxygen pressure in the tissues is low, the carbon dioxide pressure high. The blood in passing through the capillaries of the systemic circulation (e.g., of muscles, skin, abdominal organs, etc.) gives up from 5 to 7 volumes percent of oxygen (depending upon the particular type of tissue and its activity at the time) and absorbs from 4 to 7 volumes percent of carbon dioxide. The gases diffuse across the capillary membrane from plasma to tissue

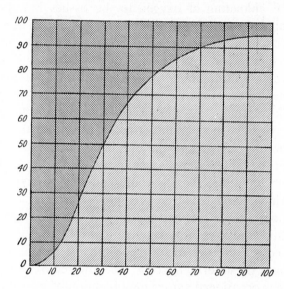

Fig. 6.19 The oxygen dissociation curve of hemoglobin. *Heavy shading* shows reduced hemoglobin, and *light shading,* oxyhemoglobin. Percentage saturation of hemoglobin with oxygen along vertical lines (ordinates); oxygen pressure (tension) in mm Hg along the horizontal lines (abscissae). (After Barcroft.)

fluid (oxygen), and from tissue fluid to plasma (carbon dioxide). (See Fig. 6.19.)

The transport of the respiratory gases in the blood. *Oxygen transport.* When human blood has been fully oxygenated (as after exposing it, at body temperature, to the atmosphere at sea level which has an oxygen pressure of about 160 mm Hg), each 100 cc contains about 20 cc of oxygen. This is the maximum quantity of oxygen which the blood will absorb, and it is then said to be fully saturated with the gas. Twenty volumes percent is, therefore, the *oxygen capacity* of normal human blood. The blood does not, however, become fully saturated with oxygen in passing through the lungs. Arterial blood contains only about 19.4 volumes percent of oxygen. In other words, it is only 97.5 percent saturated. Of the 19.4 volumes in every 100 cc of blood all but 0.24 volumes are in combination with hemoglobin. This 0.24 volume percent is in *simple solution* in the plasma. Whole blood, owing to its content of hemoglobin, can absorb, therefore, 80 times more oxygen than can an equivalent quantity of plasma.

Hemoglobin when saturated with oxygen, or nearly so, is called *oxyhemoglobin*. The oxygen is bound very loosely to the hemoglobin; the latter is said to be *oxygenated* rather than *oxidized*, for a true oxide is not formed. Hemoglobin that has given up part of its oxygen is called *reduced hemoglobin*. If hemoglobin formed a stable compound with oxygen—that is, if it formed an oxide which did not readily part with its oxygen—it would serve no useful purpose in respiration, for the unloading of oxygen to the tissues is quite as important as its rapid absorption by the blood in the lungs. The combination of oxygen with hemoglobin in the lungs and the dissociation of oxygen in the tissues proceed at nearly equal velocities. The quantity of oxygen which will combine or be held in combination with hemoglobin in the erythrocytes is dependent upon the partial pressure of oxygen in the plasma (i.e., the oxygen in simple solution). The pressure of oxygen in the plasma varies in turn with the pressure of oxygen in the alveolar air, on the one hand, and in the tissue fluids and cells, on the other (Henry's law, p. 245). For example, in passing through the lungs the plasma comes into equilibrium with the alveolar air which has an oxygen pressure of around 100 mm Hg. The hemoglobin, therefore, becomes nearly saturated with oxygen. In the tissue fluids the oxygen pressure is relatively low, and still lower in the cells. Oxygen diffuses, therefore, from the plasma to the tissue fluids and from the latter to the cells. The lowered oxygen pressure of the plasma thus occasioned causes the liberation of oxygen from the hemoglobin. Thus, through this gradient of pressure, a steady stream of oxygen from the red cells to the tissue cells is assured.

The oxygen dissociation curve of hemoglobin. The relationship between the oxygen saturation of hemoglobin and the partial pressure of oxygen to which it is exposed can be shown by placing samples of blood in a series of cylindrical glass containers (called *tonometers*) and introducing air mixtures of known oxygen and carbon dioxide pressures. The glass vessels are rotated in a water bath at body temperature; the blood is thus spread in a thin film over their interiors, and allowed to come into gaseous equilibrium with the atmosphere to which it is exposed. The percentage oxygen saturation of each of the blood samples is then determined and plotted as shown in Figure 6.19. Percentage oxygen saturation is indicated along the upright lines (ordinates), oxygen pressures along the horizontal lines (abscissae). The curve plotted in this way is called the *oxygen dissociation curve of hemoglobin.* It is important to notice the peculiar shape of this curve. It tends to flatten out at oxygen pressures above 70 mm Hg. It has been described as S shaped. At 100 mm Hg, which is the oxygen pressure in the alveolar air, the hemoglobin is over 97 percent saturated. It would become fully saturated at about 160 mm Hg. Raising oxygen pressure above 100 mm Hg can therefore cause little increase in the quantity of oxygen absorbed; and a fall in oxygen pressure down to 60 or 70 mm Hg causes a minor reduction in the oxygen saturation.

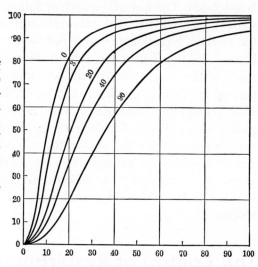

Fig. 6.20 Showing effect of increasing pressures (tensions) of CO_2 upon the oxygen dissociation curve of hemoglobin (Bohr effect at constant temp. 37° C). (After Barcroft.) Percentage saturation of hemoglobin along upright lines (ordinates); oxygen pressure in mm Hg along horizontal lines (abscissae).

The slope of the lower part of the curve (i.e., at the lower oxygen pressures) is much steeper. This means that any given reduction in oxygen pressure causes the release of a relatively large quantity of oxygen from the hemoglobin. In other words, in passing through the tissues, where the oxygen pressure is low, very free dissociation of oxyhemoglobin occurs and a relatively large quantity of oxygen is unloaded for delivery to the tissue cells.

Two factors—namely, a *rise in temperature* and an increase in *hydrogen ion concentration*—cause a shift to the right of the oxygen dissociation curve of hemoglobin. That is to say, each of these factors reduces the quantity of oxygen which hemoglobin will hold at any given oxygen pressure. Therefore, during increased tissue activity (e.g., muscular contraction) the local rise in temperature and the increase in hydrogen ion concentration, resulting from carbon dioxide and lactic acid production, cause a greater load of oxygen (per unit quantity of blood) to be delivered to the tissues. The influence of carbon dioxide pressure variations upon the form of the oxygen dissociation curve of hemoglobin is illustrated in Figure 6.20. This is known as the *Bohr effect*.

Carbon dioxide transport. Arterial blood contains from 44 to 52 volumes percent of carbon dioxide, venous blood from 50 to 60 volumes percent. A small part of this—namely, about 2.5 volumes percent (or from 4 to 5 percent of the total—is in simple solution in the plasma. A further 4 or 5 volumes percent (8 to 10 percent of the total) is combined *directly* with hemoglobin. The compound is called *carbohemoglobin*. The rest of the carbon dioxide is carried in the plasma as sodium bicarbonate. The chloride shift mechanism, through which the sodium bicarbonate is formed when carbon dioxide enters the blood from the tissues, has already been explained (p. 112). After a study of this mechanism it will be realized that, though only a small part of the carbon dioxide is carried in the blood actually combined with hemoglobin, the latter serves in an indirect way—that is, by giving up its alkali—for the carriage of over 85 percent of the total carbon dioxide. For this reason the quantity of carbon dioxide which can be absorbed by plasma, from which the red cells have been separated by centrifuging (so-called *separated plasma*), is only a small fraction of that which the plasma in whole blood (*"true plasma"*) will absorb.

The Control of Respiration

Respiration is essentially an involuntary act—that is, it is carried out automatically and without thought. Nevertheless, it is to a certain extent under voluntary control. One can, for example, cease breathing for a time, or can vary the rate or the rhythm of the respirations (as in speaking or singing). The respirations are also controlled through an effort of the will or semiautomatically (reflexly) during swallowing, coughing, sucking, etc., and are altered by emotional states. But the respiratory movements are essentially automatic in nature. The breathing cannot be suspended voluntarily for more than 45 seconds or so. At the end of this time one is compelled to take a breath.

The automatic, involuntary character of the respiratory movements is due to the rhythmical discharge of impulses from a group of nerve cells situated in the lower part of the floor of the fourth ventricle in the medulla oblongata. These constitute the *respiratory center*. Destruction of this region causes complete and permanent arrest of respiration. The impulses originating in the center are conducted down the spinal cord to the anterior horn cells of the third, fourth, and fifth cervical segments. The *phrenic nerve* which supplies the chief muscle of respiration—namely, the diaphragm—arises from these spinal segments. Impulses also descend from the center to the motor neurons in the third, fourth, fifth, and sixth thoracic segments, supplying fibers to the intercostal muscles.

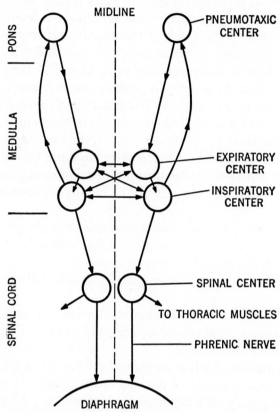

Fig. 6.21   Diagram showing the nervous connections in the respiratory mechanism.

The complete central nervous mechanism in the brain stem controlling respiration does not occupy an area as circumscribed as was at one time believed. Though we still speak of the respiratory *center,* and stimulation of a small spot in the lower part of the medulla oblongata will cause pronounced respiratory responses, modern research has revealed that the regulation of the respiratory rhythm is dependent upon a much more complex and extensive neural mechanism. There is a group of nerve cells or center in the medulla which, when stimulated electrically during inspiration, causes the immediate arrest of this movement and brings on expiration; it is called the *expiratory center*. An *inspiratory center* lies in close proximity to the expiratory center and, when stimulated, causes strong contractions of all the inspiratory muscles. In the living body, the expiratory center appears to discharge an intermittent stream of *inhibitory impulses* to the inspiratory center, interrupting its activity at regular intervals. Expiration then follows automatically and in a passive manner. In other words, expiration is the result of the cessation of impulses from the inspiratory or primary center to the diaphragm and other muscles of inspiration. A third group of nerve cells, known as the *pneumotaxic center,* situated in the lower part of the pons, is connected to the inspiratory center by nerve tracts. The function of this center is not altogether clear, but it is believed by most physiologists to receive excitatory impulses, discharged rhythmically from the inspiratory center which it relays to the expiratory center; the latter then exerts, intermittently, an inhibitory influence upon the inspiratory center as described above. All three centers are bilaterally represented (see Fig. 6.21).

The frequency of the impulses discharged along the phrenic nerves, and other nerves to the inspiratory muscles, varies rhythmically with the inspiratory movements, rising to a maximum toward the end of inspiration and falling to a minimum, or ceasing entirely during expiration.

The respiratory nervous mechanism, though fundamentally automatic in its action, is influenced by *chemical* and *reflex* factors. These will be considered separately.

Chemical factors. *Carbon dioxide* stimulates the respirations; any rise in the partial pressure of this gas in the arterial blood results in increased frequency and depth of the respirations. Under ordinary circumstances, the carbon dioxide pressure in the alveolar air, as in the arterial blood, remains remarkably constant at around 40 mm Hg, for the slightest rise suffices to increase the pulmonary ventilation. The excess gas is thus removed and the pressure restored, automatically, to the normal level. Professor J. S. Haldane and his associates found that an increase of only 0.2 percent in the carbon dioxide of the alveolar air (a rise in partial pressure of 1.5 mm Hg) doubled the volume of the air breathed per minute. The effect of carbon dioxide upon the respirations may be demonstrated by having a subject breathe an air mixture containing a high percentage (5 or 6 percent) of carbon dioxide (Fig. 6.22). The respirations become deeper, more rapid, and even violent, though the mixture contains over 90 percent of oxygen. Conversely, if a subject voluntarily increases his pulmonary ventilation by breathing quickly and as deeply as possible for a minute or so, a greater than ordinary quantity of carbon dioxide is "pumped" out of, or "blown" from, his blood. When the forced voluntary effort (*forced breathing*) ceases, spontaneous respiratory movements are not resumed for a period of from 40 to 60 seconds. This interval of suspended respiration, during which there is no desire to breathe, is called *apnea* (literally, no breathing— see Fig. 6.23). With longer peri-

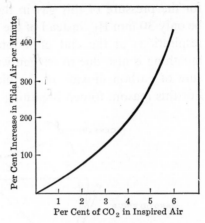

Fig. 6.22 Showing effect upon pulmonary ventilation of increasing the CO_2 percentage in the inspired air. (After Scott, redrawn and modified.)

ods of forced breathing, the apneic period may be extended to 2 minutes or more. If the subject repeats the experiment, but instead of breathing ordinary air, breathes an air mixture containing a higher concentration (4 to 5 percent) of carbon dioxide and a normal percentage of oxygen, apnea does not occur. The cessation of breathing following hyperventilation of the lungs is due, therefore, to the removal of carbon dioxide from the blood, and not to its being overcharged with oxygen. A reduction in the carbon dioxide pressure of the alveolar air by about 0.2 percent is sufficient to induce a short period of apnea.

Effects of a low pressure of oxygen in the arterial blood. The effect upon the respirations of oxygen want is seen at altitudes of 10,000 feet or more, where the oxygen pressure of the atmosphere is greatly reduced (p. 261). An increase in pulmonary ventilation then occurs. The respiratory stimulus, in this instance, cannot be carbon dioxide,

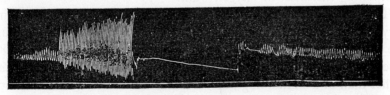

Fig. 6.23   Forced breathing for a period of 2 minutes is followed by apnea lasting for 3 minutes. This is succeeded by periodic breathing of the Cheyne-Stokes type (p. 259 and Fig. 6.25), which persists for a minute or so before normal breathing is resumed. (After Douglas and Haldane.)

for the pressure of this gas in the alveolar air at high altitudes may be only 30 mm Hg, instead of the usual 40 mm. The first return of the respirations at the end of a long apneic period caused by forced breathing is also due to oxygen want, for at this time the partial pressure of carbon dioxide in the blood is still below the normal level. For this reason, forced breathing of an air mixture containing a high

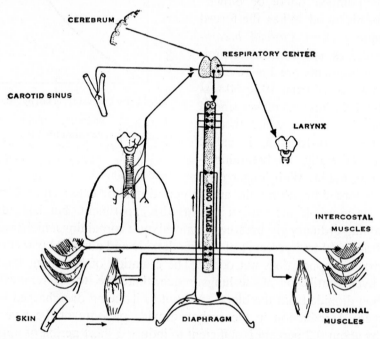

Fig. 6.24   Diagram summarizing the nervous factors in the control of respiration. (Modified from Best and Taylor, *The Physiological Basis of Medical Practice.*)

percentage of oxygen results in an extraordinarily long period of apnea (7 to 8 minutes), the large store of oxygen held in the lungs postponing the onset of oxygen want.

The stimulating effect which oxygen want exerts upon the respiratory center is now believed to be an *indirect* one—namely, through the stimulation of the chemoreceptors in the carotid body (p. 258). The *direct* effect of anoxia upon the center itself is of a depressing rather than of a stimulating nature. Under the ordinary circumstances of health, however, oxygen want is not even an indirect factor in the control of respiration, for it is not until the oxygen percentage in the atmosphere reaches a very low level (12 to 14 percent) that any noticeable effect upon respiration is produced. When one holds the breath, for example, the uncontrollable desire to breathe is due to the accumulation of carbon dioxide, and not to lack of oxygen. The intense urge to breathe occurs before the oxygen content of the blood has fallen to the point where the respirations are stimulated (through the carotid body) by oxygen want.

Reflex and chemoreflex factors. Afferent impulses originating in almost any part of the body may influence the activity of the respiratory center. The sharp inspiration which follows a painful stimulus, the inhibition of inspiration during swallowing (p. 301) or when sensory endings in the nasal mucosa are stimulated (as by some pungent odor), and the increased rate and depth of breathing caused by the stimulation of cutaneous nerves by a cold or a hot bath are a few familiar examples illustrating the effects of afferent nerve stimulation upon the respiratory movements.

The activity of the respiratory center is also influenced by proprioceptive impulses (p. 514) arising in the respiratory muscles, as well as by impulses discharged from the higher (psychic) centers of the brain. Various changes in respiratory rate, depth, and rhythm may be brought about through emotional and mental factors. The spasmodic breathing of laughter, the sobbing respirations in grief, the slow shallow breathing during attention, suspense, or apprehension, and the rapid respirations in excitement or fear may be cited (Fig. 6.24).

An outstanding reflex effect upon the rate and depth of breathing is brought about through impulses originating in afferent endings of the *vagus* situated in the pulmonary tissue itself. The adequate stimulus for the vagal endings is stretching caused by inflation of the lungs. Thus, at the end of inspiration, distension of the air sacs causes a stream of impulses to be discharged to the respiratory center. These depress the activity of the center; that is, the frequency of the impulses discharged down the phrenic and other *efferent* respiratory nerves is reduced; or the efferent discharges may cease entirely. Expiration, which, as we have seen, is brought about mainly in a passive manner, therefore follows. The arrest of inspiration brought about in this way, with the consequent onset of expiration, is called the *Hering-Breuer reflex*. Section of the vagus nerves in experimental animals, by interrupting the afferent impulses from the lungs, results in slowing and deepening of the respirations—the inspiratory phase being then prolonged.

The carotid sinuses (p. 199) *and carotid bodies* under certain special circumstances, but probably not in ordinary conditions, play a role in respiratory control. The walls of the sinus contain receptors which, when stimulated mechanically (pressure or stretch), discharge impulses to the respiratory center as well as to the cardio-inhibitory and vasomotor centers. Thus, distension of the sinus by a rise in blood pressure causes slowing of the respirations, or even complete respiratory arrest (apnea) for a short time. A fall in blood pressure has the reverse effect—namely, increased pulmonary ventilation. These effects come into play only under very unusual and special circumstances.

The carotid body is a small structure attached to a twig of a small branch of the external carotid artery close to the carotid sinus. It contains cells which have the specialized function of responding to chemical stimuli. These *chemoreceptors,* as they are called, are stimulated by a rise in the carbon dioxide tension of the arterial blood, by an increase in hydrogen ion concentration, or by oxygen lack. The nerve impulses set up by the stimulation of these chemoreceptors and discharged along the sinus nerve to the respiratory center result in an increase in the rate and depth of breathing. A rise in the carbon dioxide pressure exerts a similar, though less pronounced, effect. The carotid body plays no role, or a very minor one, in the control of the circulation (see p. 201).

As mentioned on page 257, it is only when oxygen want reaches an extreme degree that the chemoreceptors of the carotid body are stimulated. The same applies to carbon dioxide excess. The sinus mechanism, therefore, plays no part in the control of respiration under ordinary physiological conditions.

Physiological Modifications of Respiration

Laughing. Laughing consists of a deep inspiration followed by a series of short spasmodic expirations. The characteristic sound is caused by the vibrations of the vocal cords which are held tense in the path of the outgoing air. In *crying,* the respiratory movements are very similar.

Coughing. This is a reflex act usually caused by stimulation of sensory endings of the vagus nerve in the mucosa of the larynx or trachea, but it may result from the excitation of afferent vagal endings in the lungs or pleura. The act comprises a short inspiration, followed immediately by closure of the opening of the larynx (glottis), and a forcible expiratory effort. A high pressure is thus created within the lungs and lower air passages. The glottis then opens suddenly, allowing the air to escape in a blast. Thus, any irritating material which may be present in the larynx is expelled.

Sneezing. Like coughing, sneezing consists of a short inspiration, followed by a forcible expiration, but the glottis remains open. During the first part of the expiratory effort the way into the mouth is blocked by the elevation of the tongue against the soft palate, the blast of air being thus directed through the nose. Later, the resistance offered by the tongue is, as a rule, removed, the air then escaping through the mouth. The sneezing reflex is initiated by irritation of the nasal endings of the trigeminal nerve.

Yawning. Usually an indication of fatigue, sleepiness, or simply of boredom, yawning may also be induced by seeing someone else yawn. It is primarily of psychic origin. A yawn comprises a deep inspiration with the mouth fully open. *Sighing* consists of a prolonged expiration.

Hyperpnea. This term is applied to any increase in pulmonary ventilation, due to an increase in either in the rate or in the depth of breathing, or in both.

Abnormal Types of Respiration

Periodic breathing. This term is given to certain types of abnormal respiratory rhythm (see Fig. 6.25). The best known of these is called *Cheyne-Stokes breathing,* after two physicians of the last century who described it as a characteristic feature of certain diseases. This type of breathing is marked by periods of rapid and deep respiration (hy-

Fig. 6.25   Cheyne-Stokes breathing. 1, hyperpneic periods; 2, apneic periods. (After Waller.)

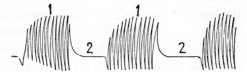

perpneic periods) alternating with intervals of complete cessation of respiration (apneic periods). At the beginning of the hyperpneic periods, the respirations are slow and shallow, but they quickly increase to a maximum rate and depth, and then, becoming smaller and smaller again, cease. The apneic periods are due to the excessive elimination of carbon dioxide from the blood during the preceding periods of hyperpnea. The latter are due, in turn, to oxygen lack, acting through the carotid body reflex, and the accumulation of carbon dioxide during the apneic periods. The respiratory center, apparently, has lost some stabilizing factor which normally prevents it from responding too vigorously to changes in the gaseous composition of the blood. Like a machine without a flywheel, the action of the center consists of uneven, relatively small changes in gas pressures causing a too sudden and unduly great respiratory effect.

Cheyne-Stokes breathing is seen in advanced kidney disease, in cases of raised intracranial pressure, and in poisoning by narcotics. In these conditions it is a symptom of very grave portent. But periodic breathing of a similar type occurs under certain physiological conditions—e.g., in animals during hibernation and sometimes in children during sleep. It is also seen when the respirations are returning after the period of apnea induced by forced breathing, or it may occur at high altitudes.

Dyspnea. Difficult breathing, or dyspnea, is seen in a number of diseased conditions.[5] The breathlessness in heart disease or in acidosis and the respiratory distress of asthma, pneumonia, and other pulmonary conditions, and at high altitudes are examples. In acidosis the respirations are increased in an effort to maintain the $\dfrac{H_2CO_3}{NaHCO_3}$ ratio at its normal value by reducing the numerator of the equation—that is, by "blowing off" carbon dioxide from the blood (p. 255). The dyspnea of heart disease, anemia, and pneumonia, and at high altitudes is caused by an inadequate supply of oxygen to the tissues, including the carotid body which is stimulated thereby.

A *rise in metabolism,* from whatever cause, brings about an increase in the pulmonary ventilation, since it is associated with an increased production of carbon dioxide. *Muscular exercise* increases the metabolism and, therefore, stimulates the respirations; and even a healthy person suffers from dyspnea after a bout of strenuous muscular effort, when he puffs, gasps, or pants and feels that he will suffocate if he does not get more air into his lungs. If, as in *hyperthyroidism* (p. 411), the resting metabolism is already above normal, dyspnea is experienced with a grade of muscular exertion which would not cause any respiratory distress in a normal person. In *anemia,* also, breathlessness occurs upon any slight muscular exertion, because the hemoglobin concentration of the patient's blood, though capable of carrying the required quantity of oxygen to the tissues when the

[5] Whenever breathing is distressing, or a person is unduly aware of the respiratory act, the term *dyspnea* may be applied.

body is at rest, is unable to satisfy the demands of even mild physical effort.

The degree of hyperpnea at which respiratory distress is experienced varies widely in different individuals according to their physical state. As compared with untrained persons, athletes are able to increase their pulmonary ventilation to a much greater extent before any difficulty in breathing (i.e., dyspnea) is experienced.

Oxygen Want—Anoxia or Hypoxia[6]

Any failure of the tissues to secure a supply of oxygen sufficient for their needs is referred to as *oxygen want* or *anoxia*. Anoxia is classified according to its cause into the following four groups: *anoxic, stagnant, anemic,* and *histotoxic.*

Anoxic anoxia. This term applies to any type of anoxia in which the blood in its passage through the lungs does not reach normal saturation (about 97.5 percent), whether as a result of a low oxygen tension in the atmosphere as at high altitudes and in vitiated atmospheres (e.g., in mines), or to some interference with breathing (e.g., obstruction of the respiratory passages, asthma, pneumonia, etc.).

Mountain sickness. The unpleasant and sometimes serious effects of the anoxia of high altitudes are referred to as mountain sickness. The first signs of mountain sickness appear at an altitude of between 8000 and 10,000 feet above sea level. At this height the percentage oxygen saturation of the hemoglobin is considerably below the normal level. For example, at a height of 14,000 feet above sea level, the atmospheric pressure is around 450 mm Hg. The partial pressure of oxygen, being reduced proportionately, amounts to $\left(\dfrac{20.96}{100} \times 450 = \right)$ 94 mm Hg, as compared with 160 mm at sea level. The oxygen pressure in the alveolar air and arterial blood is, therefore, only from 55 to 60 mm Hg. The oxygen saturation of the hemoglobin is around 82 percent as compared with the normal of about 97.5 percent, and the symptoms and signs of anoxia are apparent. These include headache, nausea and vomiting, dyspnea, and cyanosis (p. 263). Emotional outbursts (e.g., laughing or crying, quarrelsomeness or hilarity) are common. There is often a sense of exhilaration, or an exhibition of foolhardiness, boisterousness, or stubbornness. If a person remains for a

---

[6] *Hypoxia,* which means a diminished oxygen supply, is a better term than *anoxia* (literally no oxygen) and is, therefore, more correct etymologically. In the types of oxygen deficiency to be immediately described, the older word (anoxia) will be retained, since in this connection it has the sanction of long usage.

time at the high altitude, these effects gradually disappear; he becomes acclimatized. The acclimatization process consists of a rise in the red cell count (see Fig. 3.5, p. 62), and adjustments in the circulatory and respiratory mechanisms. Natives of high mountains have a red cell count of from 6,500,000 to 8,500,000, depending upon the altitude at which they live. The volume of the lungs and the size of the chest is greater than the normal for a man of the same height residing at sea level. In rapid ascents to very high altitudes (40,000 to 50,000 feet), as in an airplane, consciousness is lost rapidly unless the flyer can receive oxygen inhalations from a storage cylinder, or the plane is provided with an airtight cabin within which the partial pressure of oxygen is equal to that at an altitude of 8000 feet or less.

Stagnant anoxia. This anoxia is due to slowing of the circulation through the tissues as occurs in heart failure. The reduced velocity of the blood in the capillaries permits the hemoglobin to give up a greater fraction of its total oxygen load than normally. The venous blood contains, therefore, a proportionately larger amount of reduced hemoglobin. When the blood remains long in the capillaries, though a larger quantity of oxygen is abstracted from it, the greater part of the gas is delivered at low pressure. The tissues, therefore, receive less oxygen in a given time than when the blood flow is rapid.

Anemic anoxia. This type of oxygen want results from a reduced oxygen-carrying capacity of the blood. It includes that due to carbon monoxide poisoning as well as that resulting from anemia.

Carbon monoxide poisoning. Carbon monoxide combines with hemoglobin to form COHb, a relatively stable compound—that is, one which dissociates very slowly. Any hemoglobin in this form cannot take up oxygen, and is therefore dispossessed of any respiratory function. Carbon monoxide causes death for this reason only. The subject poisoned by the gas is deprived of the use of part of his hemoglobin just as surely as if it had been lost from the body, and the tissues, in consequence, cannot be supplied adequately with oxygen.

Hemoglobin has a very great affinity for carbon monoxide, and this is why it is so especially dangerous. When blood is exposed to an atmosphere containing equal concentrations of carbon monoxide and oxygen, it absorbs 300 parts of the former gas for every one part of the latter. In other words, the hemoglobin becomes almost completely saturated with carbon monoxide to the exclusion of oxygen. As a result of the preference shown by hemoglobin for carbon monoxide, a concentration of as little as 0.2 percent in an atmosphere otherwise normal in composition will cause death if breathed for a few minutes.

As in the anoxia of mountain sickness, in that due to carbon monoxide poisoning, the subject often becomes stubborn, perverse, or unruly. Though he is not unaware of his danger he may, owing to some fanciful idea, make no attempt to escape, and may even resist efforts of others to bring him into fresh air. This is another dangerous feature associated with exposure to this gas.

The most effective means of resuscitating a subject of carbon monoxide poisoning is artificial respiration and, when possible, using an air mixture of about 40 percent oxygen and 7 percent carbon dioxide. The oxygen tends to hasten the liberation of carbon monoxide from the hemoglobin while the carbon dioxide stimulates the respirations.

Histotoxic anoxia. In this type of oxygen deficiency, the oxidative processes of the tissues are depressed or abolished by a poison such as cyanide. The oxygen-carrying capacity of the blood is not affected, but, since cellular oxidations are greatly reduced or in abeyance, the usual amount of oxygen is not removed from the blood in the capillaries. The venous blood, therefore, has a high oxygen saturation, and is arterial in color. Cyanide poisoning is treated by the intravenous injection of a solution of sodium nitrite followed by the injection of sodium thiosulfate. However, since cyanide poisoning is so rapidly fatal, there is rarely an opportunity for applying this or any other method of resuscitation.

Cyanosis. The name cyanosis is given to the blue tint of the skin caused by an unusually high concentration of reduced hemoglobin in the blood of the capillaries composing the subpapillary venous plexus (p. 35). The blueness is usually most pronounced in the skin of the lips, ears, and finger tips. It is the visible sign of hypoxia, either of the anoxic or stagnant type. That is, the blood either does not receive a full load of oxygen in the lungs or it gives up an unusually large proportion of its oxygen to the tissues. In both these instances, the capillary blood will have an abnormally high concentration of reduced hemoglobin, which is darker in color than oxyhemoglobin. Blood contains some 15 grams of hemoglobin per 100 cc. In the cutaneous capillaries of a normal person, about 2.5 grams of this is reduced hemoglobin, the remaining 12.5 grams is oxyhemoglobin. When, as a result of either of the two types of hypoxia just mentioned, the concentration of reduced hemoglobin in the capillary blood increases to 5 grams per 100 cc, cyanosis appears. In other words, 5 grams of reduced hemoglobin per 100 cc of blood in the capillaries of the skin and mucous membranes is necessary for the production of cyanosis.

The anemic and histotoxic types of anoxia do not cause cyanosis. In the first of these, though the hemoglobin is diminished in amount, what there is of it is as fully saturated with oxygen as in health. Furthermore, a person with a very severe anemia (hemoglobin less than 5 grams per 100 cc of blood) obviously cannot become cyanosed under any circumstances; for even though all his hemoglobin should be in the reduced form, it would not be in sufficiently high concentration to cause any discoloration of the skin. On the other hand, a person whose blood had an abnormally high concentration of hemoglobin (25 to 30 grams per 100 cc, as in polycythemia, instead of the normal of about 15 grams) becomes cyanosed with a relatively mild degree of hypoxia. In the histotoxic type, the capillary blood actually contains a *lower* concentration of reduced hemoglobin than in health, for, as a result of the action of the poison on the respiratory function of the cells of the tissues, the oxygen in the blood is not utilized.

Oxygen administration. In certain acute respiratory conditions accompanied by hypoxia, the administration of oxygen in high concentration (50 to 100 percent) is of great value. Also, in heart disease in which the stagnant type of anoxia may exist, oxygen inhalations are of benefit. It must be remembered, however, that there is a limit to the amount of oxygen which the blood will take up from the lungs. In health, the blood coming from the lungs is over 97.5 percent saturated with oxygen, so, increasing the oxygen in the inspired air five times does not mean that the blood will take up five times as much oxygen as when ordinary air is breathed. The most that can be effected is to increase the oxygen saturation of the blood to 100 percent. In the stagnant type of anoxia when the *arterial* blood is at the normal of about 97.5 percent, this would mean an increase of only 2.5 percent or so. Nevertheless, this extra 2.5 percent in heart disease is often highly salutary.

The Voice

The mode of production of the human voice—with its varied tones, its range of pitch, and its volume—has long aroused the interest of physiologists. As an instrument of sound, the voice-box or larynx, with the cavities of the mouth, throat, trachea, and lungs, may be compared to the pipe of an organ. A reed and the column of air in the organ pipe are set into vibration by an air blast. In a somewhat similar manner the vocal cords within the larynx are thrown into vibration by air expelled from the lungs. The nose, mouth, throat, and chest

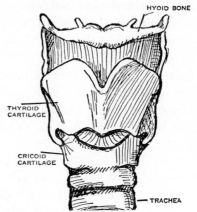

Fig. 6.26   The larynx and upper rings of the trachea. The *hyoid* is a small bone lying near the root of the tongue. The *thyroid* cartilage forms the front and side walls of the larynx. The *cricoid* is a circle of cartilage shaped like a signet ring, lying between the larynx above and the trachea below.

serve as resonating chambers. Certain notes can be played by the organist which imitate the human voice in a truly remarkable way.

The larynx (Fig 6.26) lies at the upper end of the trachea, its walls being formed of cartilage and lined with mucous membrane; the vocal cords are two thin-edged bands or membranes lying within it. The cords run from before backward, being attached behind to two small cartilaginous bodies (the *arytenoid cartilages*) and fixed in front to the wall of the larynx. By the contraction of small muscles attached to

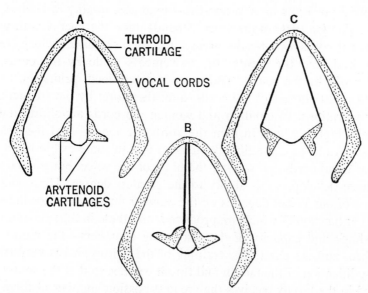

Fig. 6.27   The vocal cords viewed from above (diagrammatic) in different degrees of approximation. A, in midposition; B, in full adduction; C, in full abduction.

them, the arytenoid cartilages can be rotated when necessary. By this means the vocal cords can be swung away from one another—that is, outward against the walls of the larynx (Figs. 6.27 and 6.28), or inward toward one another until only a small chink remains between them. At ordinary times the cords lie against the wall of the larynx, the gap separating them is wide, and no sound is produced during the passage of the breath. During speech they are brought toward one another and into the current of air expelled from the lungs, which, being un-

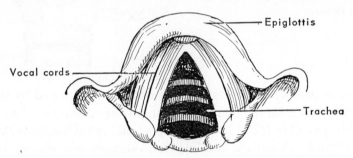

Fig. 6.28   The interior of the larynx as seen with the laryngoscope.

able to escape except through the narrow opening, sets the edges of the cords into vibration.

Sound possesses three properties—loudness, quality or timbre, and pitch. The *loudness* of the voice depends upon the energy with which the vocal cords vibrate; the greater the pressure under which the air is expired, and the greater the movements made by the cords, the louder will be the sound. The *pitch* is determined, primarily, by the length and tightness of the cords, and, therefore, by the frequency of their vibrations. In children and women the cords are short, and the voice is high pitched. In men the cords are longer, and the voice is deeper. All of us can adjust the tension and to some extent the length of our vocal cords and so alter the pitch of the voice, but trained singers have developed this ability to the greatest degree. The *quality* or *timbre* of our voices depends on the number and intensity of the overtones or harmonics which are produced, and these in turn depend upon the shape and capacity of the resonating chambers—the mouth, the trachea, and the chest. The training of the voice consists very largely in modification of the mouth and throat cavities so that the sound produced in the larynx receives the greatest possible number of these harmonics or supplementary tones.

In speech the musical sounds produced by the vibration of the vo-

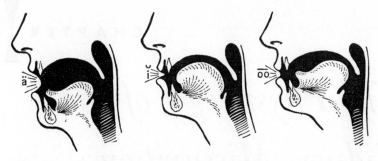

Fig. 6.29   Showing the positions of the lips and tongue and the shape of the mouth cavity when pronouncing ä, ĭ, and o͞o.

cal cords are modified by the numerous changes which may be made in the size and shape of the air passages—the pharynx and the mouth. The vowel sounds, *a, e, i, o, u,* are formed in the lower air passages and molded as it were by the mouth, the latter cavity assuming positions which are characteristic for each vowel (Fig. 6.29). When we whisper, these sounds may be produced simply by placing the mouth in the required position—that is, without vibration of the vocal cords. The consonants are formed by interrupting to different degrees the expired air in various parts of the vocal pathway.

CHAPTER 7

The Physiology of the Kidney. Micturition

The structure of the kidney. The kidney is composed of a large number of microscopical structures called *nephrons*. They are the excreting units of the kidney. Their function is the separation from the blood of water and certain materials (urea, salts, etc.) in solution which are then excreted as urine. In man, there are some 2,000,000 nephrons—1,000,000 in each kidney.

The nephron comprises (1) a spherical, vascular structure called the *renal glomerulus* or *Malpighian corpuscle,* and (2) the *renal tubule* (Figs. 7.1, 7.2, 7.4, and 7.5).

The renal glomerulus consists of some fifty separate capillaries bent into short loops to form a compact mass called the *glomerular tuft.* The upper end of each renal tubule is expanded into a structure known as Bowman's capsule. The cavity of Bowman's capsule is crescentic in cross section, owing to the encroachment of the capillary tuft which is, as it were, pushed into one side of the capsule as a ball might be pressed into the side of a partially inflated balloon. The walls of the capsule are formed of a thin membrane composed of a single layer of flat cells which, therefore, serves also as a covering for the glomerulus. This membrane and the equally thin walls of the capillaries alone separate the blood from the cavity of Bowman's capsule.

The renal tubule drains Bowman's capsule and, for purposes of description, can be divided into three parts. The first third or so is tortuous, and lies in close relation to the glomerulus; it is known as the *proximal convoluted tubule.* The walls of this portion of the tubule are composed of a single layer of columnar epithelial cells. The free

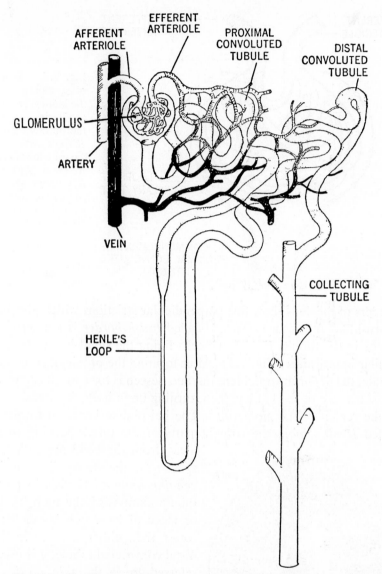

Fig. 7.1   Showing a renal unit or nephron of the cortex of the kidney, with its blood supply, and a collecting tubule. The thin part of
Henle's loop varies in length; it often extends into the ascending
limb of the loop or may even be confined to this limb.

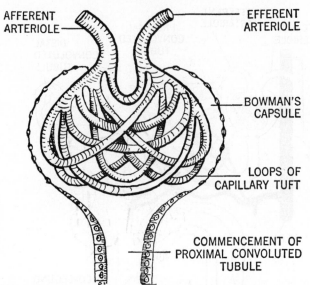

AFFERENT ARTERIOLE

EFFERENT ARTERIOLE

BOWMAN'S CAPSULE

LOOPS OF CAPILLARY TUFT

COMMENCEMENT OF PROXIMAL CONVOLUTED TUBULE

Fig. 7.2   Diagram of a glomerulus of the kidney. Note that capillaries pass from the afferent to the efferent arteriole in separate loops. There are many more capillary loops than are shown here; each glomerulus contains 50 or more.

borders of the cells show fine perpendicular striations which give them a brushlike appearance. This so-called *brush border* is not seen elsewhere in the tubule, though the cells lining the small intestine have a similar appearance (Fig. 7.3). After forming the proximal convoluted tubule, the nephron straightens out and descends for a distance through the substance of the kidney; then, turning upon itself, it ascends again to the region of the glomerulus. The hairpinlike bend, so formed, is called *Henle's loop;* the straight parts of the tubule leading to and away from the bend are called, respectively, the *descending* and *ascending limbs* of Henle's loop. The tubule composing the loop for half or more of its length is much narrower than either the proximal or distal convoluted tubule; it is usually referred to as the *thin portion of Henle's loop* (Fig. 7.1). The ascending limb passes into a second tortuous section lying in close relation to the glomerulus; this is called the *distal convoluted tubule*. The distal convoluted tubules empty the tubular fluid (now completely formed urine) into larger channels, called *collect-*

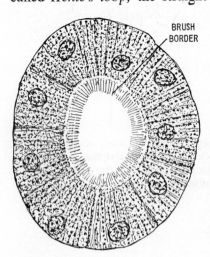

BRUSH BORDER

Fig. 7.3   Cross section of a convoluted tubule, highly magnified.

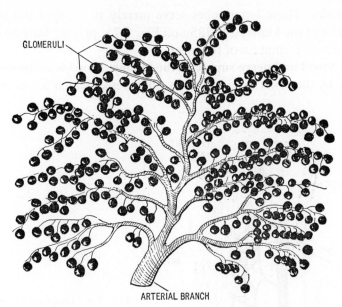

GLOMERULI

ARTERIAL BRANCH

Fig. 7.4 Drawn from a photograph of portion of a kidney after injecting its vessels with fluid that solidified, and then destroying the renal tissue with acid to reveal the glomeruli.

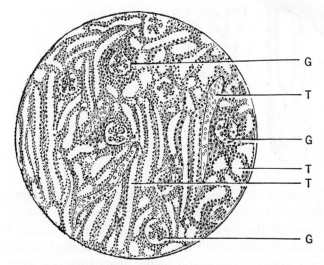

G
T
G
T
T
G

Fig. 7.5 Microscopical appearance of normal renal tissue; G, glomerulus; T, tubule.

ing tubules. These latter tubes serve merely to conduct the urine to the *pelvis* of the kidney (p. 285 and Fig. 7.7), playing little or no part in the actual formation of the urine.

The blood and nerve supply of the kidney. Blood is delivered to the kidney by the *renal artery,* a short thick vessel which arises from the

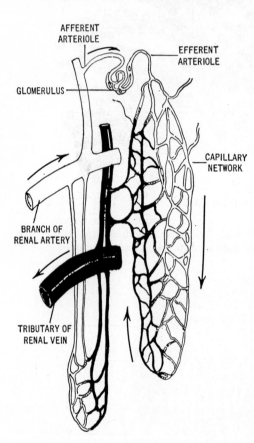

AFFERENT
ARTERIOLE

EFFERENT
ARTERIOLE

GLOMERULUS

CAPILLARY
NETWORK

Fig. 7.6 Diagram of renal circulation. Veins, black; arteries, white; hatching indicates conversion of arterial to venous blood.

BRANCH OF
RENAL ARTERY

TRIBUTARY OF
RENAL VEIN

abdominal aorta. All the blood which enters the kidney, except a small fraction for the nourishment of the covering (capsule) and connective tissue of the organ, passes through the glomeruli. The capillaries of each glomerular tuft are derived from a single arteriole called the *afferent vessel.* Converging again, the capillaries form a single effluent channel, known as the *efferent vessel* (Fig. 7.6). This is also of arteriolar construction. There is considerable disparity in size between the diameters of the two glomerular arterioles, the efferent vessel being the smaller. This arrangement makes for a relatively high pressure within the capillary loops. Furthermore, variations in glomerular capillary pressure can be brought about through changes in the relative diameters of the two vessels. Dilatation of the afferent arteriole or constriction of the efferent, the caliber of the other vessel in each instance remaining the same, causes a rise in the blood pressure in the capillaries of the renal glomerulus. Constriction of the afferent or dilatation of the efferent vessel will produce the reverse effect.

The blood, after traversing the glomerulus, is distributed to the rest of the nephron through branches of the efferent vessels which terminate in a capillary network surrounding the tubules.

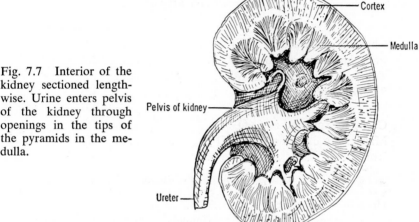

Fig. 7.7   Interior of the kidney sectioned lengthwise. Urine enters pelvis of the kidney through openings in the tips of the pyramids in the medulla.

The *nerves* of the kidney are derived from the *vagus* and *splanchnic (sympathetic)* nerves. These nerves have no secretory action, for the kidney continues to perform its functions in a normal manner after it has been completely denervated.

The renal nerves act solely upon the renal vessels controlling the volume of blood entering the organ. It is probable that they also cause changes in the distribution of blood within the kidney itself, diverting blood from one part of the renal tissue to another. It has been found within recent years that there are actually two pathways which the blood may take in its passage through the kidney—namely, through the glomeruli in the superficial part of the renal cortex, or through other glomeruli situated more deeply in the cortex near the renal medulla (Figs. 7.6 and 7.7). For example, stimulation of the central end of a cut sciatic nerve in an animal such as the rabbit causes the blood to "by-pass" the first-mentioned vessels, which is the course taken by the blood under ordinary circumstances, and to travel through the more deeply placed glomeruli. A renal vascular reflex of this sort probably occurs in surgical shock due to severe tissue injury.

The composition of the urine. The chief urinary constituents in grams per liter of urine are given in the following table.

Urea is derived mainly from the breakdown in the body of food protein; it, therefore, varies considerably with the quantity of protein in the diet. On a low protein intake, it may be less than a sixth of the

Table 7-1

Urinary constituents

I. *Inorganic constituents*

	Grams per liter
Chloride expressed as NaCl	9.0
Phosphorus expressed as P_2O_5	2.0
Total sulfur expressed as SO_3	1.5
Sodium expressed as Na_2O	4.0
Potassium expressed as K_2O	2.0
Calcium expressed as CaO	0.2
Magnesium expressed as MgO	0.2
Iron	0.003

II. *Nitrogenous constituents*

Urea
    25.0 grams containing approximately   10.0 grams nitrogen
Ammonia
    0.6 gram containing approximately   0.4 gram nitrogen
Uric acid
    0.6 gram containing approximately   0.2 gram nitrogen
Creatinine
    1.5 gram containing approximately   0.5 gram nitrogen
Undetermined nitrogen .... 0.6 gram
Total .... 11.7 gram nitrogen

value given in Table 7-1. The creatinine, on the other hand, is derived mainly from the disintegration of body tissue; its excretion is, therefore, almost uninfluenced by the protein level of the diet.

The uric acid is derived from purines (p. 366) taken in the food, as well as from the purines of body tissue. Ammonia is formed in the kidney itself from glutamine carried to it in the blood. The color of the urine is due to a pigment called *urochrome*. Normal urine does not contain glucose, except occasionally after meals; minute amounts may then appear.

The reaction and specific gravity of the urine. Under ordinary circumstances, the urine is definitely acid. The average pH is around 6.0, but the reaction varies considerably with the nature of the diet. Most fruits reduce the acidity of the urine, for they contain the salts of organic acids; the acid is oxidized, leaving the alkali, which is excreted. Starvation increases the urinary acidity, because sulfuric and phosphoric acids are formed from the breakdown of body protein, and acetoacetic and β-hydroxybutyric acids from the metabolism of body fat. A high protein diet also increases the quantity of acid excretion. Herbivorous animals, on the other hand, excrete an alkaline urine except when fasting, the urine then becoming acid. In diseases associated with the production of large amounts of organic acids in the body—e.g., acetoacetic and β-hydroxybutyric acids in diabetes—the urine is more strongly acid than normally.

The normal acidity of the urine is a manifestation of one of the most important functions performed by the kidney—namely, to aid in maintaining the alkalinity of the blood and body fluids. Blood coming to the kidney has a pH of around 7.4; the urine, as just mentioned, has an average pH of 6.0. The kidney separates acid from basic substances, retaining the latter within the body and excreting the former. This conservation of the body's base is brought about in part by the conversion in the kidney of the alkaline phosphate of the blood (Na_2HPO_4) into the acid phosphate (NaH_2PO_4). For example, the concentrations of the alkaline and acid phosphates in plasma are as 4 to 1, whereas, in urine they are as 1 to 9. Another way in which the kidney conserves fixed base (chiefly sodium) to the body is by the formation of ammonia. The ammonia then combines with acids brought to the kidney, which excretes them as ammonium salts.

The specific gravity of the urine of adults ranges under ordinary circumstances between 1.020 and 1.032; it is much lower in infants. In health, the specific gravity swings readily in one or other direction, in response to variations in the intake of fluid. For example, when a normal person drinks a large quantity of water, the urine which he passes within the next couple of hours is very dilute; the specific gravity may be as low as 1.001 or 1.002. On the other hand, after abstaining from fluids for some time, the specific gravity of the urine rises to 1.030 or higher. In the later stages of kidney disease, the specific gravity of the urine is low under all circumstances. It remains almost fixed around a value of 1.010, in spite of wide variations in the fluid intake.

The volume of the urine. In man, from 1000 to 1500 cc of urine are formed in 24 hours. The volume varies, of course, with the amount of fluid drunk and with that lost through other channels—skin, lungs, and bowels. It is reduced, therefore, in hot weather or as a result of diarrhea or vomiting. The products of protein metabolism, especially urea, increase urine production; the volume of the urine is greater, therefore, upon a high than upon a low protein diet. Urine formation is reduced during sleep, but the total excretion of urinary solids (e.g., urea, uric acids, phosphate, etc.) is about the same during the night as during a day period of equal length, the kidney merely excreting less water—that is, more water is reabsorbed from the tubules. The urine passed after rising in the morning is therefore more concentrated than ordinary day urine. A decided rise in the volume of the night urine, as a persistent phenomenon, is called *nycturia*. It is an early sign of chronic renal disease. Muscular exercise, especially of a strenuous nature, reduces the volume of the urine, as a result of the liberation of the antidiuretic hormone of the pituitary body as described on page 281.

The formation of urine. Though the renal corpuscle was described by the Italian anatomist, Marcello Malpighi, in the seventeenth century (1666), it was not until nearly 200 years later (1842) that the English anatomist and surgeon, Sir William Bowman, recognized the functional significance of this structure, and of the capsule which is known by his name. From his studies of the structure of the glomerulus, Bowman concluded that it served simply as a filter to remove water and salts from the plasma. Though others have contended that the layer of Bowman's capsule covering the capillaries of the glomerular tuft actually *secreted* these urinary constituents, the former view is now universally accepted. The glomerular membrane—that is, the walls of the capillaries and the layer of Bowman's capsule in contact with them —acts in a purely passive manner, its cells, unlike those of a true gland, possessing no secretory function.

Filtration through the glomerulus. Let us now consider the filtration process in greater detail. Filtration through a membrane may be defined as the separation, by gravity or pressure, of liquid and such materials as can pass through the membrane from other materials to which it is impervious. Water, salts, and other substances of relatively small molecular size pass through the capillary walls of the glomerulus into Bowman's capsule, but the capillary membrane offers an impassable barrier to the blood cells and the plasma colloids (proteins). If there were no proteins or other colloids of comparable molecular size in the blood plasma, the force driving water and salts from the capillaries of the tuft into the cavity of Bowman's capsule would be equal to about 65 mm Hg—that is, the difference between the capillary blood pressure (70 mm Hg or so) and the pressure in Bowman's capsule (about 5 mm Hg). But the plasma proteins, since the glomerular membrane is impermeable to them, exert an osmotic pressure (see p. 64) which opposes the blood pressure. This force acts to hold water and dissolved substances within the vessels; it, and the pressure in Bowman's capsule, must be overcome by the hydraulic force of the blood in the glomerular capillaries. The capillary blood pressure must be higher, therefore, than the osmotic pressure of the

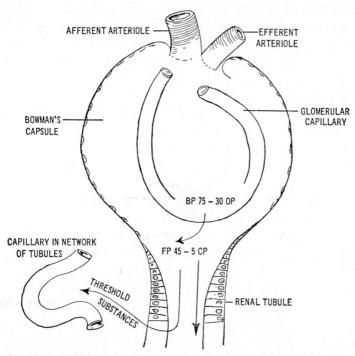

Fig. 7.8   Diagram to illustrate the forces responsible for the excretion of water and dissolved substances from the blood flowing through the glomerular capillaries, and the reabsorption of threshold substances from the tubules. BP, blood pressure; OP, osmotic pressure; FP, filtration pressure; CP, capsular pressure. All pressures in mm of mercury.

plasma colloids (proteins) and the capsular pressure combined, in order for filtration to occur. The osmotic pressure of the plasma proteins is around 30 mm Hg. Therefore, the actual driving force, or effective filtration pressure, in millimeters of mercury is as follows (see also Fig. 7.8):

70	—	30	—	5	=	45
Blood pressure		Osmotic pressure		Pressure in capsule		Effective filtration

The filtration theory of glomerular function just outlined has been confirmed in every detail by experiment. For example, a rise in blood pressure within the glomerular capillaries, without any change occurring in osmotic or capsular pressure, causes an increase in the amount of filtrate formed. Lowering the osmotic pressure while the blood pressure is kept constant, as by the intravenous injection of a saline solution (which, of course, dilutes the proteins), also increases the flow of urine. On the other hand, raising the pressure in Bowman's capsule by blocking the ureter reduces the volume of the filtrate and, when the capsular pressure just about equals the amount by which the

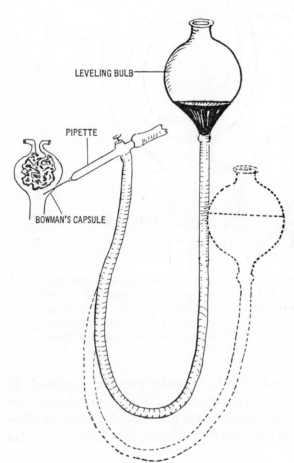

LEVELING BULB

PIPETTE

BOWMAN'S CAPSULE

Fig. 7.9   Illustrating Richards' method of obtaining a sample of glomerular filtrate. When the bulb of mercury is raised, air is expelled from the tubing; upon lowering the bulb to the position indicated by the dotted outline, fluid is sucked from Bowman's capsule.

blood pressure exceeds the plasma osmotic pressure (which would be 40 mm Hg in the example given above), urine formation ceases.

A crucial experiment was performed by Dr. Richards of the University of Pennsylvania which has finally dispelled all doubt that the glomerulus acts as a filter. He obtained a sample of fluid as it was produced by the glomerulus of the kidney of a living frog, by inserting a fine glass pipette into Bowman's capsule and sucking off the filtrate by means of a flask of mercury and a length of tubing as depicted in Figure 7.9. This fluid was found to contain glucose, chloride, and all the other constituents of plasma except the proteins. It was alkaline in reaction. In other words, it was a filtrate (or ultrafiltrate)—simply *deproteinized* plasma.

It is scarcely conceivable that the fluid of Bowman's capsule would be of exactly the same composition as that of plasma if it were produced by a secretory process.

The concentrating function of the tubules. Normal urine is much more concentrated than the filtrate in Bowman's capsule—that is, it contains a higher percentage of total solids; it is hypertonic with respect to the plasma, and has a much smaller volume. The quantity of

Table 7-2

(After Cushney)

	Blood plasma	Urine	Times increase in concentration in the renal tubules
	percent	percent	
Water	90–93	95	
Proteins, fats, and other colloids ..	7–9		
Glucose	0.1		
Na	0.30	0.35	little or none
Cl	0.37	0.6	2
Urea	0.03	2	60
Uric acid	0.004	0.05	12
K	0.020	0.15	7
NH$_4$	0.001 (?)	0.04	40
Ca	0.008	0.015	2
Mg	0.0025	0.006	2
PO$_4$	0.009	0.15	16
SO$_4$	0.002	0.18	90
Creatinine	0.001 (?)	0.075	75

filtrate formed by the human kidneys in 24 hours amounts to from 75 to 150 liters, whereas the quantity of urine secreted in the same time is only from 1 to 1½ liters. Obviously, a large volume of water—from 98 to 99 percent of that filtered through the glomerulus—must have been reabsorbed from the tubules into the blood stream. Furthermore, glucose is present in the filtrate, but is absent, in health, from the urine. Glucose, then, must be reabsorbed; in the frog sodium chloride must also be returned to the blood, for Richards, in the experiment upon the frog's kidney mentioned above, found it in the filtrate but not in the urine. Materials such as urea, phosphates, and uric acid are reabsorbed to only a small extent, while other waste products, such as creatinine and sulfates, are reabsorbed in traces or not at all. Glucose and the essential salts, since they do not escape into the urine in considerable quantities unless their concentrations in the plasma are abnormally high, are called *high-threshold substances.* Those substances which are reabsorbed to a minor extent (urea, phosphate, and uric acid) are called *low-threshold substances,* while those (creatinine and sulfates) which are not absorbed at all are called *nonthreshold substances* (see Table 7-2).

Glucose, sodium chloride, vitamin C, amino acids, and probably other essential materials are reabsorbed from the filtrate in the proximal convoluted tubule. This part of the nephron is also responsible for from 80 to 90 percent of the water reabsorbed from the filtrate. The remaining 10 to 20 percent of the reabsorbed water is returned to the renal blood from more distal portions of the tubules—probably the thin part of Henle's loop. Little or no concentration of the filtrate occurs in the proximal tubule, the water reabsorbed containing solids in about the same concentration as does the filtrate. The concentrating function is effected by the reabsorption of water in the more distal portions of the nephrons.

The change in reaction of the urine, from alkaline to acid, occurs in the distal convoluted tubule.

As already stated (p. 272), the urine after leaving the distal convoluted tubule and entering the collecting tubules undergoes little or no further change.

The process of filtration across the glomerular membrane (capillary walls and covering layer of Bowman's capsule) is purely *passive,* in so far as the membrane itself is concerned. That is to say, this membrane interposed between the capillary blood and the cavity of Bowman's capsule plays no active part in the separation of the water, salts, and other materials present in true solution in the plasma from the plasma proteins. It exhibits no selective action; no energy is expended; no oxygen is consumed in the process. On the contrary, the cells of the *tubules* exercise a selective action: some constituents of the glomerular filtrate are reabsorbed; others are discarded (excreted in the urine); energy is expended by these cells in the reabsorption process; oxygen is consumed. The process may be looked upon as a *reverse secretion*, selected materials being passed back into the blood rather than as in the secretion of an ordinary gland which, after separating certain constituents from the blood by a specific action of its cells, discharges them into the alveoli of the gland.[1]

The tubules, in some species at any rate, also have an ordinary secretory function, adding urea, uric acid, and other substances to the filtrate.

The action of hormones upon renal function. In health, the proportion of the filtered water which is reabsorbed by the *proximal* convoluted tubule is *fixed* at a value somewhere between the values already given—namely, 80 to 90 percent. That is to say, if the volume of the filtrate is 100 liters and the total volume of water reabsorbed is 98 liters, then 85 percent of this, or about 83 liters, is absorbed by the *proximal* convoluted tubule. On the other hand, the amount of water reabsorbed by the more *distal* part of the tubule varies very widely under different physiological and pathological conditions. It is solely through this variability that the urine is made less or more concentrated with corresponding changes in its volume. The foremost and most potent factor in altering the amount of water reabsorbed by the tubules distal to their proximal convoluted portions is the antidiuretic hormone of the pituitary body (see Chap. 10). This principle increases the reabsorption of water and reduces the reabsorption of sodium chloride; when it is lacking, reabsorption of water is reduced and the reabsorption of sodium chloride increased. In the absence of this hormone, the urine is, therefore, of large volume and very dilute (see *diabetes insipidus,* p. 444). The antidiuretic hormone appears to exert its effect upon the thin section of Henle's loop. One reason for believing in the truth of this statement is the fact that in animals such as frogs, whose kidneys do not have this segment, pituitary extract (containing the antidiuretic hormone) exerts no renal effect. The kidneys

---

[1] The cells of the tubules in reabsorbing water from the filtrate expend a progressively greater amount of energy as the concentration of this fluid increases and, in consequence, its osmotic pressure rises. The cells are said to perform osmotic work. When the osmotic pressure reaches a point at which it exceeds the power of the cells to perform the required osmotic work, the reabsorption of water ceases, the urine having attained its maximal concentration.

of such animals have no concentrating power; their urines are actually hypotonic with respect to the plasma.

The hormones of the adrenal cortex (p. 426) also exert an effect upon the excretion of water and sodium chloride by the kidney. They increase the reabsorption of sodium and reduce the reabsorption of potassium. Therefore, when there is insufficiency of the adrenal cortex, the reabsorption of sodium is reduced and that of potassium is increased, with consequent loss of the former from, and undue retention of the latter in, the tissues and fluids of the body (see Addison's disease, Chap. 10).

Diuresis. Increased flow of urine is called *diuresis,* and drugs which cause such an effect are known as *diuretics.* This group of drugs includes *caffeine* (of coffee and tea), *theobromine* (of cocoa), *theophylline* (of tea), *urea,* and various salts (e.g., *potassium nitrate, potassium citrate, ammonium chloride, sodium sulfate,* and certain *mercury compounds*).

It is evident from the outline of the mechanism of renal excretion just given that there are two ways in which a greater flow of urine could be produced—namely, by increasing glomerular filtration or by diminishing tubular reabsorption. Caffeine, theobromine, and theophylline cause more capillary loops to open up and, thus to increase the total filtering surface of the kidney. Sodium sulfate and the mercurial diuretics diminish reabsorption—the former by its osmotic effect after its passage into the renal tubules, the latter by its depressing action upon the readsorptive function of the cells of the tubules. Caffeine also exerts its diuretic effect by reducing reabsorption as well as by causing renal vasodilatation.

The renal response to water drinking—water diuresis. The drinking of a large quantity (1 to 3 pints) of water is followed within 60 minutes or so by the passage of a large volume of very dilute urine (specific gravity around 1.001). The renal effect lasts for 2 or 3 hours. The resemblance of this response, as well as the very dilute nature of the urine, to the characteristic renal features of diabetes insipidus (due to the lack of antidiuretic principle of the pituitary body) has long been recognized. The suspicion grew that in the mechanism of water diuresis the antidiuretic hormone of the pituitary was in some way involved. The results of recent experiments have shown how well-founded was this suspicion. Without going into details, the course of events will be briefly described. The ingested water after absorption from the intestine causes, through dilution, a slight fall in the osmotic pressure of the blood. The blood dilution exerts an effect upon certain nerve cells of the brain (their exact location is unknown) which are extremely sensitive to any change in the osmotic pressure of the blood with which they are supplied. The nerve cells—a type of receptor organ (p. 514) —are called *osmoreceptors*. In response to a lowering of the osmotic pressure of the plasma, the osmoreceptors exert an influence, either nervous or hormonal in nature, upon the cells of the posterior lobe of the hypophysis which causes a reduction or suppression of its anti-diuretic hormone. This hormone, under ordinary circumstances, is continually being secreted into the circulation and exerting its char-acteristic effect upon the formation of urine. The withdrawal of the antidiuretic action, therefore, is followed after a short interval by an increased production of urine, which is of very low specific gravity.

During a period of water deprivation, the kidney conserves its wa-ter stores. The volume of urine is reduced due to the liberation of an excess of the antidiuretic hormone. Again, the effect upon the pituitary is brought about by a change in the osmotic pressure of the blood, but now the effect is in the opposite direction for the deprivation of water has caused some slight increase in blood concentration.

The reduction in urine volume caused by the injection of a small quantity (0.001 cc) of pituitary extract into the internal carotid artery can be duplicated exactly by 10 cc of a 2.5 percent (hypertonic) solu-tion of sodium chloride or of sugar, introduced in the same manner into the cerebral circulation; such hypertonic solutions cause a rise in the osmotic pressure of the plasma of sufficient magnitude to affect the osmoreceptors.

Summary of the chief functions of the kidney. 1. The kidney main-tains the normal composition of the plasma through the elimination of excess water and the waste products of protein and purine metabolism (e.g., urea, creatinine, sulfates, uric acid, etc.), retaining at the same time the essential constituents of the blood (e.g., cells, proteins, glu-cose, and inorganic salts).

2. The kidney plays a prominent role in the regulation of the acid base balance of the body, through (a) the production of ammonia which, being then excreted in combination with fixed acids (ammo-nium salts), conserves the body's store of alkali, and (b) through the conversion of alkaline phosphate to the acid salt (Na_2HPO_4 to NaH_2PO_4).

Impairment of renal function. In *nephritis,* the commonest type of kidney disease, a proportion of the renal glomeruli are the seat of an acute or chronic inflammatory process. Some or all of the capillary loops in the diseased glomeruli are destroyed and, as a consequence, the filtering surface of the kidney is reduced. When the glomerular destruction is extensive, serious impairment of renal function results. The reader will recall that the tubules are supplied with blood which has previously traversed the glomerular capillaries. It follows, therefore, that glomerular damage must inevitably interfere with the nourishment of the tubules, with consequent impairment of their power of selective reabsorption and, thus, to concentrate the filtrate. The urine is, therefore, much more dilute, as a rule, than normal. It has been mentioned that the specific gravity of the urine in chronic nephritis cannot be raised above 1.010 or so. Nor can it be lowered much below this level by drinking a large volume of water. The changes in urine concentration (as indicated by the specific gravity) which can be accomplished so easily by the healthy kidney, in response to alterations in fluid intake, are quite beyond the power of the severely diseased kidney.

The chief manifestations of kidney disease are: (1) the retention in the blood of nitrogenous waste products (e.g., urea, uric acid, creatinine, as well as of phosphates and sulfates); (2) impaired excretion of water, or failure to concentrate the urine; (3) protein, casts, and perhaps blood in the urine; (4) edema; (5) high blood pressure (see p. 143); and (6) acidosis, in the later stages of the disease.

In severe nephritis the concentration in the plasma of urea and the other wastes mentioned above may be several times greater than in health. The difficulty in the excretion of water is shown by giving the subject a quart or so of water to drink and measuring the urine output hourly for a few hours thereafter. The normal person excretes all the ingested water within from 2 to 4 hours, but when the kidneys are seriously damaged only a part of the water is excreted by the end of 4 hours.

Normal urine is free from protein, but in kidney disease large quantities may appear. It is derived from the plasma. The diseased glomerular membrane permits the passage of serum albumin and smaller quantities of serum globulin (whose molecule is larger than that of albumin); fibrinogen, on the other hand, which has a larger molecule than those of the other plasma proteins, does not escape into the urine. When the loss of protein in the urine is excessive, its concentration in the plasma is reduced. The osmotic pressure of the latter falls in consequence, and edema results (see p. 101).

Micturition or the Voiding of Urine

The tubules of the kidney empty through a number of short ducts into a funnel-shaped membranous structure called *the pelvis* (basin) *of the kidney*. A narrow duct, containing smooth muscle in its walls and called the *ureter*, conveys the urine from the kidney pelvis to the *urinary bladder*. The urine is propelled along the ureter by peristaltic contractions; it enters the bladder in jets which occur at the rate of from one to five per minute.

The urinary bladder serves as a reservoir for the urine. It is a hollow muscular organ lined by modified stratified (transitional) epithelium. It has a maximum capacity of from a half to one pint. The most dependent part of the bladder leads into the *urethra*, through which the

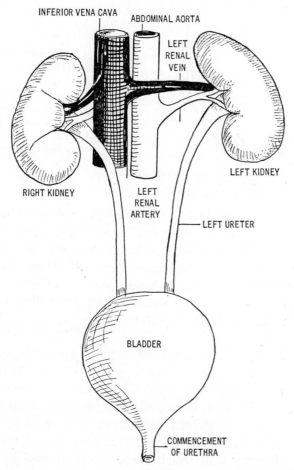

Fig. 7.10   Sketch of the urinary system from in front.

urine is passed to the exterior (Fig. 7.10). This junction of the bladder with the urethra is guarded by a collection of circularly arranged, smooth muscle fibers, called the *internal vesical sphincter*. A little above and behind the urethral opening, the bladder wall is pierced obliquely by the ureters. The triangular area of the bladder wall marked off by the urethra and the two ureteral openings is called the *trigone*. The muscle forming the rest of the bladder wall is called the *detrusor muscle*. The caliber of the first inch or so of the male urethra is controlled by striated muscle, which is generally referred to as the *external vesical sphincter*.

Evacuation of the bladder. As urine gradually collects within the bladder, the pressure within it shows very little change for a time, the tone of the detrusor muscle adapting readily to the increased volume

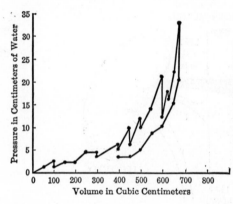

Fig. 7.11 Curve of pressure changes in the human bladder during filling (*upper curve*) and emptying (*lower curve*). Note that the internal pressure shows little sustained increase until the volume of fluid amounts to more than 200 cc. (Denny-Brown and Robertson.)

(see postural tone, p. 294). Not until the urine volume is between 200 and 300 cc does any noticeable rise in internal pressure result (Fig. 7.11). Rhythmical contractions of the detrusor muscle then occur in response to the tension exerted upon the muscle fibers. The contractions are weak at first but, gradually gaining strength as the urine volume increases, culminate in a strong reflex contraction of the bladder wall, accompanied by relaxation of the internal sphincter and trigone.

The act of micturition, though dependent upon reflex mechanisms, is, in the adult, very largely under voluntary control. The reflex contractions of the detrusor can be inhibited, and contractions of the internal sphincter induced, by an effort of the will. Thus, the reflex mechanisms can be restrained until an opportunity for voiding the urine presents itself. The restraint is then removed, and the contractions of the bladder wall which ensue are reinforced by voluntary nerve impulses transmitted along the motor nerves supplying the detrusor muscle. A rise in intra-abdominal pressure, due to contractions of the abdominal muscles and fixation of the diaphragm in the inspiratory position, usually precedes and accompanies the act of micturition. However, a voluntary movement of this character is not essential, the bladder mechanism being capable itself of expelling the urine.

The motor fibers to the detrusor muscle, and the inhibitory fibers to the internal sphincter and trigone, are derived from the parasympathetic division of the autonomic nervous system through the pelvic nerves (second, third, and fourth sacral segments). These fibers are peculiar in that, as indicated above, they transmit voluntary as well as involuntary impulses to the detrusor muscle.

The sympathetic division of the autonomic nervous system exerts an opposite effect upon the movements of the bladder. Through the hypogastric nerves it transmits inhibitory impulses to the detrusor and motor impulses to the internal sphincter and trigone (Pl. 7 B).

The external sphincter of the male, which is composed of striated muscle, is supplied with motor fibers through the pudendal nerves. The afferent nerves of the reflex arc governing micturition run mainly in the pelvic nerves.

The centers of the micturition reflex are situated in the midbrain, pons, and sacral part of the spinal cord (second, third, and fourth sacral segments). Micturition is carried out through the spinal center when the cord is severed above the sacral region. Even after destruction of the spinal center, the bladder empties automatically, its movements being then brought about through the nerve plexuses in close relation to the bladder wall.

The nervous mechanisms through which restraint is exercised in the control of micturition—that is, the inhibition of the micturition reflex—is late in developing to the state of efficiency where, as in a healthy adult, the urine can be retained in even an uncomfortably distended bladder. In infants, urine is voided involuntarily with no effort being made at restraint. In young children, though there may be complete control of the act of urination during the day, the emptying of the bladder during sleep, *"bed-wetting"* or *nocturnal enuresis,* as it is called, is of common occurrence. The age at which restraint is fully developed—at night as well as during the day—varies with the nervous constitution of the child and with his training, but is established as a rule, except for an occasional lapse under unusual circumstances, at 3 to 4 years. In persons of neurotic disposition, nocturnal enuresis may persist into adult life and, in the feeble-minded, restraint may fail to be exercised either during sleep or in the waking hours.

CHAPTER 8

Digestion

The alimentary or digestive tract comprises the *mouth, pharynx, esophagus* (or *gullet*), *stomach,* and *intestines.* The pharynx receives the food from the mouth and transfers it to the esophagus, along which it is conveyed to the stomach. The stomach evacuates its contents into the small intestine which discharges, in turn, into the large intestine (see Fig. 8.1). A descriptive outline of the structure of each part of the digestive tract, in so far as a knowledge of structure is necessary for an understanding of function, will be given in the section dealing with the physiology of that particular part.

The various processes carried on in the alimentary tract which bring about the physical and chemical changes in the food—mechanical disintegration, the decomposition of large molecules into simpler and readily soluble compounds, and the absorption of these into the blood —are all embraced under the word *digestion.* Digestion involves, therefore, mechanical factors (mastication, swallowing, and the movements of the gastrointestinal tract) as well as chemical. Digestion in the different parts of the alimentary tract will be described in order, commencing with the mouth. In each instance, a description of the chemical changes which the food undergoes during the digestive process, and of the nervous and hormonal mechanisms controlling secretion of the digestive juices, will be followed by an account of the movements of the part under discussion. First of all, a general account of *enzymes* or *ferments* and of the *properties of smooth muscle,* of which the walls of the digestive tube are largely composed, must be given.

Enzymes (G. zymē = yeast) or Ferments and Their Action

These substances—e.g., the *ptyalin* of saliva, the *pepsin* of gastric juice, and the *trypsin* of pancreatic juice—are responsible for the

288

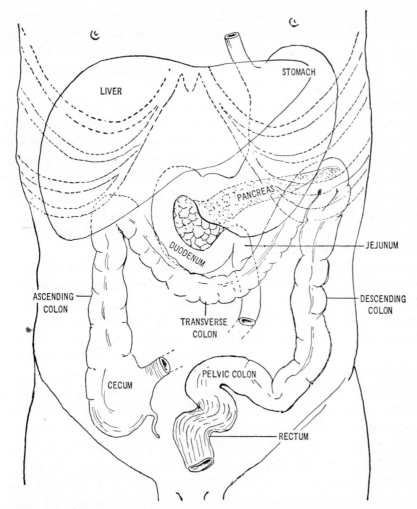

Fig. 8.1   Diagram of the gastrointestinal tract. Most of the small intestine (ileum) excised.

chemical changes which the food undergoes during digestion. The chemical changes comprise the breaking up of the large molecules of carbohydrates, proteins, or fats into smaller molecules which are able to pass through the intestinal mucosa into the blood stream. The chemical process is called hydrolysis (Gr. *hudor,* water + *lysis,* breaking up) since, as a preparatory step to the splitting of the larger molecules, a molecule of water is taken up. Thus, the cleavage of a molecule of maltose into two of glucose is represented by the following equation:

$$C_{12}H_{22}O_{11} + H_2O = C_6H_{12}O_6 + C_6H_{12}O_6$$

maltose   water   glucose   glucose

Such reactions, in order to be accomplished by the ordinary chemical methods of the laboratory, require the use of strong reagents, and usually a high temperature. The digestive ferments act at a relatively low temperature (that of the body), and without the aid of harsh chemicals.

It is not only the chemical reactions involved in digestion that are dependent upon enzyme action. These substances are concerned in the great majority of chemical reactions which occur in the tissues of both animals and plants and upon which the properties of living matter depend. Enzymes, or at least the great majority of them, are protein in nature. Though produced by living cells, they do not all require the presence of cells in order to act. Certain enzymes of yeast, for example, when expressed from the yeast cells, are capable of exerting their usual effect—the conversion of sugar to alcohol.

Several theories have been put forward to explain the manner in which enzymes act, but none can be said to have been definitely established. However, many facts are known concerning the action of enzymes which indicate that they belong to the group of substances known in chemistry as catalysts. Now, a catalyst increases the velocity of a chemical reaction, but does not actually initiate the reaction. Nor does a catalyst become altered or form a part of the product of the reaction. Catalytic action has been compared by Sir William Bayliss to the effect which a drop of oil exerts upon the speed of a metal weight moving down a glass incline. The oil hastens, but does not initiate, the movement of the weight, nor does it combine with the metal or the glass, or undergo any chemical change whatever. To take a specific instance of catalytic action: when acetic acid and ethyl alcohol are mixed, ethyl acetate is formed slowly, but the velocity of the reaction is greatly increased by the addition of a very small amount of hydrochloric acid. Thus:

$$HCl + CH_3COOH + C_2H_5OH \leftrightharpoons CH_3COOC_2H_5 + HOH$$

hydrochloric acid	acetic acid	ethyl alcohol	ethyl acetate	water

It will be seen from this equation that the hydrochloric acid does not enter into the reaction. The latter, as shown by the arrows, is reversible. That is, the combination of acetic acid with ethyl alcohol to form ethyl acetate is accompanied by a reaction in the opposite direction —namely, the breakdown of ethyl acetate into acetic acid and ethyl alcohol. When the velocities of these two opposing reactions are equal, a state of equilibrium has been reached. If the concentration of ethyl acetate is raised, the velocity of the reaction on the left is increased—that is, the reaction shifts to the left until equilibrium is reached again; if the concentrations of acetic acid and ethyl alcohol are raised, the reaction shifts to the right,[1] or the concentration of ethyl acetate is reduced by removing it as it is formed. The hydrochloric acid increases the velocity of the reaction in either direction; it is an *inorganic catalyst*. Enzymes act in the same way; they are, therefore, *organic catalysts*—that is, catalysts formed by living organisms. It should be pointed out that both types of catalyst exert their effects in very low concentrations; a small quantity of ptyalin, for example, will convert a relatively large quantity of starch to maltose; "a little leaven leaveneth the whole lump."

Enzymes differ in one important respect from most of the inorganic catalysts in being absolutely specific in their actions. Ptyalin, for example, acts upon starch, but has no effect whatsoever upon proteins or fats; pepsin converts protein to proteoses and peptones, but has no action upon the other two types of foodstuff.

Reversibility of enzyme action. The actions of most enzymes are reversible. That is to say, after catalyzing a certain reaction, they can drive that reaction in the opposite direction and cause the reverse effect. This is indicated in the equation shown above, and has already been noted for carbonic anhydrase (p. 112). But in the case of the digestive enzymes and many others, reversibility of action does not occur in the body to any appreciable degree, though it can be demonstrated *in vitro*. It has been shown, for example, that pepsin (p. 307) can synthesize a proteinlike substance from a solution containing a mixture of amino acids.

Conditions which influence the action of enzymes. 1. *Optimum temperature*. Enzymes act with maximum efficiency at a certain temperature (*optimum temperature*). Lowering the temperature below, or raising it above, this level slows the reaction. There is a certain definite temperature for each enzyme at which it acts at maximal efficiency. The digestive and other enzymes of animals act best around the temperature of the body. A high degree of heat (above 60° C) permanently abolishes their action.

2. *Hydrogen ion concentration*. The optimum pH for the different enzymes varies widely; for pepsin it is around 1.5, for pancreatic amylase about 7.0. The former enzyme is inactive in an alkaline medium, the latter in a strongly acid medium.

---

[1] These facts are embodied in the *law of mass action* which states that "the velocity of a chemical reaction is proportional to the concentrations of the reacting substances."

3. *Inorganic salts.* Enzyme action is profoundly affected by certain ions, notably chloride which is necessary for the activation of the amylases. Magnesium greatly accelerates the action of phosphatase, and trypsin is activated by calcium. Iron is essential for the action of certain respiratory enzymes in the tissues. Substances such as these, which activate or enhance the action of enzymes, are called *coenzymes.*

4. *Poisons.* Mercury, gold, copper, and several other heavy metals exert a strongly toxic effect owing, apparently, to their combining with the enzyme. Cyanides abolish the action of oxidizing enzymes of the tissues (p. 263). Fluorides, bromine, iodine, and chloroform are also toxic for some enzymes.

5. *The products of the enzyme reaction.* It has been mentioned (p. 290) that an enzyme reaction comprises two processes—decomposition and synthesis—proceeding simultaneously. As the equilibrium point is approached the velocity of the reaction gradually diminishes. For example, in the conversion of starch to maltose by ptyalin, the reaction proceeds rapidly at first, but as the concentration of maltose increases, the velocity of the opposing or synthetic reaction—maltose to starch—increases. At a certain stage the quantity of starch broken down in a given time just balances the quantity resynthesized. In other words, the enzyme reaction, to all intents and purposes, ceases as a result of the accumulation of its own products. If more starch (substrate) is added, the reaction starts again and continues until equilibrium is again reached.

Nomenclature. The material upon which an enzyme acts is called the *substrate,* and it is now the practice to derive the name of the enzyme by adding the suffix *"ase"* to the name of its substrate. For example, an enzyme which hydrolyzes starch is called an *amylase* (L. *amylum,* starch); one which acts upon protein, a *proteinase;* and on fat, a *lipase* (Gk. *lipos,* fat). *Amyolytic* (starch-splitting), *proteolytic* (protein-splitting), and *lipolytic* (fat-splitting) are corresponding terms used to denote the respective actions of these three types of enzyme. In some instances the name of the enzyme is coined by suffixing *"ase"* to the name of the reaction which it brings about. Thus an enzyme which causes deaminations (p. 363) is called a *deaminase.* and an oxidizing enzyme an *oxidase.*

Names were given to certain digestive enzymes before the system of terminology just outlined had come into use. The ferment of the saliva, for example, has long been known as *ptyalin. Pepsin* of the gastric juice, and *trypsin* (protein-splitting enzymes), *amylopsin* (starch-splitting enzyme), and *steapsin* (fat-splitting enzyme) given to the ferments of pancreatic juice are also old-established names. Corresponding terms in the new system are *salivary amylase, gastric proteinase*, and *pancreatic proteinase, amylase*, and *lipase*.

The physiological properties of smooth (nonstriated) muscle. Smooth muscle differs from skeletal muscle in the following respects: (a) slower, more sluggish contraction; (b) greater extensibility; (c) the exhibition of a sustained contraction or tonus for long periods, even though separated from the central nervous system; (d) the power of rhythmical contraction; (e) the possession of a double autonomic innervation (parasympathetic and sympathetic); (f) greater sensitivity

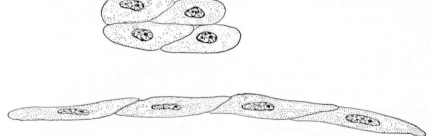

Fig. 8.2   Diagram to illustrate the manner in which muscle fibers may slide over one another and increase the capacity of a hollow organ. The *upper group* of four muscle cells is from a hollow organ whose walls are contracted and its cavity almost obliterated; the *lower group* are the same muscle fibers when the organ is full. (Redrawn from Grützner.)

to thermal and chemical influences and to certain types of mechanical stimulation, such as stretching, but a lower excitability to electrical stimulation.

Tonus of smooth muscle may be defined as the steady sustained contraction through which the muscle offers resistance to a stretching force. The rhythmical contractions are superimposed upon the tonus state which may vary independently of the rhythmical contractions themselves. The tonic contraction of smooth muscle is associated with a negligible expenditure of energy. It is relatively insusceptible to fatigue; heat production and electrical changes are not detectable; and a rise or fall in the degree of tonus is not accompanied by a corresponding change in oxygen consumption.

Certain hollow organs, such as the stomach and urinary bladder and, to a less degree, the intestines, have the remarkable ability to enlarge when their contents are considerably increased without showing any rise in internal pressure. The tone of the muscle composing the walls of these organs becomes adjusted automatically to the distending force. This *postural tone,* as it is called, is very difficult to explain. It is possible that, in the stomach at any rate, the individual fibers which are disposed in layers, instead of being lengthened by the stretching force, simply slide over one another, the wall of the organ thus being increased in area but reduced in thickness. This could occur with little strain being placed upon the fibers themselves. In Figure 8.2 will be found a diagram illustrating the manner in which this might result.

Digestion in the Mouth

The structure of the salivary glands. Saliva is secreted by three pairs of glands—the *submaxillary, sublingual* (or submandibular), and *parotid glands.* The submaxillary glands are situated beneath the floor of the mouth in close relation, one on either side, with the inner aspect of the lower jaw (mandible). The submaxillary secretion reaches the cavity of the mouth through the *duct of Wharton,* which opens beneath the tongue. The sublingual glands also lie below the floor of the mouth, but nearer the mid-line. Each sublingual gland pours its

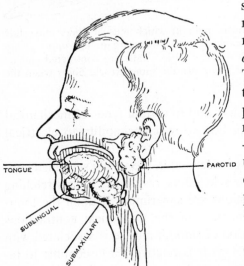

secretion into the mouth beneath the tongue through a number of small ducts—*ducts of Rivinus* and of *Bartholin.* The parotid gland lies below the ear, behind and overlapping the vertical part of the mandible (jawbone). Its duct —the *duct of Stenson*—opens upon the inner aspect of the cheek opposite the second upper molar tooth (see Fig. 8.3).

Fig. 8.3   Showing the salivary glands of one side.

The salivary glands are composed of cells arranged in small groups around a central globular cavity called the *alveolus* or *acinus.* The alveoli are drained by fine ducts which join with those from neighboring alveoli to form larger channels. Through the successive junctions of smaller ducts and the formation of larger ones, the secretion is directed into the main secretory duct or ducts (Fig. 8.4). This alveolar arrangement of the cells and the system of ducts of the salivary glands

Fig. 8.4 Showing the plan of a racemose gland such as the salivary (diagrammatic). The small globular structures are alveoli or acini, some of which are represented as having been cut across.

suggests a bunch of grapes. To these and other glands (e.g., the pancreas), showing a similar pattern, the term *racemose* (L. *racemus,* a bunch of grapes) is therefore applied.

The cells of the salivary glands are of two types, *serous* and *mucous.* The secretion of the former type is thin and watery; that of the latter type contains mucin, and is therefore thicker, and more slimy and viscous. The parotid gland is composed entirely of serous cells, whereas the cells of the sublingual gland are predominantly of the mucous type, serous cells being scarce. The submaxillary gland contains both serous and mucous cells in about equal proportions, the two types being seen in many instances in the wall of the same alveolus. The serous cells are then found on the outer side of the mucous cells which, therefore, lie between the former and the alveolar cavity. Here they appear as crescentic bodies known as the *demilunes of Gianuzzi* (Fig. 8.5).

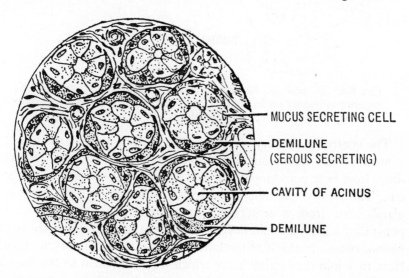

MUCUS SECRETING CELL

DEMILUNE
(SEROUS SECRETING)

CAVITY OF ACINUS

DEMILUNE

Fig. 8.5   Microscopical section of a submaxillary salivary gland, showing mucous cells and demilunes of Gianuzzi.

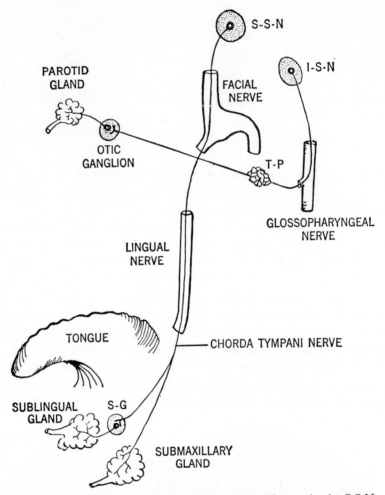

Fig. 8.6 Diagram of the nerve supply of the salivary glands. S-S-N, superior salivatory nucleus; I-S-N, inferior salivatory nucleus; S-G, submaxillary ganglion; T-P, tympanic plexus.

The control of salivary secretion. The salivary glands are under the control of the autonomic (involuntary) nervous system, receiving fibers from both parasympathetic and sympathetic divisions of this system. The *parasympathetic* fibers to the submaxillary and sublingual glands arise from a center—the *superior salivatory center*—in the pons; they leave the brain in the facial nerve and are conveyed in the *chorda tympani* branch of the latter nerve to the cavity of the mouth. Here they join the *lingual nerve* which transmits them to the floor of the mouth where, separating again from the lingual fibers, they make connections with ganglion cells situated in close relationship with the sublingual gland, or within the substance of the submaxillary gland (see Fig. 8.6). Postganglionic fibers—the axons of the ganglion cells —pass to the secreting cells.

The chorda tympani nerve also carries vasodilator fibers (p. 196) to the glands and taste fibers to the anterior two thirds of the tongue. The posterior third of the tongue receives taste fibers through the glossopharyngeal nerve. The submaxillary and sublingual glands receive, as well, secretory and vasoconstrictor fibers from the sympathetic plexus investing the neighboring branches of the external carotid artery. The parotid gland derives secretory and vasodilator parasympathetic fibers through the tympanic branch of the glossopharyngeal nerve. These fibers arise from a group of cells in the upper part of the medulla oblongata called the *inferior salivatory nucleus.* Vasoconstrictor fibers to the parotid gland are derived from the sympathetic.

Stimulation of either the parasympathetic (chorda tympani) fibers or of the sympathetic fibers to the submaxillary or sublingual gland causes a secretion of saliva. The secretion resulting from parasympathetic stimulation is, in most animals, profuse and watery in consistency; sympathetic stimulation, on the contrary, causes a scanty secretion of a thick and slimy mucinous juice. Apparently, then, the parasympathetic fibers innervate the serous cells, and the sympathetic fibers the mucous cells. Stimulation of the parasympathetic fibers to the parotid gland also causes a profuse watery secretion, whereas no obvious secretion follows stimulation of the sympathetic.

Under natural conditions, the secretion of saliva is a reflex phenomenon usually brought about by the stimulation of the taste fibers in the mouth. But stimulation of the ordinary sensory nerves in the mucosa of the mouth—that is, those fibers conveying sensations of touch, pain, and temperature—evokes a flow of saliva. We are all familiar with the salivation which results from moving some tasteless object around in the mouth, or from the manipulations of the dentist. Indeed, secretion of saliva may follow stimulation of almost any afferent nerve in the body. In animals, stimulation of the central cut end of the sciatic nerve excites salivary secretion and, in man, irritation of the nerves of the stomach or esophagus, in diseased states, is not uncommonly a cause of troublesome salivation.

Salivary reflexes are of two types. The salivary response evoked by the introduction of material into the mouth is called an *unconditional reflex.* But it is well known that salivation very often results from the sight, smell, or even the thought of food. We often hear a person say that his "mouth waters" when he sees or smells appetizing food. The response following such forms of stimulation is called a *conditioned reflex*. The unconditioned reflex is inborn; it can be elicited immediately after birth. The conditioned reflex, on the contrary, depends upon experience. In order for it to become established, an association, upon some previous occasion, must have been formed in the brain between sensations received through the nerves of taste and those gained through some other sense organ (e.g., eye, nose, ear, etc.). We need say no more here of this type of reflex; it will be considered in more detail in Chapter 12.

The characters, quantity, and composition of saliva. Normal human saliva as collected from the mouth (i.e., mixed saliva, containing secretions of all six glands, as well as the secretion of the small mucous glands scattered diffusely over the mucosa of the mouth) is slightly acid in reaction, varying between pH 6.35 and 6.85. Its specific gravity is between 1.002 and 1.008. The average adult secretes from 1200 cc to 1500 cc of saliva in 24 hours. The composition of saliva is given in the following table.

Table 8-1

I. *Salts* (approximately 0.2 percent)
    Sodium and potassium chloride
    Sodium bicarbonate
    Acid and alkaline sodium phosphates
    Calcium carbonate and calcium phosphates
    Potassium sulphocyanate (thiocyanate)

II. *Gases*
    Carbon dioxide and oxygen

III. *Organic substances*
    Ptyalin (salivary amylase)
    Maltase
    Serum albumin
    Serum globulin
    Urea
    Mucin, mainly from the submaxillary and sublingual secretions

The functions of saliva. 1. *Digestive.* The enzyme of the saliva—*ptyalin*—acts upon starch. The starch molecule is split into smaller molecules of the disaccharide, maltose. The rapid passage of the food through the mouth precludes the possibility that starch is acted upon here to any appreciable extent by the saliva. Whether starchy food, after its thorough impregnation with saliva, undergoes any important degree of digestion in the stomach has been debated. Ptyalin is active in an alkaline, neutral, or faintly acid medium, but is inactivated by strong acid. It was thought, therefore, that the highly acid gastric juice would prevent or soon terminate salivary digestion. It has been shown, however, that the latter part of the meal, which usually contains the carbohydrate, may remain in the upper part (fundus) of the stomach, and thus be protected for some time, from the acidifying action of the gastric juice, by the mass of food ingested previously. For this reason it is likely that, under favorable circumstances, the salivary digestion of starch may proceed for a considerable period after food has reached the stomach.

If boiled starch is placed in a test tube with mixed human saliva and kept at body temperature, a slow conversion of the starch into maltose takes place. The chemical change occurs in a series of stages which may be distinguished by the manner in which the product of each stage reacts with iodine. Iodine gives a characteristic blue color with boiled starch. A short time after the saliva has commenced to act, a physical change may be seen to have occurred in the starch. It loses its opalescent appearance and becomes *soluble,* though it still gives the blue color with iodine. After a short time, this soluble starch becomes partially broken down, being converted into a dextrin which, since it gives a red color with iodine, is known as *erythrodextrin.* Small amounts of maltose may also be detected at this stage. Still later, no color reaction occurs upon the addition of iodine; a colorless product —*achroödextrin*—has been formed. Finally, the starch is entirely converted into maltose and isomaltose. In the final stage, traces of glucose may also appear, due to the presence of an enzyme *maltase* present in saliva in low concentration which splits the disaccharide maltose (see p. 367) into two molecules of glucose. The following scheme illustrates the action of ptyalin:

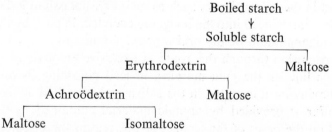

Ptyalin has no action upon cellulose, and for this reason the starch must be cooked in order to rupture the cellulose envelope surrounding the starch grains, and thus allow the enzyme to come into contact with the starch.

2. *Preparation of the food for swallowing by altering its consistency.* This is one of the most important functions of the saliva; the food is moistened, thus enabling it to be rolled into a plastic mass, which, by virtue of the slimy nature of the mucin which the saliva contains, is given a lubricant coating. Claude Bernard showed that a horse with a parotid fistula (the saliva draining to the outer surface of the cheek) had the utmost difficulty in swallowing dry hay or oats.

3. *Solvent action.* Taste is a chemical sense (Chap. 13). All solid substances, therefore, in order that they shall stimulate the taste buds, must be dissolved in the saliva.

4. *Cleansing action.* The constant flow of saliva exerts a very necessary cleansing effect. The mouth and teeth are rinsed and kept comparatively free from food debris, shed epithelial cells, foreign particles, etc.; in this way the saliva tends to inhibit the growth of bacteria by removing material which may serve as culture media. In order to realize how important its function is in this regard, one has but to consider the foul condition of the mouth that occurs in certain fevers (such as typhoid), when the salivary secretion is suppressed. Then, decomposing organic material, swarming with bacteria, collects upon the teeth and lips, and must be removed by artificial means (e.g., by wiping with moistened gauze).

5. *Moistening and lubricating action.* The saliva, by moistening and lubricating the soft parts of the mouth and lips, keeps them pliable and resilient for the purposes of articulation. Frequent sips of water are almost essential for some public speakers in whom, as a result of evaporation from the mouth during speech, or owing to nervousness with consequent inhibition of salivary secretion, the lips and mouth become dry.

6. *Excretory.* Many substances, both organic and inorganic, are excreted in the saliva. Drugs such as mercury, potassium iodide, lead, etc., when introduced into the body, are excreted, in part, by the saliva. Severe inflammation of the oral mucosa (stomatitis) may be caused by the excretion through this route of excessive amounts of mercury. The blue line on the gum margins, in lead poisoning, is due to the metal having been excreted in the saliva and deposited as the sulfide. The sulfur is provided by organic material contained in the tartar formed on the bases of the teeth. For this reason the discoloration of the gum does not occur where teeth are absent. In chronic nephritis the saliva contains a high percentage of urea; sugar sometimes appears in severe diabetes; and in parathyroid overdosage the calcium concentration of the saliva is elevated. Several types of microorganisms, some

intensely virulent—e.g., the virus of hydrophobia (rabies)—are excreted in the saliva.

Mastication. This act comprises the movements of the lower jaw, tongue, lips, and cheeks, whereby the food is reduced to a soft mass which can be easily swallowed. The incisor and canine teeth are used chiefly for tearing the food and breaking it up into small pieces, the

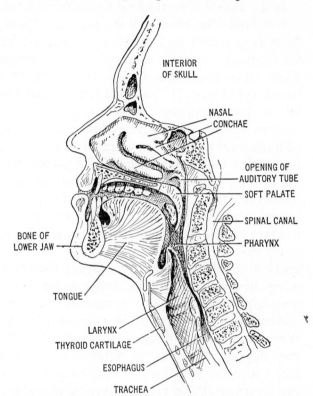

Fig. 8.7 The mouth, nose, pharynx, larynx, and the commencement of the esophagus, as exposed by a section a little to the left of the median plane of the head.

INTERIOR OF SKULL

NASAL CONCHAE

OPENING OF AUDITORY TUBE

SOFT PALATE

SPINAL CANAL

PHARYNX

BONE OF LOWER JAW

TONGUE

LARYNX

THYROID CARTILAGE

ESOPHAGUS

TRACHEA

molars for grinding it. The movements of the tongue, lips, and cheeks move the food about in the mouth, apply pressure or suction to it, and introduce fresh material between the jaws. The whole mass thus becomes thoroughly impregnated with saliva. The jaw movements are brought about by the contractions of *temporal, masseter,* and *pterygoid* muscles, all of which are supplied by the third division of the trigeminal (fifth cranial) nerve.

Swallowing or deglutition. The act of swallowing is usually described in three stages. In the *first stage,* the masticated food mass or *bolus,* as it is called, is moved to the upper surface of the tongue, which is then drawn sharply backward by the action of muscles, chiefly the mylohyoid, attached to its base. The food is thus projected into the pharynx. The opening into the pharynx, which is called the *fauces*, is limited on either side by two muscular pillars (the *pillars of the fauces*). As a result of the backward movement of the tongue, which at the same time presses against the hard palate, a pressure of 20 cm of water is created in the posterior part of the mouth and pharynx. The first stage of swallowing is a voluntary act.

In the *second stage*, the food passes through the pharynx. This stage is very brief. The muscles of the pharyngeal wall (*constrictors of the pharynx*) contract and, gripping or squeezing the food, force it into the esophagus. There are, however, three other paths which the food might take—into the nose, into the larynx, or back again into the mouth (see Fig. 8.7). The food is prevented from entering the nose by the elevation of the soft palate; the posterior edge of the latter is brought against the posterior pharyngeal wall, thus closing off the pharynx from the posterior entrance to the nasal cavities. This movement rarely fails to take place at the proper time in normal persons, but in the paralysis of the elevators of the palate, which sometimes follows diphtheria, the passage of liquids into the nose during swallowing is a common occurrence. The base of the tongue, which continues to be held in position against the fauces, and the approximation of the muscles forming the pillars of the fauces effectively block communication with the cavity of the mouth. Elevation of the larynx, which brings its opening under the shelter of the epiglottis and base of the tongue, prevents the food from entering the air passages. This upward movement of the larynx is an essential part of the swallowing act. When, as a result of disease, the larynx is fixed, swallowing becomes very difficult or impossible. When the movement is not accurately timed with the pharyngeal movements, food enters the larynx and excites the coughing reflex. Everyone at some time or another has experienced this accident.

A short inspiration (inspiration of swallowing) occurs at the commencement of the first stage; this is followed by complete inhibition of respiration, which persists until the end of the second stage.

The third stage is occupied in passing the food down the esophagus into the stomach. In man, the upper two thirds of the esophagus is composed of striated muscle, the lower third of smooth muscle. The food is carried through the tube by a peristaltic contraction (p. 336) of the muscular wall, the passage of food being much more rapid through the upper striated portion of the tube than through the lower part. The esophagus of the dog is composed throughout of striated muscle, which accounts for the amazing rapidity with which this animal can swallow food. In the lower end of the esophagus—that is, where it opens into the stomach—the muscle fibers are condensed to form the *cardiac sphincter*.[2] The sphincter at ordinary times is contracted; but it relaxes upon the approach of the food, which is then swept into the stomach by the peristaltic waves. The second and third stages of the swallowing act are entirely reflex in nature—i.e., involuntary. The reflex is initiated by the passage of the food through the fauces. Afferent nerve endings are stimulated by the contact of the food with the mucosa in the region of the fauces and pharynx. Of course, we can swallow at will, even though no food is in the mouth. It might be thought, therefore, that it was not correct to speak of the second and third stages of swallowing as being involuntary. But when one wishes to swallow, food or (if the mouth is empty) a little saliva, by a movement of the tongue, is passed backwards, to act as a stimulus. Swallowing then occurs automatically.

Innervation of the swallowing reflex. The *afferent* fibers of the reflex are contained in the branches of the trigeminal, glossopharyngeal, and vagus nerves supplying the mucous membrane in the region of the fauces, tonsil, and pharynx. Temporarily abolishing the function of the nerve endings in these regions, by the application of a local anesthetic (e.g., cocaine) to the mucous membrane, renders swallowing impossible for a time. The chief swallowing *center* is situated in the medulla oblongata, in the neighborhood of the nucleus of the vagus. The *efferent* fibers travel to the various muscles taking part in the act by the *hypoglossal* (to the muscles of the tongue), by the *trigeminal* (to the mylohyoid muscle in the floor of the mouth), and by the *glossopharyngeal* and *vagus* nerves to the muscles of the pharynx and esophagus.

The nervous control of the cardiac sphincter has for years been a question of some dispute, but in man, at any rate, the vagus appears to exert an inhibitory effect upon the muscle, while excitatory fibers are of sympathetic origin. It sometimes happens, though rarely, that the innervation of the sphincter becomes disordered, the sympathetic being overactive (or the vagus underactive). The muscle, as a result, remains tonically contracted during swallowing, and thus prevents the easy entrance of food into the stomach. Difficulty in swallowing is experienced, and the esophagus for some distance above the obstruction becomes distended by retained food. This condition is called *cardiospasm*.

---

[2] A sphincter is a circular band of muscle which, acting like a purse string when it contracts, serves to narrow the entrance to, or outlet from, certain hollow organs.

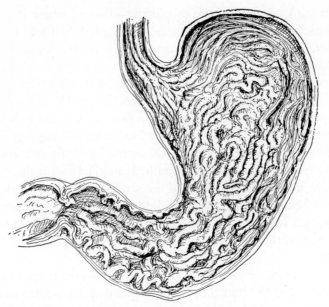

Fig. 8.8   Interior of the stomach showing rugae of the mucous membrane.

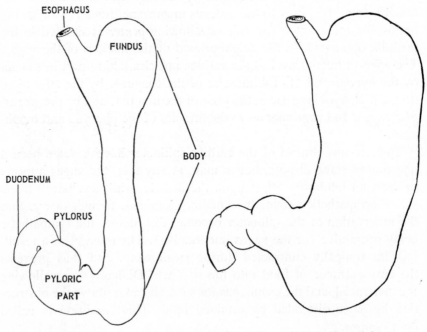

Fig. 8.9   Diagrams of the stomach, *empty* on left, *full* on right.

Digestion in the Stomach

General description of the stomach. The walls of the stomach are composed of smooth muscle fibers arranged in three layers—*longitudinal, circular,* and *oblique*—in this order from without inward, and a lining of mucous membrane. The mucous membrane contains the gastric glands; its surface epithelium is of the columnar nonciliated type. When empty, the stomach is a narrow tubular organ; its mucosa is thrown into numerous longitudinal folds called *rugae*. Its contour varies somewhat in different persons, but most commonly bears a general resemblance to the letter J (see Figs. 8.8, 8.9, and 8.11). The vertical part of the J is called the *body;* the upper part of the body is expanded into a domed chamber by a bubble of gas, and is called the *fundus*. The fundus lies in contact with the diaphragm which intervenes between it and the heart. The region of the stomach corresponding to the hook of the J is named the *pyloric part (pars pylorica).* An annular band of muscle, the *pyloric sphincter,* surrounds the opening between the pyloric part and the *duodenum* (first 10 inches or so of the small intestine). The walls of the empty stomach, except in the region of the fundus, are in contact, but the food after passing through the cardia presses steadily downward, separating the gastric walls. As the organ distends it becomes pear shaped; its rugae become flatter, and, with increasing distension, disappear. The capacity of the human stomach is from 1 to 1½ quarts.

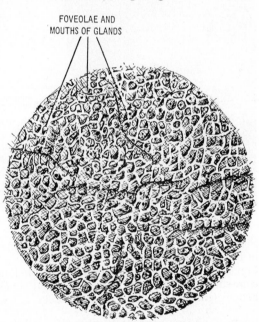

FOVEOLAE AND
MOUTHS OF GLANDS

Fig. 8.10   Mucosa of the stomach highly magnified to show foveolae.

The gastric glands. The gastric juice is secreted by the gastric glands which are scattered diffusely in large numbers throughout the gastric mucosa. The total number of glands in the human stomach is around 35,000,000. They are minute tubular or flask-shaped structures which

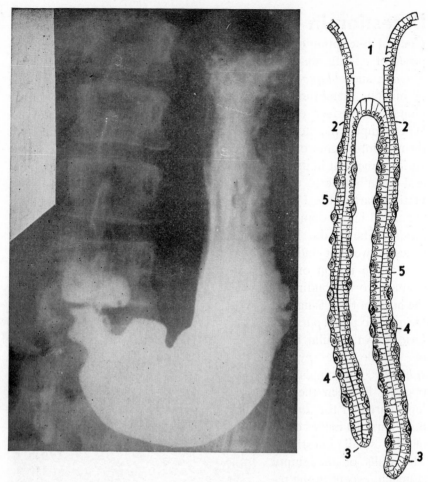

Fig. 8.11   (*Left*) X-ray photograph of a normal J-shaped stomach. (Kindness of Dr. A. C. Singleton.)

Fig. 8.12   (*Right*) Glands from fundus of stomach. 1, pit or foveola on mucous surface of stomach; 2, neck of gland containing mucin-secreting cells; 3, bottom (fundus) of gland; 4, parietal cells; 5, chief cells.

open, each one separately, into a smaller, narrow pit called a *foveola* upon the inner (epithelial) surface of the stomach. The gastric mucosa is dotted with immense numbers of such foveolae (Fig. 8.10).

The cells forming the walls of the glands are continuous with the epithelium covering the gastric mucosa, but differ from the latter both structurally and functionally. The glands in the fundus and the body of the stomach are also different in their histological appearance and in their secretory functions from those in the lower part of the stomach (pyloric region). The cells of the glands in the fundus and body of the stomach are of three types and are called, respectively, (a) *mucous neck cells* or *chief cells of the neck,* (b) *chief* or *zymogenic cells,* (c) *parietal* or *border cells.* The mucous neck cells are situated in the narrow superficial part of the gland tubule called the neck. They secrete mucus (Fig. 8.12). The chief or zymogenic cells form a continuous lining for the deeper part or body of the gland tubule. These cells secrete the enzymes of the gastric juice. The parietal or border cells do not form a continuous layer, but lie here and there along the tubule to the outer side of the chief cells. They are entirely responsible for the production of the hydrochloric acid of the juice.

The glands of the pyloric region contain only mucus-secreting cells; chief cells and parietal cells are absent; their secretion is alkaline in reaction. The mucosa for a small area near the cardia also contains glands of this type.

The composition and actions of gastric juice. The *gastric juice* contains *enzymes, mucin,* and *hydrochloric acid.* An analysis of human gastric juice is given in Table 8-2.

Table 8-2

Human gastric juice

Acidity   Free HCl, 0.50 to 0.60 percent
Total acidity, 0.45 to 0.60 percent
pH, 0.9 to 1.5

Solids   Organic, including mucin and the various ferments, 0.42 to 0.46 percent
Inorganic, 0.13 to 0.14 percent

Specific gravity, 1.006 to 1.009

Total nitrogen, 0.051 to 0.075 percent

The enzymes are *pepsin, rennin,* and *lipase.* The pepsin acts upon protein. The protein molecule, as we shall see (p. 360), is constituted of large groups of amino acids linked together. The first important action of the gastric juice upon the food is the combination of the hydrochloric acid with protein material to form *acid metaprotein.* The pepsin then acts upon the latter, splitting the protein structure into smaller molecules called *proteoses* and *peptones.* The attack made upon protein by pepsin ceases at this stage.

When the mucosa of the fundus or body of the stomach is extracted with an alkaline solution, the extract possesses little or no proteolytic activity, but becomes active upon acidification. It is, therefore, sometimes stated that pepsin is secreted as an inactive precursor which differs chemically from active pepsin, and is referred to as *pepsinogen*. A simpler and more correct explanation of the observation that an alkaline extract of the gastric mucosa is inactive is based upon the fact that pepsin, like other enzymes, acts best at a certain pH (*optimum pH*), and becomes inactive if any great change from this reaction occurs. The optimum pH for the action of pepsin is around 1.5, which is the reaction of pure gastric juice.

The concentration of hydrochloric acid in gastric juice, as the latter is secreted by the glands, is from 0.5 percent to 0.6 percent. The contents of the stomach have rarely, however, an acidity as high as this, for the juice, after it reaches the cavity of the stomach, becomes diluted by other fluids—e.g., saliva, mucus from the gastric epithelium, the alka-

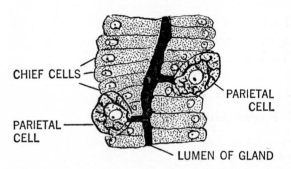

CHIEF CELLS

PARIETAL CELL

PARIETAL CELL

LUMEN OF GLAND

Fig. 8.13 High magnification of a portion of gastric gland to show intercellular and intracellular canaliculi.

line secretion of the pyloric glands, and food residues. The hydrochloric acid is formed by the parietal cells and is apparently secreted as such into the cavity of the tubules passing along fine canals (canaliculi) running between the chief cells. These intercellular canaliculi drain a network of still finer channels within the parietal cells (Fig. 8.13). The acid is not, as was at one time believed, secreted in the form of a precursor which is converted to hydrochloric acid after reaching the lumina of the tubules, or the cavity of the stomach. Indeed, it is a truly remarkable fact that the cells *do* form and secrete a mineral acid of such high concentration. Also, it may well be asked, why do not the pepsin and hydrochloric acid of the gastric juice digest the stomach itself? This is a conundrum which until recently has received no satisfactory solution. It is no answer to this question to say that the stomach is living tissue and so can protect itself, for, if the leg of a living frog is inserted into the stomach of a dog, it undergoes digestion about as readily as if it were a piece of beef.[3] It has been discovered, however, that

[3] Digestion of the mucous membranes by pepsin hydrochloric acid is a potent factor in the development of gastric or duodenal ulcer (p. 315).

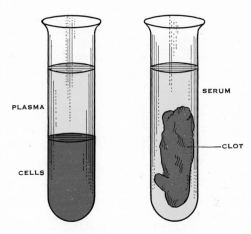

PLATE 1

Left, sample of blood immediately after centrifuging, showing the separation of cells (about 45 percent) from plasma (about 55 percent). *Right*, uncentrifuged sample of blood about one hour after it has coagulated and the clot has condensed or *retracted*.

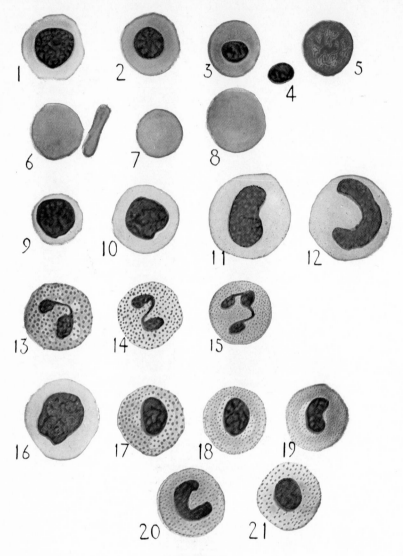

PLATE 2

The blood cells. 1–6, stages in the development of the red cells. 1, megaloblast;
2, erythroblast, note bluish tint of cytoplasm (polychromasia); 3, normoblast;
4, extruded nucleus; 5, reticulocyte; 6, fully mature erythrocyte, front and profile
views; 7, microcyte, as seen in microcytic hypochromic types of anemia; 8, mac-
rocyte, as seen in pernicious and certain other types of anemia. 9–15, varieties
of leucocytes. 9, small lymphocyte; 10, large lymphocyte; 11 and 12, two types
of monocyte; 13, eosinophil; 14, basophil; 15, neutrophil. 16–21, stages in
the development of the leucocytes. 16, myeloblast; 17, eosinophil myelocyte;
18, 19 and 20, three ages of neutrophil myelocytes; 21, basophil myelocyte.

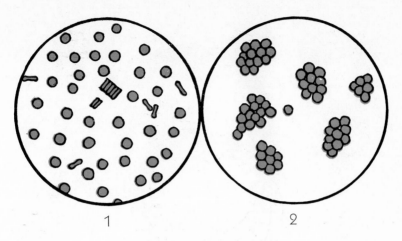

PLATE 3A

1, corpuscles mixed with compatible serum; 2, agglutination of corpuscles caused by incompatible serum.

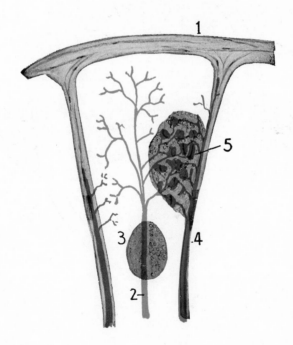

PLATE 3B

Section of a lobule of the spleen. 1, capsule; 2, branch of splenic artery; 3, Malpighian corpuscle; 4, vein; 5, splenic pulp showing blood sinuses (semi-diagrammatic).

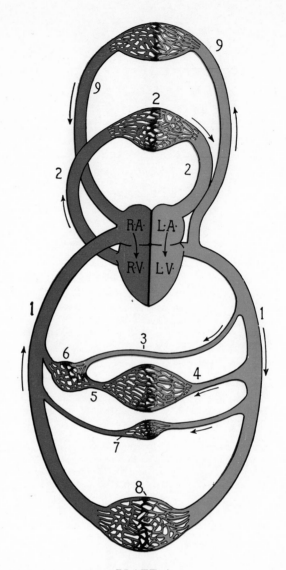

PLATE 4

Diagram of the circulation. 1, systemic circulation; 2, pulmonary circulation; 3, hepatic artery; 4, arteries to gastro-intestinal tract and spleen; 5, portal vein; 6, hepatic circulation; 7, renal circulation; 8, capillary bed of lower limbs; 9, capillary bed of head and neck. R.A., right auricle; R.V., right ventricle; L.A., left auricle; L.V., left ventricle.

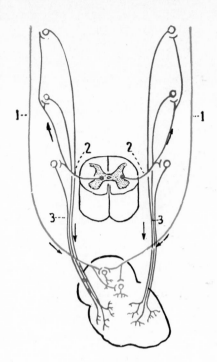

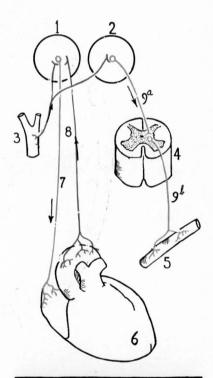

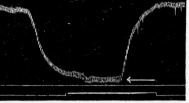

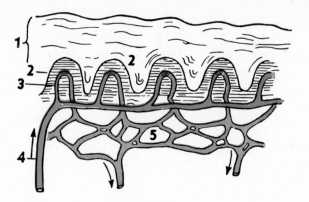

PLATE 6A

A diagram of the circulation through the skin. 1, epidermis; 2, papillae; 3, capillary loop; 4, terminal arteriole; 5, subpapillary venous plexus. The venous limb of the capillary loop and the plexus are shown in the conventional blue color, but actually the blood in these channels in health is little darker than arterial blood.

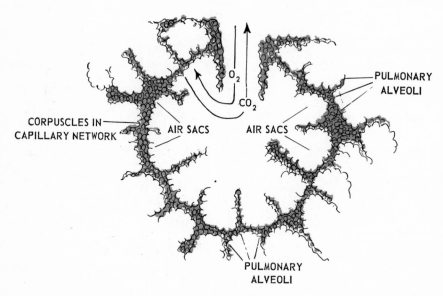

PLATE 6B

Diagram illustrating the exchange of gases between the blood and the alveolar air.

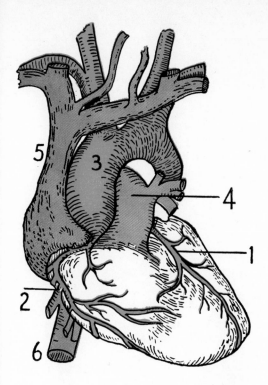

Showing the coronary arteries. 1, left coronary artery; 2, right coronary artery; 3, aorta; 4, pulmonary artery; 5, superior vena cava; 6, inferior vena cava.

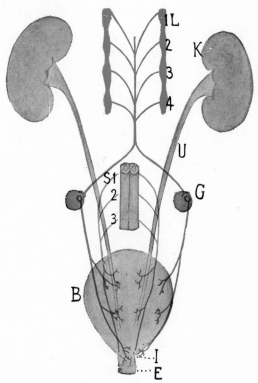

PLATE 7B

Diagram of the innervation of the urinary bladder. B, bladder; E, external sphincter; G, hypogastric ganglion; I, internal sphincter; K, kidney; U, ureter. L. 1, 2, 3, 4 refer to the ganglia of the lumbar sympathetic chain. S. 1, 2, 3, indicate the first, second, and third sacral segments of the spinal cord.

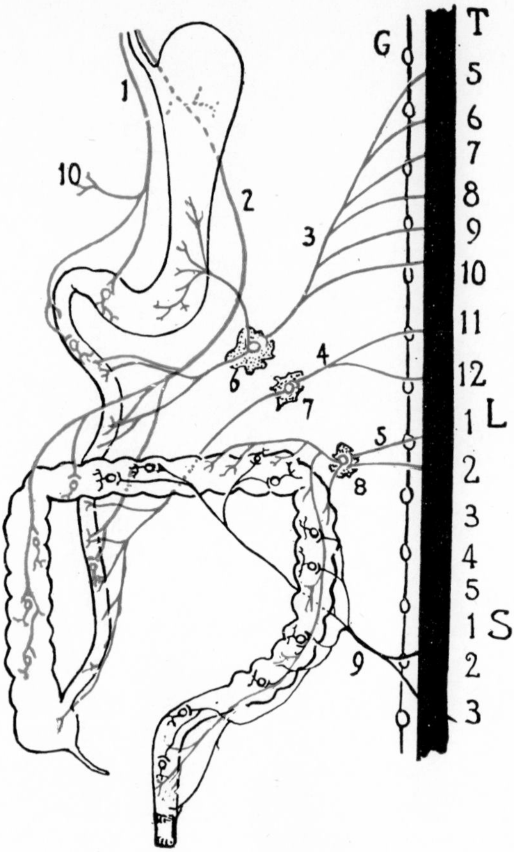

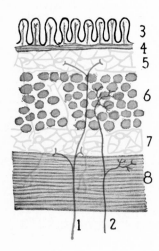

PLATE 8A

Diagram of the nerve supply of the gastro-intestinal tract. 1, 2, vagus nerves. All vagal fibers, preganglionic and postganglionic, in *red*, sympathetic in *blue*, pelvic nerve *black*. 3, 4 and 5, splanchnic nerves (sympathetic); 6, 7 and 8, prevertebral sympathetic ganglia; 9, pelvic nerve; 10, to liver; G, gangliated cord of sympathetic; T, 5–12, thoracic segments of spinal cord; L, 1–5, lumbar segments; S, 1–3, sacral segments.

PLATE 8B

Nerve plexuses of the intestinal wall. Preganglionic fibers of vagus (1) in *red;* postganglionic fibers of sympathetic (2) in *blue;* plexuses (5 and 7) in *yellow*. 3, intestinal villi; 4, muscularis mucosae; 5, submucous (Meissner's) plexus; 6, circular muscular coat, fibers shown in cross section; 7, myenteric (Auerbach's) plexus; 7, longitudinal muscular coat.

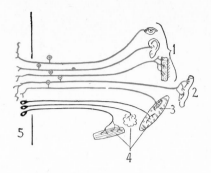

PLATE 9A

Diagram of receptor and effector organs. 1, exteroceptors; 2, interoceptors; 3, proprioceptors (muscle spindles); 4, effector organs, smooth muscle, gland and skeletal muscle; 5, central nervous system.

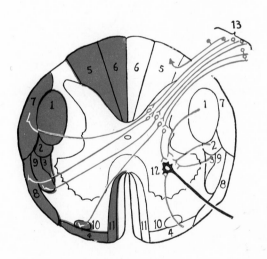

PLATE 9B

Diagram of a cross section of the spinal cord to show the main nerve tracts. Ascending tracts in blue, descending in red. 1, lateral (crossed) corticospinal tract; 2, rubrospinal tract; 3, lateral vestibulospinal tract; 4, anterior vestibulospinal tract; 5, fasciculus cuneatus; 6, fasciculus gracilis; 7, posterior spinocerebellar tract; 8, anterior spinocerebellar tract; 9, posterior spinothalamic tract; 10, anterior spinothalamic tract; 11, anterior (direct) corticospinal tract; 12, anterior horn cell (motor neuron); 13, fibers of posterior spinal nerve root connecting with secondary neurons in spinal gray matter.

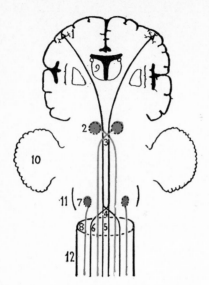

Diagram of the descending tracts of the cord. 1, Betz cell of motor area of the cerebral cortex; 2, red nucleus; 3, crossing of rubrospinal tracts (decussation of Forel); 4, decussation of pyramids; 5, anterior corticospinal tract (direct pyramidal tract); 6, lateral corticospinal (crossed pyramidal) tract; 7, vestibular nucleus; 8, vestibulospinal tract; 9, optic thalamus; 10, cerebellum; 11, medulla oblongata; 12, spinal cord.

PLATE 10B

Diagram of the ascending tracts of the cord. 1, optic thalamus (thalamus of left side not shown in order that the connections may be seen more clearly); 2, cerebellum; 3, nuclei gracilis and cuneatus in medulla oblongata; 4, (*red*), lateral spinothalamic tract pathway for pain; 5, (*yellow*), fiber conveying sensations of touch, etc., to the opposite side of the cord; 6, (*blue*), fiber transmitting touch up the posterior columns; 7 and 8, (*black*), direct and indirect spinocerebellar tracts; 9, midline.

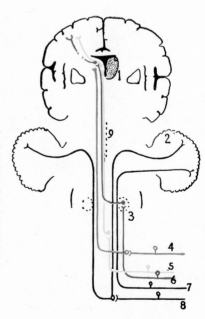

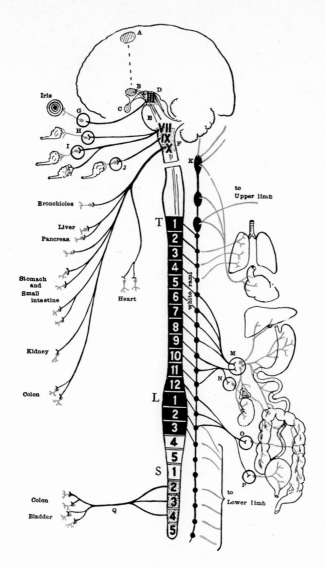

PLATE 11

Plan of the autonomic nervous system. Parasympathetic fibers on left, sympathetic on right; preganglionic in *black*, postganglionic in *red*. Parasympathetic centers in stippled shading. The Roman numerals refer to the respective cranial nerves. A, cerebral cortex; B, hypothalamus; C, pituitary gland; D, mid-brain; E, pons; F, medulla oblongata; G, ciliary ganglion; H, sphenopalatine ganglion, postganglionic fibers to lachrymal gland. I, submaxillary ganglion, postganglionic fibers to sublingual gland, submaxillary gland below, ganglion cells within the gland substance; J, otic ganglion, postganglionic fibers to parotid gland; K, superior cervical ganglion, postganglionic fibers to iris, blood vessels, sweat glands and smooth muscle of head. The middle and inferior cervical ganglia are shown below. M, N, O, P, celiac, superior mesenteric, inferior mesenteric and hypogastric ganglia, respectively; Q, pelvic nerve. The large letters T, L and S indicate, respectively, the thoracic, lumbar and sacral segments of the spinal cord.

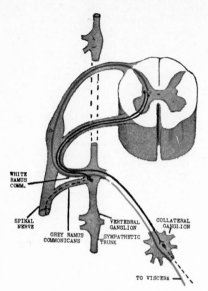

WHITE
RAMUS
COMM.

SPINAL
NERVE

GREY RAMUS
COMMONICANS

VERTEBRAL
GANGLION

SYMPATHETIC
TRUNK

COLLATERAL
GANGLION

TO VISCERA

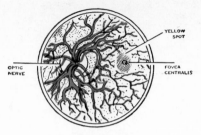

YELLOW
SPOT

OPTIC
NERVE

FOVEA
CENTRALIS

PLATE 12B

The interior of the posterior half of the left eyeball showing the entrance of the optic nerve (optic papilla or disk), retinal vessels, macula lutea, and fovea centralis.

PLATE 12A

Diagram of the connections of the sympathetic fibers. Efferent fibers in black; preganglionic, solid lines; postganglionic, interrupted lines; afferent visceral fiber in red. Collateral ganglion = prevertebral ganglion. (After Best and Taylor, *The Physiological Basis of Medical Practice.*)

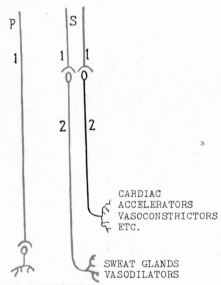

P

S

1

1 1

2 2

CARDIAC
ACCELERATORS
VASOCONSTRICTORS
ETC.

SWEAT GLANDS
VASODILATORS

CARDIO-INHIBITORS
VASODILATORS
ETC.

PLATE 12C

Diagram to illustrate the division of the autonomic nervous system into cholinergic and adrenergic types of fiber. P, parasympathetic; S, sympathetic; 1, preganglionic fibers; 2, postganglionic fibers; cholinergic fibers, *red;* adrenergic, *black.* (The figure 2 has been omitted in error from the postganglionic parasympathetic fiber.)

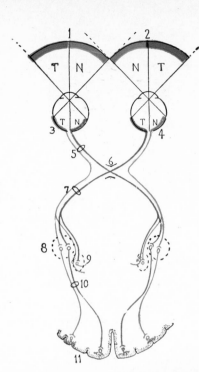

Illustrating the course of the visual fibers from the retina to the occipital cortex. 1, left visual field; 2, right visual field; 3, left retina; 4, right retina; T = temporal, N = nasal; 5, optic nerve; 6, optic chiasma; 7, optic tract; 8, lateral geniculate body; 9, superior colliculus; 10, optic radiation; 11, visual area of the occipital cortex.

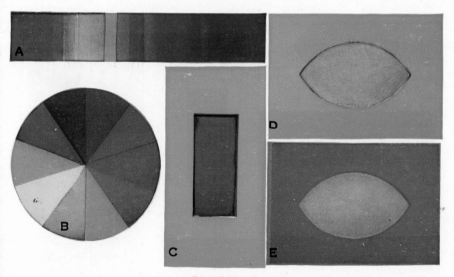

PLATE 13B

The spectrum. The series of colors — *red, orange, yellow, green, blue,* and *violet* — produced when sunlight is split into its constituents by means of a prism. B, complementary colors arranged as segments of a disk. The color pairs which are directly opposite one another are complementary. C illustrates successive contrast. If the figure is stared at for about a minute and the eyes are then directed to a sheet of white paper, the figure will float before the sight with the colors reversed, i.e., a *green* bar will be seen upon a *red* ground. D and E illustrate simultaneous contrast. The figures should be looked at through tissue paper. In D the *gray* ground takes on a *pink* tint (*red* is complementary to *green*). In E the *gray* takes on a faintly *yellow* tint (*yellow* is complementary to *blue*).

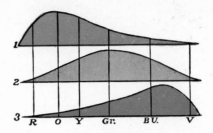

PLATE 14A

Diagram of the three primary color sensations (Young-Helmholtz theory). 1 represents the red, 2 the green and 3 the violet color sensation. The lettering along the base line indicates the colors of the spectrum. The diagram indicates by the height of the curve at which it is cut by the vertical lines the extent to which the several primary sensations of color are excited by vibrations of different wave lengths. (After Helmholtz.)

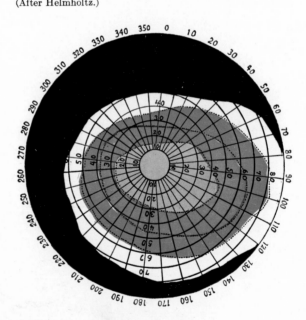

PLATE 14B

Chart showing color fields of the right retina. The entire area of the retina circumscribed by the periphery of a given colored band is sensitive to that color. Area for yellow not shown. (After Howell.)

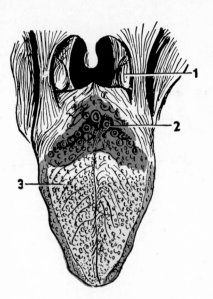

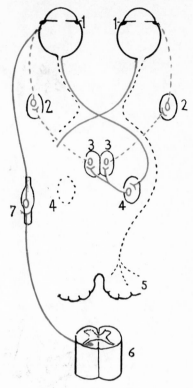

PLATE 15A

Map of tongue, showing distribution of the fundamental taste sensations. *Yellow*, sweet; *blue*, acid and salty; *green*, bitter. 1, tonsil; 2, circumvallate papillae; 3, fungiform papillae.

PLATE 15B

The nerves of the iris. Constrictor pathway (afferent and efferent) in *red*, dilators in *blue*, visual fibers *black* interrupted lines. 1, iris and ciliary muscle; 2, ciliary ganglion; 3, nucleus of oculomotor nerve; 4, superior colliculus; 5, visual area of the cortex; 6, spinal cord; 7, superior cervical ganglion.

PLATE 15C

Very early human ovum embedded in uterine wall. Note the interlocking of the tissue of the ovum (chorionic villi) with the uterine tissue (decidua). The red areas are blood sinuses. 1, amniotic cavity; 2, yolk sac; 3, embryo. (After Bryce.)

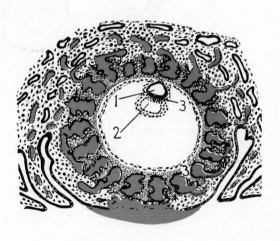

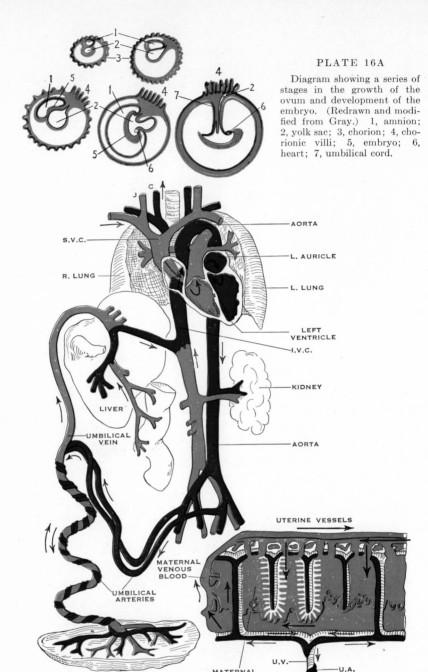

Diagram showing a series of stages in the growth of the ovum and development of the embryo. (Redrawn and modified from Gray.) 1, amnion; 2, yolk sac; 3, chorion; 4, chorionic villi; 5, embryo; 6, heart; 7, umbilical cord.

AORTA

S.V.C.

L. AURICLE

R. LUNG

L. LUNG

LEFT VENTRICLE

I.V.C.

KIDNEY

LIVER

UMBILICAL VEIN

AORTA

UTERINE VESSELS

MATERNAL VENOUS BLOOD

UMBILICAL ARTERIES

U.V.

U.A.

PLACENTA

MATERNAL BLOOD IN INTERVILLOUS SPACES

PLATE 16B

Fetal circulation. *Red*, oxygenated blood; *blue*, reduced blood; *purple*, mixed blood; C, carotid artery; I.V.C., inferior vena cava; J., jugular vein; S.V.C., superior vena cava; *small diagram below* represents a section of the placenta; only two complete villi are shown; *red* indicates maternal blood delivered into intervillous spaces, and, after giving up oxygen, is returned by uterine veins (*blue*); U.A., umbilical artery; U.V., umbilical vein.

ammonia is formed in the gastric mucosa which, being alkaline, protects the gastric tissue from the action of the acid.

The hydrochloric acid is formed from the sodium chloride of the blood, but, though several theories have been advanced, the manner in which the gland cells accomplish this chemical feat is not clearly understood.

Rennin coagulates milk, producing a flocculent mass called the *curd*, and a clear fluid known as *whey*. This action has been made use of from time immemorial in cheese making, the rennin being extracted from calves' stomachs. The curdling or clotting of milk presents a superficial chemical resemblance to the clotting of blood. As a result of the action of rennin, the soluble milk protein, *caseinogen*, is converted into an insoluble product, and, as in the conversion of fibrinogen to fibrin by thrombin, calcium is necessary for this reaction. The role played by calcium is not, however, the same in both instances. In the clotting of milk, the rennin first splits the caseinogen into two substances—*whey protein* and *paracasein*—both of which are soluble. The latter protein then combines with calcium to form *calcium paracasein* which is insoluble. The whey protein and the calcium paracasein are then digested by pepsin.

The *lipase* of gastric juice has a very weak, fat-splitting action and in the adult is of little practical importance. It acts only upon fats which are in very fine emulsion (e.g., cream and egg yolk). It may be of more value to the infant.

Mucin belongs to the class of glycoproteins (p. 361). It is present in pure gastric juice. It is secreted by the cells in the necks of the glands in the body of the stomach, as well as by the pyloric glands. The secretion of the surface epithelium of the stomach (goblet cells, p. 37) also contains a high percentage of mucin. This latter secretion is a slimy fluid which tends to cling to the surface of the mucosa. It thus serves to protect the mucosa from injury by coarse particles of food and, to a certain extent, from the action of the pepsin hydrochloric acid. It may be mentioned in this regard that mucin is capable of combining with a relatively large amount of hydrochloric acid, and of inhibiting peptic activity. Preparations of mucin obtained from pigs' stomachs have been used recently in the treatment of gastric and duodenal ulcers with the object of protecting the surface of the ulcer from the action of the highly acid gastric juice.

The secretion of gastric juice. It is now customary to speak of three phases of gastric digestion: (1) *psychic* or *cephalic*, (2) *gastric*, and (3) *intestinal*.

The psychic or cephalic phase. It was first shown by the Russian physiologist, Ivan Pavlov (1849–1936), that gastric juice is secreted while food is being chewed, and before any has entered the stomach. The more appetizing the food, the greater is its effect upon gastric secretion. Pavlov, therefore, spoke of the secretion caused in this manner as the *appetite juice.* The secretion under such circumstances is, of course, purely reflex in nature. The afferent fibers of the reflex are in the nerves of taste, the efferent fibers in the vagus nerves; the effect cannot be produced after the vagus nerves have been sectioned.

Fig. 8.14 Dog prepared with an esophageal fistula for "sham feeding."

Pavlov demonstrated this reflex in dogs by what he termed "sham feeding." An animal was first prepared by dividing the esophagus in the neck, bringing the lower end of the upper segment through the neck wound and fixing it there by sutures (Fig. 8.14). The animal, prepared in this way, relishes its food just as does any normal dog, but the food cannot enter the stomach; it simply falls from the open esophagus after it has been swallowed. Nevertheless, a flow of gastric juice results. The juice secreted by the stomach can be collected from an opening made through the abdominal wall into the stomach, and measured. It can then be analyzed for its peptic and acid concentrations, if desired; or a miniature stomach can be fashioned.

The miniature stomach, as fashioned by Pavlov's method, is shown in Figure 8.15. It offers a means of obtaining pure gastric juice, uncontaminated by food or saliva, under various physiological conditions. Since it is in connection by nerves and blood vessels with the main part of the stomach, it is therefore under the same nervous and hormonal influences as the latter.

The psychic secretion of gastric juice has been clearly demonstrated several times in man. In Dr. Carlson's laboratory in Chicago, a man was studied whose esophagus was impassable as a result of an injury received in childhood. A permanent opening had been made through the wall of the abdomen into the stomach. The man could be fed only through this opening, which is called a *gastric fistula.* Through it samples of gastric juice were withdrawn, measured, and analyzed under various physiological conditions. He could also be "sham fed," though in his case the food was chewed and then spat out. It was found that food for which this subject had a particular fondness caused the

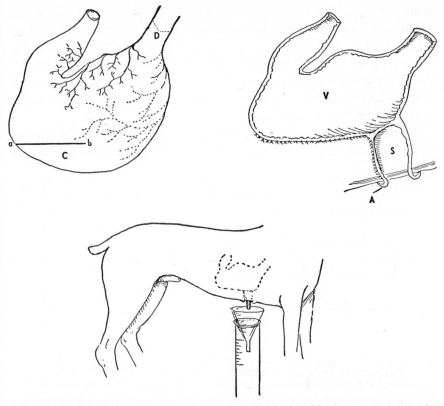

Fig. 8.15   *Upper drawings* show Pavlov's method of fashioning a gastric pouch or miniature stomach. A horizontal incision a-b is made which causes minimal injury to the gastric nerves and blood supply. *D,* vagus nerves. The flap *C* is turned down and the pouch *S* isolated from the main cavity of the stomach *V* as shown in the right-hand sketch. A, abdominal wall. The *lower drawing* illustrates the manner in which pure gastric juice can be collected from the miniature stomach while digestion is proceeding in the main part of the stomach.

greatest secretion of juice (Fig. 8.16). In some instances the mere sight or smell of food called forth a secretion. That is to say, a conditioned reflex (pp. 297 and 567) can be established for gastric secretion, as well as for the secretion of saliva.

The psychic secretion of gastric juice has also been demonstrated in persons during hypnosis. A suggestion made to the subject that he was eating some tempting piece of food stimulated gastric secretion. On the other hand, psychic influences—e.g., worry, fear, anger, and pain—are powerfully inhibitory to the gastric glands, as are also bad odors, an unsavory character of the meal, or even an unattractive appearance of its general appointments. Pleasant surroundings, contentment, delight for the eyes and ears—e.g., flowers on the table, cleanliness, and good music—tend toward an opposite effect. The importance of appetite in aiding digestion has been pithily stated by Pavlov in the words, "Appetite spells gastric juice." Macbeth at the banquet expresses a similar thought when he says, "Let good digestion wait on appetite and health on both." It is not wise, therefore, to force a child to eat food that he detests.

Variations in the secretory activity of the gastric glands are accompanied by changes in the blood supply to the gastric mucous mem-

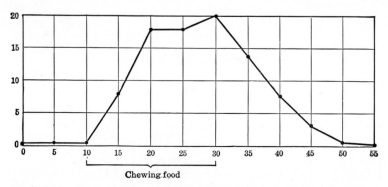

Chewing food

Fig. 8.16   Typical curve of secretion of gastric juice collected at 5-minute intervals during mastication of palatable food for 20 minutes. The rise in secretion during the last 5 minutes of mastication is due to chewing the dessert (fruit) for which the person had an especial fondness. (After Carlson.)

brane. When the interior of the stomach is viewed through a gastric fistula, or by means of a specially devised instrument known as a *gastroscope,* the mucosa is seen to blanch in response to the inhibitory influences mentioned above and to become flushed when secretion occurs.

The gastric phase. This refers to the secretion of gastric juice that occurs after the food has entered the stomach; it continues for a much longer period than does the psychic secretion. Let us now consider the mechanisms controlling the secretion at this time. The stretching of the stomach wall by the food has only a slight secretory effect. The secretion during this phase is due mainly to the action of a chemical material—a *hormone*—formed in the mucosa of the stomach. This material is absorbed into the blood stream and, reaching the cells of the gastric tubules, excites them to secretion. The hormone is produced, in turn, through the action upon the pyloric mucosa of certain substances in the food. Such substances are present in aqueous extracts of meats and vegetables (e.g., soups and beef extracts). For this reason they are referred to as *extractives*. On account of their stimulant action on secretion they are also known, from the physiological point of view, as *gastric secretogogues*.

The products of protein digestion—*proteoses* and *peptones*—and certain other materials act in a similar fashion.

When evidence for its existence was first obtained, the gastric hormone was named *gastrin;* its chemical nature was unknown. Extracts of the pyloric mucosa, obtained from an animal after a meal of meat or of other substances rich in extractives, contained the hormone. This was shown by the fact that, when such extracts were injected into the veins of an animal, a profuse secretion of gastric juice resulted.

It is now generally conceded, however, that the hormone in pyloric extracts—i.e., gastrin—is not a specific and hitherto unknown substance, but is simply histamine, which is found in other tissues as well as in the gastric mucous membrane. The discovery that histamine and gastrin are identical does not necessarily lead to the conclusion that there is no other gastric hormone. On the contrary, a considerable body of evidence suggests that a gastric hormone quite distinct from histamine is formed in the gastric mucosa during digestion. But, so far, this hormone has not been obtained by extraction.

The intestinal phase. After the partially digested food materials have reached the intestine, certain of their constituents (split products of protein digestion, meat extracts, etc.) continue to exert an excitatory effect upon gastric secretion. Little is known concerning the manner in which this effect is brought about; it may be dependent upon the formation or liberation of a hormone from the intestinal mucosa, for an extract of the latter, when injected intravenously, has an excitatory effect upon gastric secretion. Another possibility is that certain constituents of the food are absorbed into the blood stream and act *directly* as excitants of the gland cells.

The effects of different foods and of certain chemicals and drugs upon the secretion of gastric juice. The hydrochloric acid in the gastric contents is in part *combined* with food, especially in acid metaprotein and with mucus; the remainder is *free*. The combined acid and the free acid together are referred to as the *total acid*.

In man the activity of the gastric glands is investigated by giving a meal of toast and weak tea—the so-called *test meal*—and removing samples of the contents of the stomach every 15 minutes during a subsequent 2-hour period. The samples are analyzed, the percentages of *total* and *free acid* determined, and curves plotted (see Fig. 8.16).

Meat, since it is rich in extractives, stimulates the glands more power-fully than does carbohydrate. Fats have an inhibitory effect upon gas-tric secretion, as well as upon the movements of the stomach. A meal containing a high proportion of fat takes a relatively long time to leave the stomach. Fat also exerts an inhibitory effect upon both gas-tric *secretion* and *motility,* after it has reached the duodenum. The latter effect is attributed to a chemical substance (a *chalone,* p. 403) formed in the intestinal mucosa; this substance has been named *entero-gastrone.*

Among chemicals which stimulate gastric secretion, the most pow-erful are *histamine* and *alcohol. Atropine* by its paralyzing action upon the vagus endings temporarily suppresses secretion. *Alkalies* such as sodium bicarbonate in repeated small doses excite the gastric glands, but a single large dose has, as a rule, an inhibitory effect.

Abnormalities in gastric secretion. When no secretion of acid oc-curs after a test meal, the condition is called *gastric anacidity* or *achlorhydria.* About 4 percent of perfectly healthy and otherwise normal persons show this peculiarity. There may be a complete ab-sence of peptic secretion as well; when such is the case, the condition is called *achylia gastrica.* Gastric anacidity is also seen in a number of diseased states—e.g., *cancer of the stomach, pernicious anemia, chronic inflammation of the stomach, chronic arthritis, gall-bladder disease,* etc.

In some instances, the gastric glands, though failing to secrete when stimulated by a test meal, respond to histamine; the anacidity is then called *false* or *apparent.* In other instances, even a powerful stimulus, such as histamine or alcohol, is ineffective. This *absolute* failure of acid secretion is called *true anacidity.* An abnormally high acidity of the gastric contents is called *gastric hyperacidity* or *hyperchlorhydria.* In this condition, *the acidity of the gastric juice, as it leaves the gland tubules,* is not higher than usual (0.5 to 0.6 percent), but owing to a high rate of secretion or to failure of the juice to be neutralized after it has reached the cavity of the stomach, the percentages of total and free acid in the gastric contents are much above the normal values. Under normal circumstances, the acidity of the gastric contents rises after a test meal, reaching a maximum in an hour or so and then declin-ing (see chart, Fig. 8.17). The return of the curve to the resting level is due to several factors—reduced rate of secretion by the glands, emptying of the stomach, neutralization by mucus and probably also, to some extent, by the regurgitation of alkaline juices from the duo-denum. An abnormally high acidity of the gastric contents is due to failure of one or another or all of these factors; the curve of gastric acidity rises above the normal maximum, and in many instances does not return to the resting level within the normal time.

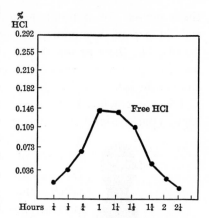

Fig. 8.17 Normal curve of free hydrochloric acid in the gastric contents following a test meal.

Gastric hyperacidity is the commonest of all digestive complaints in otherwise normal and healthy persons. It causes "heartburn" and a feeling of discomfort in the chest. The burning sensation is due to the highly acid gastric contents being carried into the esophagus by contractions of the stomach, and stimulating sensitive nerve endings in the esophageal mucous membrane. Ascending waves of contraction may carry material into the throat or the mouth. The gastric mucosa itself is insensitive to acid. Hyperacidity of the contents of the stomach is seen in a large proportion of cases of gastric and duodenal ulcer; indeed it is now generally agreed that it is the chief cause of these conditions.

In *duodenal ulcer,* for example, ulceration occurs where the gastric juice, after issuing from the pylorus, first comes into contact with the intestinal mucosa. Treatment of gastric or duodenal ulcer is therefore directed toward reducing the acidity of the gastric contents. This is accomplished by giving alkalies, or other substances which combine with the excess acid, such as preparations of mucin; by restricting the diet in respect to meat and other materials rich in extractives which stimulate gastric secretion; and by substituting foods (e.g., milk, cream, and carbohydrates) which either inhibit or exert no pronounced stimulating action upon the glands. Alcoholic drinks are forbidden, or allowed only in minimal amounts and well diluted. Excessive smoking should also be avoided. Sometimes a preparation of enterogastrone is given for its inhibitory effect on gastric secretion and motility.

A high gastric acidity is also seen when the pylorus is obstructed and, as a consequence, gastric evacuation is delayed. The distension of the stomach which results from pyloric obstruction acts further as a stimulus to secretion.

The nerves which influence gastric secretion and motility. The gastric glands receive secretory fibers through the vagus nerves. When these nerves are stimulated, the glands secrete a highly acid juice, rich in pepsin. Sympathetic fibers can also be traced to the gastric glands, but their action is less well known; it seems, however, that they innervate the glands of the pyloric region, causing a secretion of an alkaline juice consisting largely of mucus.

The movements of the stomach are under the control of both the vagus (parasympathetic) and sympathetic nerves. The vagus is motor

in action—that is, it raises the tone and increases the force of the contractions of the gastric muscle; the sympathetic is inhibitory. The vagus and sympathetic nerves are also motor and inhibitory, respectively, to the pyloric sphincter.

Movements and emptying of the stomach. The upper half or so of the body of the stomach does not show active movements, but is the seat of a steady tonic contraction. When digestion is proceeding, peristaltic contractions commence about the middle of the body of the stomach and, passing downward (i.e., toward the pylorus), become progressively more powerful (Fig. 8.18). The pyloric part is, therefore, the more actively motile region, the motility becoming more and more marked as the digestive processes progress. These movements serve to mix the food thoroughly with the gastric juice and to break up food masses that have been softened by the digestive juices. When the food has reached a consistency suitable for discharge into the duodenum, it is propelled through the pylorus by the descending waves of peristalsis.

Fig. 8.18   Drawing of x-ray of stomach showing peristalsis.

The pyloric sphincter is relaxed most of the time. It is contracted only when a peristaltic wave passes over it and closes the pyloric orifice for a moment. The latter varies in diameter from time to time, however, being wider during the later stages of digestion than at the beginning. Thus the stronger peristaltic contractions and the greater diameter of the pyloric opening, when gastric digestion is nearing completion, facilitate the evacuation of the stomach. It should be emphasized that the consistency of the food is one of the most important factors determining the time after swallowing at which it leaves the stomach. Fluids, for example, commence to leave it almost immediately after entering. Solid food in the stomach must first be reduced to a fluid or semifluid state, and those articles of diet which are most readily softened and liquefied (e.g., carbohydrates) leave before meats, which require a longer time to become reduced to a suitable consistency. Fats are evacuated most slowly, for, as already mentioned, they inhibit gastric secretion and motility. They also, for this reason, retard the evacuation of other types of food. An ordinary mixed meal is usually completely evacuated within from 3 to $4\frac{1}{2}$ hours.

The stomach contents, after they have become softened and form a nearly homogeneous semifluid or plastic mass, are referred to as the *chyme*. In this state, the food commences to pass into the duodenum. *Chyme* is an old word meaning juice, and arose from the belief that digestion in the stomach was essentially a mechanical process, the nutritive juices being expressed from the food through the pressure exerted by the contractions of the stomach. That the food underwent chemical changes in the stomach was not fully realized until the French scientist René Réaumur (1683–1757), and the Italian priest and scientist, Lazaro Spallanzani (1729–1799) (Fig. 8.19), carried out their ingenious experiments. Réaumur gave a kite and other animals small perforated metal tubes filled with meat.

Fig. 8.19   Lazaro Spallanzani.

He found, upon recovering the tubes, that the meat, which could be acted upon by the gastric juice though protected from any mechanical action of the stomach, was partially dissolved. He also showed that gastric juice would digest meat in a test tube—that is, outside the body. Spallanzani performed similar experiments upon animals and upon himself. He swallowed perforated wooden tubes filled with food and showed that, though the containers were unbroken, after passing through the alimentary tract, the food had become dissolved. He also found that gastric juice, obtained by making himself vomit, had the power to dissolve meat *in vitro*.

In the early part of the nineteenth century (1819) Dr. William Beaumont (Fig. 8.20), an American army surgeon, was offered an opportunity, unique at that time, to study the digestive processes in the human stomach. A French Canadian hunter, Alexis St. Martin, while at Fort Mackinac on Lake Michigan, received a severe wound in the abdomen from the accidental discharge of a musket. Part of the wall of the stomach was destroyed. Under Beaumont's care the man recovered but the large wound in the abdominal wall and the stomach failed to close completely. Through this opening Beaumont was able to observe the changes taking place in the food during the different stages of digestion, and performed a number of simple experiments which clarified many obscure aspects of gastric physiology.

Fig. 8.20   William Beaumont.

The experiments of these pioneers upon the chemical features of digestion had led men to forget for a time the importance of mechanical factors. The pendulum had swung too far. But today, the mechanical factors are recognized as playing a prominent role in gastric digestion, though this should not be taken to mean that nutriment is expressed from the food by any mechanical action.

Abnormalities of the motor mechanisms of the stomach are much more often the immediate cause of digestive disorders than is a failure, or even the entire absence, of the digestive power of the gastric juice. Persons in which gastric secretion is entirely lacking (*achylia gastrica*) may enjoy perfect health, and suffer no digestive discomfort whatsoever. On the other hand, disorders of the movements of the stomach—e.g., too slow or too rapid evacuation of the food, or spasm of the pylorus or of the cardiac sphincter—frequently give rise to severe gastric symptoms.

Vomiting. This is usually preceded by nausea. The ejection of the stomach contents is accomplished in the following manner. A strong contraction occurs in the pyloric part of the stomach, together with relaxation of the body of the stomach and the cardiac sphincter. Accompanying or immediately following these movements, the abdominal muscles contract forcibly, and the diaphragm descends. Thus the stomach is compressed and its contents, being prevented from passing downward by the firm contraction of the pyloric region, are forced through the relaxed cardia into the esophagus. The latter relaxes throughout its length, which permits the free passage upward of the stomach contents. The larynx is raised at the same time and its opening closed, thus preventing the passage of material into the air passages. The stomach, it will be noted, is emptied *passively;* that is, it is emptied from pressure applied from without. There is no evidence, in the adult at any rate, that an ascending peristaltic contraction of the gastric wall is instrumental in ejecting the stomach contents into the esophagus. In the young infant, however, a reverse peristaltic movement of this nature probably does occur. The purely passive role played by the stomach in vomiting was shown clearly by the French physiologist, Magendie. He excised the stomach of an animal, replaced it by a pig's bladder, and then gave an emetic which acted on the vomiting center; a typical vomiting act followed, fluid being forcibly expelled from the grafted bladder.

Vomiting is a reflex act and may follow irritation of nerve endings (vagus or sympathetic) in the stomach or duodenum. But the stimulation of afferent fibers, especially those transmitting pain impulses, in almost any organ of the body may induce vomiting. The vomiting due to disease of the appendix or gall bladder, or to some painful injury, is well known. Afferent impulses arising in a failing heart may also cause vomiting, or the act may be induced by psychic influences—anxiety, fear, or disgust. Seasickness and other forms of motion sickness are due to the stimulation of nerve endings in the utricle of the ear (Chap. 13). Nausea or vomiting not uncommonly results from eye strain, the afferent impulses initiating the reflex arising in the eye muscles.

Drugs and other substances used in medicine for the induction of vomiting are called *emetics.* Among those which act upon the nerve endings in the gastric or duodenal wall are *antimony tartrate* (tartar emetic), *copper* and *zinc sulphates,* and *salt or mustard and water.* Certain other emetics, such as *apomorphine,* act upon the *vomiting center* in the medulla oblongata. It is probable, however, that the vomiting which follows the administration of emetics of the latter type is also essentially reflex in nature. The drug acts, apparently, by raising the excitability of the center; that is, the threshold of the center to stimulation is lowered, so that impulses from various parts of the body, which normally make no impression upon it, become effective. The vomiting resulting from metabolic disturbances (e.g., in pregnancy or nephritis), or that associated with general bodily fatigue, is explained in a similar way.

Digestion in the Intestine

The intestinal tract is divided for the purpose of description into two parts—the *small intestine* and the *large intestine*. The small intestine, though of smaller diameter, is much longer than the large intestine (see Fig. 8.1). In man its length is about 21 feet. The first 10 inches or so (twelve finger breadths) are called the *duodenum*. The rest of the small intestine is divided rather arbitrarily into an upper portion (about two fifths) called the *jejunum,* and a lower somewhat narrower portion (about three fifths) called the *ileum.* The small intestine from

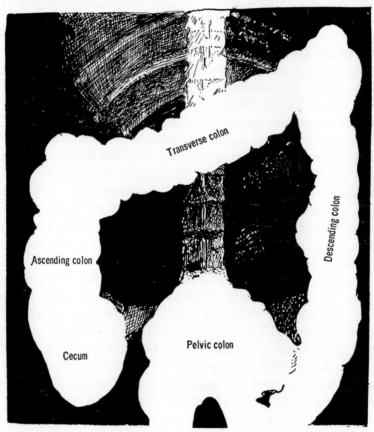

Fig. 8.21   X-ray photograph of the large intestine.

the duodenum onward is attached to the posterior abdominal wall by a fan-shaped membrane called the *mesentery* which carries vessels and nerves to the intestinal wall.

All those processes, through which the food is finally prepared for absorption, are carried out in the small intestine. Amino acids and certain other products which have escaped absorption from this part of the alimentary tract undergo bacterial decomposition in the large intestine (see p. 345), but nothing of nutritional value is prepared in this part of the digestive tract. Large quantities of water are, however, absorbed from the large intestine; it converts the fluid contents of the small intestine into the pasty consistency of normal feces.

The *large intestine* extends from the end of the ileum to the anus. It is about 5 feet long, in man, and consists of the *cecum, colon, rec-*

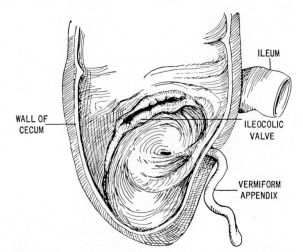

Fig. 8.22 Interior of cecum showing opening of ileum and ileocolic valve.

tum, and *anal canal.* The cecum is the saclike dilatation at the commencement of the large intestine; it lies in the lower right-hand part of the abdominal cavity. The ileum opens into its upper end and the *vermiform appendix* arises 2 inches or so lower down. The colon is described in four parts—the *ascending, transverse, descending,* and *pelvic colons.* These are shown in Figure 8.1, p. 288 and Figure 8.21. The ascending colon occupies the right side of the abdomen and is continuous below with the cecum. The transverse colon crosses the abdomen and is continued into the descending colon which occupies the left side of the abdomen. The lower part of the large intestine occupies the pelvis and consists of the pelvic colon, the rectum, and the anal canal, in this order from above downwards. The interior of the cecum is shown in Figure 8.22. The bends of the colon in the regions of the liver (i.e., at the junction of the ascending and transverse colons) and spleen (at the junction of the transverse and descending colons) are called, respectively, the *hepatic* and *splenic flexures*. The *internal anal sphincter* is situated at the lower end of the rectum. The *external anal sphincter* guards the lower aperture of the anal canal. The latter opening is called the anal *orifice* or *anus*.

The *pancreas* is a racemose gland (p. 40). It is an elongated

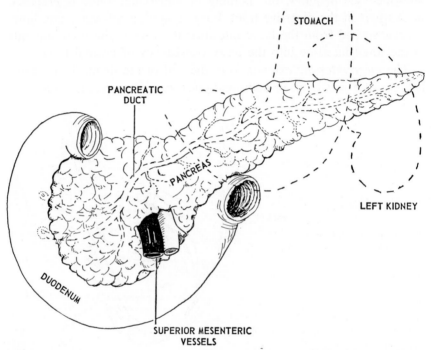

Fig. 8.23 Diagram to show the relation of the pancreas to the duodenum, stomach, and left kidney.

structure lying across the posterior wall of the abdomen; its right-hand broad part, called the *head,* fits into the curve of the duodenum (Fig. 8.23). Its body and tail are directed toward the left. The cells which form its external secretion—the *pancreatic juice*—have an alveolar arrangement resembling that seen in the salivary gland. The alveoli or acini are drained by a system of ducts. In the human subject, the main pancreatic duct (duct of Wirsung) pierces the duodenal wall obliquely, and joins the common bile duct to form a small chamber—the *ampulla of Vater*. The ampulla opens into the duodenum about $3\frac{1}{2}$ inches below the pylorus. The pancreas contains, besides the cells which form the pancreatic juice, other rounded groups of cells called the *islands* or *islets of Langerhans* (Fig. 8.24). The islet cells are of an entirely different character; they are surrounded by the acinar (external secreting) cells, but separated from them by a narrow clear space. They are responsible for the production of insulin (p. 370).

When the gland is resting (as in a fasting animal), the alveolar cells, like the serous cells of the salivary glands, contain numerous granules

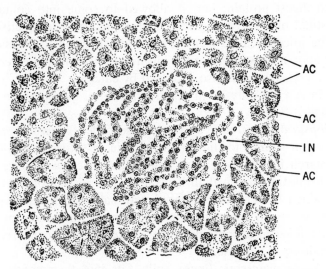

Fig. 8.24   Microscopic section of pancreatic tissue. AC, alveoli of glands which secrete pancreatic juice; IN, one of the islands of Langerhans, which produce insulin.

(p. 40); these furnish the enzymes of the juice. During secretion, the cells discharge their zymogen granules into the alveolar cavity, their cytoplasm, except perhaps for a narrow zone bordering the alveolar cavity, then appearing quite clear.

The pancreatic juice. Composition. The pancreatic juice is alkaline in reaction, due to its content of *sodium carbonate* and *bicarbonate*. Its principal ferments are *trypsin* (*pancreatic protease*), *amylopsin* (*pancreatic amylase*), *steapsin* (*pancreatic lipase*), and *rennin*.

Trypsin acts upon the proteoses and peptones formed in the peptic digestion of protein. This enzyme is also capable of attacking any protein which has escaped gastric digestion, and converting it to proteoses and peptones. Trypsin breaks the peptone molecule into smaller groups of amino acids, named *peptids*. When the amino acid groups are relatively large, they are called *polypeptids*. The final stage in the digestion of protein—that is, the complete disruption of the molecule into its individual amino acids—is brought about by the erepsin (peptidases) of the intestinal juice. But the protein molecule can be broken down into groups of four amino acids (*tetrapeptids*) and three (*tripeptids*), or even two (*dipeptids*) amino acids, during tryptic digestion.

Juice collected *directly* from the pancreatic duct has very little power to digest protein; but, if allowed to come into contact with the intestinal mucosa, it at once becomes active. The inactive material in the juice is called *trypsinogen;* its activation to trypsin is dependent upon a constituent of the intestinal juice, named *enterokinase* (p. 327). Trypsinogen is also activated by calcium.

Trypsin can act only in an alkaline medium, the optimum pH being around 8.5.

Amylopsin or pancreatic amylase (also called *pancreatic diastase*) has an action similar to that of the ptyalin in saliva (p. 298), converting starch into maltose. But pancreatic juice has a more powerful starch-splitting action than has saliva; it is also afforded a longer time in which to act. As compared with saliva, pancreatic juice is, therefore, of much greater importance in the digestion of starch. Pancreatic juice also contains some *maltase* which converts a part of the maltose to glucose.

Steapsin, or *pancreatic lipase,* splits fats into their constituents—fatty acids and glycerin (glycerol). If the intestinal contents are alkaline in reaction, the liberated fatty acids may combine with alkali to form soaps. The action of the steapsin upon the fat, *tristearin,* is shown in the following equation:

$$C_3H_5(C_{17}H_{35}COO)_3 + 3H_2O = C_3H_5(OH)_3 + 3C_{17}H_{35}COOH$$

tristearin   glycerin   stearic acid

$$C_{17}H_{35}COOH + NaOH = C_{17}H_{35}COONa + H_2O$$

stearic acid   sodium stearate
                                        (soap)

Soap formation in the intestine probably occurs to a very limited extent, for soaps can form freely only in an alkaline medium; any which may have formed become precipitated again when the medium is acidified. The intestinal contents are slightly acid in reaction except when the pancreatic secretion is at its height. Even then, it is only the duodenal contents which are rendered slightly alkaline, the contents of the rest of the intestinal tract remaining slightly acid.

The optimum pH for the action of pancreatic lipase is around 8.0.

The secretion of pancreatic juice. The secretion of pancreatic juice is brought about by a hormone formed in the mucosa of the small intestine. The existence of this hormone was demonstrated in 1902 by Bayliss and Starling. They found that a hydrochloric acid extract of the duodenal mucosa, when injected intravenously, caused the secretion of pancreatic juice. The intravenous injection of the acid by itself was ineffective. On the other hand, the introduction of hydrochloric acid into a loop of the bowel, the nerves of which had been sectioned and thus isolated from all connections with the pancreas except through the blood stream, was followed by a secretion of pancreatic juice. It was therefore concluded that in the normal course of digestion the acid chyme, after reaching the duodenum, acted upon the duodenal mucosa to cause the formation and absorption into the blood stream of a hormone which excited the pancreatic cells. The hormone was named *secretin*.[4] Later work has shown that extracts of the intestinal mucosa made with solvents other than acid (namely, water or alcohol) are active. It has also been demonstrated that bile introduced into the duodenum causes secretin to be absorbed into the blood stream and induces, in consequence, a secretion of pancreatic juice.

A second hormone having a stimulating action upon the secretion of pancreatic juice has been discovered within recent years. It has been named *pancreozymin* and, like secretin, is obtained by extraction from the duodenal mucosa. But, in contrast to the latter hormone, which increases only the water and salts of the juice, pancreozymin increases the production of the enzymes. It causes the discharge of zymogen granules from the gland cells and has little effect upon the volume (water) of the secretion.

The secretion of pancreatic juice is also brought about through nerve impulses. Stimulation of the vagus nerve causes the secretion of a juice very rich in digestive enzymes; rapid exhaustion of the zymogen granules results. Secretin, as just mentioned, appears to be responsible mainly for the secretion of the water and inorganic constituents of the juice. The vagal effect upon pancreatic secretion is, therefore, closely similar to that caused by pancreozymin and unlike that following the injection of secretin. It was shown several years ago by Pavlov that psychic factors—the taste and smell of food— were capable of evoking a secretion of pancreatic juice. These reflex secretory effects were particularly well shown by feeding experiments

---

[4] It is interesting to recall that Bayliss and Starling coined the word *hormone* to express the characters of their newly discovered secretin.

in dogs. However, the psychic or cephalic element plays a much less prominent role in pancreatic than in gastric secretion.

The villi and glands of the small intestine. The mucous membrane of the small intestine is beset with great numbers of minute, slender, fingerlike or tonguelike processes—the *intestinal villi*—which give to the naked eye the soft velvety appearance of the intestinal mucosa (Fig. 8.25). Absorption from the small intestine of water and the

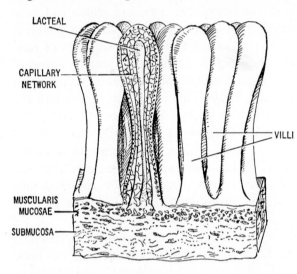

Fig. 8.25   Showing villi of the small intestine. One villus sectioned lengthwise to show vessels.

products of digestion occurs entirely through the specialized epithelium which covers the villi. The columnar epithelial cells in this situation are continuous with those lining the intestinal glands and show short delicate lines lying along and perpendicular to their free borders. In this respect these cells resemble those lining the proximal convoluted tubules of the kidney (p. 270). The striations appear to be associated in some way with the capacity of selective absorption which both the renal and intestinal cells possess.

Intestinal glands. The crypts of Lieberkühn or intestinal glands are tiny pockets lying between the villi. Their blind ends dip deeply into the mucous membrane, reaching as far as the muscularis mucosae (Figs. 8.25 and 8.36). They are lined by epithelial cells continuous with those covering the summits of the villi. Many of the epithelial cells lining the gland become converted into *goblet cells* and discharge mucus. Others (*cells of Paneth*) situated at the deepest or blind end of the crypts are filled with coarse granules and are believed to secrete the enzymes of the intestinal juice (Fig. 8.26).

The intestinal juice, succus entericus. The term intestinal juice

(L. *succus entericus*) is reserved for the secretion of the intestinal glands or crypts of Lieberkühn described in the preceding section and does not mean merely the fluid contents of the intestinal canal.

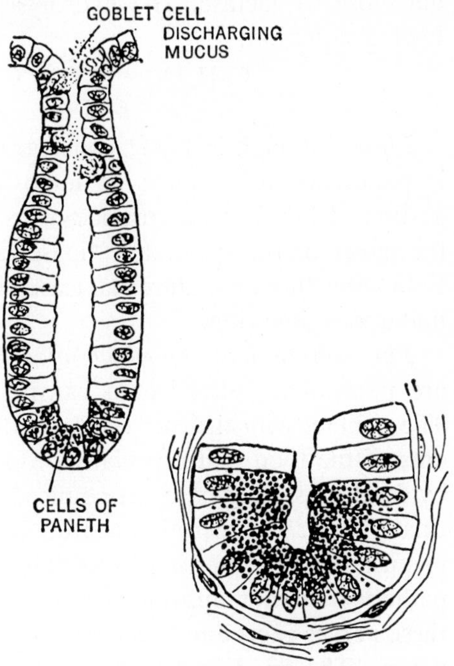

Composition. The intestinal juice is alkaline in reaction, due to its content of *sodium carbonate* and *bicarbonate*. It contains *enterokinase*, the activator of trypsin, and the following enzymes.

1. *Peptidases (erepsin),*[5] enzymes which effect the final breakdown of the protein molecule into its constituent amino acids.

2. *Sucrase, maltase,* and *lactase,* enzymes which act upon the disaccharides, *sucrose* (cane sugar), *maltose* (sugar of malt), *lactose* (milk sugar), respectively.

3. *Lipase.*

Fig. 8.26 Showing a crypt of Lieberkühn on left with goblet cells. On right, an enlarged sketch of bottom of crypt to show cells of Paneth loaded with granules.

Peptidases do not act upon unchanged protein. The protein must first be digested to the peptid stage by trypsin. Peptidases act best at a pH of about 8. The intestinal wall itself contains these enzymes and small amounts are present in other tissues of the body, including the blood. The intestinal wall also contains enzymes—*nuclease, nucleotidase,* and *nucleosidase*—capable of digesting nucleic acid and its derivatives (p. 366).

Sucrase, maltase, and lactase. Sucrose (cane, beet, and maple sugar) is split by sucrase into a molecule each of glucose and fructose; maltose, when acted upon by maltase, yields two molecules of glucose; and lactose is converted into a molecule each of glucose and

---

[5] Erepsin (Gr. *ereptomai,* to feed upon) is an old term applied to the enzymes of the intestinal juice which effect the final breakdown of the protein molecule to amino acids in the belief that but a single enzyme was responsible.

galactose by lactase. The hydrolysis of sucrose is shown in the following equation:

$$C_{12}H_{22}O_{11} + H_2O = C_6H_{12}O_6 + C_6H_{12}O_6$$

| sucrose | glucose | fructose |

Lipase, though in lower concentration in the succus entericus than in pancreatic juice, plays an important role, nevertheless, in the digestion of fat. The importance of its action is shown after abolishing the effect of the pancreatic lipase, as by tying the pancreatic duct. Following this procedure, at least 70 percent of the fat in the food undergoes digestion.

The secretion of intestinal juice. Mechanical types of stimulation are particularly effective in causing a secretion of intestinal juice. The contact with the intestinal mucosa of rough indigestible constituents of the food and especially distension of the intestinal wall itself by food masses exert a pronounced excitatory effect upon the intestinal glands. The secretion is brought about reflexly through the nerve plexuses of the intestinal wall. The extrinsic nerves (vagus or sympathetic) do not appear to have any excitatory effect. If either of these nerves exert any effect at all upon secretion, it is of an inhibitory nature. The question whether or not a hormone plays a role in controlling secretion cannot be answered definitely, though there is some evidence that secretin stimulates the intestinal glands as well as the pancreas.

The Production of Bile by the Liver. The Composition of Bile; Its Storage in, and Expulsion from, the Gall Bladder

Though it is customary to speak of the secretion of bile, this fluid, like urine, is rather in the nature of an excretion. It is produced from the constituents of the blood by the cells of the liver which are arranged in rows—the *liver cords*—radiating from a central vein (p. 208). A small aggregation of such cords, together with the central vein, is known as an *hepatic (liver) lobule.* On one side of each liver cord is a blood sinus; through these vessels, called *hepatic sinusoids,* courses a mixture of portal and hepatic artery blood (Figs. 8.27 and 8.28). On the other side lies a fine canal (*biliary canaliculus*) into which the cells of the liver cords discharge the bile formed from the constituents of the blood. The canaliculi drain into channels of progressively increasing size until a relatively large tube—the *hepatic duct*—is formed, along which the bile leaves the liver.

The composition of bile. Human bile is a clear yellow or orange-colored fluid secreted by the liver cells. Its chief constituents are the *bile pigments,* the *bile salts, lecithin, cholesterol, inorganic salts,* and *mucin.* Table 8-3 gives the average composition of human bile as it is secreted by the liver.

Table 8-3

Water	974.80
Solids	25.20
Mucin and pigments	5.30
Bile salts	9.30
Fatty acids from soaps	1.23
Cholesterol	0.63
Lecithin / Fat	0.22
Inorganic salts	8.32

Bile collected from the gall bladder is much more concentrated than liver bile (see p. 332).

The *bile pigments* are called *bilirubin* and *biliverdin.* They are derived from the hemoglobin liberated from red blood corpuscles, which at all times are undergoing disintegration in the blood stream (p. 329). The conversion of the hemoglobin to bilirubin is effected by the reticulo-endothelial cells of the spleen, liver (Kupffer cells), bone marrow, and general connective tissues (p. 94). The pigments consist of the porphyrin part of the hemoglobin molecule—that is, the remnant of the molecule after the globin and iron have been removed. Bilirubin is not quite identical, however, with the porphyrin in hemoglobin, for the chemical structure of the porphyrin group is also altered. The iron liberated in the conversion of hemoglobin to bile pigment is stored chiefly in the liver and spleen.

Bilirubin ($C_{33}H_{36}N_4O_6$) is an orange-red pigment; it is the chief pigment in human bile and in the bile of dogs. Biliverdin

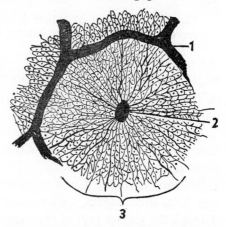

Fig. 8.27 Diagram of a liver lobule. 1, interlobular vein; 2, central vein; 3, a lobule. The fine lines converging toward the central vein and surrounding the liver cells are the hepatic sinusoids.

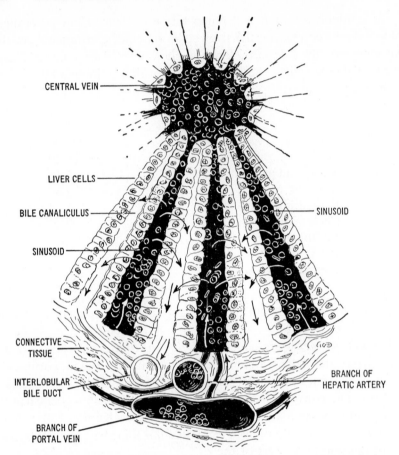

CENTRAL VEIN

LIVER CELLS

BILE CANALICULUS

SINUSOID

SINUSOID

CONNECTIVE
TISSUE

INTERLOBULAR
BILE DUCT

BRANCH OF
HEPATIC ARTERY

BRANCH OF
PORTAL VEIN

Fig. 8.28   Segment of a liver lobule (diagrammatic). White circles represent blood corpuscles. Arrows indicate bile secretion. (See also Fig. 8.27.)

$(C_{33}H_{36}N_4O_8)$ is green and constitutes the greater part of the pigment in the bile of birds and of herbivorous mammals. It is simply an oxidation product of bilirubin.

Upon reaching the intestine, bilirubin undergoes chemical reduction as a result of bacterial action. This reduction product, which gives the yellow-brown color to feces, is called *stercobilinogen* (also called *urobilinogen*). Upon exposure to air, a part of the stercobilinogen is oxidized again, and is then called *stercobilin* (or *urobilin*). Though the greater part of the stercobilinogen is passed with the feces, a part is absorbed into the portal circulation and returned to the liver, whence it is discharged again in the bile (see Fig. 8.29). In health, only minute amounts of urobilinogen, or none at all, find their way into the general circulation. Any which does escape from the liver into the systemic blood is excreted by the kidney, but the amount is so small that it does not stain the urine; it can be detected only by delicate chemical tests. The yellow color of healthy urine is not due, therefore, to this pigment (see p. 274).

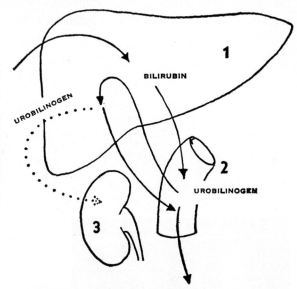

Fig. 8.29 Diagram illustrating the circulation of bile pigment. 1, liver; 2, intestine; 3, kidney. The dotted line indicates the entrance of urobilinogen into the blood and its excretion by the kidney when the liver is damaged or there is an excess of bile pigment production.

The bile salts are *sodium glycocholate* and *sodium taurocholate*. The bile acids glycocholic and taurocholic are produced in the liver by the union of *cholic acid* ($C_{24}H_{40}O_5$) with the amino acids, *glycine* and *taurine,* respectively.

The secretion of bile. We have seen that the cells forming the liver cords are exposed on one side to the blood in the sinusoids from which materials are removed and passed as bile into the biliary canaliculi on the other side (Fig. 8.28). The bile is carried through a system of channels of progressively greater size to the large *hepatic duct.* The liver forms and secretes bile continuously, but, instead of passing directly into the intestine as it is formed, the bile passes into the gall bladder from which it is discharged from time to time into the duodenum.

The storage of bile and its discharge into the intestine. The gall bladder is a small pear-shaped sac which, in the human subject, has a capacity of about 50 cc. It is situated on the under (posterior) surface of the liver (Fig. 8.30). Leading from its upper and smaller end is the *cystic duct.* The cystic duct joins the hepatic duct at an acute angle to form the *common bile duct.* The latter joins the pancreatic duct, the chamber formed by the fusion of the two ducts being known as the *ampulla of Vater* (p. 322, and Fig. 8.31). The opening of the ampulla of Vater is guarded by a ring of muscle called the *sphincter of Oddi*. The bile passes from the hepatic duct into the common bile duct, but is prevented from entering the intestine by the tonic contraction of this sphincter. When the biliary pressure reaches a value of from 50 to 70 mm of water, the bile forces its way

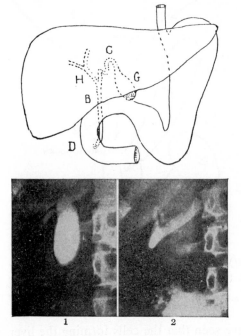

Fig. 8.30 *Upper cut* shows the relationship of the gall bladder and biliary passages to the liver and duodenum (D). B, common bile duct; C, cystic duct; G, gall bladder; H, hepatic duct. *Below* is an x-ray photograph of the gall bladder when distended (1) and after a meal of fat (2). (After Ivy.)

along the cystic duct into the gall bladder where it is stored until required. Water and salts are absorbed from the bile during its stay in the gall bladder. The bile of the gall bladder has, therefore, a much higher concentration of pigments, bile salts, cholesterol, and lecithin than has bile collected from the hepatic duct. A ten-fold increase in bile concentration may result from its stay in the gall bladder.

The wall of the gall bladder is composed of a thin layer of smooth muscle lined by mucous membrane. During a meal, the gall bladder contracts, and discharges its contents down the cystic and common bile ducts. The sphincter of Oddi at the same time relaxes, thus permitting free passage of bile into the duodenum. The gall bladder is supplied with fibers from the vagus and sympathetic nerves, and, undoubtedly, nervous influences (both conditioned and unconditioned reflexes) play a part in the mechanism of the expulsion of bile. Emptying of the gall bladder has been observed, for example, following the sight, smell, or taste of food. Nevertheless, evacuation of the gall bladder follows the ingestion of food after all nervous connections of the organ have been severed. The contractions must therefore be caused by some material carried in the blood stream. Such a material has been extracted from the mucosa of the duodenum by Dr. A. C. Ivy and his colleagues in Chicago. The hormone, for it must be classed as such, has been named *cholecystokinin*. The injection of a very small amount of this material causes contractions of the gall bladder in animals or in man. It is quite distinct from secretin, the hormone for pancreatic secretion. Not all types of food are equally effective in causing the production or liberation of the gall-bladder hormone; fatty foods, especially egg yolk and cream, are by far the most effective. Shortly after a meal of fat, the gall bladder, which may have

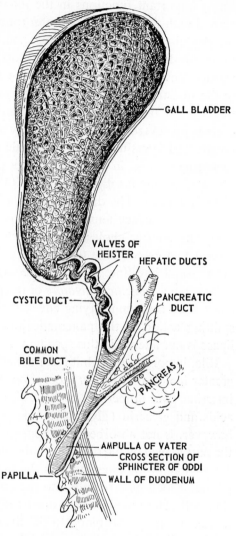

Fig. 8.31   The gall bladder and bile ducts opened.

been quiescent for several hours previously, contracts forcibly and expels its contents into the duodenum. In order to bring about its effect, the fat apparently must first have undergone digestion. That is to say, the *products* of fat digestion appear to be the essential materials which call the hormonal mechanism into play. Protein and carbohydrate foods are much less effective than fat as stimulating agents.

The functions of the bile. The bile, besides serving as a vehicle for the elimination of pigments and certain other waste products, performs important functions in the intestine. Its main function is concerned with the digestion and absorption of fat. Though the bile does not contain a fat-splitting enzyme, and, therefore, has no direct action upon the digestion of fat, the bile salts, through their power to lower surface tension, aid very greatly in the emulsification of fatty materials in the intestinal contents. The digestion of fat is materially advanced thereby, for the division of the oily materials into small globules increases by several fold the surface exposed to the action of the pancreatic and intestinal lipases. The bile salts have also the property of rendering soluble, in the aqueous fluids of the intestine, the fatty acids liberated during fat digestion. This is the so-called *hydrotropic* action of the bile salts. The dissolved fatty acids, in turn, have the property of lowering surface tension; any soaps which may be formed during digestion, and the cholesterol of the bile, have a similar action. These several factors combine to produce a fine emulsion of fatty material in the small intestine. The bile salts aid fat digestion in another way. They serve as *specific activators* of the pancreatic lipase. That is, quite apart from their emulsifying effect, they enhance very greatly the fat-splitting action of the pancreatic juice. The action of the intestinal lipase is not altered in this specific way by bile.

Bile, important though it is for the efficient digestion of fat, is of still greater importance for *fat absorption*. When bile is excluded from the intestine, over 80 percent of the fat is digested—that is, split into fatty acids and glycerin (glycerol). A large proportion of the fatty acids, however, is not absorbed, but appears in the feces. Only recently has the part played by the bile salts in the absorption of fat been elucidated. They unite in the intestine with the fatty acids to form complex compounds which pass readily into the epithelial cells covering the intestinal villi. Here the bile salts are freed again from the union, and are carried in the portal blood to the liver which excretes them again in the bile. This *circulation of the bile salts* has been known for a long time, though its significance was not apparent. The fatty acids liberated from their combination with the bile salts now combine with glycerin which has penetrated into the epithelial cells from the intestinal lumen. The products of fat digestion—fatty acids and glycerin—are thus reunited within the epithelial cells to form neutral fat. The greater part (about 60 percent) of the synthesized fat passes into the small lymphatics (lacteals) running through the centers of the villi. The course taken by the remaining 40 percent of the fat is uncertain. It is probably absorbed into the blood of the portal system. There is evidence for the view that a part of the fat is absorbed directly—that is, as fine globules of unsplit fat.

Jaundice (Fr. *jaune*, yellow) or *icterus*. In health, human plasma contains a small quantity of bilirubin. The concentration ranges in different persons from 0.1 to 0.5 mg per 100 cc. The bilirubin of the plasma is that which, having been formed by the reticulo-endothelial cells from hemoglobin derived from disintegrated erythrocytes, is on its way to the liver for excretion.

When excessive amounts of bilirubin are present in the plasma, the skin, mucous membranes, and whites of the eyes are stained yellow. The condition is called *jaundice* or *icterus*. Bilirubin then appears also in the urine and sweat, but does not pass into the saliva. An abnormally high concentration of plasma bilirubin may be due to excessive amounts of the pigment being produced, the liver and excretory channels being normal. On the other hand, the quantity of pigment formed in the body may be within normal limits, but the function of the liver is impaired as a result of some toxic or infective process, and does not remove bilirubin readily from the plasma. Again, the bile passages may be obstructed; the excretion of bile into the intestine is then prevented. There are, therefore, three types of jaundice: (1) *hemolytic,* (2) *toxic or infective,* and (3) *obstructive.*

Hemolytic jaundice is seen in conditions which cause increased destruction of red cells—e.g., pernicious anemia, hemolytic anemia, and poisoning with certain hemolytic agents. It is therefore due to the exaggeration of a normal process—namely, the liberation of hemoglobin from disintegrated blood cells. This type of jaundice is not uncommon in the newborn infant; it persists for 4 or 5 days after birth. The baby comes into the world with an excess of red cells, which undergo destruction during the first few days, the concentration of bilirubin in the plasma being thus increased to the point at which jaundice appears. Another factor is the functional immaturity of the liver. This type of jaundice of the new born is harmless, and indeed may be looked upon as a physiological phenomenon. In the hemolytic types of jaundice, the stools are dark, due to the increased pigment excretion; urobilin may appear in the urine.

In the *toxic and infective* types of jaundice, the liver cells are injured by some poison or infective process which interferes with their ability to eliminate bile pigment.

Obstructive jaundice is most often the result of blockage of the common bile duct by a gallstone within its lumen, or by a tumor pressing upon it from without. In this type, the discoloration of the skin and mucous membranes is usually intense. The feces are pale, being usually described as "clay colored," because bile pigment is, of course, excluded from the intestinal tract. The urine is usually deeply colored with bilirubin.

Movements of the small intestine. Three types of movement occur in the small intestine: (a) *peristaltic,* (b) *segmenting,* and (c) *pendular*.

A

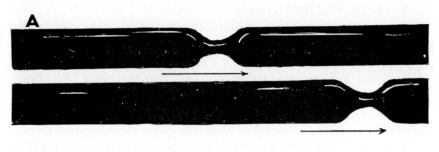

B

Fig. 8.32   Diagram of the movements of the small intestine. A, peristalsis; arrows indicate the direction of movement of the constricting band; B, segmenting movements.

Peristaltic movement (peristalsis). This kind of movement is not restricted to the small intestine, but is characteristic of hollow muscular organs in general. It has been mentioned as occurring in the esophagus during the third stage of swallowing, and in the pyloric part of the stomach. It is also seen in the large intestine, as well as in the ureter, Fallopian tube, and common bile duct. The movement consists of a ringlike contraction of the muscular wall of the tube. The annular contraction, as it travels downward, causes a certain degree of constriction of the bowel which sweeps before it any material within the lumen (Fig. 8.32A). The movement is readily started by a mechanical, an electrical, or a chemical stimulus. The most powerful stimulus is distension of the bowel—i.e., stretching of the muscle fibers. Filling of the bowel with food material provides just such a stimulus, the contraction occurring immediately behind the stimulated region. Peristaltic movements may follow one another at regular and fairly frequent intervals, the intestinal contents being moved steadily but gently along the canal. At other times a brisk peristaltic contraction appears which travels rapidly along the tube but, after moving the food a considerable distance, may not be repeated for some time. This is called the *peristaltic rush.* Especially strong stimulation, the action of a cathartic or an irritant poison, for example, may set up a peristaltic rush which travels throughout the length of the small bowel. Such a movement may also be initiated reflexly from the esophagus during swallowing, or from the stomach.

Except in the duodenum near its commencement and at the terminal part of the ileum (see Fig. 8.1, p. 288), the peristaltic movements of the normal small intestine are always from the stomach downward— that is, in a direction toward the anus. Peristalsis in the reverse direction (antiperistalsis) is occasionally observed normally in the situations just mentioned. It may also occur anywhere in the small intestine in abnormal states of the intestinal tract, especially when the canal is completely obstructed.

Segmenting movements. These movements are rhythmical constrictions of the intestine which serve to break up and knead the food, to mix it thoroughly with the intestinal juices, and to bring the intestinal contents in contact with fresh absorptive surfaces. These movements

Fig. 8.33 Diagram showing the effect of the segmenting movements upon the food mass in the intestine. A series of constrictions of the bowel wall suddenly divides the column of food, 1, into a number of segments, 2. Each of the latter is bisected again the next instant, the adjacent halves fusing as in 3, and being redivided as in 4. The process is repeated over and over again until the food is thoroughly mixed. (After Cannon.)

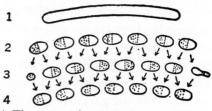

also increase the blood and lymph flow in the intestinal wall; but they exert no propulsive action upon the food. They occur at the rate of from 20 to 30 per minute (see Figs. 8.32B and 8.33).

Pendular movements. These are simple constrictions of the intestinal wall. They move up and down the bowel for short distances, giving a to and fro movement to the semifluid material in the canal, and thus lending further aid to the processes of digestion and absorption (Fig. 8.34).

The innervation of the small intestine. The small intestine receives fibers from the vagus (parasympathetic) and the splanchnic (sympathetic) nerves. The vagus is excitatory, the sympathetic inhibitory, in action (see Pl. 8A). It will be noted that the actions of these nerves

Fig. 8.34   Pendular movement; arrows indicate the directions of the movement.

upon the intestine, as compared with their actions upon the heart, are reversed. The intestinal wall itself contains two nerve plexuses. One of these lies between the two muscular coats (circular and longitudinal) of the intestine and is called *Auerbach's plexus;* ganglion cells are found among the network of nerve fibers. The other plexus, known as *Meissner's plexus,* lies in the submucosa (Pl. 8B). The vagal fibers connect with the ganglion cells of Auerbach's plexus; the impulses are thence conveyed by the axons of these cells (postganglionic fibers) to the muscle fibers. The sympathetic fibers, on the other hand, do not form junctions with ganglion cells in the intestinal wall but pass directly to the muscle cells. The postganglionic sympathetic fibers arise from cells in the celiac and superior mesenteric ganglia (Pl. 8A).

Though the intestinal movements are influenced by impulses traveling over the vagus and splanchnic nerves, they are not dependent upon them, for the three types of intestinal movement continue after all nerves of extrinsic origin have been sectioned. The peristaltic movements are then carried out through the intrinsic nervous mechanism (plexuses of Auerbach and Meissner). The segmenting and pendular movements are dependent upon the property of rhythmical activity of the muscle fibers themselves, and not upon any nervous mechanism. They continue in a denervated strip of intestinal muscle, or after paralysis of the plexus by cocaine.

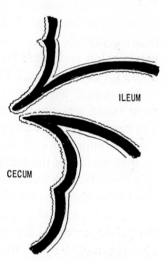

The ileocolic sphincter. The small intestine empties into the upper part of the cecum through a valvelike opening called the *ileocolic valve* (Figs. 8.35 and 8.22, p. 321). The ring of muscle surrounding the opening is called the *ileocolic sphincter*. It controls the passage of the contents of the ileum into the cecum and prevents or hinders the reflux of material into the ileum, thus protecting the small intestine from contamination by the putrefactive bacteria which flourish in the large intestine. The sphincter opens and closes during digestion to permit gushes of ileal contents to enter the cecum. During fasting it remains closed

Fig. 8.35 Diagram of the ileocolic valve in section. (See also Fig. 8.22, page 321.)

for long periods, but opens within a few minutes after a meal. This indicates a reflex action initiated by the entrance of food into the stomach. The ileocolic sphincter receives motor fibers through the sympathetic; inhibitory fibers are believed to be carried by the vagus.

The innervation of the ileocolic sphincter is, therefore, the reverse of that of the small intestine itself. A peristaltic wave in the small intestine, accompanied by relaxation of the sphincter, is brought about by vagal impulses; the ileal contents are passed into the large intestine. Relaxation of the wall of the small intestine, with closure of the sphincter, is caused by sympathetic impulses; the entrance of material into the large intestine is prevented. A discharge of impulses from a single nervous center (vagal or sympathetic) in this way either drives the semisolid contents of the ileum through the sphincter, or holds them back; thus incomplete digestion of the food is guarded against.

The movements and innervation of the large intestine. Food material reaches the cecum about $4\frac{1}{2}$ hours after a meal. Rhythmical movements resembling the segmenting movements in the small intestine may be seen occasionally in the cecum, but peristaltic contractions are absent. Regular and frequently recurring peristaltic contractions are usually absent also from the rest of the large intestine. At certain long intervals, however, a strong peristaltic wave commencing in the upper end of the ascending colon moves swiftly over the transverse colon. This *mass movement,* as it is called, is analogous to the peristaltic rush in the small intestine; it empties the transverse colon, sweeping the material into the descending and pelvic colons or into the rectum. The pelvic colon and lower part of the descending colon serve as a storehouse for the feces until the desire to defecate is aroused.

The cecum, ascending colon, and the first third or so of the transverse colon are supplied with motor fibers through the vagus nerves. The remainder of the large intestine, including the rectum and the anal canal, is supplied with motor fibers through the pelvic nerves (parasympathetic from the second, third, and fourth sacral segments of the spinal cord). The inhibitory fibers to the entire large intestine are derived from the sympathetic. These two sets of nerves act upon the internal anal sphincter in a reverse fashion; the sympathetic is excitatory, the pelvic nerve inhibitory. As stated previously, the sympathetic is also the motor nerve to the ileocolic sphincter. The external anal sphincter is under voluntary control through the pudendal nerve.

In health, the antagonistic effects of the parasympathetic and sympathetic nerves to the large intestine are nicely balanced. But the balance is sometimes upset. Relaxation and weakness of the walls of the descending and pelvic colons result from overactivity of the sympathetic innervation. The tone of the internal anal sphincter, on the other hand, is exaggerated. The colon is unable to empty itself effectually, and dilatation of its lumen, often to enormous proportions, follows. This condition is called *megacolon* (G. *megas,* large) or *Hirschsprung's disease.* When, on the other hand, the pelvic nerve (parasympathetic) is hyperactive, the descending colon becomes firmly contracted; its lumen is obliterated. This—the so-called *spastic colon* —is one cause of chronic constipation (p. 342).

Defecation (evacuation of the bowels) is a reflex act initiated by the passage of feces into the rectum. Normally the rectum is empty, except just before defecation; feces are forced into it from the pelvic colon by a mass movement. The latter movement is often started by the entrance of food into the stomach—*gastrocolic reflex.* This reflex is responsible for the desire to defecate so often experienced a short time after a meal, especially breakfast. The distension of the rectum as it becomes filled with feces acts as a stimulus to afferent nerve endings in the rectal wall. The impulses set up are conveyed to a center in the sacral part of the spinal cord. The efferent nerve fibers pass to the wall of the descending and pelvic colons, rectum, and the internal anal sphincter, via the pelvic nerves, and to the external anal sphincter and the striated muscle lying in relation to the rectum, via the pudendal nerves. A higher center for defecation is situated in the medulla oblongata. This is connected to the lower center by tracts of fibers in the spinal cord. The intrarectal pressure necessary to start the defecation reflex is from 40 to 50 mm Hg.

The movement of defecation consists of a powerful peristaltic contraction of the descending and pelvic colons and rectum, assisted usually by a voluntary contraction of the abdominal muscles, and of the muscles lying in relation to the rectum (levatores ani and rectococcygeus muscles). The contraction of the abdominal muscles is immediately preceded by an inspiratory movement (descent of the diaphragm and closure of the opening [glottis] of the larynx), thus *raising the intra-abdominal* pressure. Relaxation of the anal sphincters occurs reciprocally with the contraction of the intestinal wall—a nervous mechanism which we have already dealt with.

Constipation. Persons vary considerably in the frequency with which their bowels are evacuated. In some a bowel movement occurs twice or even three times daily, while others may feel no discomfort if an interval of two days or more elapses between movements. The majority of healthy persons have one evacuation daily, usually in the morning after breakfast. Owing to this variability, it is difficult to give a precise definition of constipation. However, when the interval between bowel movements is greater than 24 hours and the subject, as a result, suffers distress or discomfort (e.g., headaches, digestive disturbances, etc.), or if the feces are abnormally dry and hard and the evacuation of the bowels difficult, constipation certainly exists.

Constipation is caused most commonly by bad habits. As mentioned above, the desire to empty the bowel is aroused by the passage of feces into the rectum, and the stimulation of afferent nerve endings in the intestinal wall. The act can, however, be voluntarily restrained and, when this is practiced, the tone of the rectal wall is reduced, and the rectum thus accommodates its capacity to the bulk of the feces (postural tone, p. 293); the afferent nerve endings are no longer adequately stimulated, or, at any rate, are unresponsive, and the desire to defecate passes. As a result of the absorption of water, the retained feces become dry and hard. When the habit of postponing defecation in this way is persisted in, the rectum, which normally, except just before evacuation, is empty, contains feces most of the time; it becomes permanently less sensitive to distention, and its muscle, as well as that of the pelvic colon, loses its tone. It is well known that the reflex mechanisms governing the emptying of the bowel are amenable to "training." A type of conditioned reflex becomes established. When the habit of emptying the bowels at a certain hour each day is practiced for a while, the desire to do so tends to recur regularly at this time.

Other causes of constipation are: (a) *A diet* which leaves too little unabsorbed residue or one which contains too little fluid. The contents of the large intestine are, therefore, of small bulk and fail to furnish a sufficiently strong stimulus (stretching of the intestinal wall) to set up vigorous peristaltic contractions. (b) *A colon which absorbs too readily* and thus causes undue drying of the feces. (c) Hypertonic state of the muscle of the colon—*spastic constipation;* the transverse and descending colons are the seat of a strong tonic contraction which impedes the progress of the feces.

The myth of autointoxication. The general effects of constipation upon the sense of well-being are too familiar to require description. But their cause is a subject upon which there is much misunderstanding. We hear a great deal of poisons formed in the intestinal tract, and the dire effects which they are supposed to have upon the body. *Intestinal intoxication* or *autointoxication* (self-poisoning) is glibly spoken of, and advertisements in the daily press exhort one to irrigate the colon, in order to remove the noxious materials. There is no doubt whatever that small amounts of powerful poisons are formed in the large intestine as a result of the action of bacteria upon amino acids which have escaped absorption in the small intestine. They are intensely toxic if *injected* into the circulation. Some of these substances —known generally as *amines*—are formed by the removal of a molecule of carbon dioxide from such amino acids (p. 360) as *alanine, tyrosine, histidine,* etc. Among the more potent of such amines are *ethylamine* (from alanine), *histamine* (from histidine), and *tyramine* (from tyrosine). However, the production of such poisons is a perfectly normal process, and there is nothing more certain than that they cannot be held responsible for the headache, bad breath, furred tongue, or any of the other effects of constipation. The body is provided with mechanisms for rendering innocuous the poisons formed in the colon. The first line of defense raised against them is in the wall of the bowel itself; here some are destroyed or changed into harmless compounds. The second and most important detoxicating mechanism is in the liver,

where the toxic bodies are combined with sulfuric acid or with gly-
curonic acid. The resulting relatively innocuous compounds (*indoxyl
sulfuric acid* and *glycuronates*) pass from the liver to the kidney for
excretion.

To what then are the symptoms of constipation due? It is now generally conceded that they are of reflex origin. Afferent impulses set up
in the distended colon or rectum, though ineffectual in precipitating
the defecation reflex, produce reflex effects in other parts of the body,
particularly the stomach and blood vessels. The headache is probably
due to the effect upon the intracranial blood vessels. The rapid relief
from the ill effects of constipation which follows evacuation of the
bowels is a common experience, and, in itself, argues strongly against
such effects being of toxic origin, for it is inconceivable that poisons
could be freed so swiftly from the blood stream. To quote the perti-
nent comment of Dr. Alvarez, who has devoted much time to a study
of the question, "A drunken man does not at once become sober when
the whisky bottle is taken from him"; one might add, "and even after
his stomach has been emptied."

Absorption from the Intestinal Tract

The absorption of food products is, for all practical purposes, confined
to the small intestine. Some drugs and certain hormone preparations
can be absorbed in minute quantities from the mouth, especially the
mucous membrane beneath the tongue. Alcohol and a number of
drugs are absorbed from the stomach fairly rapidly. The gastric absorption of water and, to some extent, of mineral salts, also occurs,
but much more slowly. The absorption from the stomach of glucose
and other sugars in weak solution is negligible, but may be considerable if in a concentration of over 10 percent. The greatest absorption
of water relative to solids occurs from the large intestine. As a result,
the intestinal contents undergo a pronounced reduction in bulk, and
a change in consistency in their passage through this part of the intestinal tract. Unchanged protein is not absorbed, except occasionally in
minute amounts, from any part of the gastrointestinal tract.[6] Fat does
not pass from the cavity of the stomach into the circulation, though an
attempt at absorption appears to be made; for after a meal of fat, fine
droplets of oil can be detected in the gastric mucosa itself.

The alimentary tract, from a physiological point of view, must be

---

[6] The ingestion of a large quantity of raw white of egg may be followed, even
in a healthy person, by its appearance, unchanged, in small amounts in the urine.

considered as lying outside of the body proper. Food material ingested and held within the digestive tube cannot be said truly to have entered the body until it has passed across the intestinal mucosa and been absorbed into the blood. Just as the skin covers the outer surface of the body, so the mucosa of the gastrointestinal tract constitutes its inner surface. An examination of the interior of the small intestine shows how well this part of the lining of the body has been fashioned for increasing the area exposed for the absorption of food materials. The mucosa is raised into circular folds (*plicae circulares*) which, in the upper part of the intestine, may be nearly a third of an inch in depth. These and the intestinal villi (p. 327), especially the latter, increase enormously the total absorbing surface (see Fig. 8.36). It has been estimated that the number of villi in the human small intestine is around 5,000,000 and the absorbing surface not far short of 10 square meters—more than five times the skin surface. The center of each villus is occupied by an arteriole, a venule, and a lymph vessel or *lacteal*. The arteriole leads into a network of capillaries lying just beneath the epithelial covering of the villus. The central vessels are surrounded by

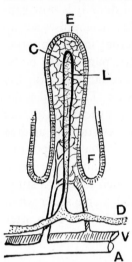

Fig. 8.36 Interior of villus. A, arteriole; C, blood vessels; D, lymph vessel; E, epithelium; F, crypt of Lieberkühn; L, lacteal; V, venule.

areolar tissue together with bundles of smooth muscle fibers. If the intestinal mucosa of a living animal is examined with the low power of the microscope, the villi will be found to be in ceaseless motion, swaying or lashing from side to side, and lengthening and shortening alternately. These movements, by their constant agitation of the intestinal fluids in the immediate neighborhood of the villi, cause thorough mixing with the digestive enzymes and bring the food material into contact with fresh absorbing surfaces; they thus aid very materially the digestive and absorptive processes.

It will be recalled that the intestinal mucosa is impermeable, or nearly so, to the large molecules of the three foodstuffs—carbohydrates (starch and the disaccharides, cane sugar, maltose, and lactose), proteins, and fats—but permits the free passage of the smaller molecules—glucose, amino acids, fatty acids, and glycerol into which the food is split by enzyme action. The absorption of these products is not, however, a simple process of diffusion, in which the intestinal mucosa acts merely as a passive membrane. On the contrary, the epithelial cells covering the villi take an active part in absorption, as is evidenced by the observation that an increase in oxygen consumption and in carbon dioxide production accompanies the process. Furthermore, the absorption, as shown by the following experiment, is selective. When the three sugars—glucose, galactose, and fructose—in equal concentrations are placed in a loop of bowel immersed in saline, glucose passes through the intestinal wall more rapidly than does galactose, and galactose more rapidly than fructose, provided that the intestinal mucosa remains viable and uninjured. After injury or death of the mucosa, the three sugars pass through it at equal rates—i.e., simply by diffusion.

After passing through the epithelium of the villi, the glucose and amino acids are absorbed into the network of blood vessels mentioned above; fat, synthesized in the epithelial cells from fatty acids and glycerin, passes, for the most part, into the lymph channels.

The reaction of the intestinal contents. The formation of feces. The reaction of the duodenal fluids is usually slightly acid but it depends upon the stage of gastric digestion at which a sample is taken; upon the degree of acidity of the gastric contents; upon the quantity of alkaline juices, pancreatic juice, and mucus secreted into the duodenum; and upon the nature of the food. It may be definitely alkaline. The contents of the remainder of the small intestine and of the entire large intestine have a reaction a little on the acid side (a pH of about 6.8). The feces are very faintly acid as a rule.

The feces are not simply and solely unabsorbed residues of the food, but are made up largely of materials *excreted* from the blood. During starvation, for example, the bulk of the feces may not be greatly less than at ordinary times, and a loop of intestine isolated from the rest of the intestine becomes filled after a few days with a pasty mass indistinguishable in consistency and composition from ordinary feces except that, of course, being isolated from the rest of the intestinal tract, it contains no bile and is, therefore, pale. Bacteria make up about 9 percent of the feces; the other main solid constituents are food residues, which vary considerably in amount with the proportion of indigestible material (chiefly cellulose) in the diet. They contain some fat, nitrogenous substances, and minerals eliminated from the blood, together with epithelial cells and leucocytes, shed from the intestinal mucosa. A very small proportion of digestible food appears in the feces. In other words, practically all the protein, fat, and carbohydrate which is eaten is absorbed, the food residues of the feces consisting almost entirely of indigestible substances. Vegetable material, since its framework is composed of cellulose, contributes more to the feces than do other foods. This indigestible material or "roughage," as it is commonly termed, serves a useful purpose in that it acts as a mechanical stimulus, increasing the motility as well as the secretions of the intestinal wall.

Substances that cause evacuation of the bowels: laxatives, cathartics, and purgatives.[7] The manifold drugs and other substances employed to stimulate the intestinal movements and cause evacuation of the bowels do not all bring about their effect after the same fashion. Some, such as *Epsom salts (magnesium sulfate), sodium sulfate,* and other saline cathartics, being not absorbable, cause through their osmotic effect a flow of water into the small intestine which, by increasing the bulk of the intestinal contents, causes distention, and consequent stretching of the bowel wall; this, we have seen (p. 337), acts as a powerful stimulus to peristalsis. Other cathartics, such as *castor oil,* contain an irritant principle which serves to excite intestinal motility. *Croton oil* is an especially powerful irritant which in very small dosage causes profuse purgation and, in larger amounts, may induce acute inflammation of the intestinal mucosa. Figs, raisins, etc., act by virtue of their indigestible residue, chiefly seeds, which serves mechanically to stimulate the intestinal movements, local reflexes being set up in the nerve plexuses of the intestinal wall. Undigested material of any sort within the bowel—e.g., the *skins of fresh fruit,* the *cellulose of raw vegetables, whole wheat, and bran*—all serve as intestinal stimulants by increasing the bulk and consequently the degree of stretch of the bowel wall. *Paraffin oil,* which is not absorbed from the intestine except perhaps in minute amounts, acts in a similar manner. There are a host of other laxatives and cathartics, many of them used from time immemorial, of which little is known definitely concerning their mode of action. Vitamin B_1 and other factors of the B complex tend to increase the tone of the intestinal musculature, and thus favor natural movements of evacuation.

Reliance upon medicines to ensure regular bowel movements should be avoided, for the intestinal musculature tends to become tolerant to their use and requires a gradual increase in dosage. Hygienic measures, diet, exercise, and habit should be depended upon whenever possible.

The sensibility of the alimentary canal. The mucosa of the gastrointestinal tract for the greater part of its length is insensitive to the

---

[7] The term *laxative* implies an agent with a milder stimulating action than either a *cathartic* or a *purgative.*

several forms of stimulation that arouse sensations from the skin, such as touch, cold and warmth, and pressure. This is not surprising, for this part of the body is never exposed to these types of stimulus, and has therefore not developed end organs that can respond to them. Pain is aroused by stretching the intestinal wall, but not by cutting, burning, or crushing. Thus distention of the stomach or intestine may cause intense pain as a result of stretching of nerve fibers in their walls. In disease, pain is often felt, not in the diseased organ itself, but in some part more or less remote. Thus in angina pectoris (Chap. 4) pain is felt in the left shoulder and arm, and even in the fingers or jaw of the same side, and occasionally in the right arm. This is called *referred pain* and has been explained upon the fact that the organ and the part in which the pain is felt have developed from closely associated embryonic structures, and, in the adult, nerves supplying them carry impulses to the same segment of the spinal cord from where they are relayed to consciousness. The pain is therefore projected to the part that receives its sensory nerve supply from this segment of the spinal cord. In other words, it is interpreted as being located in the part from which impulses of pain would normally arrive.

The only parts of the alimentary canal from which sensations of touch, warmth, and cold can be aroused are the mouth, pharynx, and anal canal, though extremes of heat and cold can be appreciated in the esophagus and, according to some, even in the stomach. Common experience may seem to contradict the statement that warmth is not felt in the stomach, but the sensation aroused by warm food or drink is attributed to the conduction of heat through the abdominal wall to stimulate end organs in the overlying skin.

Hunger and appetite. Though we have often experienced both appetite and hunger, it is possible to describe these sensations only in the vaguest terms. Appetite, though closely associated with hunger, differs from the latter in that it depends upon pleasurable memories of the taste and smell of food. Extraneous factors such as the sight of food and pleasant appurtenances of the meal also influence appetite (p. 311). Conditioned responses enter largely into its make-up. It is psychological rather than, like hunger, physiological. A newborn babe no doubt feels hunger but probably does not know appetite. Yet appetite is whetted by hunger and has, therefore, a physiological element; it is influenced by the tone and general state of the stomach. This is evidenced by the stimulating effect of an alcoholic drink taken before a meal and the increased appetite which follows the first few mouthfuls of a meal.

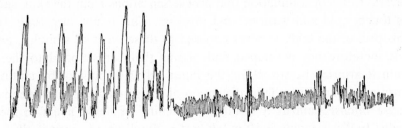

Fig. 8.37   A tracing of the contractions of the stomach in hunger.

Obviously, the sensation of hunger serves a protective function, for it controls the food intake. Its origin has a local (gastrointestinal) as well as a general (metabolic or blood composition) basis. Emptiness or fullness of the stomach and the state of its wall are potent factors influencing hunger, as is also the presence or absence of food products in the duodenum. We have all experienced that "gone" or empty feeling in the pit of the stomach when a meal has been long postponed. It is hard to say whether this arises in the stomach or the duodenum. Spasms of pain—the pangs of hunger—may occur. These are caused by contractions of the stomach and have been graphically recorded in man by Carlson by means of a balloon passed into the stomach and connected by tubing with a recording apparatus (Figs. 8.37 and 8.38).

But gastric factors are incidental rather than primary; the fundamental cause of hunger is general or metabolic rather than local. A

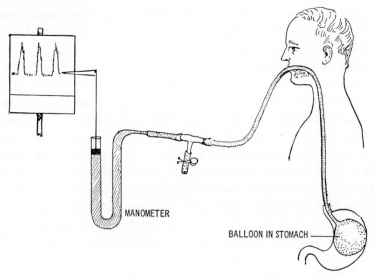

MANOMETER

BALLOON IN STOMACH

Fig. 8.38   Showing the method of recording hunger contractions.

low level of blood sugar (glucose) has been thought to be an important factor in its causation. This theory, however, does not accord with the excessive hunger characteristic of diabetes in which the blood sugar is above normal. It is more probable that the general or metabolic factor is a slow rate of glucose utilization by the tissues rather than the blood-sugar level itself. Thus during fasting, as the blood sugar falls and the rate of glucose utilization by the tissues is slowed, and in diabetes, though the blood sugar is above normal, glucose utilization is also reduced. This, which is known as the *glucostatic theory* of hunger, reconciles two otherwise irreconcilable factors. The actual control of food intake devolves upon a center in the brain (certain hypothalamic nuclei) whose cells, like those of other tissues of the body, will be subjected to changes in the rate at which glucose is used. It is postulated that a fall in glucose utilization by the cells of this "feeding center" arouses the urge to increase the food intake. The responsive hypothalamic cells have been named *glucoreceptors*. There is experimental evidence to support this conception of the hunger mechanism. A lesion suitably placed in the hypothalamus of animals is followed by an increase in the food intake. The opposite effect—reduction in the food intake—is caused by an injury placed in another but near-by part of the hypothalamus. Furthermore, it has been recognized for many years that in man disease involving this or neighboring regions of the brain may be associated with excessive hunger or with a pathological absence of hunger.

Thirst. Like hunger, thirst serves a protective function. It is nature's signal to replenish the body's water supplies. This sensation is referred to the pharynx, and is caused by the stimulation of sensory nerves in this situation. There has been much discussion as to whether the underlying cause of thirst is local—drying of the mucous membranes of the mouth and pharynx—or of a more general nature. Drying of the oral and pharyngeal mucous membranes is certainly conducive to thirst. But, if one is really thirsty, washing out the mouth or even gargling has little effect in *allaying* the sensation. Blood composition, probably the osmotic pressure of the plasma, seems to be the essential factor concerned. It seems likely that cells (*osmoreceptors*) in the hypothalamus are sensitive to changes in the osmotic pressure of the blood. We have seen that such receptors are part of the mechanism controlling the water output (see Chap. 7). It is a reasonable supposition that they also govern the water intake.

CHAPTER 9

Metabolism and Nutrition

Metabolism is a general term applied to the various chemical processes, whatever their nature, taking place in living tissues—e.g., the oxidation of food materials with the liberation of energy; the decomposition of compounds into more elementary principles; the chemical transformation of one material into another; and the synthesis of complex compounds from others of simpler constitution, as in the processes of tissue repair and growth, or in the manufacture of internal secretions and enzymes. Reactions involving decompositions are embraced by the term *catabolism;* those of a synthetic nature are referred to as *anabolism.*

Though some of the reactions taking place in the body are accompanied by the absorption of heat (endothermic reactions), in the great majority (e.g., oxidations) heat is evolved (exothermic reactions). The sum total of all the chemical reactions occurring in the body is referred to as *general metabolism,* and is expressed in terms of heat given out by the body in a given time. Those chemical changes, whether of a catabolic or an anabolic nature, which a particular substance (e.g., carbohydrate, fat, protein, purine, calcium, etc.) undergoes in the body are referred to as *special metabolism.*

General Metabolism

The sun is the source of all energy on the earth. Plant life through its possession of the green coloring matter, *chlorophyll,* is capable of utilizing the energy of sunlight to form carbohydrate material from the carbon dioxide of the atmosphere and water drawn from the soil. This process is called *photosynthesis.* The animal body, of course, cannot make direct use of solar energy; it must depend upon the energy stored by the plant or upon that provided by the tissues of other animals. The food—fat, carbohydrate, and protein—derived from either of these

350

sources therefore represents stored or potential energy. The carbon and hydrogen of the food, after absorption from the intestinal tract, are oxidized in the tissues (Chap. 6). Energy is liberated thereby for muscular activity and for maintaining the vital functions—e.g., the action of the heart, the movements of the gastrointestinal tract, the excitability of nervous tissues, etc. Thus, the various foodstuffs are to the body as fuel is to an engine; they represent a certain amount of potential energy which the body can convert to other forms of energy —mechanical, electrical, chemical, and thermal.

When the body is at rest—that is, when no external work is being performed—the energy liberated from food materials appears ultimately as heat. A heat unit, the large Calorie,[1] is therefore employed as a measure of the energy liberated in the animal body. A Calorie is defined as the quantity of heat required to raise a kilogram of water from 15° to 16° C. Of the energy expended during muscular exercise, as in lifting a weight, walking, etc., about 30 percent appears as work, the remaining 70 percent is converted to heat.

Antoine Lavoisier (1743–1794), the celebrated French scientist of the eighteenth century, pioneered in the field of metabolism. He established the crucial fact that the heat produced by a burning candle and that generated by the body were fundamentally similar processes. He showed that the body burned (oxidized) the food, the carbon being converted to carbon dioxide (CO_2) and the hydrogen to water (H_2O). He devised an ice calorimeter calculating the heat produced by the candle flame and that given out by the body of a small animal (e.g., a mouse) from the weight of ice which had melted during the period of the experiment. He came to but one false conclusion—namely, that the oxidation of the food with the production of carbon dioxide and water occurred in the lungs. We know now, of course, that it occurs in the cells of all tissues, a process which is known as *internal respiration*.

The law of the conservation of energy states that, though one form of energy is convertible into any other form, the sum total of the energy in the universe remains constant—energy cannot be created or destroyed. This law holds true for the animal body. That is to say, a given quantity of food when completely oxidized in the tissues yields its entire store of potential energy to the body—the energy intake balances the energy output, as measured by the heat produced and the work performed.

[1] The large Calorie used in physiology is written with a capital C to distinguish it from the small calorie used in the physical laboratory, which is the quantity of heat required to raise *1 gram* of water from 15° C to 16° C.

The food may not be completely oxidized in the body; a part may be stored, or, as with protein (pp. 353 and 363), a part resists oxidation and is excreted. Nevertheless, an energy balance can be struck, if any gain in weight is noted (stored energy) and the quantity of unoxidized residue of protein food in the urine is determined.

Energy is stored in the adult body as carbohydrate (glycogen) and fat, mainly the latter, whenever the food intake exceeds the energy

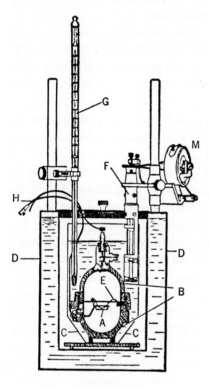

Fig. 9.1 The bomb calorimeter. A, a platinum dish upon which is placed the sample of food; B, bomb filled with oxygen; C, vessel holding water in which bomb is immersed; D, double-walled insulating jacket; E, fuse which can be ignited by an electric spark; F, water stirrer turned by a motor, M; G, thermometer; H, electric wires for ignition of fuse. (Courtesy of Emerson Apparatus Company, Boston, Mass.)

needs of the body—that is, when the energy of the food is not all expended in maintaining the vital processes, or in performing muscular work. This is by far the commonest cause of overweight (obesity). This store of energy, in the form of fat and carbohydrate, is readily available and will be drawn upon should the energy value of the diet at any time fall below the body's energy requirements. During a *prolonged* period of fasting, after the stores of glycogen and fat have been drawn upon and exhausted, the protein of the tissues is utilized to furnish energy.

In the *growing* body, a part of the food not used to furnish energy is converted to new tissue with a resulting increase in weight.

The bomb calorimeter. The potential energy of a foodstuff is determined by measuring the heat evolved when it is burned in an instrument known as a *bomb calorimeter* (see Fig. 9.1). The heat generated by the animal body may be determined in a manner identical in principle. Now, the quantity of heat liberated by 1 gram of carbohydrate or fat is the same whether the material is metabolized in the body or burned in the bomb calorimeter; 4.1 Calories are generated in the oxidation of 1 gram of carbohydrate, 9.3 Calories in the oxidation of 1 gram of fat. Protein, on the other hand, does not undergo complete combustion in the body. The nitrogenous part of the molecule resists oxidation and is excreted in the urine, mainly as urea (p. 363). A gram of protein, therefore, evolves less heat when catabolized than when burned outside the body. In the latter instance, 5.3 Calories are generated, in the former only 4.1.

Animal calorimetry. The heat generated by the body may be measured directly—*direct calorimetry*. The animal is placed in a closed chamber with double insulated walls; coils of copper tubing, through which water is circulated, are situated on the inner walls of the chamber; thus the heat given out by the animal is absorbed. The temperature of the water as it enters and leaves the chamber is recorded by thermometers.

The rise in temperature of the water in degrees centigrade, during the period of observation, multiplied by the total volume of water in kilograms which has passed through the chamber in that time, gives in Calories the heat given off by the animal. A few calorimeters of this type have been constructed for metabolic experiments on man, but their great expense precludes their general use. Indirect calorimetric methods are therefore employed almost entirely in metabolism studies upon the human subject.

Indirect calorimetry. We have seen that when carbohydrate undergoes combustion in the body, the carbon is oxidized to carbon dioxide (CO_2) and the hydrogen to water (H_2O). Thus:

$$C_6H_{12}O_6 + 6O_2 = 6CO_2 + 6H_2O$$

glucose   carbon   water
                          dioxide

The body, therefore, reverses the reaction carried out by the green plant which, as already stated, synthesizes carbohydrate from carbon dioxide and water. In the complete oxidation of a given weight of carbohydrate, whether in air or in the tissues of the body, the quantity of oxygen used and of carbon dioxide produced have definite and constant values. It is also known that for every 1000 cc of oxygen consumed when carbohydrate is the material oxidized, 5.047 Calories of heat are evolved. That is to say, there is a constant relationship between the volume of oxygen consumed and the quantity of heat evolved. It is evident, therefore, that the heat production of an animal subsisting upon carbohydrate food could be determined, provided that the quantity of oxygen consumed by the animal were known. The relationship between the oxygen consumption and the heat production varies, however, with the type of food undergoing combustion. Carbohydrate material as compared with fat is relatively rich in oxygen. Thus, $C_3H_5(C_{18}H_{33}O_2)_3$ is the formula for *triolein,* a common fat. More oxygen must therefore be supplied from a source outside the food itself for the complete oxidation of the carbon and hydrogen in fat than for the oxidation of these elements in an equal quantity of carbohydrate. The consumption of 1000 cc of oxygen, when fat is oxidized, is accompanied, therefore, by a smaller heat production—namely, 4.686 Calories as compared with the figure (5.047) given above for carbohydrate. The corresponding value for protein is 4.485 Calories. These values are termed the *heat equivalents* of the foodstuffs.

In order, therefore, to calculate the heat production of the body from the oxygen consumption, one must know the nature of the food mixture (the proportions of carbohydrate, fat, and protein) which is being metabolized. This information is obtained from the *respiratory quotient,* which will now be explained.

The respiratory quotient. The volume of carbon dioxide eliminated by the body during a given time, over the volume of oxygen absorbed, is called the respiratory quotient (R.Q.). Thus:

$$\frac{\text{Vol. } CO_2 \text{ eliminated}}{\text{Vol. } O_2 \text{ absorbed}} = \text{R.Q.}$$

From the equation given on page 353 it will be seen that, when the food undergoing combustion is carbohydrate, the volume of carbon dioxide eliminated and of oxygen absorbed is equal. When, for example, 100 grams of glucose are oxidized, 75 liters of oxygen are absorbed and 75 liters of carbon dioxide produced. The R.Q. is, therefore, $\frac{75}{75} = 1$. In the complete combustion of fat, which is relatively poor in oxygen, the volume of oxygen used (200 liters per 100 grams) is greater than the volume of carbon dioxide produced (142 liters per 100 grams). The R.Q. is, therefore, ($\frac{142}{200} =$) 0.71. The respiratory quotient for protein is 0.80 and for alcohol, 0.67.

On an ordinary mixed diet, the R.Q. of the human subject is around

Table 9-1

(After Züntz and Schumberg, modified by Lusk)

Nonprotein respiratory quotient	Calories per liter O_2	Calories derived from	
		Carbohydrate	Fat
		percent	percent
0.707	4.686	0	100
0.71	4.690	1.10	98.9
0.72	4.702	4.76	95.2
0.73	4.714	8.40	91.6
0.74	4.727	12.0	88.0
0.75	4.739	15.6	84.4
0.76	4.751	19.2	80.8
0.77	4.764	22.8	77.2
0.78	4.776	26.3	73.7
0.79	4.788	29.9	70.1
0.80	4.801	33.4	66.6
0.81	4.813	36.9	63.1
0.82	4.825	40.3	59.7
0.83	4.838	43.8	56.2
0.84	4.850	47.2	52.8
0.85	4.862	50.7	49.3
0.86	4.875	54.1	45.9
0.87	4.887	57.5	42.5
0.88	4.899	60.8	39.2
0.89	4.911	64.2	35.8
0.90	4.924	67.5	32.5
0.91	4.936	70.8	29.2
0.92	4.948	74.1	25.9
0.93	4.961	77.4	22.6
0.94	4.973	80.7	19.3
0.95	4.985	84.0	16.0
0.96	4.998	87.2	12.8
0.97	5.010	90.4	9.58
0.98	5.022	93.6	6.37
0.99	5.035	96.8	3.18
1.00	5.047	100.0	0

0.85. After fasting for 12 hours, it has a value of 0.82. When, as in the fattening of farm animals, fat is being formed from carbohydrate —that is, an oxygen-rich material is being transformed into one poor in oxygen—the R.Q. rises above 1. The heat equivalents of a liter of oxygen at different respiratory quotients are given in Table 9-1.

The respiratory quotients given in this table are for mixtures of fat and carbohydrate only (*nonprotein respiratory quotients*). For very precise work, the Calories derived from the metabolism of protein are calculated separately from the quantity of nitrogen excreted in the urine. But, as a matter of fact, only a negligible error is introduced when the figures in the table are used for calculating the heat production—that is, without any attention being paid to the protein metabolism.

The basal metabolic rate (B.M.R.). The heat production of the human body at its lowest possible level in the waking state is called the *basal metabolism* or the *basal metabolic rate* (B.M.R.). In its determination, all conditions which have a stimulating effect upon heat production must be eliminated. It is measured, therefore, 12 hours after the last meal (usually in the morning without breakfast) with the subject lying down at complete physical and mental rest, and at a room temperature of about 20° C. No strenuous muscular exertion should be undertaken for 24 hours prior to the determination. The B.M.R. is usually expressed in Calories per square meter of body surface per hour.[2] It may be determined from either the quantity of carbon dioxide eliminated, or from the quantity of oxygen consumed over a known period of time; but the figure for the latter is now most commonly employed (see Fig. 9.2). The heat value of a liter of oxygen for various

---

[2] In the early investigations of metabolic problems, it was the practice to express the heat production of the body in relation to its weight—that is, in Calories per kilogram of body weight per hour. But it was soon found that the surface area of the body rather than its weight was the determining factor in heat production. Heat is lost from the surface of the body (p. 377) and, in order to maintain a constant body temperature, must be balanced by heat production. The greater the surface area of the body the greater is the amount of heat which is dissipated. Now small animals, such as mice, rats, etc., which have a much greater surface area in proportion to their weight than have larger animals, such as dogs, cattle, horses, etc. (just as a marble has in relation to its mass a much greater surface than a baseball), have a correspondingly greater heat production on a body weight basis than have the larger animals. When, however, the heat generated is calculated and expressed in relation to the surface area of the body, it is found to be approximately the same for mammals of all sizes under comparable conditions. Thus the heat production of a mouse is around 27 Calories per kilogram of body weight per hour, while that of a man is only about 1.1 Calorie per kilogram per hour. But both have a heat production of around 40 Calories per square meter of body surface per hour. (Of course, the area of the mouse's body amounts to only a very small fraction of a square meter and the *absolute* quantity of heat given out is relatively minute.)

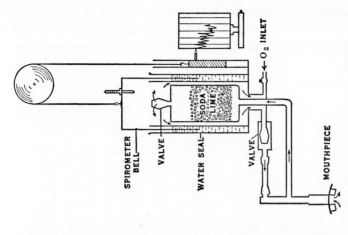

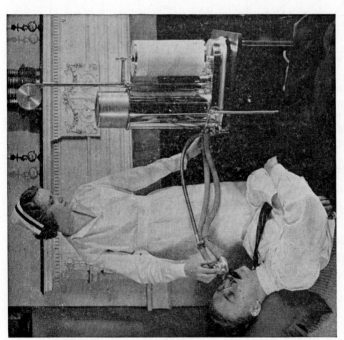

Fig. 9.2   Showing method of determining the basal metabolic rate by means of the Benedict-Roth apparatus (courtesy of Warren E. Collins, Inc., Boston). Oxygen is inhaled from the spirometer through one of the large-bored rubber tubes. The quantity consumed is recorded on the paper-covered rotating cylinder, a declining curve being inscribed on the paper by the writing point. The subject expires through the other rubber tube. The expired air passes through a canister placed within the spirometer and filled with soda lime which removes the carbon dioxide. The BMR is calculated from the oxygen consumption alone. The right-hand drawing is a diagram of the interior of the Benedict-Roth apparatus.

metabolic mixtures (carbohydrate and fat), as indicated by the respiratory quotients, is given in Table 9-1. As a rule, the R.Q. is not actually determined, but is taken to be 0.82, for this is its value after fasting for 12 hours, under which conditions, as just stated, the B.M.R. is determined.

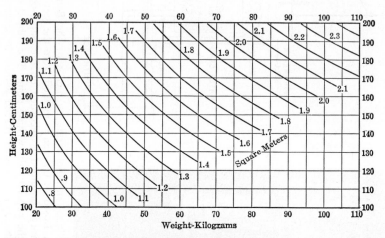

Fig. 9.3   Du Bois' chart for obtaining the surface area of the body in square meters (as indicated by the slanting lines) from a subject's height and weight. For example, a person 170 centimeters (approximately 5 feet 8 inches tall and weighing 70 kilograms (154 pounds) has a surface area of 1.8 square meters.

Sample calculation of the B.M.R. from the oxygen consumption. If the oxygen consumption over a period of 10 minutes is 2.500 liters, then the hourly heat production (under the conditions defined and at an R.Q. of 0.82) is $2.500 \times 4.825 \times \frac{60}{10} = 72.36$ Calories. If the subject has a surface area of say, 1.8 square meters, which is the figure for the average male adult, then the hourly heat production per square meter of body surface is:

$$\frac{72.36}{1.8} = 40.2 \text{ Calories}$$

The surface area of the body bears a relationship to the height and weight and may be obtained for a given person from the chart shown in Figure 9.3.

In young healthy adult males, the basal metabolic rate is around 40 Calories per square meter of body surface per hour. It is lower in women and higher in children, being around 52 Calories during the early years, and diminishing gradually throughout life. It reaches the adult value at about 20 years of age; from then it declines more slowly, reaching a value of around 36 Calories in old age. The heat production per square meter of body surface per hour for males and females of different ages is given in Table 9-2.

Table 9-2

Oxygen consumption (liters) and heat production (Calories) per square meter of body surface per hour

Ages	Male		Female	
	O_2	Calories	O_2	Calories
14–15	9.53	45.9	8.91	42.9
16–17	8.91	42.9	8.29	39.9
18–19	8.50	40.9	7.88	37.9
20–29	8.19	39.4	7.67	36.9
30–39	8.19	39.4	7.57	36.4
40–49	7.98	38.4	7.46	35.9
50–59	7.77	37.4	7.25	34.9
60–69	7.57	36.4	7.05	33.9
70–79	7.36	35.4	6.84	32.9

Note the gradual diminution in heat production with advancing years.

The physiological conditions which raise the metabolism are *muscular exercise,* a *low environmental temperature,* and the *ingestion of food,* especially protein. The term *specific dynamic action* is applied to this stimulating effect of food upon metabolism. During *sleep* the metabolism is lowered by about 15 percent below the *basal* level.

Among pathological conditions which increase the metabolism are *hyperthyroidism* (p. 411) and *fever* (p. 381); it is lowered in *hypothyroidism* (p. 408), *undernutrition, deficiency of the adrenal cortex* (p. 426), and in certain *pituitary disorders.*

The Metabolism of Protein

Protein material enters largely into the composition of all types of protoplasm, both of animal and vegetable origin. Among foods, meat (muscle), cheese, eggs, beans, and peas (legumes) are the richest sources. Its basic elements are *carbon, hydrogen, oxygen, nitrogen,* and *sulfur,* and usually *phosphorus.* Its content of the last three elements distinguishes it from either fat or carbohydrate, which contain only carbon, hydrogen, and oxygen. The body is dependent almost entirely upon protein for its supplies of nitrogen and sulfur, and mainly for its phosphorus.

The amino acids. The protein molecule is made up of a number of amino acids linked together. Some twenty-three different amino acids have been discovered. The simplest of these is called *glycine* or *glycocol,* which consists of acetic acid in which a hydrogen atom is replaced by an NH_2 group. Thus:

$$CH_3 \qquad\qquad CH_2 - NH_2$$
$$|\qquad\qquad\qquad |$$
$$COOH \qquad\qquad COOH$$
$$\text{acetic acid} \qquad\qquad \text{glycine}$$

The majority of the other amino acids are constructed upon the same general plan. They contain a fatty acid—e.g., propionic, valerianic, caproic, succinic, etc.—and one or two NH_2 (amino) groups. An incomplete list of the amino acids with their empirical formulas is given in Table 9-3.

Table 9-3

A partial list of the amino acids (see also appendix)

Glycine (or glycocoll), $C_2H_5NO_2$, or amino acetic acid
Alanine, $C_3H_7NO_2$, or α-amino propionic acid
*Threonine, $C_4H_9NO_3$, or α-amino-β-hydroxy-n-butyric acid
*Valine, $C_5H_{11}NO_2$, or α-amino isovaleric acid
*Leucine, $C_6H_{13}NO_2$, or α-amino isocaproic acid
*Isoleucine, $C_6H_{13}NO_2$, or α-amino-β-ethyl-β-methyl propionic acid
Aspartic acid, $C_4H_7NO_4$, or amino succinic acid
Glutamic acid, $C_5H_9NO_4$, or α-amino glutaric acid
*Arginine, $C_6H_{14}N_4O_2$, or δ-guanidin-α-amino valerianic acid
*Lysine, $C_6H_{14}N_2O_2$, or α-ϵ-diamino caproic acid
Cystine, $C_6H_{12}N_2S_2O_4$, or di-cysteine or di-(β-thio-α-amino propionic acid)
*Methionine, $C_5H_{11}SNO_2$, or α-amino-γ-methyl-thiol-n-butyric acid
*Phenylalanine, $C_9H_{11}NO_2$, or β-phenyl-α-amino propionic acid
Tyrosine, $C_9H_{11}NO_3$, or β-parahydroxy-phenyl-α-amino propionic acid
*Tryptophane, $C_{11}H_{12}N_2O_2$, or β-indole-α-amino propionic acid
*Histidine, $C_6H_9N_3O_2$, or α-amino-β-imidazol propionic acid

The protein molecule, being built of amino acids linked together, possesses free COOH (acid) and NH_2 (basic) groups. It is capable, therefore, of acting as a weak acid or a weak base depending upon the reaction of the medium in which it is dissolved. In alkaline solution, it behaves as a weak acid; in acid solution, as a weak base. In the blood plasma and the other body fluids (which are slightly alkaline in reaction), protein, acting as an acid, forms with bases compounds called *proteinates*. The chief base is sodium. The proteinate undergoes ionization (p. 12), into proteinate anions (P^-) and cations (Na^+, K^+, etc.). In *acid* solution, protein hydrochloride, protein sulfate, etc., are formed, the protein then acting as a weak base. At a certain reaction

Table 9-4

Classification of proteins

Simple proteins
> *Albumins*—e.g., *ovalbumin* of egg white, *serum albumin, lactalbumin,* and certain *vegetable albumins*
> *Globulins*—e.g., *serum globulin, fibrinogen, vitellin* of egg yolk, and *legumin* of peas
> *Glutelins*—e.g., *glutenin* of wheat
> *Gliadins*—e.g., *gliadin* of wheat, *hordein* of barley, and *zein* of maize
> *Scleroproteins*—e.g., *keratin* of hair, *elastin, collagen* (which yields *gelatin*) of connective tissues
> *Histones*—e.g., the *globin* in hemoglobin
> *Protamines,* in spermatozoa—e.g., *salmine* in spermatozoa of salmon

Conjugated proteins—i.e., proteins containing a nonprotein group
> *Nucleoproteins,* protein combined with nucleic acid (p. 366)
> *Chromoproteins,* protein containing a pigment group, e.g., *hemoglobin*
> *Glycoproteins,* protein containing a sugar group—e.g., *mucin*
> *Lipoproteins,* proteins whose molecule contains a fatty acid group; present in protoplasm of cells of various tissues including blood
> *Phosphoproteins,* proteins containing a phosphorus group (other than nucleoproteins)—e.g., *casein* of milk

Derived proteins, products of the action of acids, heat, or enzymes upon proteins
> *Metaproteins*
> *Coagulated* proteins
> *Proteoses*
> *Peptones*
> *Peptids, dipeptids, tripeptids,* and *polypeptids*

nearer the neutral point, ionization is reduced to zero; the protein particles, being electrically neutral, collect together into clumps. A precipitate of the protein material forms which is visible to the naked eye; this is called *isoelectric precipitation,* and the point or range of pH at which it occurs is known as the *isoelectric point* or *range.* The latter varies considerably for different proteins but is characteristic for a given protein. Proteins (or the constituent amino acids), on account of their ability to form acids or bases depending upon the H-ion concentration, are termed *amphoteric electrolytes* (Gk. *ampho,* both).

There are several proteins which contain more than 15 *varieties* of amino acids, but the assortment varies between different types of protein. The *total number* of amino acids in a protein molecule may be 200 or more. Such proteins are composed, therefore, of molecules of relatively enormous size. The molecules of certain other proteins, such as the protamines, contain much fewer amino acids and are correspondingly smaller. There is thus a very wide variation in the size of the molecules of the different types of protein. Egg albumin, for example, has a molecular weight of around 40,000, whereas the molecular weights of some other proteins are in the neighborhood of 200,000 or more. A few have a molecular weight of over a million. The shape of the protein molecule also varies. The molecules of some proteins such as the myosin of muscle and of that forming tendons and ligaments (collagen) are long and fiberlike in shape, while others, such as those of serum albumin, are globular. A short classification of proteins is given in Table 9-4.

The History of Protein in the Body

The growth of body tissue in the young animal, and the repair of protein structure in the adult body are dependent upon the protein (amino acid) content of the diet. But since the tissue protein of a given animal is different in constitution from the protein of its food, the latter as a rule must be completely broken down into its separate amino acids before it can be utilized for building body tissue.

The utilization of protein in the construction of body tissue may be compared to the building of a number of houses of different types from materials obtained from the wrecking of other structures. Each brick and stone in the old buildings is separated, and then sorted and carted to the new sites. Some of this building material will be more suitable for one type of house, some more suitable for other types. Other materials again cannot be used at all, and are therefore discarded as refuse. The new buildings, though constructed from materials taken from the old, will therefore be quite different in structure and general plan.

From this analogy, the amino acids are sometimes called the "building stones" of the protein molecule. Under the action of the peptidases of the intestinal juice (p. 327), the protein molecule is completely demolished, in the sense that it is broken up into its constituent amino acids. The separate amino acids are absorbed into the blood stream and carried therein to the tissues. Each tissue chooses those which it can make use of, rejecting others.

Those amino acids which cannot be utilized by the body are broken up; the carbon part of the molecule (i.e., the fatty acid group) is oxidized to carbon dioxide and water, thus furnishing energy to the body or is converted to body fat; the nitrogen goes to form urea which is excreted in the urine. The removal of the nitrogen (amino) group from the amino acid molecule is called *deamination;* this process occurs chiefly in the liver. Certain amino acids not used for the construction of body protein may, after undergoing deamination, be converted to glucose which is then either oxidized or stored in the liver as glycogen (p. 368). In diabetes the glucose formed from amino acids is largely excreted in the urine. The diabetic subject, therefore, continues to excrete sugar though he receives no sugar or other carbohydrate; even during fasting he continues to excrete glucose, which is then derived from the protein of his own tissues.

The *urea* in the urine is formed mainly through the deamination of amino acids composing the protein of the food. Raising the protein content of the diet, therefore, increases the output of urea in the urine and vice versa. But the urea is not entirely derived from the diet; a small part is formed from the nitrogen released by the breakdown of body protein, for the tissues are constantly undergoing disintegration and repair. The urea of the urine is thus in part *exogenous* (from food) and partly *endogenous* (from body protein). *Creatinine,* another nitrogenous constituent of the urine, is also derived from tissue protein, but unlike urea it is derived almost entirely from this source. Varying the protein of the diet, therefore, exerts little effect upon the excretion of creatinine. A small quantity of nitrogen, combined in various ways, is also eliminated from the body by passing through the wall of the intestine into the feces.

During starvation or upon a protein-poor diet, the breakdown of body protein, of course, continues. The body loses nitrogen through the so-called "wear and tear" of tissue protein, but receives none to make good the loss. That is to say, the output of nitrogen in the urine and feces exceeds that of the food; the body is then said to be in *negative nitrogen balance*. Similarly, the nitrogen output will exceed the intake, and the body will be in negative nitrogen balance, if the food protein is inadequate in amount or of poor quality (i.e., if its assortment of amino acids is unsuitable for repairing body protein, the nonutilizable amino acids being excreted in the urine). In the healthy adult receiving an adequate diet, the nitrogen excreted just balances the nitrogen taken in the food—that is, the nitrogen lost as a result of the breakdown of tissue protein is replaced from the food; the remainder of the food nitrogen is excreted. The body is then said to be in *nitrogen equilibrium.*

During growth, after a period of starvation, in pregnancy, in muscular training, or in convalescence from some disease which has caused the excessive destruction of body protein, the quantity of nitrogen excreted is *less* than that taken in the food, provided the protein intake is adequate. The body is then in *positive nitrogen balance.* In other words, nitrogen is retained for the construction of body tissue.

The "wear and tear" quota of protein metabolism is reduced by carbohydrate food. For example, the nitrogen excretion is considerably less on a diet containing carbohydrate but no protein, than in starvation. The carbohydrate diminishes the breakdown of tissue protein. This is spoken of as the *sparing effect* of carbohydrate upon protein metabolism.

We have seen that only part of the protein molecule can be oxidized in the body and thus provide energy. Civilized man cannot subsist on protein food alone, because he cannot eat and digest enough to supply the required energy. One gram of protein furnishes 4.1 Calories. A man of average size has a daily energy expenditure under basal conditions of about 1400 Calories, and between 2500 and 3000 Calories when engaged in light occupation. Now, lean meat is about 20 percent pure protein. Therefore, about

$$\frac{1400}{4.1} \times \frac{100}{20} = 1700 \text{ grams}$$

or nearly 4 pounds of meat would need to be eaten daily, in order to obtain from protein the energy required by the body, even at rest. From three to four times this amount of meat would be required to furnish the energy for heavy work. On the other hand, a carnivorous animal such as the dog, which has an energy expenditure of some 600 Calories, can consume 2 or 3 pounds of meat in a few minutes, and can therefore derive its total caloric requirement from such food. The Eskimos are also accustomed to the consumption of relatively enormous quantities of meat and fat.

The essential amino acids and the relative nutritional values of different proteins. An *essential* or *indispensable* amino acid may be defined as one which must be present in the diet in order that the growth of young animals may proceed normally, and that the health of both young and old animals be maintained. In a sense, probably all the amino acids are essential in one way or another for nutrition, but some (e.g., *glycine*) can be synthesized in the body or formed from others furnished in the diet. It is not necessary, therefore, that such amino acids shall themselves be present in the food. There are ten essential amino acids; they are marked with an asterisk in Table 9-3 on page 360.

Proteins are not all of equal value in nutrition, for the reason that the various types differ widely in their amino-acid constitution. Those which possess an amino-acid assortment most closely resembling that of the body's proteins have the highest nutritive value. Generally speak-

Table 9-5

Character of proteins in some common foods

Food	Chief proteins present	Amino-acid constitution
Milk and cheese	Casein	Complete, but low in cystine
	Lactalbumin	Complete
Corn (maize) ...	Zein	Lacks lysine and tryptophane and is low in cystine
Eggs	Ovalbumin	Complete
	Ovovitelline	Complete
Meat	Albumin	Complete
	Myosin	Complete
Peas	Legumin	Incomplete, low in cystine
Wheat	Gliadin	Incomplete lacks lysine
	Glutenin	Complete
Gelatin	Gelatin	Incomplete, lacking tryptophane and tyrosine; very low in cystine

In part from M. S. Rose, *Foundations of Nutrition.*

ing, and as might be expected, these are of animal origin—for instance, the proteins of milk, eggs, and meat. Some proteins, such as *gelatin* and *zein* (in maize) are incomplete—that is, they lack certain amino acids which are essential for growth and for the maintenance of nitrogen equilibrium in the adult. Others, such as *gliadin* (in wheat), *hordein* (in barley), and *legumin* (in peas), will serve to repair body protein in the adult but will not support growth, since they lack certain essential amino acids or contain them in insufficient amounts. Young animals which receive one or other of these as their sole protein fail to grow. Wheat, peas, and barley, however, contain other proteins which make good the amino-acid deficiencies of those which are incomplete (see Table 9-5). *Lactalbumin* of milk, and *ovalbumin* of egg white, the *proteins* of meat, and *glutenin* (of *wheat*) contain all the essential amino acids.

Purine Metabolism

Uric acid ($C_5H_4N_4O_3$), a nitrogenous compound present in normal urine and blood, is a purine derivative. Purines are constitutents of nucleic acid and this, in turn, is found in the body combined with protein, the compound being called *nucleoprotein.* Nucleoprotein is present in the nuclei of cells generally, and such tissues as those of thymus, liver, kidney, pancreas, and other glandular stuctures are particularly rich in this material. Viruses are now thought to be composed of nucleoprotein.

Nucleic acid is constituted of four compounds called *nucleotides.* A nucleotide contains a molecule each of *phosphoric acid,* the *pentose, ribose* (a sugar with 5 carbon atoms and 5 H_2O molecules), and a *purine* (*adenine* or *guanine*) or a *pyrimidine* group. The nucleoprotein of food is broken down by intestinal enzymes into protein and nucleic acid. The latter is split into its constituent nucleotides by an enzyme in the intestinal juice, called *nuclease.* The nucleotides are absorbed and, through the actions of specific tissue enzymes, are broken into their components. Prosphoric acid is first removed, leaving a pentose-purine (or pyrimidine) compound called a *nucleoside.* The sugar is then split off. The fate of the purine derivatives, adenine and guanine, only need concern us here. These, as a result of deamination (splitting off of NH_3) and oxidation by tissue enzymes, give rise to uric acid.

Uric acid is of especial interest because in gout, a painful arthritic condition, its excretion is reduced and its concentration in the blood increased. Uric acid, in the form of crystals of sodium urate, is deposited in the tissues surrounding the affected joint. Meats such as liver, sweetbreads, kidney, etc., which are rich in nuclear material and consequently in nucleic acid, tend, therefore, to aggravate the symptoms of gout.

The origin of uric acid is briefly summarized in the following scheme.

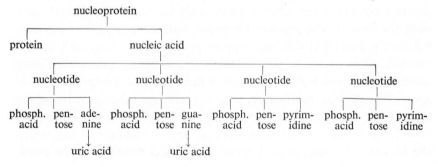

Carbohydrate Metabolism

Classification of the carbohydrates. Carbohydrates (sugars, starches, etc.) are composed of carbon, hydrogen, and oxygen. The last two elements are present in the same proportions as in water (H_2O). Thus, the three sugars, *glucose* (or *dextrose*), *fructose* (or *levulose*), and *galactose,* contain six molecules of water and six atoms of carbon, as shown by their formula, $C_6H_{12}O_6$. These sugars are therefore called *hexoses* (Gk. *hex,* six). Though they have a common empirical formula—i.e., the same number of each type of atom—the positions of the atoms in the molecule differ. The structural formulas of glucose, fructose, and galactose are given below for comparison.

glucose	fructose	galactose

Glucose is found in fruits and in the blood and tissues of animals. Fructose is the chief sugar of honey. Galactose is present, as a component of the disaccharide *lactose,* in milk, being combined in the molecule with glucose. It is also found as a constituent of certain fatty compounds in brain tissue. Other much less common sugars have molecules containing seven, five, four, three, or two carbon atoms and a corresponding number of water molecules. Employing Greek prefixes, they are called heptoses, pentoses, tetroses, trioses, and dioses, respectively. Thus a heptose is represented by the formula $C_7H_{14}O_7$, a pentose by $C_5H_{10}O_5$, a tetrose by $C_4H_8O_4$, and so on. Octoses, nonoses, and decoses, though not known in nature, have been prepared in the laboratory.

Sugars belonging to the class just outlined are called *monosaccharides,* and may be represented by the general formula $C_n(H_2O)_n$, in which n has the value 2, 3, 4, 5, 6, 7, and so forth.

Disaccharides are sugars composed of two monosaccharide molecules less a molecule of water. *Sucrose* (cane, beet, and maple sugars), *maltose* (sugar of malt), and *lactose* (sugar of milk) belong to this group. Though a disaccharide may be made up of other monosaccharides, these three, which are important food elements and, therefore, of physiological interest, consist of hexoses either of the same or of different kinds. Their formula is $C_{12}H_{22}O_{11}$. They are split (hydrolyzed) into their constituent monosaccharides by the actions of specific enzymes in the intestine. Thus—

$$C_{12}H_{22}O_{11} + H_2O = 2C_6H_{12}O_6$$

Sucrose is hydrolyzed into a molecule each of glucose and fructose,[3] maltose into two molecules of glucose, and lactose into glucose and galactose.

Polysaccharides are made up of a large number of monosaccharide molecules, which may be either pentoses or hexoses, less water. The polysaccharides of physiological importance—namely, the *vegetable starches, glycogen* ("animal starch"), *cellulose,* and *dextrins*—are constituted of glucose molecules, and are therefore given the general formula of $(C_6H_{10}O_5)_x$. Upon hydrolysis they yield glucose.

The history of carbohydrate in the body. Glycogen was discovered by the great French physiologist, Claude Bernard, in 1857. It is found in traces in most tissues of the body and in fairly large amounts in liver and muscle. Muscle may contain any amount of glycogen between 0.10 and 1.0 percent of fresh tissue. Since approximately one half the total weight of our bodies is muscle, it will be appreciated that the total quantity of muscle glycogen is very considerable. The liver often contains as much as 10 or 15 percent of its wet weight of glycogen and, though it makes up only about 3 percent of the body weight, its total glycogen content is comparable with that of the muscular tissues.

Glucose is found in all body tissues; blood contains approximately 0.1 percent, but there is considerable variation in the amount in health as well as in disease. It is the most important single carbohydrate with which we have to deal in physiology. As such it can be used as food, passing unchanged from the small intestine into the blood, while complex carbohydrates, such as the disaccharides and polysaccharides (starches and glycogen), must first be hydrolyzed into glucose or other hexoses before they can be absorbed in significant amounts.

Glucose (as well as fructose and galactose) passes from the intestine into the blood of the portal vein, and is deposited in the liver as glycogen. The conversion of glucose to glycogen is a specific function of the liver cells, and is termed *glycogenesis* (literally, glycogen formation).

[3] The mixture is called invert sugar.

The glucose in the blood is maintained at a fairly constant level by the reconversion of glycogen to glucose, which is then discharged into the general circulation. This process is termed *glycogenolysis* (literally, glycogen breakdown).

Muscle glycogen is derived from the glucose of the blood. During muscular contraction, energy is furnished mainly by carbohydrates; the muscle glycogen breaks down into its constituent glucose molecules. Lactic acid, which is ultimately produced, is in part resynthesized to glycogen and in part oxidized to carbon dioxide and water (see Chap. 11). Lactic acid, as well as the three hexoses—glucose, fructose, and galactose—is, therefore, a glycogen former. A part of the lactic acid produced diffuses into the blood and is deposited as glycogen in the liver, as well as in the heart muscle and certain other tissues. Glucose is also formed from the amino acids of food protein; in starvation or upon a protein-free diet, it is produced from body protein. This process is carried out in the liver, and is termed *gluconeogenesis* (literally, the new formation of sugar). There has been some question in the past whether sugar could be formed from fat, but it is now accepted by most authorities on carbohydrates that the conversion does occur.

The carbohydrate cycle just outlined may be represented in the following scheme.

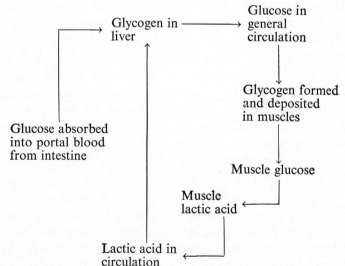

Oxidation of carbohydrate. While it appears probable that glucose is the only sugar oxidized directly in the tissue cells, there may be some utilization of fructose in this manner (see p. 367).

Diabetes and the action of insulin. Insulin, the antidiabetic hormone, is produced in the pancreas; when this gland is completely removed from animals, a condition known as pancreatic diabetes rapidly develops. This is characterized by a high blood sugar (0.2–0.5 percent, as compared with the normal of 0.1 percent) and the excretion of sugar in the urine. The extent of the increase of blood glucose (*hyperglycemia*), and of the loss of glucose in the urine (*glucosuria* or *glycosuria*) is proportional to the carbohydrate content of the diet, but even on a diet composed entirely of protein, or during fasting, the depancreatized animal excretes a considerable amount of sugar. The glucose reserves of the body (e.g., liver glycogen) are rapidly lost. Sugar is then made from tissue protein, the animal losing weight as a result. The fat depots are also called upon; the fat may be oxidized directly or first converted to glucose. At any rate, the increased rate of breakdown of fat results in the accumulation of ketone bodies in the blood (*ketosis*) and urine (*ketonuria*).

The ketone bodies are β-hydroxybutyric and acetoacetic acids and acetone. The two organic acids are normal intermediate products in the metabolism of fat, β-hydroxybutyric acid being derived, through oxidation, from acetoacetic. Both acids are present in the body in health though only in small amounts, acetoacetic acid undergoing almost complete oxidation to carbon dioxide and water. When, on the other hand, the metabolism of carbohydrate is defective, as in diabetes, for some reason not altogether clear, excessive quantities of fat are metabolized; acetoacetic acid is formed in such large amounts that it cannot be completely oxidized. It and β-hydroxybutyric acid accumulate in the blood and tissues, and are responsible for the acidosis and coma of diabetes. Acetoacetic acid is believed to be an especially toxic product. In diabetes, it is converted, through the loss of a molecule of carbon dioxide, to acetone, a volatile substance with a characteristic odor. Acetone is exhaled in the breath and excreted in the urine.

All the signs and symptoms seen in animals following removal of the pancreas are seen in human diabetes mellitus which, in most instances, is the result of disease of the islets of Langerhans in the pancreas. These structures are solely responsible for the body's supply of insulin. They can be seen in a section of the pancreas as small groups of cells lying here and there between the pancreatic alveoli which secrete the pancreatic juice (Fig. 8.24, p. 323). In diabetes there is also an accumulation in the blood of neutral fat in the form of microscopic particles called chylomicrons. This phenomenon is known as *lipemia*.

The disturbances of carbohydrate metabolism characteristic of the diabetic state may be explained on the basis of (1) failure of utilization (oxidation) of carbohydrate or (2) abnormal rate of production of sugar from noncarbohydrate sources. The results of modern research favor the second alternative.

The discovery of insulin has not solved the problem of the cause of diabetes, but has provided an effective means of treating the disease. It has also furnished a most valuable "tool" for studying carbohydrate metabolism. Insulin administered subcutaneously or intravenously eliminates all the signs of diabetes in experimental animals or in human patients. Its action is to promote the storage of glycogen in muscles and liver, to depress the wasteful new production of sugar in the liver, and to increase the oxidation of carbohydrate. The hyperglycemia and glucosuria disappear. Ketosis is eliminated. The rapid loss of body tissues is checked.

Insulin has now been prepared in crystalline form; it is a protein containing eight or more amino acids. The highly purified insulin is absorbed quickly, when administered subcutaneously, and efforts have been made to lengthen the period of absorption—i.e., to prolong its action. The most satisfactory preparation thus far developed for this purpose is protamine zinc insulin, which is made by adding protamine and zinc to insulin. Protamine is a simple protein obtained from fish sperm (see Table 9-4).

While a deficiency of insulin causes diabetes, overproduction is responsible for clinical condition called *hyperinsulinism*. The outstanding features of this disease are a low blood sugar (*hypoglycemia*), and the symptoms incident thereto. A similar condition may result from an overdose of insulin. The signs of hypoglycemia are neuromuscular hyperexcitability and hunger. If the blood sugar continues to fall, the excitability increases, leading to involuntary twitching of muscles, and later to generalized convulsions. Glucose is the best antidote for an excess of insulin. Other carbohydrates are effective in proportion to their ability to form glucose.

Other hormones and carbohydrate metabolism. The influence upon carbohydrate metabolism of certain hormones of the anterior lobe of the pituitary is dealt with on page 435, and of thyroxine and the hormones of the adrenal gland on pages 411 and 427, respectively.

These several hormones constitute a complex, but delicately balanced mechanism whereby the metabolism of carbohydrate is regulated. The various phases of, and the ceaseless changes in carbohydrate metabolism—the utilization of glucose by the tissues, the formation and storage of glycogen and its breakdown to glucose, and the new formation of glucose from protein and fat—all come under the influence of one or more of the hormones mentioned. Due to their reciprocal actions, the sugar of the blood and other body fluids is maintained at an approximately constant concentration.

The nervous system and carbohydrate metabolism. In 1855, Claude Bernard showed that injury to the brain which involved the pons and the cerebellum as well as the floor of the fourth ventricle produced hyperglycemia and glucosuria. It appears probable that these lesions set up nerve impulses which caused the breakdown of liver glycogen. This may be due to the conduction of the impulses directly to the liver or may be an indirect result of adrenaline liberation. It will be appreciated that interference with the nerve supply of any of the glands whose secretions affect carbohydrates may exert a profound influence on the metabolism of these substances.

Fat Metabolism

The neutral fats. The common fats of vegetable and animal tissues are compounds of the higher fatty acids, *palmitic* ($C_{16}H_{32}O_2$), *stearic* ($C_{18}H_{36}O_2$), and *oleic* ($C_{18}H_{34}O_2$), in combination with the triatomic alcohol, *glycerol* ($C_3H_5(OH)_3$). Each molecule of glycerol (glycerin) is combined with three molecules of one or other of these fatty acids. The resulting compound (or ester) is called a *neutral fat* or *triglyceride*. Depending upon the particular fatty acids in the triglyceride molecule, the three chief fats are named *tripalmitin, tristearin,* and *triolein,* respectively.

The fatty tissues of animals consist of connective tissue in which is deposited a mixture of neutral fats, triolein being in the greatest proportion. Tripalmitin is present in smaller and tristearin in least amount.

The triglycerides are hydrolyzed by the intestinal enzymes (lipases) into their constituents—fatty acids and glycerol. In the presence of alkali, fat is decomposed, the fatty acid then reacting to form soap. Thus,

$$C_3H_5(C_{18}H_{35}O_2)_3 + 3NaOH = 3CH_3(CH_2)_{16}COONa + C_3H_5(OH)_3$$

tristearin	sodium hydroxide	sodium stearate (a soap)	glycerol

Fatty or waxy substances–sterols, steroids, and phospholipids or phosphatides. The *sterols* are secondary alcohols which are present in animal and vegetable tissues in combination with fatty acids. The sterols are but one group of a class of fatty or waxy substances known as *steroids*. They are all closely allied chemically and include the hormones of the sex glands and of the adrenal cortex. Short descriptions of the more important steroids follow.

Cholesterol is widely distributed throughout animal tissues, both as such and as *cholesterol esters*. It was first isolated from gallstones and is an important constituent of bile, hence its name (Gk. *cholē,* bile), and of blood. It is closely related chemically to cholic acid, vitamin D, and the sex hormones. Cholesterol and its esters are especially abundant in the sheaths of nerves, in brain tissue, and in the skin.

Ergosterol is found in plant tissues; it acquires antirachitic properties upon irradiation with ultraviolet light.

The *phospholipids* or *phosphatides* are essential constituents of animal and vegetable cells. Brain, muscle, liver, bile, milk, and eggs contain these substances in especially large amounts. To this class of substance *lecithin, cephalin,* and *sphingomyelin* belong. Upon hydrolysis they yield fatty acids, phosphoric acid, and a nitrogenous base. The nitrogenous element in lecithin is *choline*.

Animal fat is formed from the fat of the food as well as from carbohydrate. It represents a store of energy which the body can draw upon as need arises (e.g., during a prolonged period of fasting). The fat of the food is, of course, not deposited in the tissues unchanged. The fatty acids derived from the ingested fat are recombined with glycerin in such proportions as to produce a fat characteristic of that of the animal's own body—that is, with the proper mixture of the three types of neutral fat.

It will be recalled that the caloric value of fat (9.3) is more than double that of either carbohydrate or protein, which makes it the ideal energy-storing material. Furthermore, fatty tissue is almost pure fat, whereas carbohydrate and protein materials are laid down in the tissues with a relatively large quantity of water.

The phospholipids are believed to play an important part in fat absorption and fat metabolism. Fatty acids, it is thought, must first be transformed to phospholipids before they can be transported across cell membranes.

The liver and fat metabolism. This organ occupies such a central position in any consideration of fat metabolism that particular attention must be directed to it. The liver is the principal if not the only site of production of the ketone bodies (see p. 370). Under a great variety of pathological conditions, neutral fats accumulate in the liver. In diabetes, in anemias, and after various types of poisoning, large deposits of fats are found in this organ. This finding suggests that, under these conditions, either the fat which normally is transported from the fat stores of the body (such as in the subcutaneous tissues or surrounding the abdominal organs) to be dealt with by the liver is, brought there in excessive amounts, or the hepatic cells are in some way functionally depressed and unable to deal with even the normal amount of fat.

Oxidation of fats. The fact that the long chain fatty acids are oxidized very readily in the body makes the detection of intermediate products a difficult matter. The observations of Knoop in the living animal suggest that the so-called β-oxidation takes place—that is, that there is successive removal of groups of two carbon atoms. The fact that the ketone bodies—i.e., those with four carbon atoms—are formed only from fatty acids with an even number of carbon atoms obviously supports the theory of β-oxidation. The results of *in vitro* experiments, however, suggest that rupture of fatty acid chains takes place at various points in the chain. It is thus apparent that our knowledge of fat oxidation is very incomplete.

The digestion and absorption of fat are dealt with in Chapter 8.

Obesity. Overweight of the body due to the excessive accumulation of fat is called *obesity* or *adiposity*. Though a very common state, it must, unless of very moderate degree, be considered an abnormality. Obesity is a definite hazard to the general health, and in several ways puts the physiological processes at a disadvantage. It places a greater than necessary burden upon the heart at all times, but especially in the performance of muscular work. Diabetes, arterial hypertension, degenerative changes in the arteries, and gallstones are among the conditions which are more common in the obese than in persons of normal or subnormal weight. Diabetes has been called the "fat man's folly." Obesity tends to reduce the body's resistance to infection, and the extremely obese person is looked upon as a poor risk by the surgeon, as well as by the insurance examiner. Someone has stated the case of the overweight person of middle age in respect to life expectancy in the epigram "the longer the belt the shorter the life." This is well borne out by insurance statistics. In persons over 45 years of age, the age at death of those who are overweight is considerably below the average, while that of lean persons is above average.

The cause of obesity. Some cases of obesity are due to an endocrine disorder, or other specific disease. But such causes are rare. The common type of obesity, which is usually referred to as *simple* obesity, is due to an intake of energy (food) in excess of the energy output (work). That is to say, the subject eats too much for the physical work he does, or he prefers foods of higher caloric value than does the person of normal weight. The excess food is deposited as fat. This conclusion has been frequently questioned, but attempts to prove otherwise, by experiments upon human subjects, have failed repeatedly to prove that it is false. The metabolic rate, for example, is not lower in the obese than in lean persons. In other words, the metabolic processes of obese persons are not more than usually economical in the conversion of food energy into work.

The Regulation of Body Temperature

The temperature of the human body is determined by placing a thermometer in the mouth, axilla (armpit), or rectum. In health, the mouth temperature is around 98.6° F. The temperature in the axilla is about a degree lower than this, and the rectal temperature about a degree higher. Even in health, the body temperature does not remain at a constant level throughout the 24 hours, but is from 1° to 1.5° lower in the early morning than in the late afternoon. The cause of this diurnal fluctuation in body temperature is unknown.

The body temperature represents the balance struck between the heat generated by the active tissues, mainly the muscles and liver, and that lost from the body to the environment. It is remarkable how steady the body temperature remains under widely varying conditions. Little change in body temperature occurs though the air temperature rises to 100° F or falls below zero, nor does the extra heat produced during light work occasion a rise in temperature. Strenuous muscular exercise may, however, cause a temporary rise in temperature of from 1° to 4° F.

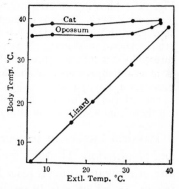

Fig. 9.4 Variation in body temperature of different types of animals by exposure for 2 hours in an environment rising from 5° to 35° C. (After Martin.)

Animals such as mammals and birds (warm-blooded animals) which can maintain a constant body temperature against variations in the temperature of their environment are called *homoiothermic*. Those species—e.g., fish, frogs, and reptiles (cold-blooded animals)—that are unable to regulate their body temperature are called *poikilothermic*. Their body temperature is that of the environment (see Fig. 9.4).

Heat balance. It is obvious that the quantity of heat produced in the body (pp. 378–9) must just balance the quantity lost to the environment. If the body produced more heat than it gave off, the retained heat would cause a rise in temperature; if it lost more than it generated, its temperature would fall. The average daily heat production—that is, the metabolism—of a man following a light occupation is around 2500 Calories. This quantity of heat is dissipated in the ways described in the following section.

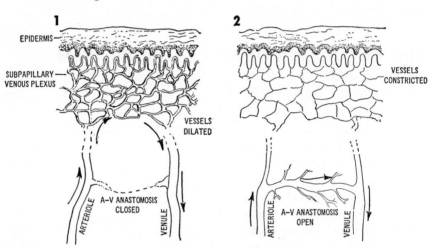

Fig. 9.5   Showing an arteriovenous anastomosis in the skin of an exposed part (e.g., ear, cheek, finger) through which warmer blood from deeper parts is conducted through the skin, just beneath the more superficial vessels. In 1, the arteriovenous anastomosis is closed, and, as at ordinary environmental temperatures, blood is directed through the subpapillary venous plexus; in 2, the blood, as at low temperatures, is shunted through the communicating vessel, a small proportion only, passing through the more superficial vessels. The continuations of the arteriole into the subpapillary venous plexus and of the small vein leading therefrom are represented merely by double rows of dotted lines.

Physical factors in temperature control. 1. *Radiation, convection, and conduction.* Through these three physical processes the body, like any other warm object, loses heat to the cooler air surrounding it, and to any cooler objects in contact with it or in its immediate neighborhood. The heat lost in this way can be increased or diminished through variations in the quantity of blood flowing through the skin. On a hot day, for example, the vessels of the skin dilate; more blood is therefore brought from the deeper parts of the body to the surface, and heat loss accordingly increased. In cool weather, the vessels of the skin constrict, a greater proportion of the total blood volume being distributed to the internal structures; heat loss is thereby reduced. When the cold is extreme, the cutaneous vessels of covered parts of the body, such as the trunk and limbs, are constricted; but in the skin of the ears, nose, cheeks, etc., anastomosing vessels existing between the arterioles, on the one hand, and small veins on the other dilate to permit a free flow of warm blood from deeper parts to the skin of the exposed regions; thus their temperature is prevented from falling too low. The anastomosing vessels lie beneath the subpapillary venous plexus from which they divert a considerable proportion of the swiftly flowing blood (Fig. 9.5 and Pl. 6 A). The skin is kept warm more effectively in this way. Thus the skin may appear pale or even of a bluish tint though quite warm; for it is the amount of blood flowing through the venous plexus and not that in the deeper cutaneous vessels which gives the skin its color (see capillaries of skin, Chap. 4).

It should be mentioned that under ordinary circumstances the amount of heat lost through conduction is negligible. Air is a very poor conductor, but the body immersed in water or on cold ground, especially if wet, loses heat rapidly by conduction.

Another important factor in temperature control is the variation in blood volume that results from changes in environmental temperature. The blood is increased in volume by heat, and is thus capable of absorbing and conveying more heat to the surface of the body for elimination through radiation, convection, and conduction. Cold causes the reverse effect—namely, a reduction in blood volume and, in consequence, a diminished heat loss.

2. *Evaporation of water from the lungs and skin.* The latent heat of evaporation of water is about 0.6 Calories [4]—that is, this quantity of heat is absorbed in the vaporization of 1 cc of water. Under ordinary atmospheric conditions, about 300 cc of water are vaporized from the lungs daily, and about 500 cc from the skin. This represents a heat loss of $(800 \times 0.6 =)$ 480 Calories.

But it should be understood that the evaporation of water from the surface of the body occurs constantly in the absence of any visible sweating, and even though the sweat glands are quite inactive or, as in some rare instances, when they are entirely lacking. Like any other moist mass, the body is continually losing weight by evaporation. The water "seeps" (diffuses) into the skin from the underlying tissues and is vaporized from the surface. This water loss, together with that from the lungs, was first observed and studied by an Italian physician Sanctorio Sanctorio (1561–1636), upon himself and called by him *insensible perspiration.* The quantity of body water lost from the skin surface as visible sweat and as insensible perspiration varies, not only with the temperature of the air, but also with the degree to which the

[4] The latent heat of the evaporation of sweat is 0.59 Calorie.

atmosphere is saturated with moisture—i.e., with the relative humidity. If this is very high, a large part of the sweat may simply drip from the skin, and such unevaporated sweat exerts no cooling effect. The relative humidity of the atmosphere is, therefore, of the greatest importance with respect to our comfort on a hot day.

It is clear that when the environmental temperature is higher than that of the body, heat cannot be dissipated by radiation and convection; the body would gain rather than lose heat were it entirely dependent upon these processes. At such temperatures, evaporation of water from the skin and lungs plays the leading role in the regulation of body temperature. The sweat glands are stimulated, and visible sweating appears when a rise of from 0.5 to 1° F in body temperature occurs. The rise in body temperature may result from an increase in the temperature of the environment or from increased heat production, as in muscular exercise.

The effect upon the sweat glands is brought about through a center in the brain from which they receive impulses through the sympathetic nerves. A rise in temperature of the blood supplying the center is the most potent factor in causing the secretion of sweat. This is shown by the fact that heating the carotid artery in the cat causes sweat secretion from the toe pads, though the paws themselves are kept cool. But sweating may also be induced reflexly—that is, from the stimulation of afferent nerves in the peripheral tissues, skin, muscles, and so forth.

Table 9-6

Daily heat loss

	Calories
Radiation, convection, and conduction	1850
Evaporation from the skin	400
Vaporization of water from the lungs	175
Warming inspired air to body temperature	80
Urine and feces (i.e., heat of these excreta over that of the food)	50
Total daily heat loss	2555

In dogs and cats, functional sweat glands are absent from the body surface, being confined to the skin of the pads of the paws. In these animals, rapid breathing (panting), with increased vaporization of water from the lungs as a consequence, is relied upon to increase heat loss at high temperatures.

3. Of the total heat lost from the body, over 95 percent is elimi-

nated through (1) and (2) discussed above. The remaining 5 percent is lost in the urine and feces, and in raising the inspired air to body temperature.

The quantities of heat lost daily in each of the several ways just described are given (in round numbers) in Table 9-6.

Variations in the quantity of heat lost through these physical factors are capable, under ordinary circumstances, of maintaining the body temperature at the normal level. However, at very high environmental temperatures or when, as in strenuous muscular effort, heat production is very greatly increased, the mechanisms of temperature control may be inadequate; the body temperature then rises.

The chemical factors in temperature control. At low environmental temperatures, the physical mechanisms alone are incapable of reducing heat loss sufficiently to prevent a fall in body temperature. Chemi-

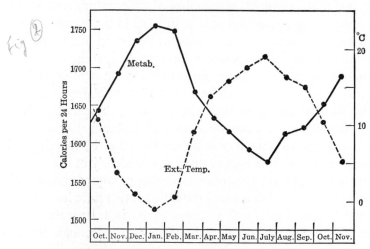

Fig. 9.6   Showing the effect of external temperature upon metabolism. (From Martin after Gessler from observations upon himself.)

cal regulation then comes into play—i.e., heat production increases. The body's fires, so to speak, are fanned. The point in the temperature scale where physical factors are aided by chemical means in the control of body temperature is called the *critical temperature*. It varies, of course, with the nature and thickness of the clothing, but for the naked human body it is around 28° C (82° F). Cold, therefore, acts as a powerful stimulus to metabolism (heat production). The greater heat production in response to cold is brought about mainly by increased tone of the skeletal muscles and, in some instances, by involuntary contractions of these muscles (shivering) and of the smooth muscle of the skin (goose flesh). When cold, a person usually indulges, also, in some form of muscular activity—walking, swinging his arms, or stamping his feet—which very materially increases his heat production (see Fig. 9.6).

At temperatures between 28° and 30° C, the body (naked) is able to establish a balance between heat production and heat elimination without calling accessory mechanisms into play—sweating on the one hand or muscular contraction (shivering or voluntary muscular movements) on the other—and one, therefore, feels quite comfortable. This temperature range, or correspondingly lower temperatures for the clothed body, is for this reason called the *comfort zone*.

In cold climates protein food, owing to its specific stimulating effect upon metabolism (*specific dynamic action*, p. 359), gives valuable assistance to the chemical mechanism of temperature control. On the other hand, a high protein diet is unsuitable in hot weather, since the greater heat production which it induces throws an additional burden upon the mechanisms responsible for heat dissipation.

Heat-controlling centers. The main center for the control of body temperature is situated in the fore part of the hypothalamus—that region at the base of the brain near the origin of the pituitary stalk (p. 541). Isolation of this region by section of the brain stem or upper spinal cord renders an animal poikilothermic—that is, incapable of maintaining the height of its temperature independently of the temperature of the environment. This operation also paralyzes the skeletal muscles; the power to increase heat production is therefore lost. Stimulation of the hypothalamic center causes a rise in temperature. The center exerts its influence upon body temperature through the autonomic nervous system causing vasoconstriction or vasodilatation, sweating, increased muscular tone, contraction of smooth muscle in the skin (shivering), and the liberation of adrenaline from the adrenal medulla which, as mentioned below, stimulates heat production.

These effects upon the sweat glands, vessels, and the adrenal gland are largely reflex in nature, the center being influenced by afferent impulses initiated in the temperature receptors of the skin. But such effects are also induced by a rise in the temperature of the blood supplying this region of the brain.

The endocrines and heat regulation. The secretions of both the thyroid and adrenal glands stimulate heat production. This effect, known as the *calorigenic action* of these hormones, enables an animal to withstand a greater degree of cold than is possible for one that has been deprived of either or both of these endocrines; the temperature of such animals is usually subnormal. Prolonged exposure to cold (over a period of weeks) causes an overproduction of the thyroid hormone. At any rate, the thyroid glands of rats who have been so treated show pronounced indications of increased activity, and a rise in heat production. The latter effect does not appear in thyroidectomized animals similarly treated.

The hypersensitivity of hypothyroid patients to cold and of hyperthyroid to a warm environment is well known.

Fever or pyrexia. A rise in body temperature above the normal level, unless of a temporary nature as in strenuous exercise or as a result of exposure to a high air temperature, is called fever or pyrexia. The highest body temperature compatible with life is between 110° and 112° F. The rise in temperature is due primarily to an *impairment of the mechanisms for heat elimination* (e.g., increased blood volume, vasodilatation, and sweat secretion) and not to increased heat production. At the commencement of a fever, for example, the skin is pale and dry; the metabolism is not increased. Heat elimination is reduced; heat is therefore retained in the body and the temperature rises. Having reached a certain height, the temperature remains fairly steady, for now heat elimination keeps pace with heat production; a balance is struck, but at a higher level than in health. Though, as just mentioned, increased heat production is not responsible for the onset of the fever, the higher temperature induced through heat retention

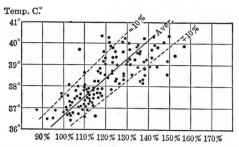

Fig. 9.7   Chart from Du Bois showing the effect upon metabolism of an increase in body temperature (fever).

causes, in turn, greater heat production; for the heat generated in the body is the result of chemical reactions, mainly oxidative in nature and, like chemical reactions in general, they are accelerated by a rise in temperature (see Fig. 9.7). A rise of 1° F in body temperature increases the metabolism by about 7 percent.

In acute infectious diseases and in bacterial infections generally, the accompanying fever is due to an action of the bacterial toxin upon the heat-regulating centers; in animals whose brain has been cut across below these centers, the injection of a toxin, which in a normal animal would cause a sharp rise in temperature, does not cause fever. In some instances, the bacterial toxin may act *directly* upon the heat-regulating centers. As a rule, however, its action is probably an *indirect* one, the first effect being to produce chemical changes in the tissues which alter the osmotic pressure of the tissue fluids, causing the withdrawal of water from the vascular system and, as a consequence, a reduction in the dissipation of heat by radiation. Furthermore, the reduced blood volume causes the drainage of blood from the cutaneous vessels; the skin, thus becoming cold, stimulates cold receptors, and brings about a reflex response from the centers controlling heat production. Cutaneous vasoconstriction occurs, which further reduces heat dissipation accompanied by shivering. One of the first symptoms at the onset of an acute infectious fever is a feeling of intense cold, often with goose flesh, shivering, chattering of the teeth and shaking of the limbs; for, as just mentioned, the withdrawal of warm blood from the skin has stimulated receptors sensitive to cold. The temperature taken in the mouth at this time of the "chill" is found to be high, though the skin may feel cold even to another person, and the patient's lips and nose appear pinched, pale, and even of a bluish tint. The mechanism of a "chill" at the commencement of a fever may be compared (though not exactly) to that controlling the temperature of a room isolated from a temperature-sensitive device which has been exposed to a cold draft. The cold-sensitive device corresponds to the cold receptors in the skin; the thermostat to which it is connected by wires, and which controls the furnace, is comparable to the heat-regulating centers; and the isolated room, to the deeper tissues.

The effect of certain drugs upon the body temperature. There are many drugs which have a fever reducing or *antipyretic* action. Among such agents are *aspirin, salicylates, antipyrine,* and *quinine.* Some of these drugs appear to bring about their antipyretic effect by increasing the blood volume, and thus increasing heat dissipation; for the greater volume of fluid available for circulation through the vessels near the body surface, the greater the amount of heat which will be radiated to the surroundings. The increase in blood volume is thought to be due to the rise in blood sugar which these drugs induce; water is drawn into the vessels by the raised osmotic pressure of the blood plasma caused by the increased sugar concentration. On the other hand, *reduction* in circulating fluid, as in dehydration, may cause fever. Other drugs such as *morphine, alcohol* in large amounts, and *general anesthetics* (ether, chloroform, etc.) are capable of reducing even a normal body temperature through their depressant action upon the heat-controlling centers.

There are other agents which raise the body temperature above the normal. *Dinitrophenol,* a drug which has been used—not without danger—as a cure for obesity, raises the body temperature by increasing the rate of oxidation in the tissues. The action of the hormones, adrenaline and thyroxine, in this regard, has been referred to on pages 413 and 422.

Heat stroke, heat exhaustion, and sunstroke. After a person has been exposed to a high temperature for a time, his heat-regulating mechanism may fail, and very serious symptoms, even death, may result. The effects of extreme heat fall into two categories known, respectively, as *heat stroke* and *heat exhaustion.* In the former, a person exposed to great heat, often while undergoing some physical exertion, suddenly becomes unconscious. The body temperature is found to be very high, and in a severe case may reach 108° or 110° F. Sweat secretion is suppressed; both blood volume and urine volume are increased. In heat exhaustion, the symptoms develop more gradually and consist of abdominal cramps, rapid pulse, low systolic blood pressure, and sometimes dizziness and dyspnea. The blood and urine volumes are reduced, and the chloride of the blood and urine are much below normal (due to loss of chloride in the sweat). Sunstroke is merely a form of heat stroke or heat exhaustion, the body absorbing heat from the direct rays of the sun. There is no special effect of the sun's rays, apart from their heat, which causes the symptoms of so-called sunstroke.

Heat cramps. Men working in a very hot environment for a long period may suffer severe cramplike contractions of the muscles. The muscles are rendered hyperexcitable by the reduction in the salt concentration of the tissue fluids; and this is due, in turn, to the excessive loss of sodium chloride in the sweat.

The Vitamins

It was discovered nearly 50 years ago that diets composed of purified protein, fat, and carbohydrate, and containing the essential minerals would not support life. It was concluded, therefore, that foods in their natural state contained substances which, though present only in minute amounts, were nevertheless essential to life. Sir F. Gowland Hopkins, of Cambridge University, was among the first to suspect the presence of such materials in natural foods. In 1906, he expressed his views in the following words, "No animal can live upon a mixture of pure protein, fat, and carbohydrate; and even when the necessary inorganic material is carefully supplied, the animal still cannot flourish." The chemical nature of these materials was unknown, so they were called simply *accessory food factors*. Later these vital elements were thought to belong to a group of nitrogenous substances known as amines. They were therefore named *vitamines*. It was soon found, however, that this conclusion was false. The name was retained, however, but it was suggested that the terminal "e" be dropped. The generic term *vitamin* was then generally adopted. There are a number of different vitamins. Each is designated by a letter of the alphabet. The vitamins A, D, E, and K are soluble in fats and fat solvents (the fat-soluble vitamins); the vitamins of the B complex and vitamin C are soluble in water (the water-soluble vitamins).

The growth of our knowledge of the vitamins within the past three decades ranks as one of the most brilliant achievements of physiological and biochemical research; the practical application of this knowledge has conferred immense benefits upon mankind.

Table 9-7

Summary of the vitamins

Vitamin A (antixerophthalmic)

Vitamin B complex
- thiamin or vitamin B_1 (antineuritic)
- riboflavin, B_2 or G
- nicotinic acid or niacin
- pyridoxin, B_6
- pantothenic acid
- folic acid
- antipernicious anemia factor, B_{12}
- biotin
- inositol
- para-aminobenzoic acid
- choline

Vitamin C (antiscorbutic)
Vitamin D (antirachitic)
Vitamin E (antisterility)
Vitamin K (antihemorrhagic)

Vitamin A ($C_{20}H_{30}O$), the antixerophthalmic vitamin. The chief sources of vitamin A[5] are fish liver oils (e.g., cod and halibut), dairy

---

[5] There are actually two vitamins A. Each is derived from a separate carotene (carotene-α and carotene-β), which differ slightly chemically. The vitamin A first discovered and present in mammalian livers, and in the commoner types of food is now known as vitamin A_1; it is derived from carotene-α. The second vitamin A,

products, and many vegetable foods. The following is a list of materials especially rich in this vitamin.

Fish liver oils
Butter and cream
Egg yolk
Carrots, yellow maize (corn), alfalfa, spinach, peas, beans, and other yellow and green vegetables

It is not strictly correct to say that plants contain vitamin A. They contain rather a yellow pigment called *carotene* ($C_{40}H_{56}$) which, after being taken into the animal body, is converted by the liver into vitamin A according to the following equation:

$$C_{40}H_{56} + 2H_2O = 2C_{20}HO_{30}$$

Carotene, being a precursor of the vitamin, is called *provitamin A*. The green and yellow parts of plants contain more of the provitamin than do the paler portions. The contents of vitamin A in milk and butter varies with the carotene content of the fodder of the cow. After ingestion the carotene is transformed in part to vitamin A and secreted as such in the milk. A part of the carotene is also secreted unchanged. Vitamin A itself is colorless, so that a pale milk may be just as rich a source of the vitamin as one more deeply colored. The vitamin A of fish liver oils is also derived ultimately from plant life. Small invertebrates of the sea, known as copepods, feed upon marine plants, and serve in turn as food for small fish. The latter convert the carotene, originally formed by the plant, into the vitamin. Larger fish devour the smaller fish and store the vitamin so obtained in their livers.

Vitamin A deficiency. When the diet is deficient in vitamin A (and in the provitamin), the epithelium lining the respiratory and alimentary tracts as well as the ducts of certain glands, becomes abnormal; it undergoes transformation to the stratified squamous type. Such mucous surfaces are especially susceptible to infection. Inhibition of lacrimal secretion, followed by drying of the cornea (*xerophthalmia*), is an outstanding effect of vitamin A deficiency. In some instances softening of the cornea (*keratomalacia*), which may progress to ulceration and consequent blindness, results. Vitamin A is necessary for the regeneration of the visual purple of the retina which, in health, readily takes place after the eyes have been exposed to light (Chap. 13).

designated A_2, is absent from mammalian liver but is the chief vitamin A found in the livers of fresh-water fish; its provitamin is carotene-β.

Night blindness (*nyctalopia*) is, therefore, a common accompaniment of vitamin A deficiency. A sufferer from night blindness sees well in bright light, but is quite or almost blind in dim light. Vitamin A deficiency may also lead to degenerative changes in the long fiber tracts of the spinal cord, and in certain of the peripheral nerves.

An adequate supply of vitamin A is also required for the normal growth of bone. In experiments upon growing animals, pronounced localized overgrowths of bone results, causing deformities. These abnormalities were particularly noticeable in the bones of the skull and spinal column. Pressure upon nerves issuing from the cranial cavity or vertebral column by the redundant bone are largely responsible for the abnormalities of the nerves mentioned above.

The diets of persons on this continent are rarely deficient in vitamin A to the point where serious abnormalities supervene; but in India, China, and other Eastern countries the diet is frequently deficient in this and other vitamins. In localities far removed from larger centers of population, owing to difficulties of transportation, such as in lumber camps of the north country, especially in winter, night blindness and other signs of vitamin A deficiency occasionally make their appearance. Infants reared upon a badly planned artificial diet may also suffer from deficiency of vitamin A (Fig. 9.8).

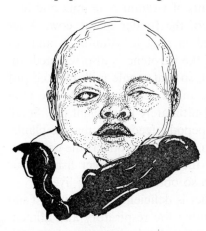

Fig. 9.8   Xerophthalmia in a child caused by vitamin A deficiency. (Drawn from a photograph after Bloch.)

The vitamin B complex. The first of this large group of vitamins to be discovered was thiamin, or vitamin B_1, the antineuritic vitamin. Severe deficiency of this vitamin is the cause of a disease known as *beriberi*. Beriberi is a disease of rice-eating countries. Its chief features are paralysis of the limbs (due to degenerative changes in the peripheral nerves—*polyneuritis*), dilation of the heart, and edema. It was shown by Eikjman, a physician working in the Dutch West Indies, to be due to a dietary deficiency. He demonstrated that the essential factor missing from the diet was contained in the coverings of the rice kernel. Persons who live almost exclusively upon a diet of *polished* rice—that is, rice from which the pericarp (bran) and germ have been removed in the milling process—

develop the disease, but are readily cured when they are given un-
polished rice or an extract prepared from the rice "polishings." This
factor in the polishings of rice which protected against beriberi was
designated *vitamin B* or the *antineuritic vitamin*. From researches of

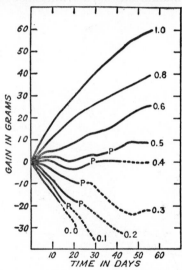

Fig. 9.9   *Upper figure* (after
Harris): *left,* distended stomach in thiamine (B₁) deficiency
due to loss of tone of gastric
muscle; *right,* normal stomach.
Lower figure: curves showing effect of graded quantities of vitamin B₁ upon growth of nine
groups of rats; P, point where
polyneuritis developed; broken
lines are drawn from the points
where some individuals of the
group died. Figures from 0.0 to
1.0 indicate grams of whole
wheat (B₁) received by the respective groups. (After Chase.)

recent years it has been shown that so-called vitamin B is actually a
complex substance consisting of several vitamins, only one of which is
protective agains beriberi. This latter, the antineuritic principle, is now
known as vitamin B₁, or *thiamin.*

Other effects of vitamin B₁ deficiency are (a) *gastrointestinal disorders* (e.g., reduced motility of the stomach and intestines resulting
in constipation, inhibition of the digestive secretions, and loss of appetite); and (b) *retarded growth* (see Fig. 9.9).

In birds (e.g., pigeons) a condition analogous to human beriberi

Fig. 9.10 *Left,* pigeon suffering from polyneuritis; *right,* the same bird an hour after treatment with vitamin B_1. (After Funk, redrawn.)

results from vitamin B_1 deficiency. Its chief features are paralysis due to involvement of the peripheral nerves (polyneuritis), retraction of the head, and convulsions. The condition is cured in a remarkably short time by feeding a concentrated preparation of vitamin B_1 (see Fig. 9.10). Vitamin B_1 deficiency in a dog and its rapid cure by administration of the vitamin is shown in Figure 9.11.

Thiamin has been synthesized. It exists in the tissues as an integral

Fig. 9.11 *Upper drawing,* dog with polyneuritis showing paralysis of the hind limbs due to a deficiency of vitamin B_1. *Lower drawing,* the same animal cured by the vitamin given in the form of tomato juice. (Drawn from a photograph after Cowgill and Mendell.)

part of an enzyme system essential for the metabolism of carbohydrates. In its absence, carbohydrate metabolism does not proceed normally. Lactic acid accumulates in the blood, heart, and brain. The accumulation of lactic acid in the brain substance appears to be responsible for the head retraction seen in birds.

There are several other vitamins of the B complex (see Table 9-8, p. 396), the most important of which in respect to human nutrition are *riboflavin* and *nicotinic acid* (*niacin*).

Riboflavin. This is one of a group of yellow fluorescent pigments found in animal tissues. Liver, kidney, and milk are especially rich sources of this factor of the B complex. When it is lacking from the diet, reddening of the eyes, due to the growth of fine blood vessels

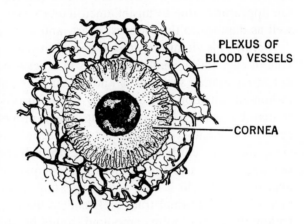

Fig. 9.12 Vascularization of the cornea due to severe riboflavin deficiency. Note the growth of vascular loops into the cornea, which normally is bloodless, from the vessels at the periphery (*limbic plexus*).

PLEXUS OF BLOOD VESSELS

CORNEA

into the cornea, results, together with opacities of the cornea (Fig. 9.12). A sensation of burning and itching of the eyeballs is experienced. There is intolerance to light which may be so severe that the eyes cannot be opened in an illumination of even ordinary intensity (photophobia). Another effect of deficiency of this vitamin is the development of fissures in the skin radiating from the angles of the mouth.

Animals with riboflavin deficiency grow slowly. Chicks on a diet in which it is lacking develop a degenerative disorder of the peripheral nerves, a type of paralysis resulting known as "curled toe."

Nicotinic acid (*niacin*). A disease occurring among the poor of the southern United States and less commonly in some European countries has within recent years been recognized as being due, mainly at least, to a deficiency of this vitamin. The chief features of this disease, which is known as *pellagra,* are reddening and drying of the skin together with, in the severer cases, nervous and gastrointestinal disturbances. It occurs in those who subsist mainly upon maize.

Pyridoxin. Rats on a diet deficient in pyridoxin develop a cutaneous disorder consisting of reddening and scaliness of the skin and loss of hair. There is some indication that this factor is concerned with the synthesis of hemoglobin and the manufacture of erythrocytes. The regeneration of blood following hemorrhage is hastened by feeding pyridoxin. Deficiency of this vitamin has not been observed in man.

Pantothenic acid. Most animal and vegetable tissues contain this acid. It stimulates the growth of yeast. Its role in human nutrition is unknown. But when lacking from the diet of chicks, it causes dermatitis and degenerative changes in the nervous system. In rats, pantothenic acid deficiency causes graying of the fur and "spectacle eyes" (an appearance due to an inflamed hairless ring around the eyes), as well as damage to the kidneys, heart, and adrenal cortex.

Biotin. This vitamin is present chiefly in yeast, liver, kidney, and the yolk of egg, and in smaller amounts in other foods. Its deficiency does not occur in man so far as is known, but it is important, nevertheless, in human nutrition, for deficiency has been produced experimentally in man by giving a diet containing a high proportion of raw white of egg. Unpleasant symptoms, including drowsiness, greasiness of the skin, and some cardiac distress, developed. In rats fed upon a diet of raw egg white, a severe dermatitis accompanied by "spectacle eyes" appears. A protein in raw egg white known as *avidin* combines with biotin in the intestinal tract and renders the latter unavailable in nutrition; the avidin-biotin compound cannot be utilized.

Choline. A constituent of the lipid known as lecithin, choline when lacking from the diet results in fatty livers in animals. Deficiency of choline apparently does not occur in man. Nor has *inositol* deficiency been observed in man. This vitamin is found chiefly in cereals as a complex compound with calcium, phosphorus, and magnesium. It is also present in animal tissues such as liver and ordinary meats. Mice fed upon a diet deficient in inositol show patches of baldness, but it does not appear to be related to loss of hair in man. *Para-aminobenzoic acid* deficiency has not been observed in man and, though deficiency in rats causes graying of the hair, there is no evidence that this vitamin is related in any way to the loss of color of human hair. Para-aminobenzoic acid's chief interest lies in the fact that it is necessary for the growth of certain disease-producing bacteria (see footnote, p. 221).

The role played by *folic acid* in blood formation is described on page 74, and of *vitamin B_{12}* on page 76.

A number of vitamins of the B complex are essential for the growth of several types of microorganism, and are dietary requirements for chicks, rats, mice, and other laboratory animals, but only *thiamin, riboflavin, niacin, folic acid,* and *vitamin B$_{12}$* have been shown to be indispensable constituents of human diets. This does not necessarily mean that those which are not required in the diet are not utilized by the human body. Several are synthesized by intestinal bacteria, and such synthesis probably occurs in the human intestine. Most of the factors of the vitamin B complex have been shown to exist as integral parts of tissue enzyme systems with which their functions are intimately associated.

Vitamin C, the antiscorbutic vitamin. Vitamin C is present in greatest amounts in citrus fruits (e.g., lemons, limes, oranges, and grapefruit). It is also contained in most other fruits and green vegetables. Tomatoes and red and green peppers are exceptionally rich sources; potatoes, turnips, meat, and milk contain moderate amounts. Vitamin C has been identified chemically as *ascorbic acid* ($C_6H_8O_6$). It possesses high reducing powers; it has been synthesized in the laboratory, and by the intestinal bacteria of many animals.

Vitamin C serves the important function of maintaining a healthy state of the walls of the capillaries. When it is lacking from the diet, the cement substance interposed between the endothelial cells, and holding them together, becomes deficient. The vessels, as a consequence, develop leaks which permit the escape of blood into the surrounding tissues.

Vitamin C is in relatively high concentration in the cortex of the adrenal gland (see p. 428).

Scurvy (*scorbutus*) is caused by vitamin C deficiency. The chief manifestation of this disease is bleeding from the mucous membranes, beneath the skin and into joints. The skin, as a result of numerous capillary hemorrhages (*petechiae*), may show extensive mottling. The gums are swollen and inflamed, and bleed easily. The subjects become anemic, weak, and emaciated. Unless fresh food containing the vitamin is supplied, death results. Scurvy, though unusual in the general population except in times of famine, was a common disease in sailors, soldiers, explorers, and others who, of necessity, subsisted upon diets lacking in fresh fruits, vegetables, meat, and milk. Scurvy is readily produced in guinea pigs by placing them upon a diet of hay and oats —i.e., one lacking in green stuffs. The disease is sometimes seen in persons living on the outskirts of civilization, such as lumbermen, especially during the winter months when fresh food is difficult to procure, and provision for a supply of vitamin C in concentrated form has not been made. The disease may also appear in infants who are artificially fed; infantile scurvy (*Barlow's disease*) should, however, never occur, since the administration of tomato or orange juice is a certain preventive.

Vitamin D ($C_{28}H_{44}O$), the antirachitic vitamin. This vitamin is formed by the action of ultraviolet light upon certain waxy compounds known as sterols. Among such compounds are *ergosterol,* found in yeast, and *cholesterol,* present in the skin and other animal tissues. The ultraviolet rays cause a rearrangement of the atoms in the sterol molecule, thereby endowing it with the properties characteristic of vitamin D. Vitamin D is formed naturally by the action of sunlight upon a sterol in the skin closely associated with cholesterol. This sterol is known chemically as 7-dehydrocholesterol. The antirachitic vitamin is prepared commercially by irradiating yeast (rich in ergosterol) by means of the mercury vapor lamp or the carbon arc. Such artificial preparations of vitamin D are referred to as *viosterol,* or simply as *irradiated* or *activated ergosterol.* The wavelengths in the ultraviolet part of the spectrum which are effective in the formation of this

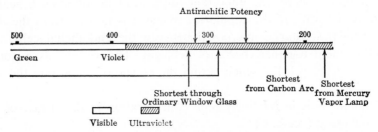

Fig. 9.13   Scheme of wavelengths of spectrum, showing the range of those possessing antirachitic power. Figures in millimicrons ($m\mu$). (Redrawn and modified from Blunt and Cowan.)

vitamin have a range of from 250 to 313 $m\mu$[6] (see Fig. 9.13). Vitamin D has been synthesized in the laboratory. It is a yellow crystalline substance which has been named *calciferol.* The richest natural sources of the vitamin are fish liver oils, especially those from the cod and halibut. These large fish obtain the vitamin from smaller species upon which they feed (e.g., herring, whiting, etc.). The small fish in turn acquire the vitamin from invertebrate marine forms, such as copepods and mollusks, which probably synthesize it. Some authorities believe that the cod and certain other fish are also capable of synthesizing

[6] $m\mu$ = millimicron, the one millionth part of a millimeter.

vitamin D. There are several vitamins D. The two of medical interest are the two just mentioned. They are designated D_2 (irradiated 7-dehydrocholesterol of skin and in cod liver oil and other fish oils) and D_3 (irradiated ergosterol, calciferol). There is no vitamin D_1.

The following is a list of the chief sources of vitamin D.

> Fish liver oils (e.g., halibut and cod)
> Irradiated ergosterol (of yeast)
> Irradiated milk
> Irradiation of the skin

The main action of vitamin D is upon the metabolism of calcium and phosphorus; it is essential for the mineralization of growing bone, and for maintaining the normal mineral composition of the adult skeleton. It also plays an important role in dental health; defective tooth structure, leading to decay of the teeth (*dental caries*), results when the diet is deficient in the antirachitic vitamin. When the vitamin in the form of viosterol is administered in excessively large doses, a marked rise in the calcium of the serum (hypercalcemia) results, calcium being drawn from the skeleton to the blood. The calcium of the urine is increased. Vitamin D acts, in this respect, like the hormone of the parathyroid glands. Toxic symptoms resembling those caused by overdosage with parathyroid extract also follow the administration of large amounts of viosterol. The manner in which the vitamin, in physiological dosage, exerts its effect upon calcium metabolism is not altogether clear. But it is generally believed to increase the absorption of calcium from the intestinal tract; its chief action, however, appears to be upon the skeleton, influencing, in some manner not understood, the deposition of calcium and phosphorus in the developing bone.

Rickets (rachitis) results from vitamin D deficiency. It is a disease of young children, chiefly, between the ages of 6 months and 3 years. Its essential feature is defective development of the bones. The deposition of phosphorus and calcium is interfered with; the bones are, therefore, soft and yielding. Deformities of the limb bones and spine and defective ossification of the skull bones result. Small round swellings are found at the junctions of the ribs with the sternum; these are referred to as the "rachitic rosary." The head is somewhat larger than normal with a prominent brow; soft areas may be felt in the skull. The abdomen is large and round, which has given rise to the term "potbelly" (see Fig. 9.14). The disease occurs most often in bottle-fed infants, especially in those who are growing rapidly and receiving a diet containing a large proportion of carbohydrate. Rickets is readily cured

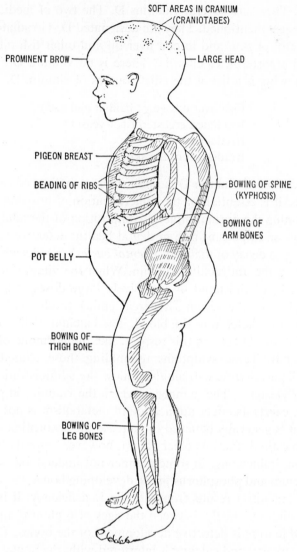

SOFT AREAS IN CRANIUM
(CRANIOTABES)

PROMINENT BROW

LARGE HEAD

PIGEON BREAST

BEADING OF RIBS

BOWING OF SPINE
(KYPHOSIS)

BOWING OF
ARM BONES

POT BELLY

BOWING OF
THIGH BONE

BOWING OF
LEG BONES

Fig. 9.14   Diagram showing the chief features of infantile rickets. (After Harris, redrawn.)

or prevented by the administration of vitamin D, either in the form of
cod liver or halibut liver oil, viosterol or irradiated milk, or by exposing
the child to ultraviolet radiations (sunlight, the mercury vapor lamp,
or carbon arc). The value of sunshine in the treatment of rickets was
pointed out over 70 years ago (1880) by Palm, an English physician,
but it is little more than 30 years since the curative effects of ultraviolet
irradiation and of cod liver oil have come to be generally recognized.

Rickets is seen most commonly in the large cities of northern latitudes, since infants in these localities are less exposed to sunshine than are those in southern climates. The disease is almost unknown in the tropics. The smoke and dust of cities also act as a screen through which the shorter wavelengths of the sun's rays cannot penetrate, or do so to a minimal extent. It should be remembered, furthermore, that window glass is opaque to radiations shorter than 320 mμ. Sunshine that has passed through ordinary glass therefore possesses no antirachitic action. On the other hand, in order to gain benefit from ultraviolet radiation, a person need not be in direct sunshine. The sun's rays reflected from the sky (skyshine), or from water, snow, or light-colored objects are effective.

Osteomalacia (soft bones) is a disease—essentially the same as rickets—which occurs in adults in eastern countries, especially India and China. Women are mainly affected with the disease since they, as well as receiving in common with the general population little vitamin D in their diet, are often confined within doors and thus deprived of the benefit of sunshine.

Vitamin (or vitamins) E, the antisterility vitamin. Vitamin E is necessary for normal reproduction. Female rats upon diets lacking in vitamin E though they become pregnant, do not bear living young. The embryos, after developing for a short time, die. In male rats, vitamin E deficiency results in degenerative changes in the testes; spermatozoa are not produced and the sex instinct is lost. The addition of lettuce or other food containing vitamin E corrects the defects of either the male or female reproductive functions.

Vitamin E is fat soluble and has been obtained in crystalline form. Its chief sources are green vegetable foods—e.g., lettuce, peas, alfalfa and the germ of various cereals. Wheat germ oil has a very high vitamin E content.

Besides the vitamin E first discovered, two other compounds, closely related to it chemically, have been shown to have similar physiological actions. We may now speak of vitamins E. All three belong to a class of compounds known as the *tocopherols*. The three vitamins E are, therefore, frequently referred to by their chemical designations. Prefixing the Greek letters to distinguish them, they are known as *alpha, beta,* and *gamma* tocopherol, respectively.

Vitamin E exerts an influence upon the metabolism of muscular tissue (nutritional disorders of muscle occur in animals when it is lacking from the diet) and upon the biochemical processes in the nuclei of cells generally; its action is exhibited especially upon rapidly growing

Table 9-8

Summarizing the principal facts concerning certain vitamins

Name	Chief functions	Effects caused by deficiency	Chief sources
Vitamin A antixerophthalmic	Maintains the integrity of epithelial tissues. Essential for the regeneration of visual purple.	Xerophthalmia. Keratomalacia. Conversion of columnar epithelium to squamous type. Night blindness.	Carrots. Lettuce. Alfalfa. Yellow corn. Butter, cream, and milk. Egg yolk.
Thiamin (B₁, aneurin) antineuritic	Essential in the metabolism of carbohydrate serving as a coenzyme in the tissues. Maintains the tone of the gastrointestinal tract. Promotes appetite.	Beriberi. Polyneuritis in animals (especially birds). Loss of tone of gastrointestinal tract. Loss of appetite.	Yeast, germ of wheat, and other cereals.
Riboflavin (B₂, vitamin G)	Essential component of certain tissue enzymes.	Vascularization of cornea with opacities. Fissures around lips. Retarded growth. Loss of hair (in rats).	Liver. Kidney. Milk.
Nicotinic acid (Niacin)	Coenzyme in tissue respiration.	Pellagra.	Liver, meats. Brewer's yeast. Wheat germ.
Pyridoxin (B₆)	Coenzyme in the metabolism of tyrosine, tryptophane, and certain other amino acids.	Retarded growth (in rats). Anemia in pigs, dogs, and rabbits. The effects of its lack in human nutrition unknown.	Milk. Wheat germ. Yeast. Meats, kidney, and vegetable fats.
Pantothenic acid	Stimulates the growth of yeast.	"Spectacle eyes" and graying of fur in rats; anemia in dogs; deficiency in man not observed.	Widely distributed in animal and vegetable tissues.
Biotin	Tissue enzyme concerned in carbohydrate metabolism.	"Spectacle eyes" and nervous (spastic) symptoms in rats. Deficiency (except experimental) not observed in man. Deficiency produced by feeding raw egg white.	Yeast, kidney, liver, and egg yolk.
Para-aminobenzoic acid	Essential for some enzyme system in bacterial cell (see footnote, p. 221).	Graying of fur in black rats. Deficiency not observed in man.	Various animal tissues; cultures of certain bacteria (e.g., Staphylococci).
Vitamin C antiscorbutic	Maintains the integrity of the capillary walls.	Scurvy.	Citrus fruits. Tomatoes. Turnips.
Vitamin D antirachitic	Regulates calcium and phosphorus metabolism. Essential for the normal development of bones and teeth.	Rickets. Osteomalacia. Dental caries.	Cod liver and halibut liver oils. Exposure of the skin to ultraviolet irradiation.
Vitamin E antisterility	Essential for reproduction.	Death of young in uterus. Sterility of male, degenerative changes in testes, failure of spermatogenesis.	Lettuce. Water cress. Wheat germ.
Vitamin K antihemorrhagic	Necessary for the production of prothrombin by the liver.	Hemorrhagic tendency.	Alfalfa and other green foods.

structures. It has been employed, but on the whole with disappointing results, in the treatment of certain wasting diseases of the muscles; and, in consideration of its influence upon the reproductive functions, it has been given to pregnant women who have had repeated miscarriages or abortions (*habitual abortion*) with the hope that they will be able to give birth to a living child.

Vitamin K (the antihemorrhagic vitamin). This vitamin is found in largest amounts in alfalfa, spinach, cauliflower, cabbage, and other green foods and less abundantly in cereals, carrots, and yeast. Chicks and other farm birds develop a fatal hemorrhagic disease when this vitamin is lacking from the diet. The hemorrhages are due to a low concentration of prothrombin in the blood. This, as mentioned on page 103, is an essential factor in the coagulation of the blood. Hemorrhages in the human subject are rarely if ever due to the lack of vitamin K in the diet because vitamin K is synthesized by bacteria in the intestine of man. For the same reason it has not been found possible to induce a hemorrhagic tendency in other mammals by feeding them a diet lacking in this vitamin. But vitamin K is not absorbed from the intestine in the absence of bile. Therefore, in obstructive jaundice in which bile does not enter the intestine, a tendency to bleed is a common feature. It is now the custom to give vitamin K by injection or by mouth accompanied by bile or bile salts before operating upon a patient with obstructive jaundice. The prothrombin concentration of the blood is raised thereby and the defect in the clotting mechanism corrected.

A grave hemorrhagic disease occurs in newborn infants due to an insufficient amount of vitamin K received by the fetus from the mother. The prothrombin concentration of the infant's blood, when this occurs, is less than 50 percent of the normal. Death may occur within the first few hours after birth. If the child is untreated but survives longer than this, the condition usually corrects itself, for bacteria swallowed in the milk synthesize the vitamin in the intestine. The disease can now be treated at the first sign of its appearance, and quickly corrected by the intravenous administration of vitamin K.

The Principles of Dietetics

The importance of a well-balanced diet for the normal growth and development of the young, and for the health of both young and old, is recognized today as never before. There seems little doubt that the finer physique and better health of the present generation is largely the result of the more varied and ample character of modern diets (see

Fig. 9.15 *Upper photograph,* class of elementary school children at Southwark, England, in 1894. *Lower photograph,* corresponding class 30 years later. The improvement of this group over that in the upper photograph is attributed largely to the more adequate diet received by the children in the lower group. (After Harris.)

Fig. 9.15). Deficiency diseases which have been so prevalent in the past, especially among the poor, are now comparatively rare. Rickets and scurvy, for example, have almost vanished from civilized communities and, were the knowledge which has been gained from modern research sedulously applied, the eradication of these and other diseases due to defective diets—such as beriberi and pellagra—would soon be an accomplished fact. In planning a diet, the following factors must be taken into account:

1. The caloric (energy) requirement of the subject.
2. The proportions of the three main types of food — carbohydrate, protein, and fat.
3. Essential fatty acids.
4. The vitamin requirement.
5. The mineral constituents.

Determination of the caloric requirement. A man of average size and following a light occupation has an average energy output of from 2500 to 3000 Calories daily. In order that the body's tissues shall not be called upon to furnish any of the required energy, the caloric value of the diet must not be less than the energy expenditure; otherwise the body would lose weight. Nor should the caloric value of the diet be greater than the energy expended. The excess energy would then be simply stored as fat (see p. 374). Excess of energy intake over energy output is the usual cause of obesity. In order, therefore, to calculate the caloric requirement in any given case, one must first know the energy expenditure during the resting state, that is, the basal metabolism (p. 356). To this is added the energy expenditure of the particular occupation in which the person is engaged.

The energy expended daily by different persons, or by the same person at different times, varies widely, depending upon the extent of the exercise undertaken. The energy allowances for work of several grades are given in the following table.

	Daily energy expenditure (above basal) Calories
Sedentary life	500– 700
Light work—e.g., professional and business-men	700–1200
Moderate work—e.g., mechanics	1200–1500
Heavy work—e.g., laborers, lumbermen, athletes, etc.	1500–4000 and upward

The metabolism during sleep is lower than the basal metabolism by from 15 to 20 percent. The lower metabolism of the 8 hours of sleep must therefore be taken into account in determining the caloric requirements. The calculations just outlined are exemplified in the following table in which the figures are for a man following a light occupation.

Basal metabolism (16 hours)	1200 Calories [7]
Metabolism during sleep (8 hours)	500 "
Allowance for light work	800 "
Total	2500 Calories

Since the food itself has a stimulating effect upon metabolism (see specific dynamic action, p. 359), an allowance of from 6 to 10 percent must be made in order to establish the energy balance. In the example given above, this would amount to between 150 and 250 Calories. If this allowance is not made, the subject would lose weight, for his own tissues would be drawn upon to furnish the extra heat production associated with the specific dynamic action.

The basal metabolism of a normal subject can be derived from his height and weight (see chart, Fig. 9.3, p. 358). The energy values of the various articles of diet are obtained from standard tables, and the quantities apportioned accordingly. For example, beef (with a medium amount of fat) has an energy value of about 1300 Calories per pound; butter (almost pure fat) yields 3600 Calories per pound; milk, 325; eggs, 765; cheese (largely protein), 2200; sugar, 1860; and white bread, 1200. Children, owing to their greater activity and the requirements of growth, should receive a more ample diet in proportion to their size than that of the average adult. A boy of 16 years, for example, especially if he is growing rapidly and taking part in athletics, requires at least as much food as a full-grown man engaged in moderately heavy work.

The proportions of carbohydrate, fat, and protein. A little over 50 percent of the total caloric requirement should be furnished by carbohydrate food, about 35 percent by fat, and 12 percent by protein. The protein in the diet of the average adult should be from 70 to 90 grams daily, or around 1 gram per kilogram of body weight. Children, especially in the early years of life, require a higher protein intake (2 to 3.5 grams per kilogram) than do adults, and a larger proportion (60 to 90 percent) of the total protein should be of the highest biological value, such as is furnished by milk, eggs, and meat. In adults receiving 80 to 90 grams of protein daily, at least 50 percent should be first class, as in meat and eggs. If the protein is mainly of low biological value (e.g., vegetable proteins), the total allowance must be larger.

Fat is an indispensable element of the diet. Fats not only contain fat-soluble vitamins, but also certain unsaturated fatty acids (linoleic and

[7] This is about 40 Calories per hour for a man having a surface area of 1.8 square meters.

linolenic acids) which cannot be synthesized in the body, yet are essential for normal nutrition.

The mineral requirements. *Sodium, potassium, magnesium,* and *phosphorus* are present in adequate amounts in a diet which is ample in other respects and, as a rule, no special attention need be paid to them. Sodium chloride, for example, besides that which is present naturally in many foodstuffs is added in cooking, and as table salt in quantities determined by individual taste. Protein foods constitute the chief source of the phosphorus of the diet and, when the allowance of protein is adequate, the phosphorus intake takes care of itself. Potassium and magnesium are derived from cereals and vegetables, and are also present in sufficient amounts in an ordinary diet.

The minerals in which the diet is most likely to be deficient are *calcium, iron,* and *iodine*. The intake of calcium, which enters so largely into the composition of bone, is especially likely to be inadequate in the diets of children. According to Professor Sherman, children require at least a gram of calcium per day. The adult requirement is about 0.8 gram daily. As a result of the deposition of mineral in the bones of the fetus, the demand for calcium increases during pregnancy when the allowance should be from 1.5 to 2 grams daily. The mother should also receive a high allowance of calcium after childbirth if she nurses her baby at the breast, for the secretion of milk is a severe drain upon the body's calcium stores. By the same token, milk is especially rich in calcium, containing about a gram per quart. Cereals and certain vegetables (such as beans, peas, and turnips) are also good sources of this mineral, but the calcium of milk, as compared with that of vegetables, is more readily absorbed. Only a small part of the calcium in cereals and vegetables is utilized by the body. Meat contains minimal amounts. Milk is therefore, especially for children, the best source of calcium.

Iron is an indispensable constituent of the diet, since it is necessary for the synthesis of hemoglobin. The daily requirement is from 15 to 20 mg. The chief sources of food iron are meats (especially liver), eggs, and such vegetables and cereals as spinach, beans, and peas, whole wheat, and oatmeal. Milk is very poor in iron.

Iodine is an essential constituent of the thyroid hormone; goiter (p. 412) results when the diet is deficient in this element. Sea foods are the chief natural sources of iodine, though many brands of table salt (*iodized salt*) contain small quantities (1 part in 100,000) which have been added by the manufacturer. The daily requirement of iodine is placed at about 100 micrograms.[8]

[8] A microgram or gamma (γ) $= \frac{1}{1000}$ milligram.

There are a number of other mineral elements which are required to be taken in minute quantities for special purposes—e.g., the elaboration of certain hormones and enzymes or for the incorporation into particular tissues. Among these so-called *"trace elements"* are: *cobalt* (in vitamin B_{12}, p. 74), *zinc* (in insulin, p. 371), *manganese* (in tissue enzymes), and *copper* (required in hemopoiesis). No attention need be paid to these elements in planning a diet since the small amounts required are present in a diet adequate in other respects. Traces of *fluorine,* which is a constituent of osseous and dental tissues, are indispensable for the formation of teeth of normal structure. The drinking water is the most usual source of this mineral.

CHAPTER 10

The Endocrine Glands

Glands such as those of the mouth, stomach, and intestines, which deliver their secretions into the alimentary tract, or those such as the lachrymal, mammary, and sweat glands, which discharge upon the surface of the body, are called *glands of external secretion* or *exocrine* glands. The glands which we are about to consider do not possess ducts or any openings to the exterior; their secretions pass into the blood stream, and are thus conveyed to the various tissues of the body upon which they exert their action. These glands are therefore called *endocrine glands or organs, ductless glands,* or *glands of internal secretion.*

The secretions of the endocrine glands are for the most part excitatory in their actions; they *stimulate* the growth and development, or the functional activity of certain tissues; internal secretions acting in this manner are therefore called *hormones* (Gk. *hormaō,* I excite). The term hormone is not, however, restricted to the secretions of the ductless glands. Any substance formed by a tissue of the body and carried in the blood stream to act as an excitant to some other tissue or organ may be called a hormone. Thus, secretin (p. 325), pancreozymin, and even carbon dioxide (p. 254), since it is carried by the blood and acts upon the respiratory and vasomotor centers, come into this category. *Chalone* is an allied term, sometimes used to designate an internal secretion having an *inhibitory* action, such as enterogastrone (p. 314).

Methods of investigation. Our knowledge of the endocrines has been advanced enormously in the past thirty years, and especially within the last twenty. The chief methods used in the investigation of endocrine function are three in number. *First,* an extract of the gland tissue may be prepared, which is then injected into animals and a study made of its effects. *Second,* a given gland may be excised, and the subsequent life history of the animal followed, careful notice being taken of its development and growth, or of any unusual feature. *Third,* studies may be made upon human subjects in whom one or other gland is known to be deficient or overactive. The first and second methods are often employed together. For example, after extirpation of the gland, the animal is treated with an extract prepared from the same type of gland, observations being made of the power of the preparation to correct the defects resulting from the operation. This is called the *substitution* or *replacement* method.

The general chemical nature of the hormones. The active principles of the endocrine glands have a complex chemical structure. Those of the male and female sex glands and of the adrenal cortex belong to the large class of fatty and waxlike substances known as steroids (p. 373). Their chemical formulae are well known, and many have been synthesized in the laboratory. The hormones of the pituitary gland, the parathyroid hormone, and insulin, on the contrary, are proteins; little is known more precisely of their chemical constitution. The thyroid hormone, thyroxine (see p. 412), is an amino acid.

Potent extracts of a number of ductless glands have now been prepared. These preparations, with the exception of thyroid extract and some forms of the male and female sex hormones, are relatively or quite inactive when given by mouth; their full effect is exerted only when given by injection.

Most of the ductless glands are present in all orders of vertebrates, and an extract obtained from the gland of one order exerts, as a rule, its specific effect when administered to a member of another order. Thus the hormone of the sheep's thyroid influences the growth and development of frog larvae (tadpoles).

The Thyroid Gland

The thyroid gland is composed of two *lobes* which lie one on either side of the larynx (see Figs. 10.1 and 10.2). Under the microscope, the glandular tissue is seen to be composed of a mass of alveoli (also called *acini* or *follicles*) lined by a single layer of cuboidal epithelial cells. The alveolar cavities are filled with a homogeneous viscous material called *colloid;* this is secreted by the lining cells and contains the thyroid hormone.

The thyroid is supplied with nerves, but whether these have any secretory function is questionable. It is certain, at any rate, that a hormone liberated by the pituitary gland (thyrotrophic hormone, p. 435) is of much greater importance than are nerve fibers in the control of thyroid activity.

Excision of the thyroid (thyroidectomy) in young mammals (e.g., pigs, goats, calves, rabbits, etc.) results in retardation of skeletal growth, and failure of sexual development (Fig. 10.3). Tissue oxidations are depressed, the basal metabolic rate falling after the operation to 60 or even 50 percent of the normal. The skin becomes thick and leathery in texture, the hair sparse, dry, lusterless, and brittle. The

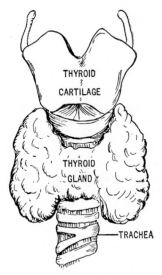

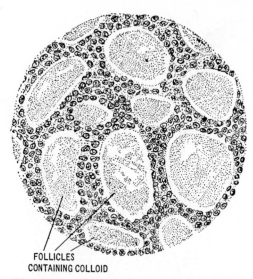

Fig. 10.1 Showing the relation of the thyroid gland to neighboring structures.

Fig. 10.2 Microscopic section of normal thyroid tissue.

long bones continue to grow in thickness, but longitudinal growth is very slow. The administration of thyroid extract after thyroidectomy prevents the onset of these effects or, if they have appeared, abolishes them or at least arrests their progress.

The effects following thyroidectomy in lower orders are even more striking. Thyroidectomized tadpoles, for example, do not develop into frogs. Metamorphosis is at once resumed, however, upon the addition of thyroid extract to the water in which the thyroidless animals live (Fig. 10.4). Furthermore, the administration of thyroid extract to normal tadpoles causes them to metamorphose in about a third of the usual time. The effect of thyroid extract upon the axolotl—an aquatic form allied to the frog—is still more extraordinary. In the adult form, this animal is purely aquatic in its habits, possessing gills, a finned tail, and four short limbs, suggesting some fabulous gigantic tadpole whose metamorphosis, after proceeding so far, has become arrested (Fig.

10.5). Thyroid feeding causes this creature to lose its gills and fin, to develop air-breathing organs, and forsake the aquatic life of its kind.

Goiter. This term is applied to chronic enlargement of the thyroid. When the enlargement is not associated with any general effects referable to disturbed function of the thyroid, it is called *simple goiter*. Goiter may, however, be accompanied by underfunctioning or by over-

Fig. 10.3 The effects of thyroidectomy on growth and development. The kid on the right was thyroidectomized soon after birth; both kids are the same age. (Drawn from a photograph after Sutherland Simpson.)

functioning of the thyroid—*hypothyroidism* and *hyperthyroidism,* respectively.

The histological appearance of the goitrous thyroid varies. In one type, the alveoli are enlarged, irregular in size and shape, and filled with colloid material. This is called *simple colloid* goiter (Fig. 10.6). Colloid goiter may progress to atrophy of the secretory cells, and their replacement by fibrous tissue; the signs of thyroid deficiency (hypothyroidism) then make their appearance. In a second type, the cells lining the alveoli enlarge and multiply; the wall of the alveolus is thrown into folds which project into, and almost obliterate, its cavity. This form, which is known as *diffuse parenchymatous goiter,* may be associated with signs of increased functional activity of the gland (hyperthyroidism). In the third type, the gland contains a tumor of thyroid tissue (*adenoma*); the surrounding glandular tissue may be normal. This form is called *adenomatous goiter.* It too may give rise to hyperthyroidism.

All forms of simple goiter are due to a deficiency of iodine in the food and drinking water. Other forms of goiter, in many instances at any rate, are also believed to be due to some deficiency of this element. It is, therefore, in regions where iodine is low, such as those far

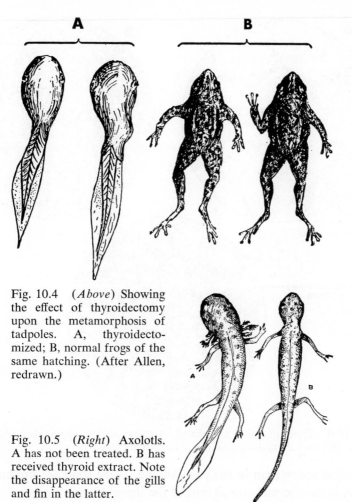

Fig. 10.4   (*Above*) Showing the effect of thyroidectomy upon the metamorphosis of tadpoles. A, thyroidecto-mized; B, normal frogs of the same hatching. (After Allen, redrawn.)

Fig. 10.5   (*Right*) Axolotls. A has not been treated. B has received thyroid extract. Note the disappearance of the gills and fin in the latter.

removed from the sea (which contains large stores of iodine), that goiter is prevalent. The inhabitants of mountain villages—e.g., in the Alps, Pyrenees, and Himalayas—have been among the chief sufferers. Through the ages iodine has been leached from the soils of these regions and, as a consequence, the water and food have a very low iodine content. In certain parts of North America, especialy in areas near the Great Lakes, and in some inland and hilly counties of England, there is a poverty of iodine, and goiter is occasionally seen, even today. Since the importance of iodine for normal thyroid function has been recognized, small amounts of iodine are taken by the population of goitrous districts; as a result of this preventive measure, goiter is much less

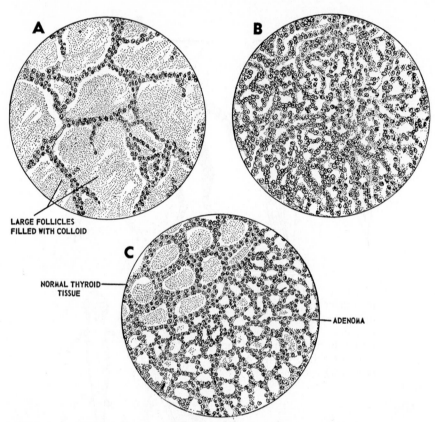

LARGE FOLLICLES
FILLED WITH COLLOID

NORMAL THYROID
TISSUE

ADENOMA

Fig. 10.6   Types of goiter as defined by microscopical appearance. A, colloid goiter; B, parenchymatous goiter; C, adenomatous goiter.

prevalent today than in the past. Iodine, as we shall see presently (p. 412), is an essential constituent of the thyroid hormone.

Hypothyroidism (*thyroid deficiency*). In infants and young children, thyroid deficiency produces effects essentially similar to those seen in animals following thyroidectomy. The defects of physical, sexual, and mental development form a characteristic picture to which the term *cretinism* is applied; the child is called a *cretin*. These young victims of thyroid deficiency are dwarfed to a marked degree and, unless the condition is corrected at an early age by the administration of thyroid extract or of thyroxine (p. 412), their height when they reach adult age

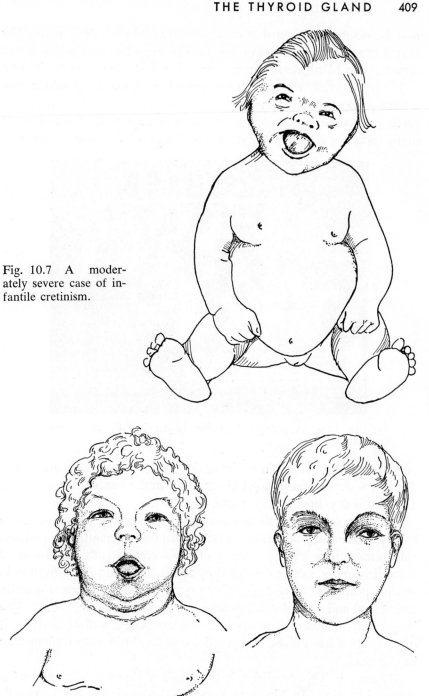

Fig. 10.7 A moderately severe case of infantile cretinism.

Fig. 10.8   Cretinism. On *left* at age of 3½ years (before treatment); *right*, same subject (after treatment with thyroid hormone) at the age of 7 years. (Drawn from a photograph after McCullagh.)

may be no greater than that of a normal child of 7 or 8 years. The sexual organs do not develop, nor do the secondary characters of sex appear. The basal metabolic rate is lowered. Mental growth is, as a rule, very seriously retarded; many cretins are imbecile or idiotic, and a large proportion are deaf mutes (Figs. 10.7 to 10.9). The facial features are coarse; the bridge of the nose is depressed; the tongue in many instances is enlarged and, as if too large for the mouth, protrudes

Fig. 10.9   A group of cretins in an institution. (After Falta.)

between the lips. The skin of the entire body appears thick and puffy, due to the deposition of a gelatinous fluid in the subcutaneous tissues. The hair is dry, brittle, and sparse.

Cretinism is very commonly associated with goiter, and is therefore most prevalent in goitrous districts; for as already mentioned, goitrous enlargement may lead to atrophy of the secretory cells. Cretinism, if recognized early, can be corrected by continued treatment with thyroid extract, powdered thyroid gland, or thyroxine. Almost normal growth, and sexual and mental development can be induced (Fig. 10.8). The longer that treatment is postponed, the less benefit will be derived; if the condition has existed untreated for years, little improvement can be expected.

Myxedema. This condition is the result of thyroid deficiency commencing in adult life. Its general features—namely, the low metabolic rate, the thickness and puffiness of the skin (myxedema) from which the condition originally got its name, the scantiness and dryness of the hair—are similar to those just described for cretinism. But inasmuch as full development—skeletal, sexual, and mental—has been attained before the onset of the disease, many of the characteristic features of cretinism are absent. Myxedematous subjects, though they are apathetic and lethargic and think slowly, are not mentally defective.

Fig. 10.10   Myxedema. *Left,* before treatment with thyroid extract. *Right,* after treatment. (Drawn from a photograph after Joll.)

The myxedematous subject is very quickly restored to normal by thyroxine or thyroid extract.

Hyperthyroidism, thyrotoxicosis (*overactivity of the thyroid gland*). Hyperthyroidism occurs in two forms, considered on the basis of the microscopical appearance of the gland. In the first form, called *exophthalmic goiter,* the whole gland is enlarged. The chief features of this condition are (a) enlargement of the thyroid; (b) elevation of the basal metabolic rate; (c) disturbances of carbohydrate metabolism (e.g., reduction in the glycogen stores, hyperglycemia, and glucosuria); (d) nervousness and tremor; (e) rapid action of the heart; and (f) protrusion of the eyeballs (*exophthalmos,* see Fig. 10.11).[1]

---

[1] Exophthalmos, or protrusion of the eyes, often to the extent that the whites of the eyes show above the iris, is due to the accumulation of fluid (edema) in the tissues behind the globes. The eyeballs are literally pushed forward and may be partly dislocated from their sockets; in extreme cases, the lids cannot be closed over them. The surfaces of the eyes then become dry and inflamed and may ulcerate. Exophthalmos is not due, as might be thought, to an excess of the thyroid hormone itself, but to the thyrotrophic hormone of the anterior lobe of the pituitary body (p. 435); it can be produced in *thyroidectomized* animals by the continued administration of this hormone.

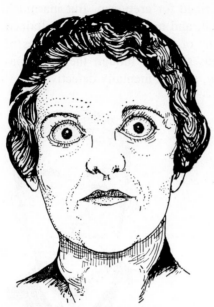

Fig. 10.11 Exophthalmic goiter. Note the staring eyes and the enlargement of the thyroid.

The name given to this type is not always appropriate since there may not be exophthalmos; and this may be present in the second form called *toxic adenoma,* in which the gland contains one or more tumors of thyroid tissue (*adenoma*) surrounded by normal appearing thyroid tissue. In both types, the affected thyroid tissue shows signs of great activity, presenting those features described on page 406 as parenchymatous goiter.

The thyroid hormone. It was shown over 60 years ago that the thyroid was a gland of internal secretion. An English physician, George Murray, in 1891 prepared a glycerin extract of sheep's thyroids. This preparation, when administered by injection to a subject of myxedema, restored him to normal within a very short time. It was discovered later that thyroid tissue, dried and powdered and given by mouth, was equally effective. At this time, nothing was known regarding the chemical nature of the hormone, but it was soon found that thyroid extracts contained iodine combined with protein. This iodine-protein compound was called *thyreoglobulin* (or *thyroglobulin*). The active principle of the extract was later obtained in crystalline form. It was shown to contain a large proportion (60 percent) of iodine; it was named *thyroxine*. Thyroxine—the thyroid hormone—has since been synthesized. It is an amino acid derived from the amino acid, tyrosine, and has the following formula:

$$HO \diagdown \bigcirc \diagup - O - \diagdown \bigcirc \diagup CH_2 \cdot CH(NH_2)COOH$$

thyroxine

Thyroxine, whether prepared from thyroid tissue or synthesized, has an action identical with that of the dried gland, but is much more potent. A fraction of a milligram, given daily, is sufficient to maintain the basal metabolic rate of a subject of myxedema at the normal level.

The thyroid hormone appears to act as a catalyst (p. 290), hastening very greatly oxidation in the tissues. When given to a normal animal, the metabolic rate is raised and the other signs of hyperthyroidism (except exophthalmos) make their appearance. The effects are not observed, however, until the lapse of several hours after the hormone has been administered, and are not fully developed until the lapse of from 8 to 10 days. But, even though a single dose is given, the effects persist for 5 or 6 weeks.

The production of the thyroid hormone and its discharge into the circulation are automatically controlled through the hypothalamus and the anterior lobe of the pituitary (thyrotrophic hormone, p. 435). This controlling mechanism is a very complicated one; several factors are

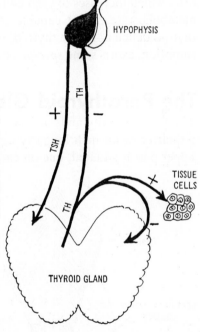

Fig. 10.12 Diagram to illustrate the principal factors controlling the production and discharge of the thyroid hormone. Plus and minus signs indicate, respectively, an increase or a decrease in action upon the structure to which the arrows point. (See text.) TSH = thyroid stimulating hormone; TH = thyroid hormone. Thus, a fall in TH of the blood causes increased production of TSH.

concerned, but probably the most important one is the concentration of the thyroid hormone in the blood. A fall in the concentration of thyroxine in the circulation stimulates the hypothalamic-pituitary mechanism, and more of the thyroid-stimulating (thyrotrophic) hormone is released from the pituitary. Any tendency for the thyroid hormone concentration in the blood to increase beyond the body's requirements causes a depression of the production of the thyrotrophic hormone. Thus the thyroid hormone governs its own production (see

Fig. 10.12). It is also probable that an excess of thyroid hormone in the circulation acts directly upon the thyroid, "backfires" as it were, to depress hormone production. Furthermore, it is most likely that the nervous system, through the hypothalamus, exerts an influence upon the production of the thyroid-stimulating hormone of the pituitary.

Summary of thyroid function. The thyroid gland extracts iodine from the blood together with the amino acid, tyrosine, and from these synthesizes its hormone thyroxine, whose molecule, as will be seen from the formula shown above, contains four atoms of iodine (I). Thyroxine presumably acts upon all tissues as a catalyst, hastening oxidative processes. It is tempting to attribute the developmental retardation caused by thyroid deficiency to the reduction in the rate of tissue oxidations, but the problem is not so simple as this, for dinitrophenol, a drug which increases oxygen consumption by the tissues and raises the metabolic rate, is not capable of replacing thyroxine in a subject of thyroid deficiency. The thyroid, apart from increasing the oxygen consumption, exerts some *specific* effect upon the tissue cells.

The Parathyroid Glands

The parathyroid glands are two pairs of small oval structures (about a quarter of an inch long) lying in close relation to the thyroid. The upper pair is situated, one on each side of the mid-line, behind the upper poles of the thyroid lobes; the lower pair lies behind, or a little below, the inferior poles of the thyroid (Fig. 10.12). Sometimes the parathyroids, especially the upper pair, are embedded in the posterior part of the thyroid.

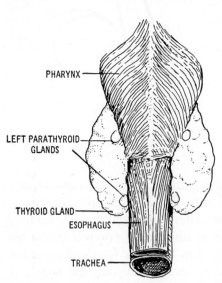

PHARYNX

LEFT PARATHYROID GLANDS

THYROID GLAND

ESOPHAGUS

TRACHEA

Fig. 10.13   The thyroid region of the neck from behind.

Removal of the parathyroids (*parathyroidectomy*) causes increased excitability of the neuromuscular tissues, which culminates in a severe convulsive disorder known as *tetany*. The manifestations of tetany, as they occur in animals after parathyroidectomy, are as follows: (a) twitching and spasmodic contractions of the muscles, which usually increase in violence until the whole body is thrown into convulsions; (b) rapid breathing; (c) acceleration of the heart; (d) rise in temperature; (e) death, usually occurring from exhaustion or from asphyxia resulting from spasm of the muscles which close the opening of the larynx (*laryngeal spasm*).

Parathyroid deficiency resulting in tetany is sometimes seen in the human subject following removal of the thyroid for goiter, the parathyroids having been inadvertently or unavoidably removed with the thyroid, or severely injured. The phenomena of parathyroid deficiency in man are usually much less pronounced than those which follow parathyroidectomy in animals. Twitchings, nervousness, and an occasional spasm of the facial or limb muscles are often the only manifestations. In other instances, tetany is in a latent form and is revealed only by means of special tests or under special circumstances (p. 417).

The function of the parathyroid glands. Normal blood contains from 5 to 6 mg of calcium per 100 cc; this is all contained in the plasma, so that the concentration of calcium in the plasma (or in the serum, for

Fig. 10.14 The effect of parathyroid extract on the calcium of the blood in parathyroid tetany. A single dose of extract was given when the serum calcium had fallen to 6 mg percent and the symptoms of tetany had reached their height. (After Macleod and Taylor.)

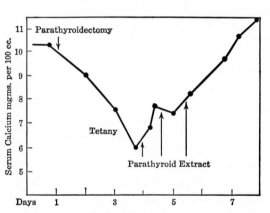

none is removed in the clot) is from 9 to 11 mg per 100 cc (i.e., 6 mg per 100 cc of blood). Parathyroidectomy causes a pronounced fall in the serum calcium (*hypocalcemia*). When the serum calcium level falls to about 6 mg percent, tetany appears and increases in severity with further reduction in the serum calcium concentration. Injections of calcium relieve the condition within a few minutes; there is no doubt, then, that calcium deficiency and the development of the tetanic state are directly related. These observations led to the conclusion that the parathyroids are concerned in some way with the control of calcium metabolism. This view of parathyroid function was amply confirmed in 1925, by the important discovery made by Professor J. B. Collip.

He found that an extract prepared from the parathyroid glands of cattle, when administered by subcutaneous injection to parathyroidectomized animals, raised the serum calcium and abolished all the manifestations of tetany (Fig. 10.14).

When *normal* animals are given repeated doses of parathyroid extract, the serum calcium is raised above the normal level (*hypercal-*

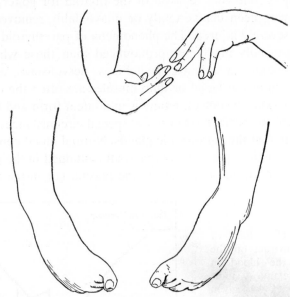

Fig. 10.15   Carpopedal spasm. The positions of the hands and feet in tetany.

cemia); it may be increased to 20 mg or more per 100 cc of serum. The excretion of calcium and phosphorus in the urine and feces is increased. The excess calcium in the serum is derived from the bones. The skeleton, especially the ends of the long bones, contains stores of calcium and, under normal circumstances, these are released by the action of the parathyroid hormone. Thus the normal level of calcium in the blood is maintained.

Other forms of tetany. Tetany occurs from other causes than parathyroid deficiency. It is not uncommon in young children (*infantile tetany*), and is then usually an accompaniment of rickets, the parathyroids being very rarely at fault. The serum calcium, however, is low and, as in parathyroid tetany, it is the hypocalcemia which is directly responsible for the tetanic seizures. Tetany is also seen in *osteomalacia* (p. 395), an adult form of rickets occurring in China and India; in *sprue,* a rare condition associated with defective absorption of calcium from the intestine; and in certain other conditions but especially in *alkalosis,* which may result from persistent vomiting (loss of HCl), forced breathing (excessive elimination of CO_2), or the administration of large doses of an alkali, such as sodium bicarbonate.

In the tetany of children, the hands and feet assume characteristic attitudes (see Fig. 10.15). This phenomenon is referred to as *carpopedal spasm*. Spasm of the laryngeal muscles with asphyxial attacks are common; the child becomes blue (cyanosis), but, presently, the obstruction to breathing is overcome, the air being then drawn into the chest with a highpitched "crowing" sound. In other instances, generalized convulsions occur.

In either infants or adults, the serum calcium is sometimes reduced below the normal level, but not quite low enough to bring on a tetanic attack, under ordinary circumstances. This is called *latent tetany.* A typical tetanic seizure may be precipitated, however, by some upset in the general health. Latent tetany may be detected by the following tests: (a) Tapping over the facial nerve in front of the ear causes twitchings of the muscles of the face, if latent tetany exists. This is called *Chvostek's sign*. (b) *Erb's sign*. The muscles show increased excitability to stimulation by a galvanic current (applied to the skin overlying a muscle). (c) *Trousseau's sign*. Tying a tourniquet around the arm above the elbow, so as temporarily to occlude the blood supply, causes the hand to assume the characteristic attitude.

Hyperparathyroidism (excess of the parathyroid hormone). In *animals,* overdosage with parathyroid extract causes (besides the hypercalcemia and the increased excretion of calcium and phosphorus, already mentioned) very grave effects—e.g., depression of spirits, muscular weakness, and hemorrhages into the stomach and intestines. Death occurs within a few days. If given in smaller doses over a long period, softening of the bones, as a result of the removal of calcium, results. In *man,* there is little doubt that excessive amounts of the extract would produce similar effects.

A rare disease, known as *osteitis fibrosa cystica,* is caused by overactivity of the parathyroid glands themselves. A tumor of one or other of the four glands is usually present; this secretes excessive amounts of the parathyroid hormone into the blood stream, producing effects closely similar to those resulting from overdosage with parathyroid extract—namely, hypercalcemia, increased excretion of calcium and phosphorus in the urine, and softening of the bones, which in some cases leads to marked deformity. The bony tissue, which normally is dense and contains a high percentage of mineral, becomes demineral-

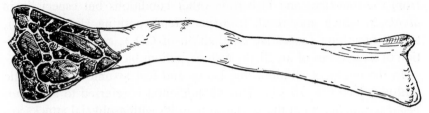

Fig. 10.16   Longitudinal section of bone (tibia) showing structural changes in osteitis fibrosa cystica. (Drawn from a photograph.) Note deformity of shaft and cystic cavities in the head of the bone.

ized and more fibrous in character. In places, the bone structure is replaced by cavities (cysts) of various sizes and shapes (see Fig. 10.16). *Renal stones (calculi)* are common in this disease and are due to the deposition of calcium excreted in excess by the kidney. They are formed from part of the excess calcium brought to the kidney for excretion.

The Adrenal Glands (or Suprarenal Capsules)

These are two somewhat pyramidal structures lying, one on each side of the body, in contact with the upper pole of the kidney (Fig. 10.17). Each gland measures from 1 to 2 inches in length. The adrenal

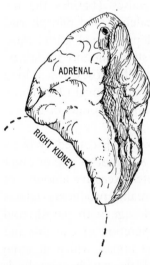

Fig. 10.17   The   adrenal gland.

gland, however, is actually two glands in one, for each consists of two functionally distinct parts—a central portion which is called the *medulla,* and a surrounding zone of tissue called the *cortex.* The cells of the medulla give a specific chemical reaction—namely, an affinity for the salts of chromic acid, by which they are stained brown. They are therefore referred to as *chromaffin cells.* In certain fish (*the elasmobranchs*) the two parts are quite separate (Fig. 10.18). The tissue corresponding to the mammalian adrenal medulla is present as several small masses of cells lying in close relation to the ganglia of the sympathetic chain. In man, also, small collections of chromaffin cells are to be found in close association with the sympathetic ganglia. They are known as *paraganglia*. The two parts of the adrenal gland have quite different origins, and there is but little evidence that their functions are closely related. The medulla develops from a group of cells, split off from the neural crest of the early em-

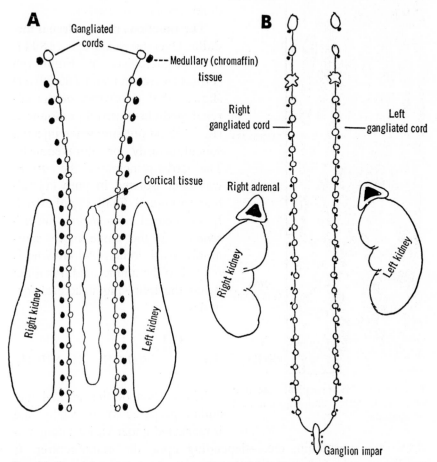

Fig. 10.18   Adrenal tissue, in elasmobranch fish (A), in mammals (B); medullary (chromaffin) tissue, black; cortical tissue, white. The small masses of chromaffin tissue lying close to the sympathetic ganglia are the paraganglia.

bryo, to which the ganglion cells of the sympathetic nervous system also trace their ancestry. It is important to remember this fact in order to understand the functions of this part of the gland. The cortex, on the other hand, arises from the multiplication of cells in close relation to those from which the sex glands (testes and ovaries) are developed. A microscopical section of the adrenal cortex is shown in Figure 10.19.

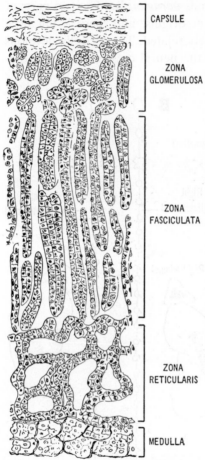

CAPSULE

ZONA GLOMERULOSA

ZONA FASCICULATA

ZONA RETICULARIS

MEDULLA

Fig. 10.19 Microscopical section of adrenal cortex and adjacent part of medulla.

The cellular structure of this part of the gland shows three distinct zones—an outer (*zona glomerulosa*), a middle (*zona fasciculata*), and an inner lying next the medulla (*zona reticularis*).

The functions of the adrenal medulla. Over 60 years ago (1894), two physiologists in Edinburgh (Professor Schafer and Dr. Oliver) showed that an extract of the adrenal medulla caused a pronounced rise in blood pressure when injected subcutaneously or intravenously. The active principle of the extract was later isolated in pure crystalline form and finally synthesized. It was named *epinephrine,* but *adrenaline* is the name more commonly used today. Adrenaline is related to the amino acid, tyrosine; it has the following structural formula:

$$HO \underset{}{\overset{OH}{\bigcirc}} CH(OH) \cdot CH_2 \cdot NHCH_3$$

The extract of the adrenal medulla is prepared commercially, and is marketed under various names—adrenalin,[2] suprarenin, etc.—depending upon the manufacturer. It was discovered a few years ago that the adrenal medulla contained another hormone which was similar to but not identical with adrenaline. This was named *noradrenaline* or *norepinephrine.* The commercial extract is, therefore, a mixture of the two hormones. The description which follows applies to the actions of the commercial extract.

Actions of a commercial extract of the adrenal medulla. The rise in blood pressure following the injection of a commercial extract of the adrenal medulla (Fig. 10.20) is the result of constriction of the small

[2] *Adrenalin,* as a name for a commercial extract, is spelled without the terminal *e.* When referred to as a separate hormone, it is spelled with the *e.*

blood vessels (arterioles), chiefly of the skin and abdomen. The vessels of the heart (coronaries) and of the skeletal muscles are *dilated* by the extract. The heart is slowed; this action is the reflex result of the rise in blood pressure (Marey's law, p. 190); for if the vagus nerves are first cut, the heart is accelerated. The quantity of the extract required to cause cardiac acceleration is minute. The denervated heart—that is, the heart completely isolated from nervous control by interruption of the vagus and sympathetic pathways—is increased in the rate of its

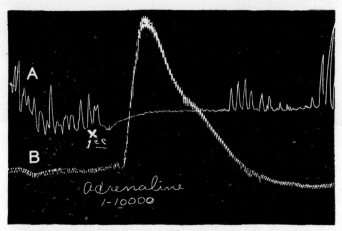

Fig. 10.20   Showing effect of adrenaline upon intestinal contractions, A, and blood pressure, B. 1 cc of 1 in 10,000 adrenaline solution injected at X. (Modified from Jackson.)

beating by as little as 1 part of the material in 1,400,000,000 parts of blood. The denervated heart therefore provides the most sensitive test object for detecting the presence of adrenaline in blood or other fluid.

Other effects produced by an extract of the adrenal medulla are *inhibition of the movements of the intestine,* and *contraction of the pyloric, iliocolic, and internal anal sphincters.* It *relaxes the smooth muscle of the bronchioles,* thus causing dilatation of these parts of the bronchial tree. It is, therefore, of great value in relieving spasm of the bronchioles in attacks of asthma. It *inhibits the wall of the urinary bladder,* but causes *contraction of the ureter,* and of the *sphincter of the bladder.* In most animals, the *uterus contracts* under its influence. It dilates the *pupil of the eye* and contracts the *smooth muscle of the skin* through which the hairs or feathers are elevated. It exerts a favorable effect upon the contraction of skeletal muscle; an isolated muscle subjected to repeated stimulation fatigues less readily if treated with the extract (Fig. 10.21).

An extract of the adrenal medulla also raises the metabolic rate; this is spoken of as its *calorigenic* action. It increases the sugar content of the blood by causing an increased breakdown in the liver of glycogen to sugar. The decomposition of muscle glycogen is also accelerated, lactic acid being produced which, escaping into the circula-

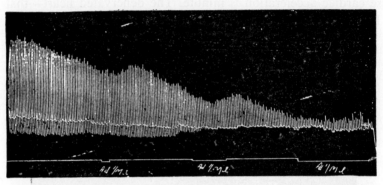

Fig. 10.21   Showing the effect of adrenaline in postponing muscular fatigue. Note the increase in the height of the contractions following each injection of adrenaline.

tion, raises the level of the lactic acid in the blood. The lactic acid is carried to the liver and there reconverted to glycogen. These effects in their relation to the carbohydrate cycle are shown in the following scheme:

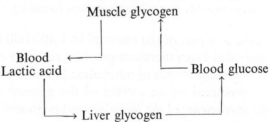

Adrenaline hastens the clotting of blood; but this effect is brought about only if the hormone is injected into the body. It exerts no effect upon the clotting process when added to blood after it has been shed —i.e., when added to blood in a test tube. This difference in the action of adrenaline upon the clotting process within and outside the body suggests that the hormone acts in the former case, not directly, but through some other tissue or organ acting as an intermediary. The nature of the intermediary is unknown.

Most of the effects listed above as following the administration of an adrenal extract can be produced by stimulation of sympathetic nerve fibers. Indeed, the actions of the hormones of the adrenal medulla may be summed up by saying that they imitate the effects of sympathetic excitation. This remarkable *sympathomimetic* action is perhaps not so surprising when we recall that the adrenal medulla and sympathetic nerve cells have a common origin (p. 419). See also p. 566.

The actions of adrenaline and noradrenaline compared. Information concerning the separate actions of adrenaline and noradrenaline is not yet complete, but the following comparisons can be drawn. Noradrenaline is a general vasoconstrictor, showing little or no selective action in respect to different sets of blood vessels, whereas adrenaline, while it constricts the cutaneous vessels, dilates the coronary vessels and the vessel of the muscles. Its effect upon the vascular system as a whole is dilatation, the vasodilator action overshadowing the vasoconstriction. The peripheral resistance (Chap. 4) is therefore reduced. Since the overall effect of noradrenaline is vasoconstriction, it increases the peripheral resistance. The action of a commercial extract upon the heart is a pure adrenaline effect, noradrenaline having no effect upon cardiac action. The effect upon plain (smooth) muscle—stomach, intestine, bronchioles, etc.—is also due mainly to adrenaline; noradrenaline has but little effect upon smooth muscle, nor does the latter hormone act to postpone the fatigue of skeletal muscle. The effects of the extract upon carbohydrate metabolism and upon heat production (calorigenic action) are chiefly due to adrenaline.

The emergency theory of the function of the adrenal medulla. By a great number of ingenious experiments, Professor Cannon and his several associates at Harvard University have demonstrated that the hormone of the adrenal medulla serves an *emergency function.* It reinforces the action of the sympathetic nervous system to raise the defense mechanisms of the body against the dangers and rigors of the environment to a high level of efficiency. These workers experimented with cats in which the heart had been denervated by cutting the vagus nerves and excising the stellate ganglion of the sympathetic chain which gives rise to or transmits the sympathetic fibers to the heart.[3] It was found that fright (caused by a barking dog), exposure to cold, asphyxia, the administration of an anesthetic, pain, or muscular contraction caused acceleration of the heart. Since the cardiac acceleration could not have been caused by nervous influences, and did not

[3] The heart receives directly a few fibers from the sympathetic chain below the stellate ganglion which must also be severed to completely denervate the heart.

occur after removal of the adrenals, it must have been due to the action of adrenaline discharged from the animal's own adrenal glands.

Under quiet, resting conditions the blood contains only a negligible amount of adrenaline, about one part in one or two billion; but during states of excitement or any of the conditions just mentioned about .004 mg per kilogram of body weight may be discharged from the glands per minute. It is believed, therefore, that the adrenal medulla functions only under circumstances which demand some special effort on the part of the body, as when an animal is defending itself or running down its prey, fleeing from danger, or exposed to cold. It will be recalled that the reactions of an animal under such circumstances —e.g., the bristling of fur or the ruffling of feathers (caused by the contraction of the smooth muscle in the skin), the dilatation of the pupil, the acceleration of the heart, and, in certain cold-blooded species, the contraction of the melanophores (pigment cells) of the skin —are characteristic of sympathetic stimulation or of adrenaline administration. Other physiological adjustments which increase the efficiency of the body to the maximum in times of stress—such as the mobilization of sugar from the liver (fuel for muscular work), the rise in blood pressure, and the diversion of blood from the skin and splanchnic region to the vessels of the brain, heart, and contracting muscles, the dilatation of the bronchioles, and the postponement of muscular fatigue—are brought about through the sympathetic nervous system, as well as by the hormone of the adrenal medulla. The increased coagulability of the blood caused by adrenaline would also seem to be a part of the general defense reaction, for should a wound be sustained, bleeding will be more quickly staunched.

The *secretion of the adrenal medulla* is under the control of the sympathetic nervous system. Stimulation of the splanchnic nerve causes the liberation of adrenaline, and prolonged stimulation causes exhaustion of the adrenaline stores. It is a very interesting and significant fact, in view of the functional relationship between the adrenal medulla and the sympathetic nervous system, that the fibers to the adrenal, unlike any other sympathetic fibers, do not form connections with ganglion cells but pass directly to the cells of the medulla. The adrenal cell thus appears to take the place of the sympathetic ganglion cell. A center, controlling adrenal secretion, is situated in the medulla oblongata. A higher center is present in the hypothalamus, and in the cerebral cortex.

When the blood-pressure-raising (pressor) effect of adrenal extracts was first discovered, it was naturally suggested that the adrenal glands were responsible for maintaining the normal arterial blood pressure. The fallacy of such an idea is proved by the observation that destruction of the medullary tissue of both adrenals is not followed by a fall in blood pressure. Animals subjected to this operation show no abnormality. The adrenal medulla then, unlike the adrenal cortex, is not indispensable. Nor is there any evidence that so-called *high blood pressure* (*essential arterial hypertension*) is due to the secretion of excessive amounts of adrenaline. However, a rare type of arterial hypertension, which occurs usually in paroxysms, is caused by the secretion of excessive amounts of adrenaline and noradrenaline. Certain tumors composed of adrenal tissue, or hypertrophy of the adrenal medulla itself, are associated with such hypersecretion of the hormones.

Sympathin. It has been shown by Professor Cannon and his colleagues that the sympathetic nerves bring about their effects through the medium of a chemical substance (or substances) liberated from their terminals. This substance, though resembling adrenaline in its actions, was found to differ in certain respects. In view of its origin at sympathetic nerve endings, it was called *sympathin*. It was later concluded that there were two such substances, one excitatory, the other inhibitory. It now appears that the first of these, which was named sympathin E, is *noradrenaline* and the second or sympathin I is *adrenaline*.

The functions of the adrenal cortex. Animals die in from 10 to 15 days after complete removal of both adrenal glands. We have seen that excision of the adrenal medulla alone is not fatal; the cortex, therefore, is the part of the gland which is essential to life. If one sixth or so of the total amount of adrenal cortical tissue is left, the animal survives; this part of the gland must, therefore, produce a highly potent hormone.

During the time that the animal survives after double adrenalectomy, the following effects are observed: (1) loss of appetite, vomiting, fall in blood pressure, muscular weakness and, just before death, profound prostration; (2) subnormal body temperature and reduced basal metabolic rate; (3) concentration of the blood, due to a loss of plasma water; (4) reduction in the sodium chloride of the blood and a rise in the potassium, calcium, phosphate, and nonprotein nitrogen; (5) hypoglycemia; (6) signs of renal failure.

Foremost among the functions of the adrenal cortex is the influence that it exerts upon the metabolism of water and salts. In the absence of the adrenal cortex, sodium and water are excreted in excessive amounts, whereas potassium escapes into the body fluids from the tissue cells, where normally it is in relatively high concentration. Excretion of this mineral by the kidneys is also impaired; its concentration, therefore, rises in the blood and other tissues.

The adrenal cortex also exerts an influence upon carbohydrate metabolism which is due to a hormone other than that controlling the metabolism of water and salt.

Destructive disease of the adrenal cortex, usually of a tuberculous nature, occurs in man. The manifestations of this condition, which is known as *Addison's disease,* are similar to, though less acute than, those just described as resulting from adrenalectomy in animals. The disease, if untreated, is gradually progressive, death occurring within 2 or 3 years. A bronze or dirty gray discoloration of the skin, which is not seen, as a rule, in animals after adrenalectomy, is a prominent feature in Addison's disease. The skin may be mottled, pale areas of depigmentation lying adjacent to overpigmented areas. Anemia and gastrointestinal disturbances are also outstanding features of adrenal insufficiency in the human subject. The pigmentation is due to an increase in the normal pigment (*melanin*) of the skin. The disturbances in water and salt metabolism, already described as occurring in adrenalectomized animals, are prominent features.

Addison's disease is treated by the administration of a hormone (usually desoxycorticosterone, cortisone, or both, see below) obtained from the adrenal cortex (or prepared synthetically) in combination with a diet high in sodium content and low in potassium.

The active principles isolated from the adrenal cortex. Several active principles have been extracted from the adrenal cortex and prepared in crystalline form. Chemically they all belong to the class of fatty or wax-like substances known as steroids (p. 372) and are referred to collectively as corticoids. They are basically similar in molecular structure to the sex hormones. A hormone was isolated from the adrenal cortex some years ago by Dr. E. C. Kendall of the Mayo Foundation. It has a long chemical name [4] but is known more briefly as Kendall's compound E. More recently, owing to the possible confusion with vitamin E, it has been designated *cortisone.* It was discovered by Dr. P. S. Hench and his associates of the Mayo Clinic that this principle exerts a most favorable effect upon the course of chronic (rheumatoid) arthritis and acute rheumatic fever.

The physiological action of cortisone is upon the redundant connective tissues (collagenous fibers) surrounding the affected joints. This principle has also been employed in affections of the skin associated

[4] 17-Hydroxy-11-dehydrocorticosterone.

with disorders of the collagenous tissues. Besides the diseases mentioned, it has been used in a wide variety of pathological states (e.g., leukemia, asthma, multiple enlargement of lymph nodes, etc.), sometimes with considerable benefit, though the improvement is usually only temporary. The mode of action of cortisone in many of these disorders is not clearly understood. The secretion of cortisone, like that of

Table 10-1

The corticoids

Name	Principal actions
Corticosterone	On carbohydrate, protein, and fat metabolism; antagonizes the action of insulin.
11-Desoxycorticosterone	On water and mineral metabolism, increases the retention of sodium and the excretion of potassium.
Aldosterone	Similar to preceding but more pronounced.
11-Dehydrocorticosterone	On carbohydrate metabolism.
17-Hydroxycorticosterone	On carbohydrate metabolism; on connective tissues; antirheumatic.
17-Hydroxy-11-dehydrocorticosterone (cortisone)	On carbohydrate metabolism; on connective tissues; antirheumatic.
17-Hydroxy-11-desoxycorticosterone	On connective tissues; antirheumatic.

other hormones of the adrenal cortex, is under the control of the adrenocorticotrophic hormone (ACTH) of the pituitary body. So far as is known, the latter hormone is the sole means whereby the function of the adrenal cortex is controlled. Unlike the adrenal medulla, the liberation of its hormones is not regulated by nerves.

Among the other steroid principles obtained from the adrenal cortex are *corticosterone* and *desoxycorticosterone*. The former exerts its chief action on the metabolism of carbohydrate, causing the formation of sugar from protein, increase in the glycogen stores, and hyperglycemia. The action of desoxycorticosterone is directed mainly to the metabolism of sodium and potassium, increasing the retention in the

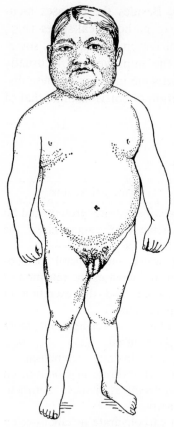

Fig. 10.22 Child aged 4½ years suffering from adrenal tumor. Note the florid "beefy" face and the precocious development of the genital structures. (Drawn from a photograph after Guthrie.)

body of the former, and stimulating the renal excretion of the latter. More recently, a hormone has been isolated from the adrenal cortex that has a much more powerful effect upon salt metabolism than has desoxycorticosterone. It is called *electrocortin* or *aldosterone;* like desoxycorticosterone, it causes the retention of sodium and the excretion of potassium, but, as just mentioned, to a much more pronounced degree. The principal corticoids and their actions are given in Table 10-1.

The adrenal cortex also contains the female sex hormones *estrone* and *progestin,* as well as one with male hormone activity known as *adrenosterone.*

The adrenal cortex is relatively rich in cholesterol and in vitamin C (ascorbic acid). The former is probably the chief substance from which the steroid hormones of the adrenal are synthesized in the body. The concentrations of both these substances are reduced when the adrenal cortex is stimulated, as by the adrenocorticotrophic hormone of the pituitary (p. 435), to liberate its hormones. But the role played by vitamin C with respect to the function of the adrenal cortex is unknown. It is not essential for the production of the hormones, for they continue to be formed in animals who have been rendered severely deficient in vitamin C.

Other functions of the adrenal cortex. The adrenal cortex performs other functions besides those just described. Several observations suggest that it influences the development of the sex functions. Enlargement of the adrenal cortex, for example, or tumors of cortical tissue sometimes occur, accompanied by sexual abnormalities. In children with such growths, precocious development of the sexual organs and of the secondary sex characters (see p. 444) is seen; these subjects often also show unusual muscular development for their age, and sometimes an abnormally "beefy" florid face. Such an appearance has prompted the comparison with "a burly brewer's drayman" (Fig. 10.22). Little girls, subjects of this disease, also show precocious sexual development, and in appearance resemble stout women in miniature. Menstruation may occur as early as 3 or 4 years of age. Women who are the victims of cortical enlargement or tumor become obese,

Fig. 10.23   Virilism due to a tumor of the adrenal cortex. On *left,* at age of 24 years; on *right,* at age of 32, about one year after the onset of the disease. (Drawn from photographs after Hare, Ross, and Crooke.)

and masculine in appearance; hair grows upon the face and chest, and their disposition tends toward "mannishness." This condition is referred to as *virilism* (Fig. 10.23).

The cortex of the adrenal, as well as the medulla, appears to play a role in states of stress, for when such a state as exposure to extreme cold, hemorrhage, bacterial infection, or severe mechanical injury is suffered by an animal, the output of the adrenal cortex is increased. See also Cushing's disease, page 444.

The Pituitary Body or Gland (Hypophysis Cerebri)

Development and structure. The pituitary gland is connected by a narrow stalk, called the *neural stalk* or *infundibulum,* to the base of the brain just behind the optic chiasma. In man it is an ovoid body and measures a little over half an inch in its longest diameter. It is lodged within a small recess in the bone of the base of the skull, known as the *sella turcica* (L., Turkish saddle). The pituitary consists of an anterior and a posterior portion. These have separate origins and are different in structure and function. The anterior part arises from the embryonic mouth cavity as a hollow pouch (*Rathke's pouch*); the posterior part is formed by a downgrowth of nervous tissue from the floor of the third ventricle at the base of the developing brain. Rathke's pouch grows

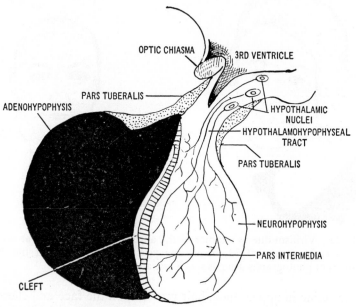

OPTIC CHIASMA   3RD VENTRICLE

PARS TUBERALIS

ADENOHYPOPHYSIS

HYPOTHALAMIC NUCLEI

HYPOTHALAMOHYPOPHYSEAL TRACT

PARS TUBERALIS

NEUROHYPOPHYSIS

PARS INTERMEDIA

CLEFT

Fig. 10.24   Diagram of the pituitary body (hypophysis cerebri).

upward and, meeting the downgrowth from the brain, fuses with it. The cavity of Rathke's pouch becomes reduced to a narrow cleft by pressure against the posterior part; the anterior wall of the pouch—that is, the portion lying in front of the cleft becomes thickened and is now called the *adenohypophysis, pars distalis,* or *pars anterior* of the pituitary (Fig. 10.24). The posterior wall of Rathke's pouch is represented by a thin shell of tissue, closely applied to the anterior aspect of the posterior part of the gland; it is called the *pars intermedia.* That portion of the pituitary developed from the base of the brain and lying behind the pars intermedia is known as the *neurohypophysis, neural lobe,* or the *pars nervosa.*

The part of the pituitary situated in front—that is, the adenohypophysis—is readily separated from the rest of the gland and is very commonly referred to as the *anterior lobe;* whereas the portion lying behind the natural line of cleavage offered by the cleft is called the *posterior lobe*. The latter term, therefore, includes both the pars intermedia and the neurohypophysis. A part of the tissue of Rathke's pouch also extends upward as far as the base of the brain, where it covers a mass of nerve cells in this situation known as the *tuber cinereum*. This part of the pituitary, which—having the same origin as the anterior lobe—is usually included with it, is called the *pars tuberalis*. As development proceeds, the connection of the pituitary with the mouth cavity disappears, but that with the base of the brain persists and, as mentioned above, is called the neural stalk or infundibulum.

The nomenclature of the parts of the pituitary is confusing owing to varied designations which different authors from time to time have adopted. The different terms are given in the following table, with the names in most common use today given first and the older terms in small brackets.

Origin	From the mouth cavity	Adenohypophysis [pars distalis, pars glandularis, pars anterior]	Anterior lobe
		Pars tuberalis	
		Pars intermedia	
	From the base of the brain; floor of 3rd cerebral ventricle	Neurohypophysis [neural lobe, pars nervosa] Neural stalk [infundibulum]	Posterior lobe

The adenohypophysis consists of cords of cells separated by relatively wide blood channels (sinuses). The cells are of three main types: (a) those which are stained poorly by ordinary dyes—*chromophobe* cells; (b) those which stain with acid dyes—*acidophil* (*alpha*) cells; and (c) those which stain with basic dyes—*basophil* (*beta*) cells (see Fig. 10.25).

The posterior lobe of the pituitary receives numerous fibers from nerve cells situated in the region of the brain near the origin of the infundibulum (see hypothalamus, p. 541). A few nerve fibers have been traced into the anterior lobe, though it is believed that they are not secretory, but entirely vasomotor in function. The structure of the neural lobe is quite different from that of the anterior lobe. It contains nerve fibers, spindle-shaped cells called *pituicytes,* neuroglial cells, and hyaline bodies. These latter are cells filled with a clear homogeneous material; their function is doubtful, though they are believed by some to furnish the active principle of the posterior lobe secretion.

The functions of the anterior lobe. The functions of the anterior lobe of the pituitary are many. The growth of the skeleton, the development of the sex glands, and the activity of the thyroid, adrenal, and parathyroid glands are dependent upon this part of the pituitary. Within the last 15 years or so the anterior lobe has been the object of intensive investigation. A number of separate active principles or hormones, each of which exerts its specific effect when injected into animals, has been obtained by the extraction of anterior lobe tissue. It has been aptly termed the master gland of the endocrine system (see Fig. 10.48, p. 455). Its hormones are protein in nature.

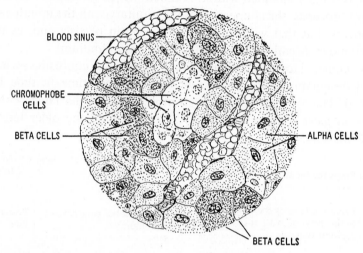

Fig. 10.25   Microscopical section of the adenohypophysis.

The pituitary principles which upon injection give relatively pure effects, and are probably distinct and separate hormones, are as follows:

(1) The growth hormone
(2) The thyrotrophic hormone (TTH)
(3) The adrenocorticotrophic hormone (ACTH)
(4) and (5) Two gonadotrophic hormones (FSH and LSH)
(6) Prolactin

Certain effects other than those produced by the foregoing more-or-less pure principles can be produced by relatively crude (unfractioned) extracts of the anterior lobe. These effects are:

(1) Diabetogenic
(2) Glycotropic
(3) Ketogenic
(4) Parathyrotrophic
(5) Pancreotrophic

Arrest of skeletal growth follows removal of the pituitary (*hypo-physectomy*) from young animals, and the sex glands do not develop:

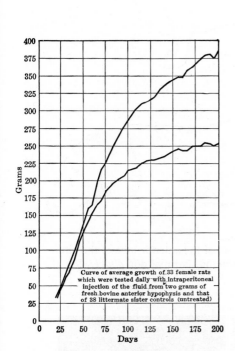

Fig. 10.26 Curves showing the effect upon the growth of rats of daily injections of an extract of the anterior lobe of the pituitary. *Upper curve,* treated animals; *lower curve,* untreated litter mate sisters. (After Evans.)

Fig. 10.27 Drawing of an hypophysectomized white rat (*left*) and its normal litter mate.

the thyroid and cortex of the adrenal atrophy. The daily transplantation of anterior lobe tissue into the hypophysectomized animals is followed by the resumption of growth, by the regeneration and normal development of the atrophic testes or ovaries, and restoration to normal of the adrenal cortex and thyroid gland. The effects of hypophysectomy can be corrected also by anterior lobe extracts, and extracts have been prepared which will abolish one or other defect caused by hypophysectomy but leave the others almost or quite uncorrected. That is to say, extracts more or less pure in one or other of the pituitary hormones as listed above are now available. These extracts are also capable of causing their respective effects in normal animals.

Fig. 10.28   The effect of an extract of the anterior lobe of the pituitary upon the growth of the dachshund. Normal dog *above;* dog of same litter *below,* injected. (Drawn from a photograph after Van Dyke.)

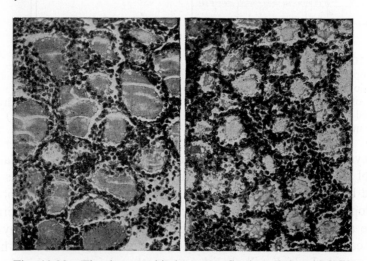

Fig. 10.29   The thyrotrophic hormone. Section of thyroid from normal guinea pig on the *left,* that of litter mate treated with 8 mg of anterior lobe substance on *right.* Note the greatly increased cellularity of the latter and the infolding of the follicular walls. (After Van Dyke.)

Young rats treated daily with a purified *growth hormone* attain a size nearly double that of untreated animals of the same litter (Figs. 10.26 and 10.27). The characteristic effect of the growth hormone has also been demonstrated on puppies (Fig. 10.28).

The *thyrotrophic* [5] *hormone* (TTH) exerts its effect upon the thyroid gland. An animal receiving an extract containing this hormone shows marked hypertrophy and increased activity of the thyroid gland and, in consequence, a rise in the basal metabolic rate (Fig. 10.29).

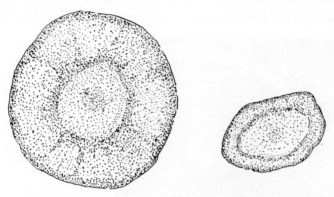

Fig. 10.30   Showing effect of hypophysectomy upon the size of the adrenal. Adrenal from an hypophysectomized animal on the *right,* from normal animal on the *left.* Note that the effect is exerted chiefly upon the cortex. (After P. Smith.)

The *adrenocorticotrophic hormone* (ACTH) maintains the functional activity of the adrenal cortex. It stimulates the elaboration and output of cortisone and the other corticoids (see Fig. 10.30).

The *gonadotrophic hormones* are essential for the normal development of the gonads and for the production of the respective sex hormones of the male and female animal. They will be considered in the section on the sex hormones (p. 449). *Prolactin,* which stimulates the secretion of milk, will also be dealt with in that section.

The *diabetogenic* and *glycotropic* effects appear to be due to different principles in anterior lobe extracts. A crude extract, given over a period of days, produces a permanent diabetes—hyperglycemia, glycosuria, increased production of urine (polyuria), thirst, and wasting. The glycotropic effect is a temporary hyperglycemia and glycosuria.

[5] It has been recommended that the suffix *tropic,* derived from the Greek *tropē* (a turning), be changed to *trophic,* from the Greek *trophē* (nourishment), on the grounds that the latter more correctly expresses the action of these pituitary principles. The ending *tropic* is used in such words as geotropic, heliotropic, glycotropic, etc.

This action is antagonistic to that of insulin. The effect upon carbohydrate metabolism exerted by the anterior lobe of the pituitary can also be demonstrated by the following experiments.

(a) Hypophysectomy, by removing the source of the sugar-raising principle, results in a fall in the blood sugar. (b) Excision of the pancreas alone (removal of the source of insulin, p. 370) causes hyperglycemia and the other signs of diabetes, but if the pituitary is removed as well, little or no rise in blood sugar occurs; there may, indeed, be hypoglycemia when the animal is fasting. The transplantation of anterior lobe tissue into such a pancreatectomized-hypophysecto-

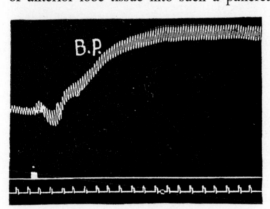

Fig. 10.31   Showing the effect of pituitrin upon the arterial blood pressure. B.P., carotid blood pressure; white square indicates the injection of 0.5 cc pituitrin. (After Herring.)

mized animal causes the appearance of the usual effects of pancreatectomy. A pituitary extract with an effect upon carbohydrate metabolism, but entirely free from growth effects, has not been prepared. It is probable that the diabetogenic effect is simply a manifestation of the growth hormone.

The ketogenic effect is evident when an anterior lobe extract is injected into a fasting animal, or better, into one on a diet of fat, when ketone bones—*acetoacetic acid* and β-*hydroxybutyric acid*—appear in relatively high concentration in the blood and urine. Associated with the ketogenic effect are a reduction in body fat and increase in the fat of the liver.

The relationship between the pituitary and parathyroid glands is rather indefinite, but it does appear that the master gland exerts an influence upon the activity of the parathyroids (*parathyrotrophic effect*). The effect of a crude anterior lobe extract upon the pancreas is more definite, and following the administration of such an extract, the growth of the insulin-producing cells (islands of Langerhans, p. 323) in the pancreas is stimulated. This is the so-called *pancreotrophic* effect.

The physiology of the posterior lobe. An extract of the posterior lobe of the pituitary has been used in medicine for a number of years. It is sold under various trade names—e.g., *pituitrin, infundin,* etc. It produces the following effects when injected subcutaneously:

(a) A rise in arterial blood pressure occurs as a result of general vasoconstriction (Fig. 10.31). This action differs from that of an extract of the adrenal medulla, for all vessels—cutaneous, muscular, coronary, etc.—are constricted alike, there being no relationship between its effects upon various structures and those caused by sympathetic stimulation.

(b) Contraction of the smooth muscle of the uterus, intestine, gall bladder, urinary bladder, and ureter, as well as of that in the walls of

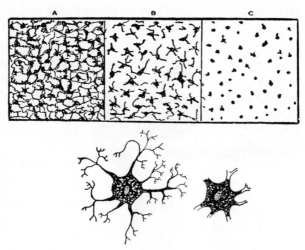

Fig. 10.32 Melanophores of frog's skin. A, fully expanded; B, partially contracted; C, fully contracted—i.e., collection of pigment at centers of the cells. (Redrawn from Hogben.) *Below,* enlarged views of a melanophore, expanded on the *left,* contracted on the *right.* The branching processes are invisible in the latter because they contain no granules.

the follicles and ducts of the mammary gland. The contraction of the uterine muscle is called its *oxytocic* action. The potency of a posterior pituitary extract is assayed by testing its oxytocic action upon the excised uterus of a virgin guinea pig. It is for this effect that the extract is most often employed in medicine, being administered in the later stages of labor to stimulate uterine contractions. It is also used to stimulate the muscle of the intestinal wall and thus to relieve troublesome abdominal distention, especially after operation upon the abdomen. The effect of pituitary extract upon the mammary gland is called its *galactogogue* action (Gk. *gala* [*galact*—], milk + *agōgos,* drawing forth), for it causes the expression of milk from the follicles and along the ducts to the surface of the nipple. This is not a true secretory effect—that is, a production of milk by the gland cells—but merely an expression of *preformed* milk from the alveoli and ducts by the contraction of smooth muscle fibers surrounding these structures. The commencement of the milk flow in cows at milking time, and what farmers speak of as the "letting down" of the milk, is thought to be due to the galactogogue principle.

(c) *Reduced production of urine—antidiuretic effect* (p. 281).

(d) *Hyperglycemia, glucosuria, and reduction of liver glycogen.*

(e) *"Expansion" of the melanophores* in the skin of various kinds of cold-blooded vertebrates. The skin of the frog is abundantly supplied with melanophores. These are irregularly shaped cells possessing several branching processes and granules of a dark pigment (Fig. 10.32). The processes of adjacent cells interlace with one another to form a rich network. The pigment at one time may be concentrated near the center of the body of the cell; the next moment the granules may migrate and fill the processes. In the former event the skin is pale, in the latter it is dark. The movements of the pigment granules, and the consequent darkening or lightening of the skin, depend upon the illumination of the environment; thus, by changing its color to match its surroundings, the animal is rendered less conspicuous to its enemies. An injection of pituitrin causes the granules to move into the branching processes, the animal then becoming a deep brown or green (Fig. 10.33). Hypophysectomy, on the contrary, by removing the supply of posterior lobe principle, results in permanent pallor of the skin. Blinding the animal, as by sealing its eyes with wax, also abolishes the skin responses so long as the eyes are closed. The skin color remains unaltered in light or shade. The effects are evidently initiated by light reflexes, and are brought about in the following way. The pituitary secretes the melanophore-ex-

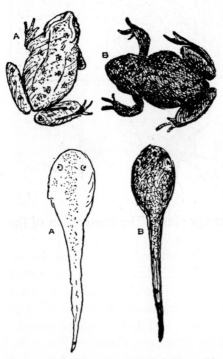

Fig. 10.33 *Upper drawing*, A, the color of a normal frog. B, the same frog after the injection of an extract of the posterior lobe of the pituitary. (Redrawn from Hogben.) *Below*, the effect of hypophysectomy upon the color of tadpoles. A, hypophysectomized; B, normal.

panding principle continuously, so long as no light, or light of low intensity, falls upon the retina; the skin is then dark. Retinal illumination, on the other hand, sets up nerve impulses which suppress temporarily the pituitary secretion; the skin, therefore, becomes pale. Many species of fish and certain lizards and toads possess a similar mechanism for altering the depth of color of their skins in conformity

Fig. 10.34   An example of giantism. Father on *right* and boy on *left* are of average height.

with the illumination of their immediate environment. The pigment granules in some forms are red (*erythrophores*), in others yellow (*xanthophores*).

The several effects of posterior lobe extract are due, not to one, but to at least three and possibly four, distinct principles. A short time ago two substances in the form of white powders were separated from the relatively crude posterior lobe extract (pituitrin). These are known as *pitressin* and *pitocin* (or *oxytocin*). The former is vasoconstrictor (pressor), intestine stimulating, and antidiuretic in action; the latter contains the uterine-stimulating (oxytocic) principle. Both raise the sugar of the blood. The melanophore-expanding effect is caused only by pitressin, though it appears that this effect is due to a separate principle which is merely associated as a contaminent with pitressin; there is convincing evidence that it is a separate hormone elaborated by the *pars intermedia,* and has been named *intermedin.* Indeed pitressin and pitocin are far from being pure substances, and it is possible that the antidiuretic effect of the former is also due to a distinct hormone.

Disorders of the pituitary in man. *Giantism and acromegaly—hyperpituitarism.* The great stature of those persons whom one sees in

Fig. 10.35   Acromegaly. (Drawn from a photograph after Lisser and Goldberg.)

circuses or occasionally reads about in the daily papers is caused by overactivity of the anterior lobe of the pituitary. Some of these *giants* are between 8 and 9 feet tall (Fig. 10.34). Of course, general overgrowth of the skeleton can occur only if the hyperpituitarism commences during the normal period of growth. Hypersecretion of the growth hormone of the pituitary after adolescence does not cause an increase in stature. Nevertheless, the stimulating effect of the hormone upon growth is seen in the bones of the face, hands, and feet. This condition, resulting from hyperpituitarism in adult life, is called *acromegaly* (Gk. *acron,* extremity + *megas* (*megal-*), large); the appearance of a person suffering from it is characteristic. The nose and lower jaw, especially the latter, are abnormally large and prominent, and the forehead unusually massive (beetling) where it ordinarily forms a slight eminence above the eye sockets. The skin of the face is thick and coarse. There may be overgrowth of hair upon the chest; in women hair may appear upon the face. There are often signs of overproduction of other hormones of the anterior lobe of the pituitary—e.g., hyperthyroidism (thyrotrophic hormone), signs of overstimulation of the sex functions (gonadotrophic hormones), or hyperglycemia, glucosuria, and other diabetic manifestations (diabetogenic principle). The disease is gradually progressive (see Fig. 10.35). In most instances a pituitary tumor composed of acidophil cells is found after death.

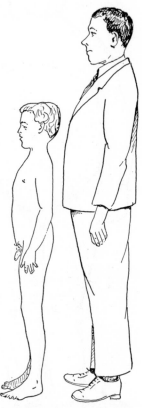

Fig. 10.36   Lorain type of pituitary dwarf, age 21 years. Man on the right 5 feet 7 inches. (Drawn from a photograph after Lisser.)

Dwarfs—hypopituitarism. Deficiency of the anterior lobe secretion in childhood produces dwarfism. There are two main types of pituitary dwarf. In one type, the diminutive body is of normal proportions, or rather, shows the proportions of the normal young child, the head being large, relatively, to the rest of the body (see Fig. 10.36). These subjects may or may not show failure of sexual development. This variety of dwarf is usually intelligent, and not unattractive in appearance; it is referred to as the *Lorain type*. The midget of the circus belongs to this group.

In the second type of pituitary dwarf, the chief features, other than the stunting itself, are obesity and arrested sexual development. Children affected by this pituitary disorder are often subnormal mentally, usually lethargic or somnolent, and have large appetites, especially for sweets. The fat boy of *Pickwick Papers* was undoubtedly an example of this disorder. The condition is called *dystrophia adiposogenitalis* or *Fröhlich's type* of dwarfism. Diabetes insipidus often accompanies this condition. It is thought to be due to destructive disease involving the neurohypophysis or the base of the brain in the region of the origin of the pituitary stalk (hypothalamic region), together with deficiency of the growth hormone of the anterior lobe (see Fig. 10.37).

Essentially the same disorder occurs in adolescents or adults but,

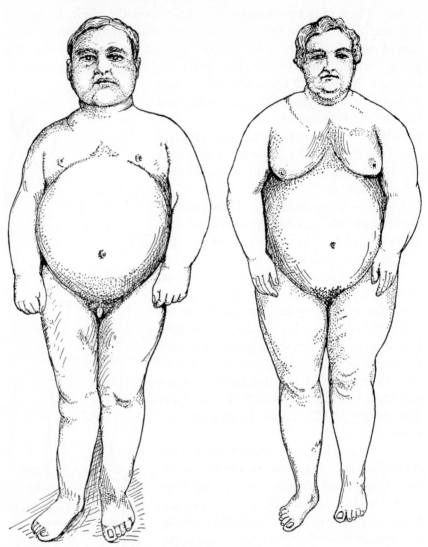

Fig. 10.37   Frölich's type of dwarfism (juvenile form of dystrophia adiposogenitalis. (From a photograph
after Cushing.)

Fig. 10.38   Dystrophia adiposogenitalis in a woman. (Drawn from a
photograph.)

of course, dwarfing is absent. The obesity is often extreme; the sex functions are suppressed. When it occurs in the male, the fat has a feminine distribution—that is, over the hips, thighs, and chest; the skin is smooth and soft; the hair is scarce or absent from the face and body, but fine and plentiful on the head; such persons tend toward effeminacy in temperament and disposition (see Figs. 10.38 and 10.39).

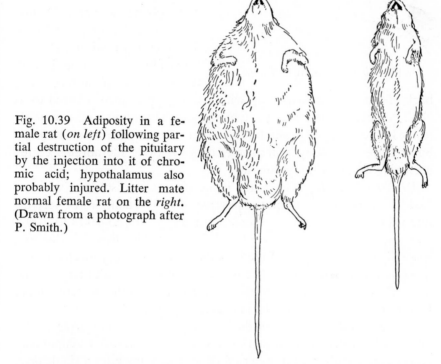

Fig. 10.39   Adiposity in a female rat (*on left*) following partial destruction of the pituitary by the injection into it of chromic acid; hypothalamus also probably injured. Litter mate normal female rat on the *right*. (Drawn from a photograph after P. Smith.)

Pituitary cachexia or Simmond's disease. This is a rare but very grave disease of the pituitary, more commonly affecting women. It is due to atrophy of the anterior lobe, occurring in early or middle adult life. The manifestations of the condition are those of a premature senility. For example, a young woman giving every appearance of healthy youth may within 5 years or so show all those features which one ordinarily associates with old age. The skin becomes dry, sallow, and wrinkled, the hair gray and sparse, the body emaciated, and the sexual organs atrophic; menstruation ceases. The bones are frail and appear to diminish gradually in size. Hypoglycemia (due to deficiency of glycotropic principle) often occurs. Mental changes ultimately supervene. In a large proportion of cases, the changes in the pituitary which lead to this grave condition follow pregnancy.

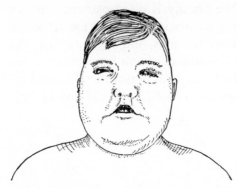

Fig. 10.40   Cushing's disease.

Cushing's disease or syndrome. Hypersecretion of the adrenocorticotrophic hormone of the anterior lobe of the pituitary causes a state first described by Dr. Harvey Cushing of Boston. It is marked by obesity involving the face and trunk, but not, as a rule, the limbs. The face is round and the features almost obscured by fat, the so-called "moon face." The back of the neck is heaped up with fat, an appearance referred to as "buffalo neck." There may be hypertension. This disease may not only result indirectly from a pituitary disorder affecting the adrenal cortex, but may be caused by hypertrophy or a tumor of the adrenal cortex occurring as the primary disease.

Diabetes insipidus. This is the name given to a disorder characterized by excessive thirst and the passage of large quantities of very dilute urine. The urine has a specific gravity of around 1001 to 1002, and may have a daily volume of over 20 liters. The disease is due to a lesion involving any part of the hypothalamico-pituitary mechanism—namely, the hypothalamus, the posterior lobe of the pituitary, or the nerve fibers descending from the hypothalamus to the posterior lobe. Failure of the secretion of the antidiuretic principle of the neural lobe is quite evidently the cause of the excessive production of urine (polyuria). Administration of posterior lobe extract (pituitrin) temporarily relieves the condition. For a period of several hours after a single dose has been given by hypodermic injection or sprayed into the nostrils, the urine is reduced in volume and much less dilute (see also Chap. 7).

The Sex Glands or Gonads

The sex glands or gonads of the female are called the *ovaries,* those of the male, the *testes* (see Chap. 14). The gonads are also referred to as the *primary organs of sex*. The uterus, Fallopian tubes, and vagina of the female and the epididymis, seminal vesicles, prostate, and penis of the male are called the *accessory organs of sex*. Those changes which make their appearance at the time of sexual maturity (puberty), and which in many species distinguish at a glance the male from the female, are known as the *secondary sex characters*. In the human subject these include the growth of hair upon the pubis and in the axillae of both sexes, the bass voice and beard of men, and the development of the breasts of women. The large comb, wattles, spurs, and tail feathers of the domestic cock (rooster) and the antlers of the stag are other examples of secondary sex characters.

Excision of the sex glands, whether of the male or female, is called castration. Excision of the female gonads is also termed *ovariectomy,* or *spaying.* The effects of castration upon the male have been known from ancient times. When this operation is performed upon the male chicken (cockerel), the secondary sex characters do not appear; sex instinct is suppressed. The body weight of the castrated birds, which are known as *capons,* is greater, however, than that of uncastrated males of the same age. Castration of young stags prevents the development of the antlers. In boys who have been castrated before the age of puberty (a practice even of modern times, in certain countries), the larynx does not develop, and the voice remains high pitched, the accessory organs of sex do not mature, and the secondary sex characters fail to appear. The operation exerts an effect upon fat deposition, the subjects tending toward obesity. The proportions of the skeleton are also altered, the bones of the lower limbs tending to be abnormally long in relation to the trunk. That the gonads are endocrine organs is shown by the fact that the effects of castration in animals can be prevented by grafting tissue of the excised gland into some other part of the body. Any influence which the transplanted tissue can then exert upon other tissues must, obviously, be solely through the blood stream.

The sexual phenomena of the mature female. The organs of sex in both the male and the female animal mature at a definite age which varies in different species. At this time, which is called *puberty,* the reproductive functions commence. Sex desire is aroused and mating occurs. The *reproductive period* extends throughout the greater part of the animal's life; it ends with atrophic changes in the sex organs and the gradual suppression of sexual activity. In the human species, puberty occurs at from 13 to 15 years of age, usually being a little earlier in girls than in boys. The secondary sex characters already described now make their appearance.

In the majority of animal species, the female will receive the male only at a certain period or periods of the year. These so-called *mating seasons* are characterized by certain sexual phenomena which are generally referred to by animal breeders as "heat" and by physiologists as *estrus* (also spelled *oestrus*). Estrus, and the sex phases immediately preceding and following it, are together referred to as the *estrus cycle.*

The phase preceding estrus is called *proestrus;* that following it *postestrus.* The changes during proestrus consist of swelling and increased vascularity of the vulva and vagina. The uterus becomes enlarged and its glands hypertrophy. In some animals, at this time, bleeding occurs from the uterus and appears externally. The changes of proestrus are preparatory in nature, the female organs being brought into a condition suitable for the reception of the male and the fertilization of the ovum. The Graafian follicles in the ovary (p. 648) are undergoing maturation. Estrus itself is the period during which ovulation occurs and the female will mate. The changes occurring during postestrus are anticipatory to the implantation of the fertilized ovum in the uterus.

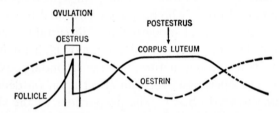

Fig. 10.41   Diagram of the estrus cycle. (Modified after Corner.)

The uterine mucosa hypertrophies and its glands show increased secretory activity. During postestrus the corpus luteum is developing. The uterine changes in postestrus resemble those taking place during pregnancy which, indeed, are an extension or continuation of the former.

In a number of animals the postestrus preparation of the uterus for the implantation of the fertilized ovum—i.e., for pregnancy—is a very prominent feature of the estrus cycle. Postestrus in such species is therefore called *pseudopregnancy.* If fertilization of the ovum by a sperm cell occurs, the uterine changes of postestrus merge into those of pregnancy. If fertilization does not result, the uterus returns to its resting state and all sexual activity subsides until the commencement (proestrus) of the next estrus cycle.

Some animals, such as the dog, are called *monestrous,* since a single estrus cycle occurs in each mating season. The term *anestrus* is applied to the quiescent periods intervening between the mating seasons. In other species, such as the cow, mouse, and rat, two or more estrus cycles occur during each mating season; such animals are termed *polyestrous.* The interval elapsing between any two estrus cycles is then termed *diestrus* and the period between mating seasons, as in the case of monestrous animals, is called anestrus.

The phases of the estrus cycle in a monestrous animal are shown in the following scheme and in Figure 10.41.

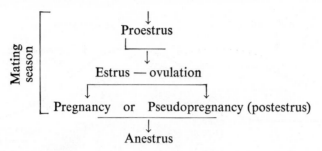

The menstrual cycle. The rhythmical series of changes in the sex organs, which occurs about every 28 days throughout the reproductive life of women, is analogous to the estrus cycle of lower animals. It is called the *menstrual cycle* (L. *mens,* month). In one phase of the menstrual cycle, uterine bleeding occurs. This phase is referred to as *menstruation* or the *menstrual period;* it has a duration of from 3 to 5 days. Ovulation occurs about midway between the menstrual periods—that is, somewhere between the thirteenth and seventeenth days following the commencement of the bleeding (see Fig. 10.42).

Though, as just mentioned, the menstrual cycle corresponds to the estrus cycle, the two differ in this respect: bleeding, which is a prominent feature of the former, is absent or inconspicuous in the latter. It is not possible to say to what phase of the estrus cycle (whether to proestrus or postestrus) menstruation itself corresponds. Since bleeding in certain species occurs in proestrus, it has been assumed by some that such bleeding is analogous to menstruation; others have thought that menstruation corresponds to the end of postestrus—that is, to the breakdown of the uterine mucosa built up during postestrus. There are objections to both these views.

Conspicuous histological changes occur in the uterine mucous membrane (endometrium) during the menstrual cycle. Though these changes have been very minutely described and divided into stages, it will suffice to give a brief outline here. The endometrium becomes thicker and more vascular, the small arteries become tortuous and coiled in a corkscrewlike fashion; the surface epithelium hypertrophies. The glands of the mucous membrane elongate and show secretory activity. The hypertrophy of the epithelium and the vascular changes are due to the action of estradiol (*follicular phase* of the cycle); the somewhat later glandular changes are caused by progestin (*luteal phase*). Should fertilization and implantation of the ovum (p. 669) occur, the stimulating effects of the ovarian hormones become more pronounced, and merge with those of the pregnant state. If, on the other

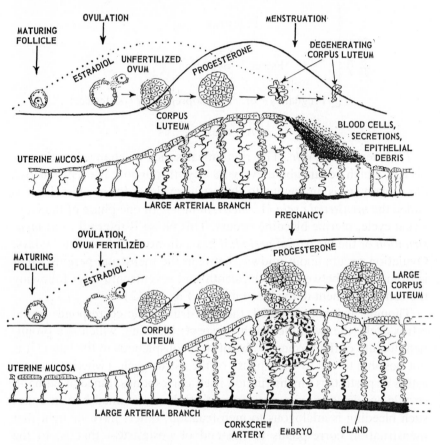

Fig. 10.42   Diagram of the menstrual cycle. Note the thickening of the mucosa, the increasing tortuosity of the vessels and glands as progestin production increases. Breakdown of the mucosa with menstrual bleeding occurs as the corpus luteum degenerates or retrogresses.

hand, the ovum is not impregnated by a male sex cell (spermatozoon, Chap. 14), it degenerates as does the corpus luteum. The hypertrophied endometrium cannot be sustained in the absence of the latter; its epithelium is shed, and bleeding (menstruation) then occurs. Menstruation, therefore, is the sign that a fertilized ovum has not become implanted in the uterine mucous membrane, in other words, the pregnancy has not commenced. After from 3 to 5 days of menstrual bleeding, repair processes restore the surface epithelium, the vascular and glandular activities of the endometrium subside, and the uterus returns to the resting condition; the menstrual cycle has been completed.

The first menstrual cycle commences at puberty. Toward the end of the reproductive period, the cycles become irregular and finally cease, usually between 45 to 50 years of age; the cessation of the menstrual cycles at this time is called the *menopause*. It is accom-

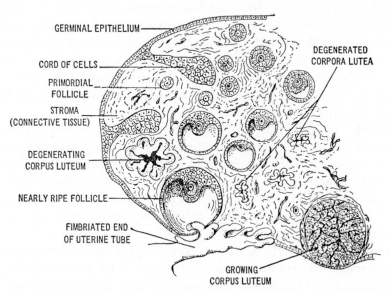

GERMINAL EPITHELIUM

CORD OF CELLS

PRIMORDIAL FOLLICLE

STROMA (CONNECTIVE TISSUE)

DEGENERATING CORPUS LUTEUM

NEARLY RIPE FOLLICLE

FIMBRIATED END OF UTERINE TUBE

DEGENERATED CORPORA LUTEA

GROWING CORPUS LUTEUM

Fig. 10.43   Section of a portion of an ovary showing Graafian follicles in various stages of development.

panied by atrophic changes in the ovaries and the accessory organs of reproduction. Psychic phenomena, depression, or irritability are common during this period. Instability of the vasomotor system, causing sudden flushing of the face, and a sensation of warmth—*hot flushes*—are of frequent occurrence.

Ovarian hormones. The phenomena of the estrus and menstrual cycles, described in the preceding section, are dependent upon hormones produced in the ovary. The Graafian follicles of the ovary increase in size during proestrus (or, in the human subject, in the phase of the menstrual cycle immediately following menstruation) and become filled with fluid; the ova enlarge and approach maturity. A hormone called *estradiol* or the *follicular hormone* [6] is produced at this

[6] Other substances closely similar chemically and possessing the physiological activity of the follicular hormone have been obtained from the ovaries, as well as from female urine and other body fluids and tissues. *Estrone* (also known as *thee-*

time by the cells lining the follicles. When a follicle reaches maturity, it ruptures and discharges the ovum. This event, called *ovulation,* occurs in animals during estrus, and in women midway between the menstrual periods—that is, about 18 days after menstruation. The cells lining the ruptured follicle then multiply and form a mass or body called the *corpus luteum (yellow body),* for the cells composing it contain a yellow, fatty material known as *lutein.* The corpus luteum replaces the small blood clot which filled the follicle immediately after its rupture and the discharge of the ovum. The corpus luteum is virtually a small temporary ductless gland (see Figs. 10.42 and 10.43), for it produces an internal secretion—the *hormone of the corpus luteum.* This is more commonly referred to as *progestin* or *progesterone.* The latter is a chemical term and is used more especially when referring to the hormone in pure crystalline form.

Estradiol is responsible for the changes in the accessory organs of reproduction during proestrus and estrus, for the psychic phenomena of estrus, and for the development of the secondary sex characters (p. 444) of the mature female. It is, therefore, sometimes called the female sex hormone, and corresponds to the male hormone elaborated by the testes (p. 451). As already mentioned, removal of the ovaries of a young female animal prevents it from becoming sexually mature. The accessory organs fail to develop, estrus does not occur, the secondary sex characters do not appear, and the sex instinct is never manifested. Injections of the female sex hormone into such an animal correct all these effects of ovariectomy. On the other hand, young immature animals treated with estradiol show precocious sexual development. The role played by estradiol in pregnancy and parturition is described in Chapter 14.

The *hormone of the corpus luteum—progestin* or *progesterone*— prepares the uterus for the reception of the fertilized ovum. It is responsible for the uterine changes characteristic of postestrus or pseudopregnancy, and for the development of the placenta—the organ which enables the embryo to receive nourishment from the mother during pregnancy (p. 670). For example, if a pregnant rabbit is castrated

---

lin), which differs from estradiol in chemical structure to a minor extent, was formerly thought to be the naturally occurring hormone produced by the maturing Graafian follicle. Estradiol has been synthesized and has also been isolated in crystalline form from the urine of pregnant women.

Estrin is an earlier term given to the follicular hormone before its chemical structure was fully known. It is still in use as a physiological term but carries no precise chemical meaning. *Estrogen* is another name with a purely physiological connotation; it is applied to any agent, whether of biological or other origin, which is capable of inducing estrus and often other effects of the follicular hormone.

(ovariectomized) early in pregnancy or if the corpora lutea are excised, the embryo dies and is expelled from the uterus (*abortion*). The hormone of the corpus luteum can be prepared most conveniently from hog's ovaries. This preparation, when injected into ovariectomized animals after they have become pregnant, permits pregnancy to continue to full term. Normally, if fertilization of the ovum occurs, the corpus luteum continues to increase in size until the later months

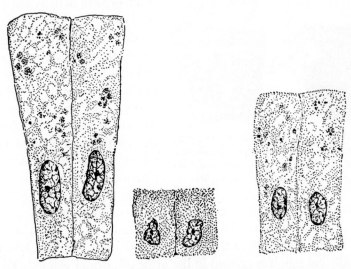

Fig. 10.44   Cells of seminal vesicles of rat. *Left,* of normal animal; *middle,* 3 weeks after castration; *right,* of castrated animal after daily injections of male hormone.

of pregnancy, its hormone exerting a constant influence upon the growth and functional integrity of the placenta. On the other hand, if the ovum remains unfertilized, the life of the corpus luteum is short. After exerting its hormonal influence for a time and causing the uterine changes characteristic of pseudopregnancy, it undergoes degeneration. In the human subject, changes in the uterine mucosa occur after ovulation analogous to those of pseudopregnancy but, again, failure of the ovum to become fertilized is followed by degeneration of the corpus luteum. The uterine mucosa then reverts to its resting state; it is at this time that menstruation occurs (see Figs. 10.41 and 10.42).

Progestin also brings the mammary glands to full maturity during pregnancy, induces multiplication of the uterine muscle fibers, and inhibits contractions of the uterus (see Chap. 14).

The male hormone—testosterone. In 1929 McGee obtained the male hormone in crude form by the extraction of bull's testes with acetone.

This preparation was shown to cause the growth of the comb and wattles of the castrated cockerel (capon) and to bring about the normal development of the accessory organs (penis, seminal vesicles, and prostate) of castrated male rats (Figs. 10.44 and 10.45). In immature rats treated with the extract, the accessory sex organs develop and sexual maturity is reached prematurely. The extract also stimulates the comb growth in hens and inhibits ovulation—masculinizing effect.

Fig. 10.45   Castrated cockerel (capon) on *left;* note the undeveloped comb and wattles. Capon after receiving daily injections of male hormone, on *right.*

More recently, the hormone has been obtained in crystalline form from testicular tissue. This purified material is called *testosterone,* and has the empirical formula $C_{19}H_{30}O_2$. The hormone has also been obtained in crystalline form from male urine. Chemically, this latter material differs slightly from testosterone and has been designated *androsterone;* its activity is also much less (one seventh to one tenth) than that of testosterone. The male hormone does not appear in the urine of boys until after the tenth year, but oddly enough it is present in the urine of normal women. The male hormone belongs, with the ovarian hormones, to the class of substances known as steroids (p. 372). Both testosterone and androsterone have been synthesized in the laboratory from cholesterol. This suggests the possibility that the male hormone is formed in the body from this substance, which is a constituent of nearly all animal tissues.

Cells in the interstitial tissue of the testes—the so-called *cells of Leydig*—are generally believed to manufacture the male hormone. That these cells and not the spermatogenic cells (p. 656) are responsible seems evident from the fact that castration effects do not follow irradiation of the testes with x-rays which destroys the spermatogenic cells but leaves the cells of Leydig unaffected.

The relation of the anterior lobe of the pituitary to the sexual functions—gonadotrophic hormones. The anterior lobe of either the male or female pituitary contains two hormones which act upon the gonads. In the female, one of these *gonadotrophic hormones* stimulates the growth and maturation of the Graafian follicles in the ovary. Thus indirectly this hormone causes the production of the follicular hormone. It is called the *follicle-stimulating hormone* (FSH) of the anterior pituitary. The other gonadotrophic hormone of the pituitary acts upon the second phase of the ovarian cycle—i.e., it stimulates the growth of the corpus luteum. This gonadotrophic hormone is therefore known as the *luteinizing hormone* (LH), or as the *lutein-stimulating hor-*

A

Fig. 10.46   A, showing the effect of hypophysectomy on the uterus of rabbits; of normal animal *on left;* of hypophysectomized animal *on right.* B, showing the effect of an extract of the anterior lobe of the hypophysis upon the ovary, untreated *on left;* after a period of daily injections *on right.*   **B**

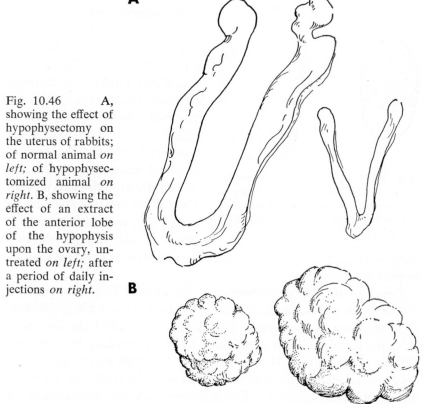

mone (LSH).[7] It therefore, through its stimulating effect upon progestin formation, indirectly causes the changes in the uterine mucosa characteristic of pseudopregnancy and of the corresponding phase of the menstrual cycle, or, if pregnancy ensues, of the development of the placenta (cf. p. 670). Both gonadotrophic hormones, whether derived from female or male pituitaries, produce analogous effects upon the testes. The follicle-stimulating hormone acts upon the elements of the testes corresponding to the lining cells of the Graafian follicles—

[7] The growth of the corpus luteum after it has been formed and its maintenance in a functioning state depends, not upon the lutein-stimulating hormone but upon another pituitary hormone. This has been given the name of the *luteotrophic hormone.* It now appears, however, that it is simply prolactin (p. 454).

namely, the spermatogenic cells. The luteinizing hormone stimulates the interstitial cells of Leydig (Chap. 65). On this account it is also known as the *interstitial-cell-stimulating hormone,* abbreviated ICSH.

Removal of the pituitary is followed by atrophy of the gonads and, secondarily, of the accessory sex organs (Figs. 10.45, 10.46, and 10.47). Transplantation of tissue of the anterior lobe or injections of anterior lobe extracts prevent these otherwise inevitable results of hypophysectomy. The anterior lobe of the pituitary is therefore ultimately responsible for the sexual development of the male or female animal. The phenomena of puberty—namely, the development and maturation of the gonads and, through the intermediary of the hormones liberated by the latter, the growth of the accessory organs of sex and the development of the secondary sex characters—are dependent upon the gonadotrophic hormones.

Fig. 10.47   The effect of hypophysectomy on the testis; of hypophysectomized rat *on left;* of normal rat *on right.* (Drawn from photographs after Van Dyke.)

Prolactin, the lactogenic hormone. The anterior lobe of the pituitary also liberates a principle which stimulates milk secretion in the mother, after the birth of the young. This hormone is called the *lactogenic principle* or *prolactin.* It is obtained from the pituitary by extraction with an acid solution. If the pituitary is removed late in pregnancy, only a small quantity of milk is secreted after the young are born, and the secretion soon dries up. This hormone evidently also exerts an influence upon the maternal instinct, for hypophysectomized animals do not care for their young like normal mothers. Furthermore, injections of prolactin arouse the maternal instinct in young virgin rats; they commence to build a nest from straw, wool, or other soft material which they can gather.

Prolactin is also responsible for the growth of the corpus luteum during pregnancy (see footnote, p. 453).

The liberation of prolactin from the hypophysis and its stimulating action on the secretion of milk coincide so closely with the termination of pregnancy that curiosity must naturally be aroused concerning the mechanism underlying such accurate timing.[8] Many details of the

[8] Some secretion of milk into the follicles of the mammary gland occurs before

highly complex mechanism are obscure, but it appears from the great volume of experimental work carried out within recent years that the *immediate* or *direct* cause the flow of milk from the breasts is hormonal rather than neural in nature. There is abundant evidence that prolactin is not concerned alone, but that the galactogogue principle (p. 437), estradiol, and progestin, a hormone of the adrenal cortex,

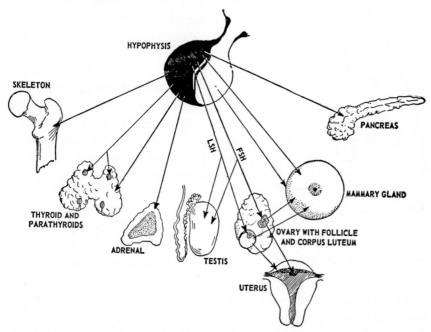

Fig. 10.48   Diagram showing the influence of the hormones of the hypophysis upon endocrine and other structures; anterior lobe, black; posterior lobe, white.

and even the thyroid hormone also play their parts. However, the liberation of prolactin from the hypophysis is initiated by nervous impulses. The latter set up in the nipple by the act of suckling and conveyed to the pituitary body (through autonomic nerves) constitute probably the most important single nervous factor in inducing the production and liberation of the lactogenic hormone. Suckling also causes the passage of the galactogogue principle into the circulation. But that there are other nervous influences affecting milk secretion can be attested to by any dairyman. Contentment of milking cows, and even music in the stable, facilitates the "letting down" of the milk, an effect which is be-

the end of pregnancy, but as a rule, it is not until the uterus has been emptied that milk appears externally. This milk secreted before the birth of the offspring and retained by the gland is yellow in color and creamy in consistency; it is known as *colostrum.*

lieved to be due, at least in part, to the release of the galactogogue principle and the resulting stimulation of the smooth muscle in the walls of the milk follicles and ducts. During pregnancy progestin is in high concentration in the blood and, according to some investigators, this depresses prolactin production but, when toward the end of pregnancy a rather abrupt reduction in the blood content of this hormone occurs, prolactin liberation follows automatically.[9]

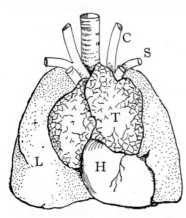

Fig. 10.49 Showing the relation of the thymus to the thoracic viscera and great vessels. C, common carotid artery; H, heart; L, lung; S, subclavian artery; T, thymus.

The actions of the various hormones of the anterior lobe of the pituitary body are summarized in Figure 10.48.

The hormones of the placenta. The placenta contains two hormones. One of these is estradiol, the other, called by Collip the *anterior pituitarylike* (APL) principle, acts upon the ovary, stimulating the growth of the corpus luteum. It also stimulates, though to a slight extent, the maturation of the Graafian follicles. The estradiol found in the placenta is apparently manufactured by this organ, and does not simply represent a store of the hormone produced by the ovary. This conclusion is justified by the observation that in pregnancy large quantities of the follicular hormone continue to appear in the urine, though the ovaries have been removed. APL also appears in the urine of pregnant women. This fact is the basis for a well-known test for pregnancy. Two German workers, Aschheim and Zondek, found that the injection of a small quantity of urine of a pregnant woman into a young (sexually immature) mouse caused within 100 hour the following effects:

(a) The onset of estrus

(b) Small hemorrhages into some of the Graafian follicles

(c) The formation of corpora lutea

[9] In certain abnormal states of the hypophysis associated with overactivity of the anterior lobe, such as acromegaly, milk may be secreted in the absence of pregnancy, or even in males. This is due presumably to the production and liberation of prolactin. Also the mammary glands of newborn infants of either sex sometimes secrete milk. This was long known as "witch's milk" and is now attributed to prolactin in the infant's circulation derived from the blood of the mother before birth.

The action of prolactin upon the crop glands of doves and pigeons is of especial interest. These glands secrete a creamy material with which the birds feed their young. The crop glands of virgin pigeons enlarge and secrete an abundance of crop milk when injected with a potent preparation of the lactogenic hormone.

The Aschheim-Zondek test for pregnancy is almost infallible; its error is only about 1 percent. The close resemblance between the effects of the urine of pregnancy and those of the gonadotrophic principles of the pituitary, led Aschheim and Zondek to the conclusion that

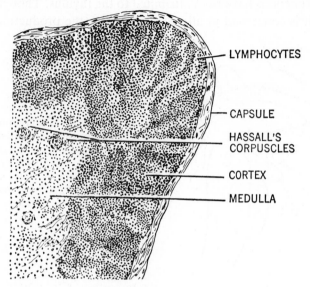

Fig. 10.50   Microscopical section of a follicle of the thymus.

during pregnancy the pituitary principles were produced in excess and excreted in the urine. It is now generally agreed, however, that the characteristic effects of the urine of pregnant women are due to a single substance, and that it is *not* derived from the pituitary, but is the anterior pituitarylike principle (APL) of the placenta.

The Thymus

The thymus lies behind the upper part of the breast bone and extends upward for a short distance into the neck. Below, it lies in relation to the base of the heart and the great vessels (Fig. 10.49). It is of relatively large size in the infant, but commences to shrink at about the age of puberty and, by adult life, it is reduced to little more than a vestigial structure. In the infant, it is soft and pink. When sectioned, it is seen to be made up of a large number of lymph follicles, in each of which an outer zone or *cortex* and an inner zone or *medulla* can be distinguished (Fig. 10.50). The cortex is composed of masses of lymphocytes supported by a meshwork of slender branching cells. The medulla also contains lymphocytes but in much smaller members, and the meshwork is coarser. It also contains peculiar bodies called *Hassall's corpuscles,* formed of epitheliallike cells arranged concentrically around a mass of granular cells.

Many functions have been attributed to the thymus. Though proof is lacking, it is concerned in all probability with the production of lym-

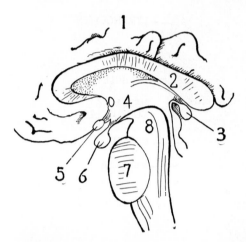

Fig. 10.51   Diagram to show position of the pineal gland. 1, cerebral hemisphere; 2, corpus callosum; 3, pineal; 4, third ventricle of the brain; 5, optic chiasma; 6, pituitary; 7, pons; 8, midbrain.

phocytes. The structure of the cortical portion of its follicles suggests such a function. Several endocrine functions at one time or another have been attributed to it, but most of the theories which have been advanced are based more upon conjecture than upon fact.

The Pineal Body

The pineal is a small body lying deep in the brain under the shelter of the posterior extremity of the corpus callosum (p. 530, see also Fig. 10.51). Though its structure suggests the possibility that it serves some endocrine function there is no reliable evidence that such is the case.

CHAPTER 11

The Physiology of Nerve and Muscle

The structure of the nerve fiber. A nerve fiber is the elongated extension of a nerve cell whose body is situated in the central nervous system (brain or spinal cord), or in an outlying ganglion (of the sympathetic gangliated cord or of a posterior spinal nerve root).(See also Chap. 12). Some nerve fibers transmit messages (e.g., of touch, pain, sound, light, etc.) from the periphery to conscious centers and give rise to the respective sensations. They are, therefore, *sensory* in function. Others carry messages to the muscles, causing them to contract; these are therefore called *motor* nerve fibers. Certain nerves are composed entirely of sensory fibers; some contain only motor fibers; others, again, contain both types of fiber, and are called *mixed* nerves (see also Fig. 12.2, p. 508). The peripheral nerves—that is, the nerve trunks distributed to the various parts of the body—are constituted of nerve fibers, often in great numbers, bound together into a variable number of bundles. Each bundle is surrounded by a connective tissue sheath called the *perineurium*. The individual fibers are enveloped in turn and separated, each from its neighbor, by a thin covering of connective tissue known as the *endoneurium*. Finally, the entire nerve trunk is enclosed and separated from other structures by a thick connective tissue sheath called the *epineurium* (see Figs. 11.1 and 11.2).

The message transmitted by the nerve fiber is called the *nerve impulse;* its nature will engage our attention later.

The nerve fiber, then, whether in a peripheral nerve or in the central nervous system itself, is the conducting unit of the nervous system, and may be compared to a single wire in an electric cable or in the central exchange of a telephone system. Nerves which transmit impulses from the periphery to the nerve centers are called *afferent;* those which transmit impulses in the opposite direction are called *efferent.* Now, of course, all sensory nerve fibers are afferent, but not all afferent fibers are sensory, for some transmit impulses which make no impression upon consciousness—they arouse no sensation. Similarly, all motor fibers are efferent, but not all efferent fibers are motor, since certain

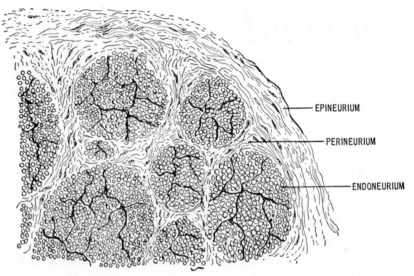

EPINEURIUM

PERINEURIUM

ENDONEURIUM

Fig. 11.1   Cross section of a portion of a peripheral nerve. The small circles represent the nerve fibers.

fibers of the autonomic nervous system terminating in glands are secretory in function.

Each fiber entering into the composition of the motor and sensory nerves consists of a delicate filament of protoplasm—the *axis cylinder* —ensheathed by a layer of fatty material called *myelin.*

Nerve fibers which possess a sheath of this fatlike substance, and they constitute the great majority comprising the tracts in the central nervous system and in the peripheral nerves, are called *myelinated* or *medullated* fibers. Fibers which have no myelin sheath, such as the postganglionic fibers of the autonomic nervous system, are called *amyelinated* or *nonmedullated* fibers.

The layer of myelin enveloping the axis cylinder—*the myelin sheath*—is enclosed, in turn, by a very thin, transparent nucleated membrane known as the *neurilemma* or *sheath of Schwann.* The myelin sheath is interrupted at regular intervals; at these points the neu-

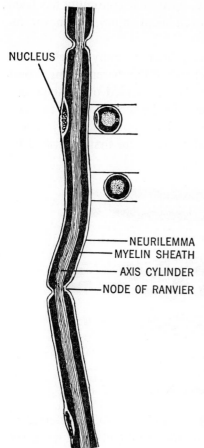

NUCLEUS

NEURILEMMA
MYELIN SHEATH
AXIS CYLINDER
NODE OF RANVIER

Fig. 11.2 Drawing to show the structure of a nerve fiber, in longitudinal section and in cross section at two levels.

rilemma dips sharply toward, and comes almost into contact with, the axis cylinder. These interruptions give the impression of a series of equally spaced constrictions along the nerve fiber; they are called the *nodes of Ranvier*. The axis cylinder contains a number of fine thread-like strands known as *neurofibrils* which run throughout its length (see also p. 506). The endoneurium, mentioned on page 459, encloses the nerve fiber, lying immediately outside the neurilemma.

The myelin sheath is believed by some physiologists to serve as insulation and thus to prevent the passage, crosswise, of the impulses from fiber to fiber. Others consider that it is chiefly nutritive in function, and that its metabolic processes are closely related to those of the axis cylinder. There is no conclusive evidence to support either of these ideas.

The myelinization of nerve fibers is a progressive process and does not occur simultaneously in the various types of nerve. It is not complete at birth; its completion appears to coincide with the establishment of function. The tracts of the spinal cord supplying voluntary nerve fibers to the lower limbs, for example, are not fully myelinated in infants until about the second year, or about the time that the child has learned to walk. The association tracts of the brain are myelinated still later, whereas myelination of the sensory tracts of the cord occurs early (fourth month) in fetal life.

Nuclei are to be seen in the neurilemma at fairly regular intervals, one to each section of nerve between the nodes of Ranvier. The sheath of Schwann is absent from the fibers of the central nervous system and from the fibers of the optic nerve. Its presence is absolutely essential for the regeneration of an interrupted nerve fiber (p. 464); fibers in the situations just mentioned, therefore, once their continuity has been destroyed as a result of disease or mechanical injury, are never regenerated.

Degeneration of nerve. Since the nerve fiber is simply the elongated process of a nerve cell, its nutrition depends upon its remaining a part of the cell. When, therefore, a nerve fiber is divided or crushed, degenerative changes begin almost at once in the section distal to (i.e., on the side away from the body of the cell) the point of injury. These changes, as they occur in a peripheral nerve, were first described by

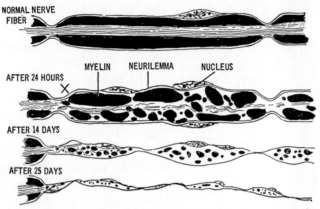

Fig. 11.3   Degeneration of nerve. Nerve injured at X.

Waller, a physiologist of the last century, and are usually referred to as *Wallerian degeneration.* The first alteration in the fibers of the nerve appears within 24 hours after the injury. The neurofibrils in the axis cylinder become wavy or tortuous, and then break up into sections. Next, the myelin sheath swells and droplets of myelin appear (Fig. 11.3). The myelin itself undergoes decomposition into its constituents —fatty acids, etc. Finally, usually within two or three weeks following the injury, the debris resulting from the degenerative process is cleared away, nothing remaining of the nerve fiber but an empty tube—the neurilemma which remains intact. The nerve fiber on the proximal side of the point of division (i.e., on the side toward the nerve cell) also degenerates as far as the first node of Ranvier, and even the body of the cell itself may show degenerative changes (*retrograde degeneration*), consisting of the disappearance of the Nissl bodies (p. 507) and shrinkage of the nucleus.

The degenerative changes just described are readily detected by treating the tissue with a suitable stain and examining thin sections of it beneath the microscope. Most of the knowledge which we possess of the origin and course of the various fiber tracts in the brain and cord (Chap. 12) has been gained from experiments upon animals in which a lesion is made in some or other region and the degenerated fibers traced microscopically through successive levels of the nervous system, or from the examination of nervous tissue of subjects who have died of certain nervous diseases which have caused the degeneration of nerve fibers. The location of the degenerative changes following experimental injury to fibers in one or other part of the brain or cord, or resulting from disease, indicates the direction from which the affected fibers originated. For example, if after section of a fiber tract in the cord degeneration occurs above the point of section, the cell bodies of the sectioned fibers must be situated below. Also, by destroying a group of nerve cell bodies in one or other situation and examining tissue taken from different parts of the nervous system for degenerative changes, the course taken by the fibers of the injured cells can be traced (see also Fig. 12.16, p. 525).

Degeneration of the peripheral nerves may result from causes other than mechanical injury. Peripheral nerve degeneration is seen in poisoning by certain chemicals (e.g., lead, arsenic, alcohol), in vitamin deficiency (A and B_1), and in certain nervous diseases (e.g., anterior poliomyelitis which causes the destruction of nerve cells in the spinal cord). It is most important in such conditions, or following mechanical injury to a nerve trunk, to have some means of detecting the presence of degeneration, and of determining the extent to which the degenerative process has progressed. Such information is afforded by testing the affected nerve or nerves with an electric current. The current is applied to the skin overlying the motor nerve trunk. When the nerve is completely degenerated, it fails to respond (as shown by the absence of a contraction of the muscle) to either the faradic (interrupted) or to the galvanic current. When the current is applied directly over the muscle, a sluggish response is obtained with the galvanic current, but none with the faradic. These abnormal responses of the nerve and muscle to electrical stimulation constitute the *reaction of degeneration.*

Nerve regeneration. Provided that the two ends of a divided nerve are not too widely separated, the continuity of most nerves ultimately becomes restored—the nerve is said to have undergone regeneration. The neurofibrils of the proximal section of the nerve fiber (i.e., the part extending from the cell body to the point of section) grow distally and, entering the empty neurilemmal tube of the degenerated fiber, gradually extend throughout its entire length (Fig. 11.4). The nuclei of the neurilemma multiply. The neurofibrils later become embedded in a ground substance or matrix of protoplasm. Thus, a new axis cylinder is formed. The rate of growth of the axis cylinder varies in different types of nerve from 0.25 to 2.5 mm per day. A myelin sheath is formed later, and finally the function of the nerve may be completely restored. The sprouting neurofibrils sometimes cross a gap of several millimeters separating the two segments of the nerve—a truly remarkable phenomenon. The force or influence which directs or attracts them into their proper channels is unknown. A neurilemma is abso-

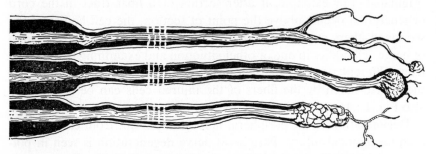

Fig. 11.4   Regeneration of nerve; three types of ending.

lutely necessary for the regeneration process. The fibers of the central nervous system and of the optic and auditory nerves, which do not possess neurilemmal sheaths, are incapable of regeneration after interruption of their continuity, whether this has been caused by disease or mechanical injury.

The regeneration of nerve fibers makes possible the junction by operation of one nerve with another. In facial paralysis, for example, the power to move the muscles of the face can be restored by suturing the proximal end of a sectioned hypoglossal nerve to the distal end of the degenerated facial nerve. The latter nerve is regenerated by the growth of neurofibrils which grow down the empty tube formed by the neurilemma of the degenerated facial nerve. If the operation has been successful and the neurofibrils have reached the facial muscles, the patient, after a period of re-education, can control the movements of the previously paralyzed side of the face.

Nerve cells (i.e., the cell bodies) never regenerate after injury; when destroyed, they are replaced by the nonspecific neuroglia.

The physiological properties of the nerve fiber. *Excitability* and *conductivity* are the outstanding properties of the nerve fiber. Though many living tissues possess these properties, they are developed to the highest degree in nerve. When the nerve fiber is stimulated by means of an *electric shock, mechanically* (as by a pinch), *thermally* (as by the application of a heated glass rod), or *chemically* (as by touching it with a crystal of common salt), a disturbance is set up at the point of stimulation which is called the *local excitatory state*. If the stimulus is sufficiently strong to raise the latter to a certain critical value, a disturbance spreads at high velocity along the nerve. This propagated disturbance or wave of excitation, set up by stimulating the nerve fiber, is called the *nerve impulse*.

When a constant (galvanic) current of moderate strength, such as that derived from an ordinary dry cell, is used as a stimulus, it is found

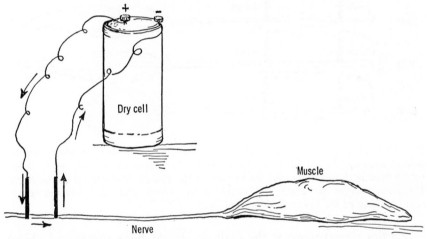

Fig. 11.5   Illustrating stimulation of a nerve by means of a constant current.

that excitation of a nerve, muscle, or other excitable tissue occurs at the instant that the current is closed, and again when the current is opened. Though, of course, the current continues to flow during the intervening period, it does not excite the tissue, provided that its intensity remains unchanged. The closing or making current (make shock) causes excitation of the nerve or muscle at the *cathode*—that is, at the point where the current leaves the tissue. The opening or breaking current (break shock) causes stimulation at the *anode*—that is, where the current enters the tissue (see Fig. 11.5). The stimulus caused by making the current is the stronger of the two, so that, when the current strength is gradually reduced, a point is reached at which a response occurs only with a make shock.

Electrotonus. The passage of a constant current through a nerve causes changes in excitability and conductivity of the nerve fibers.

These effects are generally referred to as *electrotonus*. When the current is "made," both these properties of the nerve are increased in the region of the *cathode;* whereas they are depressed in the region of the *anode.* The changes produced at cathode and anode are called, respectively, *catelectrotonus* and *anelectrotonus.* The effects are reversed when the current is "broken," a momentary enhancement of excitability and conductivity occurring at the anode and depression of these

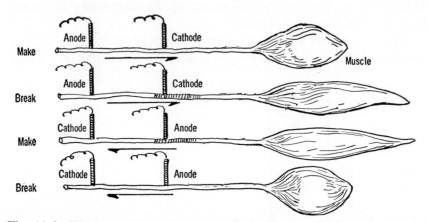

Fig. 11.6 Diagram of a nerve-muscle preparation illustrating electrotonus; arrows indicate the direction of the current—ascending or descending from or to the muscle. Shortening and thickening of the muscle indicate its contraction. Hatched areas on nerve near the muscle in the second and third sketches represent blocking of the nerve as described in the text.

properties supervening at the cathode. It has been mentioned above that, with a moderately strong current, excitation of the nerve, which may be made evident by using a nerve attached to its muscle, causes excitation with both make and break shocks but, upon gradual reduction in the strength of the current, a point is reached when excitation occurs only at the make. If, however, the current is very strong, and the electrodes are so placed upon the nerve that the cathode is nearer to the muscle than is the anode—that is, the current is *descending* in the nerve toward the muscle (see Fig. 11.6)—excitation also occurs only on the "make," because on the "break" the depressed conductivity at the cathode blocks the impulse initiated at the anode. If, on the other hand, the electrodes are reversed—that is, the current is *ascending* in the nerve from the muscle—excitation occurs only on the "break," for the impulse arising at the cathode is blocked by the depressed conduction at the anode occurring on the "make" of the current (see Table 11-1).

Table 11-1

Strength of current	Descending current		Ascending current	
	Make	Break	Make	Break
Very weak................	C	O	C	O
Moderate.................	C	C	C	C
Very strong..............	C	O	O	C

The qualities of a stimulus. The prime factors in excitation of nervous or muscular tissues are *intensity, rate of change,* and *duration* of the stimulus.

1. *Intensity or strength of the stimulus.* An electric shock, which is the most convenient and commonest type of stimulus used in the laboratory, must be of a certain minimal voltage. The electric stimulus whose voltage is just sufficient to excite is said to be of *threshold* or *liminal* strength. A stimulus weaker than this is called *subthreshold* or *subliminal.*

2. *The rate of change in the intensity of a stimulus.* An electric stimulus which is just capable of exciting the nerve when its intensity increases rapidly, may be quite ineffective if it reaches its maximum value more gradually. In order to be effective at the slower rate of change, the strength of the current must be increased. In other words, the threshold of excitation rises as the rate of increase in the current strength diminishes. This relationship between the threshold of excitation of the nerve and the rate of change in intensity of the stimulus is referred to as *accommodation.* Rate of change is a factor of just as great importance in other types of stimulation. We are all familiar with the fact that changes in the environment, whether of temperature, sound, or movement, are more likely to be effective stimuli if they occur suddenly.

3. *Duration—chronaxie.* Since, as mentioned above, a constant current excites only at the make and break, though the current continues to flow in the intervening period, it had been thought that the *duration* of a current played no part in excitation. But it is known now that the current must flow for a certain minimal time, measured in thousandths of seconds, in order to excite. That is to say, if the time elapsing between the make and break of the current is too short, the tissue is not excited, no matter how strong the current may be. Thus, alternating currents of very high frequency but having a strength of several thousand volts, do not stimulate when passed through the body.

The length of time during which a current must flow in order to excite a nerve or muscle varies with the strength of the current, the time being shorter with a strong than with a weak current. The excitability of a given nerve or other tissue may be measured by determining the minimal intensity of a current which, if allowed to flow for an indefinitely long period, will excite—that is, the time factor is not considered. On the other hand, the excitability can be measured by using a current of a *standard strength,* and determining the minimal time dur-

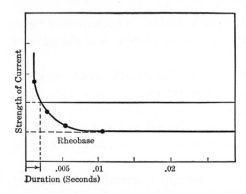

Fig. 11.7   Strength-duration curve. The chronaxie is the time interval marked by the intersection of the vertical interrupted line with the upper horizontal line, the latter representing a strength of current twice the rheobase. The chronaxie value in this instance, as indicated by the arrow, is .002 second.

ing which it must flow in order to excite. The current of a strength just sufficient to excite, but of indefinitely long duration, is called the *rheobase.* A current of double this strength is then employed as the standard, and the minimal duration for excitation measured. This time factor is called the *chronaxie* of the tissue in question. In other words, chronaxie is a measure expressing the *shortest duration for excitation of a current having a strength twice the rheobase* (Fig. 11.7).

The chronaxies of the different types of excitable tissue and of nerves and muscles of the different species, as well as of the same species, show very wide variation—namely, between 0.1 and 100 milliseconds (thousands of seconds). The chronaxie of the muscles of the human arm, for example, is around 0.1 millisecond, whereas that of the smooth muscle of the frog's stomach is about 100 milliseconds. The chronaxie of the human sciatic nerve is about 0.3 milliseconds (see Table 11-2, p. 469). Rapidly acting tissues, such as voluntary muscle, have shorter chronaxies than the more slowly acting, such as smooth muscle. The tissues of warm-blooded animals have, in general, shorter chronaxies than those of cold-blooded species. The chronaxies of thick nerve fibers, which conduct at high velocity, are shorter than those of fibers of smaller diameter and slow conduction. A nerve and the muscle which it supplies have chronaxies of nearly the same value, and certain

Table 11-2

Species	Structure	Chronaxie (milliseconds)
Man	Flexors of arm	0.08–0.16
	Extensors of arm	0.16–0.32
	Retina	1.2
	Vestibular nerve	14–22
	Sciatic nerve	0.3
Dog	Muscle of	
	ventricle of heart	2.0
	Auriculoventric-	
	ular bundle	6.0
Frog	Stomach	100
	Gastrocnemius	
	muscle	0.3
	Ventricular	
	muscle	9.0
Crab	Muscle of claw	12

drugs—such as curare—which paralyze voluntary muscle are be-lieved by some to cause their effect by increasing the disparity be-tween the chronaxie values of the muscle and its nerve.

Electrical changes in nerve. The nerve impulse is accompanied by a change in electrical potential. Any part of a nerve in the excited state is electrically negative, relatively, to all other parts of the nerve. The excited part is as the negative pole (copper) of a battery; any inactive part corresponds to the positive pole (zinc). If, therefore, a pair of electrodes are in contact, one with an excited part of the nerve, the other with a resting part, and the two electrodes connected through a sensitive electric recording ap-paratus, a current flows and causes a movement of the indicator of the instrument. The direction taken by the current is from the unexcited part of the nerve (+) to the ex-cited part (−), through the instru-ment, and from excited to unexcited part through the nerve. Thus, the electric circuit is completed (see Fig. 11.8 A). A similar electrical

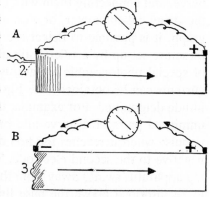

Fig. 11.8 Diagram illustrating ac-tion current, A, and current of injury, B. 1, galvanometer; 2, stimulus; 3, in-jured part of tissue (see text).

phenomenon occurs in muscle and other excitable tissue—*any active region of a tissue being relatively negative to an inactive region.*

The current thus set up in excited tissue is called the *action current.* Injured nerve or other tissue is also relatively negative to healthy tissue; the current set up when the injured and uninjured sections of the tissue are connected by a conductor is called the *current of injury* or *demarcation current* (see Fig. 11.8 B).

As we have seen, the excited state—the nerve impulse—travels rapidly over the nerve fiber. By placing electrodes upon a length of

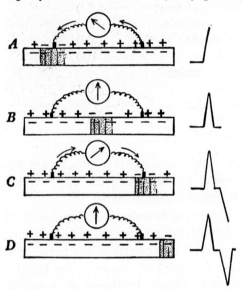

Fig. 11.9   Showing the production and recording of a diphasic action current (see text). Stippled area indicates wave of contraction.

nerve, and connecting them with a sensitive electric apparatus, such as the string galvanometer, or with an amplifier and cathode-ray oscillograph, it is possible to detect the passage of nerve impulses, whether these are set up by artificial stimulation or occur naturally. By means of special photographic apparatus, a permanent record of the action currents can be obtained (see Fig. 11.9), and their velocity and magnitude determined. For example, if the electrodes are placed upon two uninjured parts of a nerve and one end of the nerve stimulated, the impulse when it reaches the first electrode causes this to be relatively negative to the second electrode. The indicator of the electric recording apparatus swings away from the zero position. This causes a stroke to be inscribed above the base line in the photographic record (Fig. 11.9 A). When the impulse passes from beneath the first electrode, but has not yet reached the second (i.e., the nerve beneath each electrode is inactive and so of equal electrical potential), the indicator of the instrument returns to zero and a downstroke is inscribed in the record (see Fig. 11.9 B). When the impulse arrives at the second electrode, this becomes relatively negative to the first; a current flows through the instrument in the opposite direction, a curve below the base line appearing in the record (Fig. 11.9 C). Thus a *diphasic curve* is produced (Fig. 11.9 D).

If, instead of placing both electrodes upon uninjured tissue, the nerve beneath the second electrode is crushed, as is the usual practice in recording the action currents, the current resulting from the dif-

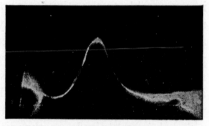

Fig. 11.10 Action-potential wave recorded by means of the cathode-ray oscillograph. (After Erlanger and Gasser.)

ference in potential between the injured and uninjured portions (current of injury) undergoes a sharp reduction in strength when the impulse reaches the first electrode; that is, the action current opposes the current injury. This variation in strength (negative variation) of the injury current appears as a single wave in the record. A second wave, directed oppositely to the first, does not appear, since the impulse cannot reach the electrode placed upon the crushed section of nerve. Such a record is called *monophasic* (see Fig. 11.10).

The most convenient and reliable means which we possess for investigating the properties of the nerve impulse is provided by the analysis of the electrical changes recorded from the nerve. The strength of the action current, as indicated by the amplitude of the recorded curves, their frequency and velocity, can be readily determined; such values are taken as corresponding to those of the nerve impulses themselves.

The Nature of the Nerve Impulse

The "all-or-none" or "nothing" principle (or law). The "all-or-none" principle, as it applies to the contraction of heart muscle, has been already defined (p. 159). This principle applies also to the nerve impulse and to the contraction of the individual fibers of skeletal muscle. For example, a stimulus just strong enough to excite the nerve fiber causes the transmission of an impulse which, as gauged by the action current, is of the same magnitude and has the same velocity as one set up by a stimulus of much greater strength. In other words, a stimulus which is capable of causing a response at all causes the *maximum* response. Nor can the impulses in the nerve fiber, as can the contractions of a muscle fiber, be summed—that is, the impulses as measured by the electrical response, cannot be increased in magnitude by raising the rate of stimulation. Each impulse remains separate.

The nerve impulse may therefore be compared to a spark traveling in a fuse of gunpowder; for, of course, it is immaterial, in so far as the size of the spark and the rate of its transmission are concerned, whether the fuse has been ignited by a small or by a large flame (which is comparable to the stimulus applied to the nerve). For the sake of illustration other comparisons may be drawn between the nerve fiber and a fuse of gunpowder. The nerve impulse and the spark are self-propagated; both derive the energy for their transmission from the material through which they pass. They, therefore, do not undergo any diminution with distance, differing in this respect from a sound wave, a wave in water, or from an electric current, each of which is reduced in magnitude as the distance from its point of origin increases.

If a section of the nerve fiber is treated with a narcotic—that is, ether or alcohol—conduction in the narcotized region is depressed; the impulse (as indicated by the action current) is reduced in magnitude by passing through this region. But the impulse, upon entering the unnarcotized section of nerve, regains its original value—further proof for the statement that the conduction of the impulse is dependent upon energy derived from the nerve fiber itself. A wave in air or water, or an electric current, once having undergone a reduction in force as a result of some resistance in its path, is not restored to its original value after having emerged from the medium offering the resistance. The spark in gunpowder behaves, however, like the nerve impulse. If a section of the fuse is dampened, the spark is less intense and travels more slowly through this section, but at once flares up again upon reaching the dry section of powder beyond.

It is therefore evident that the nerve impulse, though inseparable from an action potential, is not merely an electric current transmitted along the nerve as along a wire.

Lillie's iron wire model of the nerve fiber. An electrochemical phenomenon most closely comparable to that of the nerve impulse is exhibited by an iron wire immersed in a solution of acid of appropriate concentration. A nerve model so constructed was devised by Dr. Ralph Lillie of Chicago, and is generally known as *Lillie's iron wire model.* If an iron wire is immersed in strong nitric acid, it becomes coated with a layer of iron oxide. If the wire is then placed in a glass tube filled with a solution of acid suitably diluted, and "stimulated" by scratching its surface at one point so as to break the film of oxide, a disturbance consisting of effervescence and the formation of a dark compound is set up and travels rapidly along the wire; the film of oxide gradually re-forms in the wake of the propagated electrochemical change. The wire can also be "stimulated" electrically. The model shows several of the phenomena associated with the passage of the nerve impulse. An action potential can be recorded from the wire as the propagated disturbance passes over it. Electrotonic effects (p. 465) and a refractory period (see below) can also be demonstrated. The latter is that period following the "impulse" during which the oxide coating is being re-formed and the wire cannot be "stimulated."

The membrane theory of nerve excitation and conduction. The electrochemical change in the wire following its "stimulation" is quite evidently a surface phenomenon. The nerve impulse is thought to be of

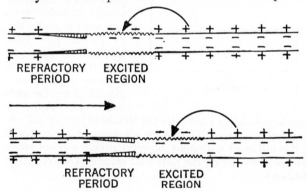

REFRACTORY   EXCITED
PERIOD   REGION

REFRACTORY   EXCITED
PERIOD   REGION

Fig. 11.11   Illustrating the nerve membrane theory. *Straight arrow* indicates the direction taken by the impulse; *curved arrow,* the potential difference. The part of the nerve marked by wavy lines is depolarized, and is negative to the polarized part. The refractory periods in which the nerve is being repolarized are represented by hatching; following this again repolarization has occurred, and the ability of the nerve to conduct an impulse has been restored.

the same nature, occurring at the surface of a membrane or film enveloping the nerve fiber. This conception has been embodied in what is known as the *depolarization* or *membrane theory* of the origin and spread of the nerve impulse. According to this theory, the nerve fiber in the resting state is *polarized*—that is, the ions in the fluids in contact with the two sides of the film or membrane are arranged with the cations on the outside and the anions on the inside (Fig. 11.11). Thus, positive and negative electric charges are balanced on either side of the membrane which remains impermeable to them so long as the nerve is at rest. Upon stimulation of the nerve, some chemical change is brought about which renders the membrane permeable to the ions; it becomes *depolarized* at the point of stimulation. An electrical potential is set up between the adjacent polarized and nonpolarized regions of the nerve, which acting like the original stimulus causes the spread of depolarization down the nerve; thus the impulse is propagated automatically. Excitation of the nerve is not restored until the depolarized region is repolarized. The period during which the nerve is depolarized corresponds to the absolute refractory period.

The absolute and relative refractory periods of nerve. The nerve fiber, after the passage of an impulse, is for a short time unable to conduct. This is due, if we accept the membrane theory, to its being in the depolarized state. This brief interval following the passage of the im-

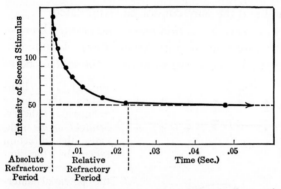

Fig. 11.12 Curve of the recovery in the sciatic nerve of the frog. Two stimuli were applied to the nerve, the second stimulus being separated from the first by various time intervals and of just sufficient strength to excite. Intensity of stimulus is plotted along the ordinate, time along the abscissa. The interrupted horizontal line indicates the threshold strength of current required to excite the resting nerve. During the absolute refractory period (about 0.003 second in this instance) a stimulus, however strong, will not excite. The excitability returns gradually during the next 0.02 second (relative refractory period). (After Adrian.)

pulse, and during which the fiber will not conduct, is called the *absolute refractory period* (see Fig. 11.12). The nerve fiber in this state may be likened to the gunpowder fuse after the spark has passed, leaving only a trail of ash; a fresh train of powder must be laid before a second spark can travel the same path. The duration of the absolute refractory period of frog's nerve is from 0.002 to 0.003 second, and of mammalian nerve about 0.001 second. It is followed by a longer period during which repolarization of the nerve fiber is occurring. This is called the *relative refractory period;* it has a duration of from 0.01 to 0.02 second. During this time, the excitability and conductivity of the fiber is below normal, a stronger stimulus than usual being required to set up an impulse which, as judged by the action current, is of smaller magnitude. These properties improve progressively, reaching the values for resting nerve at the termination of the relative refractory period.

The velocity of the nerve impulses. In mammalian myelinated nerves, the impulse travels at a velocity of from 90 to 100 meters per second—that is, at about the speed of a revolver bullet. The impulses in unmyelinated mammalian nerve and in all nerves of cold-blooded animals, whether myelinated or unmyelinated, travel at much slower rates. Nerve fibers of large diameters transmit impulses at a higher velocity than those of small diameter. In the small nonmedullated fibers of some cold-blooded animals, the rates of conduction of the nerve impulse are less than 2 meters per second (Table 11-3).

Table 11-3

Nerve velocities

Mammalian nerve, myelinated, at body temperature	100–125 meters per second
Dogfish nerve, myelinated, at 20° C ..	35 meters per second
Frog's nerve, myelinated, at 20° C ...	30 meters per second
Crab's nerve, amyelinated, at 22° C ..	1.5–5 meters per second

That there are at least two types of sensory nerve with different conduction velocities can be deduced from a common experience. When, for example, one stubs one's toe or receives a hard knock upon the shin, a sharp evanescent pain is felt which after a short interval is followed by a duller more enduring and much more unpleasant kind of pain. The impulses causing the initial pain are carried by nerves of relatively large diameter with a rapid conduction rate; the second pain is dependent upon nerves of smaller diameter and of slower conduction. Upon the nerves conducting at the more rapid rate (30 to 100 meters per second), the protective or withdrawal reflexes depend. Were consciousness not apprized of an injury until the slowly conducted impulses arrived, irreparable damage might be inflicted upon a part before the warning message to protect it had been received.

The frequency of nerve impulses. The length of the absolute refractory period determines the maximum frequency at which the nerve fiber is capable of transmitting impulses. In mammalian nerve, for example, the absolute refractory period has a duration of $\frac{1}{1000}$ second. In other words, a period of $\frac{1}{1000}$ second must elapse after the passage of an impulse before the fiber can again conduct. The maximum frequency is, therefore, around 1000 per second. Action currents of this frequency have actually been demonstrated by means of the cathode-ray oscillograph. A *single* fiber in the nerve trunk was separated from its neighbors by careful dissection and laid across a pair of electrodes connected to the recording apparatus.

The relation of the frequency of the impulses to the magnitude of the response. It has been mentioned above that the individual nerve impulse cannot, so far as is known, be varied in magnitude or in any other character by altering the strength of the stimulus. It may naturally be asked then, "Why does a stronger stimulus produce a greater effect?" A strong stimulus, for example, causes a more intense sensation than a weaker one when applied to a sensory nerve ending, or a more powerful contraction when applied to a motor nerve. The greater sensation caused by the stronger stimulus is due entirely to the higher frequency of the impulses. Increasing the strength of the stimulus causes a rise in the frequency of the impulses discharged along each nerve fiber; when applied to a nerve trunk, the stronger stimulus also excites more nerve fibers than the weak one. These two factors, namely, the frequency of the impulses in each nerve fiber and the number of fibers involved—that is, the number of impulses reaching consciousness in a unit of time—determine the intensity of the sensation.

Similarly, the magnitude of the muscular response when a motor nerve is stimulated is related to the frequency of the impulses discharged along the individual nerve fibers, as well as upon the number of fibers excited. Each nerve fiber of a mammalian motor nerve terminates by dividing into some hundred branches, each of which supplies a muscle fiber.[1] Now, as we shall see (p. 488), when a muscle is stimulated by a single electric shock, it gives a single contraction or *twitch* but, if stimulated by a series of such shocks in rapid succession, the resulting twitches become fused into a sustained contraction or *tetanus,* which exerts a force considerably greater than that of the single twitch. In a voluntary movement of the human arm, for example, the impulses pass from the central nervous system to the muscles at varying frequencies—from 5 to 50 or more per second. At the lower frequencies, the individual contractions are incompletely fused and only a proportion of the muscle fibers are activated; the movements are weak. Complete fusion of contractions occurs at the higher frequencies, a powerful movement resulting.

In some types of contraction, such as the tonic contraction of the muscles which maintain the body's posture, the impulses are transmitted at moderately high frequencies, but only a proportion of the nerve fibers going to the muscle are active at one time—that is, the impulses are discharged from the central nervous system asynchronously along the several fibers composing the motor nerve. As a consequence, the

[1] The single motor nerve fiber and the group of muscle fibers which it supplies is called a *motor unit.*

fibers of the muscle are never all contracted at once; they contract in rotation. Since the muscle fibers respond in relays, some resting while others contract and vice versa, this type of contraction, though generally less powerful than that which results in movement, is able to be maintained for relatively long periods without fatigue.

The nature or quality of sensation. The sensation aroused by stimulating a sensory nerve ending varies with the particular nerve ending excited. For example, stimulation of certain nerve endings in the skin causes a painful sensation, of others a sensation of touch, of others, again, a sensation of heat or of cold. The optic nerve transmits impulses which arouse visual sensations. The acoustic and olfactory nerves and the nerves of taste, when stimulated, give rise to their own peculiar sensations. To what is this specificity of the sensory nerves due? There are two possibilities: (a) The fibers constituting the several types of nerve may differ in some fundamental way from one another, so that the impulses set up may have some distinguishing characteristic. In other words, each type of fiber may convey to consciousness a message peculiar to that type of fiber. (b) The fibers themselves may be unspecific and the impulses which they transmit may be all alike, the different kinds of sensations—pain, touch, visual, auditory, etc.—being then dependent upon the particular region of the brain where the impulses are received. That is to say, the different regions of the brain interpret, each in its own way, the messages that come to them, though such messages are all identical in their general characters.

The latter conception appears to be the true one. All the evidence indicates that the impulses, along whatever type of nerve they are transmitted and though they may differ in minor details, are essentially the same in character. For example, the action currents recorded from the optic nerve, from a motor nerve, or from a cutaneous sensory nerve, show no characteristic differences which might reasonably be considered as a basis for the several qualities of sensation. The center in the brain in which the impulses arrive is the determining factor. Impulses reaching one part of the cerebral cortex cause a visual sensation but, if these same impulses could be directed to the auditory center of the brain they would, according to this view, give rise to a sensation of sound. Or again, if it were possible to stimulate the receptors of the eye by a sound, and those of the ear by a light, the sensation to which such stimulation gave rise would still be one of light or of sound, respectively. For example, though the rods and cones of the retina are the receptors for sight, and are so specialized that light rays constitute the most effective, indeed the only really adequate, stimulus, we know from our own experience that they, or the optic nerve fibers, can be excited by mechanical means—e.g., a blow or firm pressure upon the eyeball, when a flash or a ring of light is seen.

By way of summary, it may be said that whereas the intensity of a sensation (the brightness of a light, the loudness of a sound, etc.) depends upon the *frequency* of the impulses, the *nature* of the sensation is dependent upon the area of the cerebral cortex in which the impulses are received.

Chemical changes in nerve. Until some years ago attempts had failed to demonstrate any increase in oxygen consumption or of carbon dioxide production by nerve during its activity. Nor could any rise in temperature of the nerve be demonstrated during the passage of the impulse. It was therefore thought that the conduction of the nerve impulse was a purely physical process. By the application within recent years of more refined methods of investigation, it has been shown quite conclusively, however, that conduction in nerve is essentially chemical in nature. A resting nerve produces a small quantity of heat (70×10^{-6} calories per gram of nerve per second) which is increased by over 50 percent during activity. The resting nerve also consumes oxygen and produces carbon dioxide, the gaseous exchanges undergoing a definite increase when the nerve is stimulated.

Carbohydrate is not, apparently, the fuel from which the energy for the conduction of the impulse is derived. During stimulation, no reduction in the glycogen content of the nerve occurs, the disappearance of sugar is not accelerated, and lactic acid is not produced. Nerve conduction differs, therefore, in this respect from muscular contraction (p. 497). The immediate source of the energy for nerve conduction is furnished by the explosive breakdown of phosphocreatine. The phosphocreatine undergoes resynthesis after the passage of the impulse— i.e., during the refractory period—the conductivity of the nerve being thus restored. The source of the energy for the recovery process is unknown. That the recovery process is essentially different from that occurring in muscle is evident from the fact that it occurs in the absence of oxygen. A nerve placed in nitrogen will therefore continue to respond to stimulation for a relatively long time—3 hours or so.

The Physiology of Skeletal (Voluntary) Muscle

The minute structure of skeletal muscle has been briefly described in Chapter 2.

Functional anatomy. The characteristic and outstanding property of muscle is its contractility; and the most obvious function of skeletal muscle is to move the limbs, head, trunk, and other parts. The muscle fiber is a highly complex mechanism primarily directed toward the conversion of energy derived from chemical reactions to mechanical energy which is exhibited as movement or some kind of force. Most skeletal muscles, as the name implies, are attached to bony structures, though a few, such as those of the face, are attached to skin; others are attached to cartilage and some to ligaments or to other muscles. One of the bones to which a muscle is attached is usually held more or less stationary by the action of other muscles; the *prime mover* (see below) thus is provided with a fixed point for its contraction. This attachment of the muscle is usually called its *origin*. The other extremity of the muscle, especially of a limb muscle (e.g., the biceps of the arm), is most usually attached to a bone

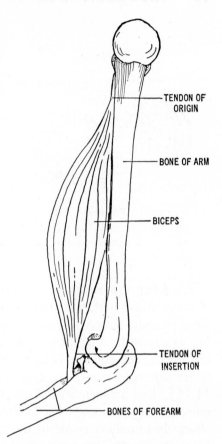

Fig. 11.13   Showing the action of a muscle crossing a joint. When the muscle (in this case the biceps of the arm) contracts, it pulls upon its insertion into the bone (radius) of the forearm and bends (flexes) the elbow joint.

which moves upon some type of joint when the muscle contracts; this attachment is called the *insertion* of the muscle. In the case of the muscles of the limbs and of certain other parts, the muscles are situated with their insertions distal to their origins (i.e., more toward the fingers or toes) and, when the muscle contracts, its insertion moves toward its origin, which remains stationary (Fig. 11.13). Most voluntary muscles are inserted not directly into the bone, but through the medium of a strong, tough, inelastic fibrous cord called a *tendon* (or sinew, in popular language, Fig. 11.14). Tendons vary greatly in length; in man, this may be from a fraction of an inch to more than a foot. Sometimes a muscle has a tendon at each of its extremities.

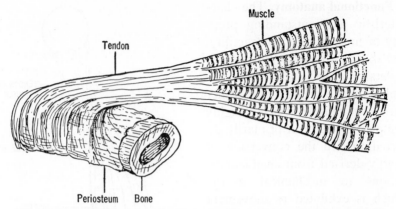

Fig. 11.14   Showing the blending of voluntary muscle fibers with fibers of the tendon, and of the tendon with the periosteum (covering of the bone).

The form of muscle and the arrangement of its fibers. Muscles are of many shapes and sizes. Their shapes are variously described as *fusiform* (spindle shaped), *quadrilateral* or *rhomboid, triangular, straplike* (such as the long muscle on the front and inner side of the thigh and knee), and *pennate* (like a feather) in which the fibers pass from either side to a central tendon which they join obliquely (see Fig. 11.15). This arrangement of the fibers is called *bipennate.* In other muscles, only one half of a feather is represented, the fibers passing obliquely to only one side of the tendon; they are called *unipennate.* In most muscles, however, the fibers pass in a direct line—line of

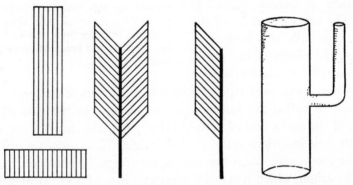

Fig. 11.15   Diagram showing four different types of arrangement of the fibers in voluntary muscles. (Description in the text.)

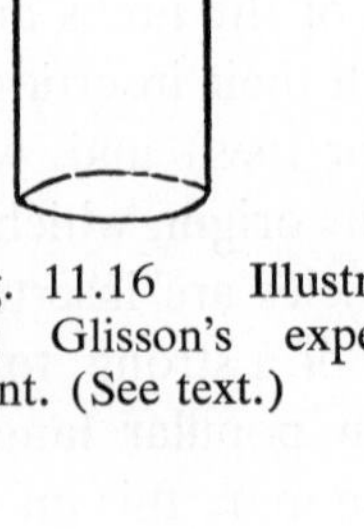

Fig. 11.16   Illustrating Glisson's experiment. (See text.)

pull—from origin to insertion.

When a muscle (e.g., the biceps of the arm) contracts, it appears to increase in volume, and the ancient and medieval physicians thought that such actually occurred as a result of what they called animal spirits flowing into the muscle through its nerves. Francis Glisson, an English physician (1597–1677), showed by a very simple experiment that the

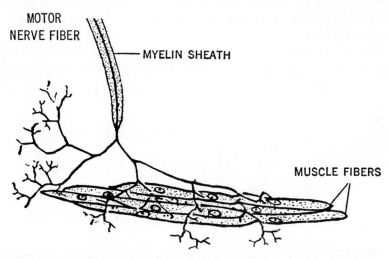

Fig. 11.17   Showing the branches of a single nerve fiber terminating in a group of muscle fibers of a motor unit.

muscles of the human forearm did not increase in volume when they contracted; they actually diminished a little in bulk. He had a man insert his arm up to the elbow into a tall glass vessel provided with a side tube (see Fig. 11.16). The vessel was then filled with water to the brim and a bandage bound around the top of the vessel and the arm at this point in such a way as to prevent leakage. When the muscles of the arm contracted, no rise in the level of fluid in the side arm occurred; a slight fall was observed.[2]

Red (dark) and white (pale) muscles. We are all familiar with the dark and light flesh of fowl. In mammals, also, there are two types of muscle, the dark red and the light colored. The division into these two types is more pronounced in the cat and rabbit than in the monkey or man. The pale muscles (like the wing muscles of birds) contract more rapidly than the dark colored, and require a higher frequency of stim-

---

[2] The slight reduction in volume was probably due to the expression of blood from the vessels by the compressing force of the contraction.

ulation in order to tetanize them (p. 488). The two kinds of muscle differ histologically; the fibers of the dark variety have, as compared with those of the pale muscles, more abundant sarcoplasm, are more opaque, and show less distinct cross-striations. The dark muscles as well as giving a slower contraction also fatigue less readily. They constitute, in man, mainly those muscles (e.g., the extensors of the thigh) which are capable of sustaining a position of the body, such as standing, for a long period. In some human muscles, both kinds of fiber are present together.

The innervation of skeletal muscle, motor end-plate, and motor units. Each muscle cell receives both a motor and sensory innervation. Each nerve fiber of a spinal motor nerve, which is an axon of a cell in

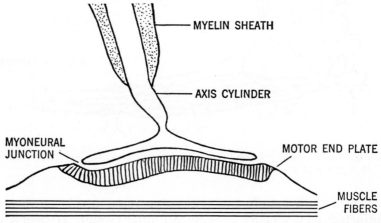

Fig. 11.18   Showing a nerve fiber ending in a muscle—the myoneural junction. (After Couteau, redrawn.)

the anterior horn of the spinal cord, divides into some 100 branches which supply a corresponding number of muscle fibers. The anterior horn cell (including its axon, the nerve fiber) is called a *motoneuron,* and the group or "bunch" of muscle fibers which it innervates is designated a *motor unit* (Fig. 11.17). The muscle cell possesses a specially organized structure known as the *motor end-plate.* Each axon branch of the motor nerve fiber, as it approaches the muscle fiber for which it is destined, loses its myelin sheath and terminates on the motor endplate as a flat expansion. This contact (there appears to be no actual union) between the terminal of the nerve fiber and the end-plate is called the *myoneural* or *neuromuscular junction* (Fig. 11.18). It exhibits many of the properties of the synapse existing between neurons (p. 510).

The sensory nerve fibers also lose their myelin sheaths and end in a special fusiform organ within the fiber known as the *muscle spindle*. The spindle consists of a group of muscle fibers differing from those of the rest of the muscle and enclosed in a well-defined capsule. It is a receptor of kinesthetic sense (p. 514 and Pl. 9A).

Muscular movements. Muscles which bend a limb at a joint—e.g., those which raise the thigh at the hip joint, or bend the elbow or knee—are called *flexor muscles* (or *flexors*). Those which straighten the limb—lower the thigh at the hip joint, or straighten the arm at the elbow or the leg at the knee—are called *extensor muscles* (or *extensors*). Muscles which move the limb or other part in a direction away from the mid-line of the body, or of a limb, are called *abductors;* and those executing the opposite movement—that is, bringing the limb or other part toward the mid-line of the body or of a limb—are known as *adductors*. There are also muscles which rotate a limb. In the case of the movements at the ankle joint, confusion is avoided by adding the qualifying prefixes, *plantar-* and *dorsi-* to the word *flexor*. Thus, turning the foot upward upon the ankle joint is called *dorsiflexion;* depressing the foot toward the ground is called *plantarflexion. Dorsiflexors* and *plantarflexors* are corresponding terms given to the muscles which carry out these movements.

In performing a given movement—e.g., bending of the leg at the knee or of the arm at the elbow—the several muscles carrying out the movement act as a "team." In the bending of the arm at the elbow, for example, the muscles which execute the actual movement (biceps, etc.) are called *prime movers,* but we shall see (p. 517) that the oppositely acting (extensor) muscles must relax; the muscles which straighten the elbow (such as the triceps) are therefore called *antagonists*. The functions of these muscles are, of course, reversed when the elbow is extended, the triceps is now the prime mover and the biceps the antagonist. *Fixation muscles* are those which hold stationary the bone or bones giving origin to the muscle, thus enabling it to move the bone into which its tendon is inserted. Thus, in raising the arm from the side, muscles about the shoulder joint contract to hold the shoulder blade (scapula) and collarbone (clavicle) steady. Muscles that serve to steady a joint crossed by the tendon of the prime mover, and in this way enable the prime mover to contract to best advantage without loss of power, are called *synergists*. Thus, when the muscles (flexors of the fingers and wrist) which clench the fist contract, there is a tendency for the wrist to be sharply flexed. Normally this does not occur because the muscles on the back of the forearm (extensors of the wrist), whose

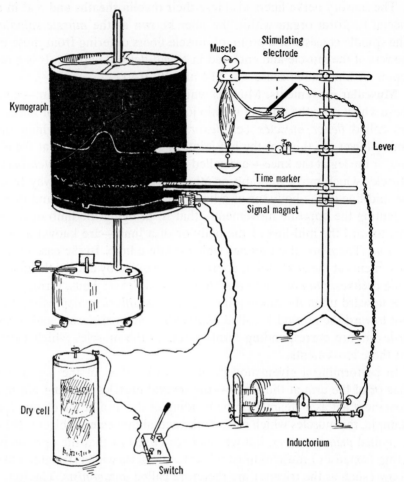

Fig. 11.19   Showing apparatus for stimulating an isolated frog's muscle and the method of recording the contraction.

tendons cross the back of the wrist, contract, and thus give rigidity to this joint.

Method of recording contractions of an isolated muscle. Our knowledge of the physiology of muscular contraction has been gained largely from studies of the isolated muscle of the frog. The muscle of the calf—the *gastrocnemius*—is the one most generally employed. This muscle is attached above to the lower end of the thighbone (femur) and below, through a strong tendon called the tendon of Achilles (tendo Achillis or tendo calcaneus), to the bone of the heel. In preparing the muscle for an experiment, it is removed from the animal together with its nerve supply, the sciatic, and the lower end of the femur. The preparation is then suspended by fixing the section of bone in a clamp, and fastening the lower tendinous end of the muscle to a light lever, as shown in Figure 11.19. The writing lever is adjusted so as to make light contact with the surface of a revolving drum, motivated by clockwork and covered with smoked paper. This instrument is called a *kymograph.* As the drum revolves, the soot is removed by the point of the lever, which thus traces a white horizontal line so long

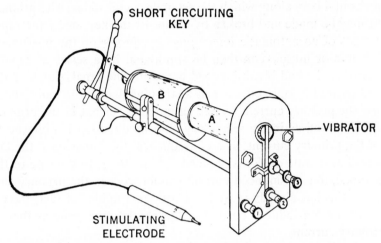

Fig. 11.20   The inductorium. A, primary coil; B, secondary coil.

as the lever remains stationary. Any shortening (contraction) of the muscle causes an upward movement of the lever which then inscribes a curve on the rotating drum.

A tuning fork of the required frequency of vibration (e.g., $\frac{1}{100}$, $\frac{1}{50}$ per second) is arranged with a writing point to mark the time intervals at the bottom of the tracing; or some device run by clockwork may be used. A signal magnet is also set up in the primary circuit of the inductorium (see below) to indicate the instant that the stimulating current, which also activates the signal, is made or broken.

The inductorium. The induced electric current is usually employed in classroom experiments for stimulating muscle and nerve; it can be finely graded in strength, and a series of rapidly repeated shocks can be applied to the excitable tissue. The instrument employed for this purpose is called an *inductorium,* and consists of two cylindrical spools or coils of wire called *primary* and *secondary* (Fig. 11.20). The primary coil has an iron core around which are made a few turns of thick wire. It receives current from a dry cell, a switch or key being interposed in the circuit. The secondary coil is composed of many turns of fine wire. Its core being hollow, it is capable of being slid like a sleeve over the primary coil. It runs on parallel metal bars and can be pivoted as well around its transverse axis. When the current from the dry cell enters the primary coil, a current is induced in the secondary coil. The low electromotive force of the primary circuit is transformed to the high electromotive force of the induced current which is led off to stimulating electrodes fastened to binding posts, one on either end of the horizontal bars along which the secondary coil slides. The primary circuit may be made and broken by means of the key, or by the rapid movements of an automatic *interrupter* or *vibrator* on the instrument itself. Nerve or muscle can then be stimulated by a series of rapidly alternating make and break induced currents. The break shock of the induced current is more effective as a stimulus than is the make shock because the primary current causes an induced current in the primary coil itself as well as in the secondary, and its direction is opposite to that of the primary current; as a consequence, the intensity of the latter as well as its rate of rise is reduced (see p. 467). In the case of the break shock, the self-induced current cannot weaken the primary current since this has already ceased to exist. As a matter of fact, the direction of the self-induced current at the break is the same as that of the primary current.

The current induced in the secondary coil is increased or diminished by sliding this coil toward or away from the primary coil. The induced current can also be graded by rotating the secondary coil upon its pivot, and altering the angle which it makes with the primary coil. When the secondary and primary coils have their long axes at right angles to one another, there is no induced current. A current is induced as the secondary coil is moved from the right angle toward the horizontal position, and increases steadily the farther it is turned in this direction, reaching a maximum for any given distance from the primary coil, when the long axes of the two coils are in line.

The simple muscular contraction or "twitch." Muscle, like nerve, responds to any one of the four types of stimulus—*electrical, mechanical, thermal,* or *chemical.* The muscle may be stimulated directly—that is, by placing the electrodes in contact with its surface—or through its nerve. When stimulated in either of these ways and with a single stimulus—e.g., a make or break shock—the muscle contracts and, having raised the writing lever to a certain height, relaxes again and allows the lever to return to its original position. Thus a curve, such as that shown in Figure 11.21, is inscribed. This simple brief contraction is called a muscle *twitch;* it is due, of course, to the shortening (contraction) in unison of the numerous fibers of which the muscle is composed. A simple contraction or twitch does not occur in the living animal under ordinary physiological conditions, but the reflex contraction of the extensor muscles of the thigh caused by a tap on the patella tendon (knee jerk) is of this nature. The curve shown in Figure 11.21 is marked off into three parts to represent corresponding phases of the muscular response. The stimulus is applied at A; shortening of the muscle commences at B, and relaxation at C. The distance from A to B indicates the period elapsing from the application of the

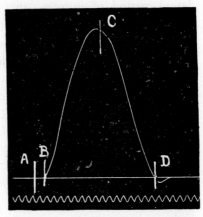

Fig. 11.21 Record of a muscle twitch. A-B, latent period; B-C, contraction phase; C-D, relaxation phase. Time indicated by lower tracing ($\frac{1}{100}$ second) caused by a vibrating tuning fork. (After Stirling.)

stimulus to the commencement of the contraction. This is called the *latent period;* its duration is about 0.01 second. The next period (B-C), during which the lever rises from the horizontal line (base line) to the summit of the curve, is the *contraction phase;* it lasts for approximately 0.04 second. The part of the curve from C to D represents the *relaxation phase.* This has a duration of about 0.05 second.

As determined by the method described above, the total duration of the contractile process of the frog's gastrocnemius muscle, including the latent period, is found to be about a tenth of a second. The muscles of warm-blooded animals have considerably shorter contraction times.

The latent period of the muscle, as measured from the instant of stimulation of its nerve, is made up of: (a) the time taken for the impulse to travel along the nerve from the point of stimulation to the muscle; (b) the very brief interval during which the initial chemical changes are occurring in the muscle fiber and tension is being developed; (c) the inertia of the lever. The last mentioned, (c), can be almost entirely eliminated by refined methods of recording—e.g., some form of recording in which the contraction of the muscle moves a mirrored surface. This reflects a beam of light which is photographed. The light beam, which is substituted for the material lever, is free from inertia. Furthermore, its length can be such that great magnification of the movements of the reflecting surface can be obtained. The true latent period of muscle—that is, the interval (A-B) between the stimulation of the muscle fiber itself and the commencement of the shortening process—varies between 0.0025 and 0.004 second.

The effect upon the force of the contraction of increasing the intensity of the stimulus. If a series of stimuli of gradually increasing strength is applied directly to the muscle, contraction curves of graded heights will be obtained (see Fig. 11.22). The weakest stimulus which will excite the muscle is called the *minimal* or *threshold stimulus.* As the strength of each successive stimulus is increased, a greater and greater response is obtained from the muscle. Ultimately, a point is reached where the muscle contracts maximally—that is, no further in-

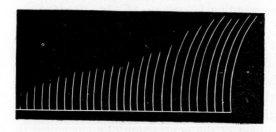

Fig. 11.22   Record of a series of contractions caused by a succession of stimuli of graded strength. The muscle lever traced each of these lines while the drum of the kymograph was at rest, and was then moved by hand to a fresh position after each contraction.

crease in the height of the contraction curve results from increasing the strength of the stimulus. This is called the *maximal stimulus.*

It was stated on page 471 that muscle, like nerve, obeys the "all-or-none" law. The grading of the muscular response to stimuli of graded strength, as just described, appears to contradict this statement. The explanation is that a muscle is composed of a number of units—the muscle fibers. The force of the contraction of the whole muscle is dependent upon the number of fibers excited by the stimulus. A strong stimulus excites a larger number of fibers than does a weak one, and with a maximal stimulus the current spreads to involve all the fibers. Studies made upon a single muscle fiber have shown that it does not respond by graded responses as the strength of the stimulus is increased. It responds maximally or not at all—that is, it obeys the "all-or-none" law.

Summation and tetanus. If a second stimulus is sent into an isolated frog's muscle within the latent period of the first, no obvious effect is produced. If, however, the second stimulus is applied while the muscle is contracting in response to the first stimulus, it contracts again; the second contraction is added to the first, the shortening of the muscle being then greater than that caused by a single stimulus. The greatest effect of the second stimulus is observed when it is applied to the muscle near the height of the contraction caused by the first. This phenomenon, whereby one contraction is added to a previous one to produce a greater total shortening of the muscle, is called *summation* (Fig. 11.23). A third contraction may be added to a second, a fourth to a third, and so on. When the stimuli sent into a frog's gastrocnemius

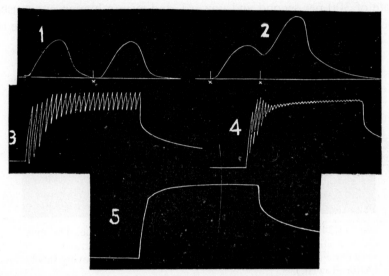

Fig. 11.23   Illustrating summation and tetanus. 1, the second stimulus x was applied after relaxation of the muscle, two separate contractions of equal amplitude result; 2, summation, the second stimulus x being applied at a shorter interval after the first than in 1; 3 and 4, incomplete tetanus caused by a series of stimuli applied at short intervals apart; 5, complete tetanus resulting from a still more rapid rate of stimulation, the individual muscular responses being completely fused. (After Stirling and Howell.)

muscle are at a slower rate than from 15 to 30 per second, the individual contractions can be distinguished—that is, they are not completely fused. The contraction curve shows smaller or larger waves synchronous with the rate of stimulation. At rates of stimulation higher than this, the responses are completely fused, the contraction curve being perfectly smooth. The curve rises to a maximum height, which is considerably greater than that caused by a single stimulus, and remains at this height as long as the stimulation lasts or until the muscle becomes fatigued. A sustained contraction of this nature is called *complete tetanus*. The contraction caused by slower rates of stimulation, and in which the individual responses are distinguishable, is referred to as *incomplete tetanus*.

The rate of stimulation at which complete fusion of the contractions occurs varies with the speed at which a given type of muscle normally contracts. Thus, rapidly acting white muscles require a higher rate of stimulation to produce tetanus than do the more slowly acting red muscles, and the rate required by smooth muscle is slowest of all (5 stimuli per second). In the rapidly acting muscles of the wings of insects, contractions are not fused until the rate of stimulation reaches a rate of 300 per second and upward, and even a human eye muscle (internal rectus) requires a stimulation rate of 350 per second. The re-

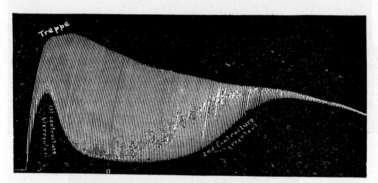

Fig. 11.24   Illustrating treppe, contracture, and fatigue. The muscle was stimulated at intervals of 1 second. The contractions are very close together because the kymograph drum was moving slowly. (After Howell.)

quired rate for red muscle of the human calf, on the other hand, is only 30 stimuli per second. In man, the voluntary contractions of the muscles of the limbs are brought about by the discharge of impulses along the motor nerves at rates of from 5 to 50 per second. At the lower rates, the contraction is an incomplete tetanus, but at the higher frequency complete fusion of the contractions results (see also p. 476).

Treppe or the "staircase" phenomenon. When a muscle is stimulated repeatedly at regular intervals, the first few contractions of the series increase successively in amplitude. This phenomenon has already been described for heart muscle (p. 160). It is due, apparently, to the beneficial effect exerted upon the irritability of the muscle by the chemical products of the first few contractions, and by the rise in temperature (Fig. 11.24).

The effect of loading upon the contraction of a muscle. A muscle contracts more forcibly if suitably loaded. The increase in the height of the contraction increases up to a point with each weight that is added to the scale pan suspended from the muscle, as shown in Figure

11.19, page 484. The force of the contractions then decreases again as the load is gradually increased (Fig. 11.29, p. 495). For an isolated frog's muscle, the maximum height is attained at a loading weight of between 30 and 50 grams. When a loaded muscle is stimulated to contract, the first effect is a sudden lengthening of the muscle fibers. This sudden stretch causes tension in the muscle which is immediately followed by shortening. The stretching of the fibers in some way enables the muscle to mobilize more energy than is possible for the unweighted muscle. We have seen the same phenomenon in the case of cardiac

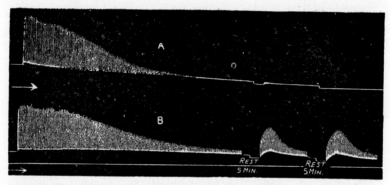

Fig. 11.25   Showing the effect of oxygen lack upon the onset of fatigue. Records from a pair of sartorius muscles of frog, stimulated at 1 second intervals. A, in nitrogen; B, in oxygen. (After Fletcher.)

muscle (p. 193). Throughout the shortening of the muscle, the tension remains constant. This type of contraction is therefore called *isotonic* (Gk. *isos,* equal + *tonus,* tension). But if the muscle is loaded with a weight that it is unable to lift, or is attached to a stiff spring that it cannot bend, only a very slight shortening of the muscle fibers can occur. Such a contraction is called *isometric* (Gk. *isos,* equal + *metron,* measure).

Fatigue. If *direct* stimulation of an excised muscle—that is, with the electrodes placed upon the muscle—be continued after the contractions have reached their maximum amplitude, the irritability of the muscle gradually becomes depressed, due to the accumulation of lactic acid (Fig. 11.25). The concentration of lactic acid at which loss of irritability of the muscle occurs, and at which it fails to respond to stimulation, is around 0.5 percent.

The onset and development of this state of *fatigue* are more rapid, the higher the rate of stimulation. Isolated muscle, or one in the intact animal the blood supply of which has been occluded, also fatigues more rapidly than one receiving an adequate oxygen supply. Oxygen is required for the removal of the lactic acid produced during contraction. In the muscle deprived of its blood supply this, of course, does not readily occur. Lactic acid accumulates, and it is to such accumulation that the loss of irritability of the muscle is attributed (see p. 498).

When a muscle is stimulated, not directly, but *through its nerve,* fatigue supervenes much sooner—long before the lactic acid concentration has reached the value at which it depresses muscular irritability. We know that nerve is highly resistant to fatigue. There must, then, be

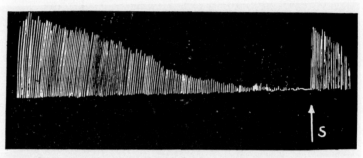

Fig. 11.26 Illustrating the ready fatigability of the myoneural junction—i.e., before the muscle itself. The muscle was stimulated *through its nerve* to the arrow, S, and then *directly.*

a third structure or tissue in the nerve-muscle preparation that is peculiarly susceptible to fatigue; this is the junction between nerve and muscle—the *myoneural junction*—which exhibits the properties of a synapse. The early fatigability of the myoneural junction can be demonstrated by a simple experiment. If the nerve to the muscle is stimulated repeatedly until the muscle fails to respond, a stimulus of the same strength as before applied directly to the muscle causes a vigorous contraction (see Fig. 11.26).

Contracture. Under certain conditions, relaxation of the muscle takes place very slowly; it may remain in the partially contracted state for a considerable length of time. This state of the muscle is referred to as *contracture.* If a muscle in a state of contracture is stimulated at relatively long intervals, it responds by further shortening, each contraction being then superimposed upon the sustained contraction caused by the previous stimulus. Contracture is brought about by the action of certain drugs, especially *veratrine,* and by *fatigue.* It also sometimes occurs in apparently normal muscle during the first of a series of contractions and then passes off (Fig. 11.24).

The effect of temperature upon muscular contraction. Warming a muscle causes it to respond more rapidly and vigorously to stimulation. Contraction and relaxation phases are both shortened; the latent period is also of shorter duration. Lowering the temperature of the muscle exerts the opposite effect, the contraction being weaker and all its phases lengthened. Cold-blooded animals, such as snakes and frogs, whose body temperature varies with that of the environment, move

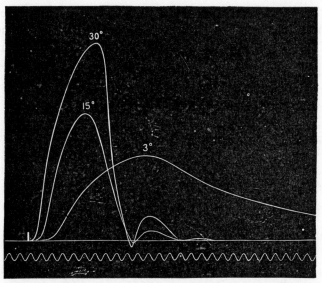

Fig. 11.27   The effect of temperature upon the contraction of a frog's gastrocnemius muscle. Tracing should be read from left to right. Figures are the temperatures (°C) of the salt solution in which the muscle was immersed. (After Pembrey and Phillips.)

sluggishly, therefore, in cold weather. The activity of mammals, on the other hand, whose muscles are maintained at a constant temperature of around 98.5° F, is not influenced by changes in the temperature of the environment. Nevertheless, the more efficient action of the muscles after the commencement of exercise is due, in part, to the local rise in temperature resulting from the earlier contractions. "Warming up" to one's work is a familiar expression (Fig. 11.27).

The effect of temperature upon the speed of muscular contraction conforms with Van't Hoff's law, which states that the velocity of chemical reactions, which, of course, are the basis of muscular contraction, is increased to between two and three times by a rise in temperature of 10° C.

Muscle is inexcitable at very low temperatures. Frog's muscle, for example, fails to respond at temperatures of from 32 to 35° F. On the other hand, at an excessively high temperature (105 to 110° F for frog's muscle) the muscle proteins are coagulated, and death of the muscle results. At the same time, the muscle undergoes pronounced shortening and loses its natural translucency. This state is called *heat rigor*. It resembles *rigor mortis,* a term given to the stiffening of the muscles of the body generally which occurs in from 1 to 7 hours after death.

Electrical changes in muscle. Like nerve and other excitable tissues, an action potential is developed in muscle when it contracts, the active region of the muscle being negative to the inactive region. A current of

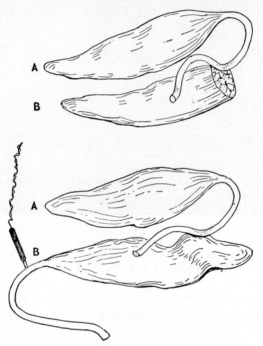

Fig. 11.28   The rheoscopic preparation. (See text.)

injury can also be demonstrated when one electrode is placed on a crushed or cut end of the muscle, the other upon the uninjured surface, and the two electrodes connected through a galvanometer (see Fig. 11.8, p. 470). The action current or the current of injury in muscle can be used to excite the nerve of another isolated muscle. This so-called *rheoscopic preparation* is shown in Figure 11.28. When the nerve of muscle A (*upper sketch*) is placed so that one part rests upon the cut surface of muscle B, and another part of the nerve is made suddenly to touch a point on the uninjured surface of B, a slight twitch of A occurs each time the contact is made. Similarly, if B (*lower sketch*) is stimulated to contract, a twitch of A occurs as the wave of contraction passes beneath a nerve which touches the contracting muscle at two points, a potential difference being established as the contraction wave spreads between the active (contracting) part of the muscle and the inactive (resting) part.

Muscular work and efficiency. Work, as defined by the physicist, is the product of the load (expressed in grams, kilograms, or pounds) and the vertical distance (in millimeters, centimeters, meters, or feet) through which it is raised. According to the units of distance and weight employed, the work is expressed in grammillimeters, gramcentimeters, kilogrammeters, or foot-pounds.

The isolated muscle can be made to perform work by stimulating it to contract and lift a weight. A load of a known weight is attached to the lever at the point of attachment of the muscle, which is then stimulated. The height above the base line of the tracing inscribed by the lever is measured. This measurement, however, is not the actual distance through which the weight has been raised, for the shortening of the muscle has been magnified by the lever. The distance as measured must therefore be divided by the magnification of the lever, which is usually five.

The work performed by the gastrocnemius muscle of the frog is most suitably expressed in grammillimeters (gmm). For example, a muscle that lifts a weight of 1 gram to a height of 2 mm does 2 gmm

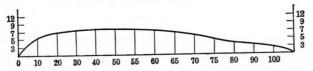

Fig. 11.29   Diagram to show the method of measuring muscle work. Heights of contractions along vertical lines, weights in grams along the horizontal line. (After McKendrick.)

of work. The muscle, when loaded with a heavier weight, may not raise it so high, yet may do more work. Thus, if it lifts a weight of 4 grams only 1 mm it does 4 gmm of work. Starting with a light load and gradually adding to it for a number of successive contractions, it is found that the work performed increases up to a maximum and then falls off. There exists, therefore, an optimum load—that is, a load with which the muscle performs the maximum amount of work (see Fig. 11.29).

Since the work, as just defined, is the product of the load and the lift, no work is done by an unloaded muscle when it contracts; nor by one that contracts against a weight that it is unable to lift. In both these instances, however, there is an expenditure of energy which is derived from chemical processes taking place in the muscle; all of this energy appears ultimately as heat.

The fibers of a muscle contracting against a resistance, such as a weight that it cannot move or a stiff spring that it cannot bend, of course, do not shorten. The tension within the muscles increases, however. Such a contraction is called *isometric* (Gk. *isos,* same + *metron,* measurement). An *isotonic* contraction, on the other hand, is one in which the muscle shortens, but its tension remains almost constant throughout the contraction. In the body both types of contraction take place. The isometric type is seen in those muscles that maintain the body's posture, such as the extensors on the front of the thigh. These exert a constant pull upon the leg, and thus hold the limb in the extended position to afford a firm support for the body. The movements of the limbs, as in walking, lifting objects with the hands, or throwing a ball, are brought about by isotonic contractions.

Of the total energy expended by any machine, a part appears as mechanical work, the remainder being dissipated as heat. The efficiency of the machine is defined as the percentage of the total energy that appears as work. Thus:

$$\text{Efficiency} = \frac{\text{work}}{\text{total energy (work} + \text{heat)}}$$

As mentioned above, a muscle contracting isometrically or without a load performs no work; all the energy is dissipated as heat. Contracting with an optimum load, on the other hand, muscle has an efficiency of from 25 to 30 percent, which compares favorably with that of the best type of gasoline engine. By measuring the heat produced by a muscle during its contraction and the work done, its efficiency can be readily calculated from the equation given above. In making the calculation, the energy appearing as work and as heat must, of course, be expressed in the same units. We may express the work in heat units (e.g., microcalories). Now, the heat equivalent of a grammillimeter is .00235 microcalorie. Therefore, if the heat produced is 8.4 microcalories, and the work performed is 1200 gmm, then the total energy expenditure expressed as heat can be calculated as follows:

Heat produced = 8.4 microcalories
Work   = 1200 gmm
Heat equivalent of the work = 1200 × .00235 = 2.8 microcalories

The total energy expenditure is, therefore, 8.4 + 2.8 — 11.2 microcalories.

The efficiency is $\dfrac{2.8}{11.2}$ = 25 percent

The chemical constitution of muscle. Fresh muscular tissue, which composes the lean part of beef, pork, etc., contains about 20 percent of protein and around 75 percent of water. The remaining 5 percent is made up of minerals and various organic compounds (glycogen, glucose, lipids, steroids, and nonprotein nitrogenous compounds). The principal mineral in the muscle cell (fiber) is potassium, which has a concentration of around 400 mg per 100 grams; magnesium, phosphorus, sodium, and calcium are present in much lower concentrations. The chief nonprotein nitrogenous substances are *creatine, phosphocreatine, adenosinetriphosphate, carnosine,* and *urea.* The main proteins composing the contractile elements of muscle (the micellae) are *myosin* and *actin.* These two proteins are in very close functional association in the micellae; the combination, known as *actomyosin,* is of essential importance in the contractile process.

The pigment of muscle, called *myoglobin* or *muscle hemoglobin,* is closely allied chemically, as well as in function, to hemoglobin.

The chemistry of muscular contraction. Muscle derives the energy for its contraction, ultimately, from the combustion of carbohydrate; in the final step of this process, oxygen is consumed and carbon dioxide (CO_2) and water (H_2O) produced. The actual contraction of the muscle, however, is brought about by the explosive separation of a molecule of phosphoric acid from *adenosinetriphosphate* (abbr. ATP), a compound composed of adenylic acid (a nucleotide, p. 366) and three molecules of phosphoric acid. *Adenosinediphosphate* (ADP) is thus formed. This reaction is the very first to occur when the muscle fiber contracts. The molecule of phosphoric acid split off from ATP combines with glycogen present in the muscle fiber. Instantaneously with the acquisition of phosphoric acid, the glycogen splits off a molecule of phosphorylated glucose, called *glucose phosphate,* which is converted through a series of intermediate reactions to *fructose diphosphate* (i.e., fructose combined with two molecules of phosphoric acid). The fructose diphosphate passes through a series of complicated reactions to form lactic acid. After the transfer of phosphorus from ATP to glycogen and the formation of ADP, *phosphocreatine* splits into *creatine* and *phosphoric acid*. The liberated phosphorus is taken up by ADP and ATP reformed, thus:

$$phosphocreatine \longrightarrow creatine + phosphoric\ acid$$
$$phosphoric\ acid + ADP \longrightarrow ATP$$

The conversion of ATP to ADP, as just stated, is the immediate source of the energy for the contraction of the muscle fiber. From the breakdown of phosphocreatine is derived the energy for the reformation of ATP from phosphoric acid and ADP. Phosphocreatine is also resynthesized, the energy for the resynthesis being derived from the breakdown of glucose phosphate to lactic acid.

Of the lactic acid produced, one fifth is oxidized to carbon dioxide and water. The remainder (four fifths) is resynthesized to glycogen in the liver, muscles, and other tissues of the body. Each of the several chemical reactions described above is dependent upon a specific enzyme. Only one of these need be referred to, and it will be spoken of later.

The removal of phosphoric acid from ATP and its resynthesis, as well as the breakdown of phosphocreatine, can be carried out in the absence of oxygen. The breakdown of glucose phosphate to lactic acid and the resynthesis of phosphocreatine can only occur in the presence of oxygen. There are, therefore, two phases in the contractile process— a *nonoxidative, anaerobic,* or *contraction phase* and an *oxidative, aerobic,* or *recovery phase.* This latter is necessary to restore energy-producing substances and permit continued contraction of the muscle.[3]

In so far as its energy relationships are concerned, the muscle fiber has been compared to a submarine which, while submerged, is driven by energy stored in electric batteries, oxygen being not required; this period corresponds to the anaerobic phase of the process in the muscle. The batteries are recharged when the submersible reaches the surface, oxygen being then necessary. This corresponds to the aerobic or recovery phase of the muscle.

Though it will be clear from the foregoing account that the reactions leading to lactic acid formation are required for the continued activity of muscle, contractions, nevertheless, can proceed for a time after

[3] A muscle deprived of oxygen (i.e., in an atmosphere of nitrogen) is, therefore, capable of responding to stimulation for a considerable time. Lactic acid, however, is not removed by oxidation and resynthesis to glycogen, but, accumulating, reduces the irritability of the muscle. The concentration of lactic acid at which the muscle fails to respond is around 0.5 percent. This is called the *lactic acid maximum*. When oxygen is supplied to a muscle fatigued by repeated stimulation in nitrogen, the lactic acid is removed and the irritability of the muscle restored.

the production of lactic acid has been entirely suppressed; the reaction is therefore not essential for the actual contraction. The production of lactic acid from the breakdown of carbohydrate in the isolated muscle can be prevented by treating it with a drug called *sodium iodoacetate;* yet the muscle so treated responds to stimulation for some time, or until the phosphocreatine store of the muscle is exhausted. But phosphocreatine cannot be reformed, since the energy for the resynthesis is derived from the glycogen to lactic acid reaction. A muscle poisoned by iodoacetate obviously cannot continue to respond for as long a time as can a normal muscle. The glycogen to lactic acid reaction, therefore, though not directly responsible for the contraction, serves, as it were, to "rewind" the contractile mechanism—to "set the trigger" for the next contraction. Carbohydrate, then, is the ultimate source of the energy for the activity of the isolated muscle.

Table 11-4 presents a summary of the chemical changes occurring during and immediately after its contraction.

Table 11-4

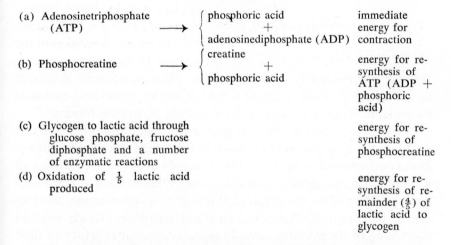

(a) Adenosinetriphosphate (ATP) ⟶ { phosphoric acid + adenosinediphosphate (ADP) } immediate energy for contraction

(b) Phosphocreatine ⟶ { creatine + phosphoric acid } energy for resynthesis of ATP (ADP + phosphoric acid)

(c) Glycogen to lactic acid through glucose phosphate, fructose diphosphate and a number of enzymatic reactions — energy for resynthesis of phosphocreatine

(d) Oxidation of $\frac{1}{5}$ lactic acid produced — energy for resynthesis of remainder ($\frac{4}{5}$) of lactic acid to glycogen

The transformation by the muscle fiber of chemical energy into mechanical energy resulting in movement. The shortening (contraction) of the micellae is the fundamental mechanical change that occurs in the muscle fiber when it is excited to contract. We must now consider the possible way in which the loss of a molecule of phosphoric acid from adenosinetriphosphate (ATP) brings about this change. The contraction of a whole muscle is simply the sum of the shortening taking place in the millions of micellae that the muscle contains, and it is strongly suggested that the shortening of the micellae is due, in turn,

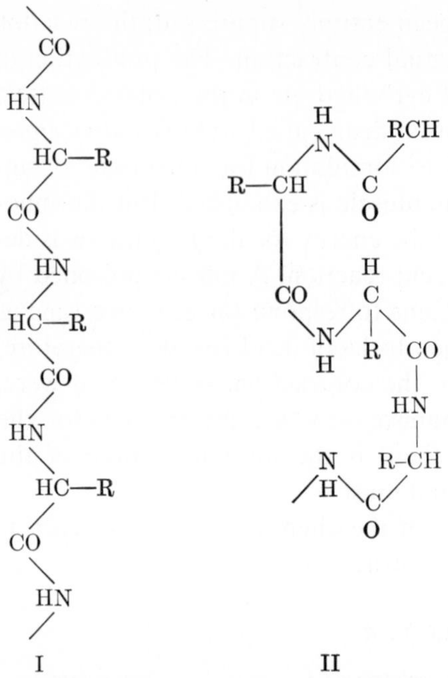

```
    \
    CO
    /
   HN                          H        RCH
    \                          N
    HC—R              R—CH      C
    /                  |        O
   CO                  |
    \                  |        H
   HN               CO         C
    /                 \N        |
   HC—R              H  R  CO
    \                          |
    CO                        HN
    /                          |
   HN                    N     R–CH
    \                   /H     C
    HC—R                       O
    /
   CO
    \
   HN
    /

    I                    II
```

Fig. 11.30 Showing a myosin molecule in an extended (I) and in a folded or contracted state (II).

to the shortening, by folding or rolling up, of the long chains of molecules constituting the muscle proteins (Fig. 11.30).

In the ultramicroscopic study of proteins of hair (e.g., wool, feathers, etc.), it has been found that their molecules are arranged in long roughly parallel and more or less folded chains. The hair can be lengthened by stretching it; when released it returns to its original length. This property of such structures is due, it is believed, to the unfolding and refolding, like a concertina, of the long amino-acid chains of its constituent protein. When heated, or treated with a strong chemical, the natural condition of the protein in the hair is altered; the hair is permanently shortened and its inherent elasticity destroyed as a result of the tight irreversible folding of the amino-acid chains of its proteins. Thus is explained the shrinkage of woolen fabrics.

Now, myosin, like the fibrous proteins of wool and other hairs, is composed of long chains of amino-acid molecules. A chemical change in the environment of the molecules (brought about by the splitting of a phosphoric acid group from adenosinetriphosphate it is supposed) causes folding of the molecular chains and, as a consequence, shortening of the micellae. When the chemical conditions which induced shortening of the micellae have disappeared, the latter return to their previous length; the muscle fiber relaxes.

A chainlike molecule of a fibrous protein in the folded (contracted) and in the unfolded (relaxed) state is shown in Figure 11.30.

Myosin, an enzyme. The surprising discovery was made a few years ago (1939) that myosin—one of the essential proteins in the muscle fiber, and which, with actin, largely composes the micellae—appears to be itself an enzyme required for the splitting, with lightninglike rapidity, of adenosinetriphosphate.[4]

---

[4] Following the usual practice of naming enzymes, myosin is also known as *adenosinetriphosphatase.*

As a machine the muscle fiber is unique. There is no man-made mechanical device with which it can be compared satisfactorily. The muscle is a chemical machine and a comparison has been drawn between it and the internal combustion engine in which the firing of a mixture of gas and air moves a piston. The comparison would be closer if an engine were conceived in which the spark which ignites the gas mixture and the piston were one and the same. A piston raised to a high temperature would, in a way, be comparable to myosin, for this protein, being the moving part of the muscle as well as an enzyme through which the initial energy is liberated, corresponds to both piston and

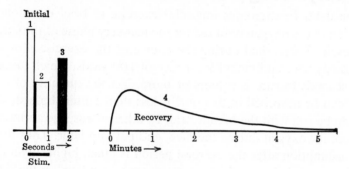

Fig. 11.31   Diagram showing the stages of heat production by muscle during and following a short tetanic contraction. The three rectangles represent the initial heat. 1, heat produced at the commencement of the contraction; 2, that produced during the maintenance of the contraction; 3, relaxation heat; 4, recovery heat. (After Evans, *Recent Advances in Physiology*.)

spark. But the muscle fiber is not, like the gasoline motor, a heat engine utilizing the pressure generated by heated gas molecules for power. Muscle gains the energy for its contraction largely from the bonds which hold certain phosphoric acid groups to organic compounds, such as adenosinetriphosphate and phosphocreatine.

Heat production in muscle. It has been mentioned that during the isometric contraction of muscle, the total energy expended appears as heat. The heat production is divided into two phases, termed the *initial* heat and the *recovery* heat. The initial heat comprises the heat produced in chemical reactions during the contraction of the muscle (*contraction heat*) together with a smaller quantity which appears during relaxation (*relaxation heat*). The latter results from the conversion to heat of the energy exhibited as tension during the contraction phase. The initial heat is produced during the anaerobic phase of the contractile process; it, but not the recovery heat, is therefore generated by a muscle contracting in nitrogen. The recovery heat appears after relaxation is over, and is due mainly to the oxidation of lactic acid (Fig. 11.31).

The phases of heat production are summarized in the following table:

1. *Initial heat* = 45 percent of the total heat,
   a. Contraction heat 65 percent of the initial heat,
   b. Relaxation heat 35 percent of the initial heat.
2. *Recovery heat* = 55 percent of the total heat.

The Physiology of Muscular Exercise

Oxygen debt. In strenuous muscular exercise of brief duration, only a fraction of the oxygen required for the recovery phase of the contracting muscles is breathed during the course of the exercise. For example, the oxygen requirement for a race of 100 yards, which takes only a few seconds to run, is 6 liters or more. Yet the quantity of oxygen which can be absorbed in this time is less than 1 liter. Indeed, a short race can be run with the breath held. In other words, the sprinter goes into debt for oxygen during the race, and pays up later. Thus the oxygen consumption after the exercise period is much higher than during an ordinary period of rest. The extra oxygen is utilized in the removal of the lactic acid produced during the exercise. The size of the oxygen debt for any piece of work is determined by measuring the oxygen consumption of the after-period of exercise, and subtracting from the result the figure for the oxygen consumption of a corresponding period of rest. During very strenuous muscular effort, the oxygen debt may amount to 15 liters or more.

The ability of the muscles to contract, without receiving the full oxygen requirement until the work has been completed, has an obvious advantage. Short periods of strenuous exercise can be undertaken which would otherwise be impossible, for the respiratory and circulatory systems are quite unequal to the task of furnishing, during the exercise, the great volume of oxygen which is ultimately used in the recovery process. The maximum quantity of oxygen that can be delivered to and consumed by the tissues of a large healthy man is not more than about 2 liters per minute and, of most persons, considerably less than this.

In light exercise no oxygen debt is incurred. The lactic acid is removed as it is produced; in other words, the body, in so far as oxygen consumption is concerned, "pays as it goes." Lactic-acid production and its removal are nicely balanced; a "steady state" is established.

When the "steady state" has been reached, a person engaged in an athletic performance of some duration—such as running, rowing, etc.—breathes with less effort. As the expression goes, he has got his "second wind."

The source of the energy for muscular work. We have seen that the energy for the contraction of the isolated muscle is ultimately derived from carbohydrate. Glycogen is broken down through glucose phosphate and fructose diphosphate to lactic acid. In the numerous studies of the respiratory exchanges of the isolated gastrocnemius muscle of the frog during contraction, respiratory quotients of 1.0 (p. 354) are obtained. In the intact animal carbohydrate is also the fuel for short bouts of muscular exercise. After a sprint, for example, a fall in blood sugar may occur, and the ingestion of glucose prior to a race is now recognized as a valuable means of postponing fatigue and enhancing muscular performance. In prolonged and exhausting work the carbohydrate stores become depleted; fat is then burned to furnish the required energy. Protein apparently is not utilized in muscular exercise, or, if so, to a very small extent.

The adjustments in the respiratory and circulatory systems in muscular exercise. During strenuous muscular effort, the quantity of air breathed is from 300 to 400 percent greater than during a resting period of the same length. The greater pulmonary ventilation is brought about by an increase in the respiratory rate, as well as by an increase in the volume of each breath. The increased breathing occurs at the very outset of exercise; indeed, it has been shown in experiments upon man that it may actually anticipate the exercise by a brief interval—that is, an effect upon the respirations may be noted at the instant a signal has been given to start some muscular act, and before the muscles contract. Changes in heart rate and blood pressure may also precede the contractions of the muscles. The influence upon the respiratory and circulatory systems at the commencement of or preceding the exercise is due to impulses from psychic levels of the brain, and probably also from the motor area of the cerebral cortex, upon the centers in the medulla. The efficiency with which the work is performed is also undoubtedly influenced by emotional factors. These act most likely by bringing about more perfect coordination of respiratory and circulatory mechanisms, but also, probably, through a direct effect upon the muscular contractions themselves. A man is spurred to greater effort, and is a more effective worker, if the work interests him than if he is bored with it, or does it as a matter of routine. In emergencies or during excitement—"in the heat of the moment"—feats of strength of endurance are accomplished which, in the absence of the emotional factor, would be impossible. It is likely that adrenaline liberated into the blood stream through nervous influences plays a role in some instances (pp. 420–1).

If the exercise is severe, chemical factors soon come into play to increase the pulmonary ventilation. The production of lactic acid and carbon dioxide in the muscles causes a slight increase in the hydrogen ion concentration of the blood which acts as a stimulus to the respiratory center. The greater carbon dioxide produced by the exercise is thus eliminated.

The adaptations of the circulatory mechanism in exercise are of a highly complex nature. The blood pressure rises to from 160 to 180 mm Hg, as a result of constriction of the vessels in the splanchnic region. The carotid sinus depressor reflex is in abeyance or neutralized by pressor reflexes. The vessels in the muscles themselves dilate. A larger proportion of the blood volume is diverted, therefore, to the active muscles than during rest. The vasodilatation in the muscles is due, mainly, to chemical substances—namely, carbon dioxide and lactic acid, products of the contractile process—acting directly upon the vessels. Not only do the muscles receive a greater proportion of the total blood volume during exercise than during rest but, as a result of the contraction of the spleen, the volume of circulating blood may be increased by from 20 to 25 percent. The blood also circulates more rapidly; the output of the heart and, consequently, the quantity of blood pumped per minute through the systemic and pulmonary vessels is increased many fold. In a large robust man performing arduous work, the output of the heart may amount to 35 liters (nearly 8 gallons) or more per minute. The greater cardiac output is the result of the greater venous return—that is, of the increased volume of blood flowing through the contracting muscles and carried along the great veins to the right side of the heart.

The effect of muscular exercise upon the heart rate varies in different persons. In those untrained to muscular work, the heart accelerates markedly, a rate of from 110 to 120 per minute being not unusual, whereas the heart of the athlete may show little or no acceleration during muscular feats of a highly exacting character, such as sprinting or rowing. Through the respiratory and circulatory mechanisms just described, the maximum load of oxygen is delivered to the contracting muscles. The oxygen supply is further augmented through the effect which the carbon dioxide and lactic acid produced in the muscle, and the local rise in temperature, exert upon the liberation of oxygen from oxyhemoglobin. As mentioned on page 251, increased acidity and a rise in temperature cause the hemoglobin to give up a greater part of its oxygen load.

Athletic training causes a moderate enlargement of the normal heart. The enlargement is purely physiological, and is commensurate with the accompanying increased bulk of the skeletal muscles. Enlargement (dilatation and hypertrophy) of the heart occurs when the heart is damaged; and athletes, of course, like anyone else, may be subjects of heart disease. Because some athletes have shown cardiac dilatation and hypertrophy or other evidence of heart disease, it used to be thought that athletics, if engaged in too enthusiastically, led to heart disease. It is now generally admitted, however, that the well-conditioned heart of the young adult is not damaged by even strenuous exercise. The skeletal muscles fatigue before a healthy heart does. In other words, the heart free from disease can perform the greatest task which is ever demanded of it. The work of the heart consists in discharging the blood conveyed to it, and the skeletal muscles are not capable of driving enough blood along the veins to tax its powers. On the other hand, a person with a diseased heart, should he indulge in strenuous exercise, runs a serious risk, if not of inducing cardiac failure, of at least causing serious damage to his heart. In apparently healthy persons after middle age, the state of the heart muscle is an unknown quantity, and for this reason excessive muscular effort should be avoided.

CHAPTER 12

The Central Nervous System

The structure of nervous tissue. The brain and spinal cord are composed of *nerve cells* with their processes—the nerve fibers—and *neuroglial cells.* The bodies of the nerve cells, and their processes for a short distance from their origin, compose the *gray matter* of the central nervous system. The nerve fibers, collected into bundles or tracts, constitute the *white matter. Neuroglial cells* perform no essential nervous function; they form a supporting framework for the nervous elements proper. There are three types of neuroglial cells, called, respectively, *oligodendroglia* (or oligodendrocytes), *astrocytes,* and *microglia* (see Fig. 12.1). The last mentioned are elements of the reticuloendothelial system.

The *nerve cell* or *neuron* is the structural unit of the nervous system. It consists of a *body* and one or more *processes.* The cell bodies in different parts of the nervous system vary widely in size (4 to 25 microns) and in shape (triangular, multiangular, round, spindle- or pear-shaped). In respect to their internal structure, however, all possess certain characteristics in common. The typical nerve cell has a relatively large globular nucleus situated near the center of the cell and containing, as a rule, a single nucleolus. The cytoplasm, or *pericaryon* —that is, the part of the body of the cell exclusive of the nucleus— shows, after suitable staining procedures, fine fibrils—the *neurofibrils.* These course through the cell body from pole to pole, sweeping around the nucleus. Their presence in the nerve fiber has been mentioned on page 461. When stained with an appropriate basic dye, the cytoplasm of the nerve cell exhibits a striated or mottled appearance, due to the

506

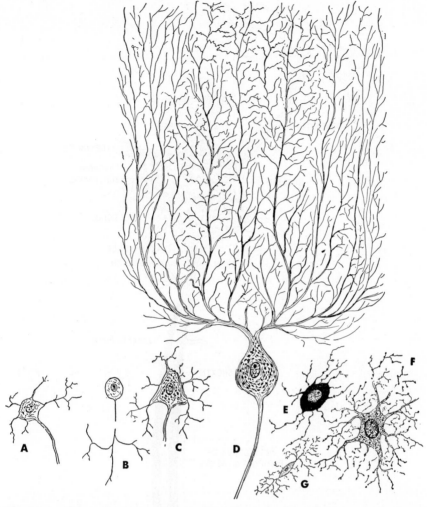

Fig. 12.1   Types of nerve and neuroglia cells. A, motor cell from anterior horn of the spinal cord; B, unipolar nerve cell; C, giant pyramidal cell from the motor area of the cerebral cortex; D, Purkinje cell from the cerebellar cortex; E, oligodendroglia cell; F, astrocyte of neuroglia; G, microglia.

presence of irregularly shaped particles, resembling the chromatic material of the nucleus. These particles are called *Nissl bodies* or (from their tendency to be arranged in rows, thus suggesting a tiger's stripes) *tigroid bodies* or the *tigroid substance* (see Fig. 12.2).

In 1949 Dr. Murray Barr made the astonishing discovery that the nerve cells of females could be distinguished histologically from those of males. The nucleolus in the nerve cells of the former shows adjacent to it a minute body composed of chromatin. This "nuclear satellite,"

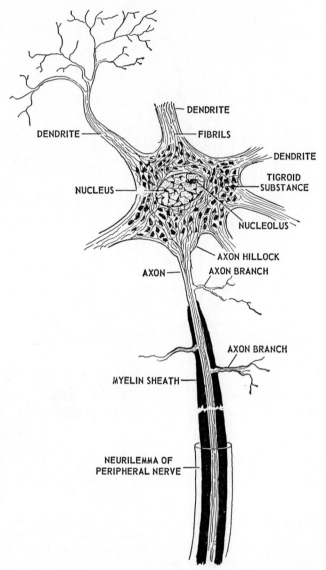

DENDRITE

DENDRITE

FIBRILS

DENDRITE

NUCLEUS

TIGROID
SUBSTANCE

NUCLEOLUS

AXON HILLOCK

AXON

AXON BRANCH

AXON BRANCH

MYELIN SHEATH

NEURILEMMA OF
PERIPHERAL NERVE

Fig. 12.2 A drawing (semidiagrammatic) of a nerve
cell. All but one dendrite have been cut.

as it was originally called, is not found except very rarely in the nerve
cells of males. The dot of chromatin has since been shown to be present in the cells of the other tissues of the body in which it lies near the
nucleolar membrane; it is now more usually referred to as the *sex
chromatin* (see p. 666).

A nerve cell possesses, as a rule, many processes which vary very

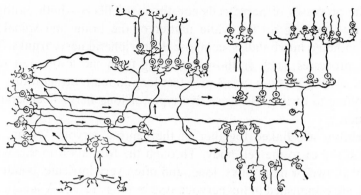

Fig. 12.3 Diagram to show how a few nerve cells may communicate with a great number of others in different parts of the central nervous system.

widely in length, thickness, and general appearance, according to the type of cell. These processes are of two kinds called, respectively, *dendrites* and *axons*. The dendrites which are usually multiple, though they may be single or even absent, *conduct impulses toward the body of the cell;* the axon *conducts from the cell body.* A typical dendrite has many branches (Gk. *dendron,* a tree), whereas the axon, which usually arises from the opposite pole of the cell is, as a rule, a long slender fiber with no branches near the cell body; it branches near its termination, or it may give off twigs at intervals along its length and more or less at right angles to it. The axon is always single.

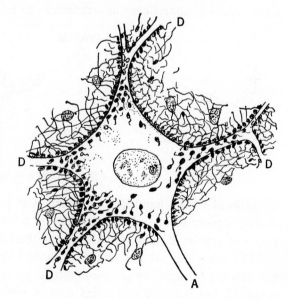

Fig. 12.4 End feet (represented by small black ovals) or *pieds termineaux* making contact with the body and the dendrites of a nerve cell; A, axon; D, dendrites.

The processes of nerve cells constitute the fibers—both motor and sensory—making up the white matter of the brain and spinal cord and, gathered into bundles, compose the peripheral nerve trunks. Thus, some processes, such as those extending from the lower part of the spinal cord to the toes, are 3 or 4 feet long in man. Structurally, there is nothing to distinguish these two types of long nerve fiber from one another.

Neurons are linked together in the central nervous system, axon to dendrite or to the cell body. Through the formation in this way of chains of two or more links, long, and often very intricate, conducting paths are established in the nervous system (Fig. 12.3). A junction between the axon of one neuron with a dendrite or the cell body of another is called a *synapse*. There is no actual structural union of two neurons at the synapse—merely contact. The axon terminates in a small swelling called a *synaptic nob, end foot,* or *pied termineau,* through which it makes contact with the dendrite or body of another nerve cell (Fig. 12.4).

Reflex Action

A nervous reflex is an involuntary act brought about by the stimulation of an afferent nerve ending or receptor (p. 514). Familiar examples of actions which are purely reflex in nature are the following: the quick closure of the eyelid when some object touches the eyelashes, or even suddenly approaches and threatens to strike the eye; the sudden

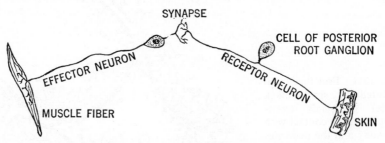

Fig. 12.5   Diagram of the simplest conceivable reflex arc.

withdrawal of the hand or foot when it is painfully stimulated; the sharp recovery of one's balance when, as a result of a slip, the body's center of gravity is suddenly shifted; and the jerk of the leg (knee jerk, p. 518) when the patellar tendon is tapped sharply. Though such reflex acts are brought about involuntarily, we are aware that they have occurred, but innumerable reflex acts of which we are quite unconscious—e.g., the movements of the gastrointestinal tract, variations in heart rate and respiration, changes in caliber of the small blood vessels, the secretion of glands, etc.—are continually taking place in the body.

The reflex arc. The structural basis of reflex action is the *reflex arc.* The latter may be described in its *simplest conceivable* form as consisting of two neurons, linked together in the central nervous system, axon to dendrite (see Fig. 12.5). The two neurons are thus arranged, one with its axon, the other with its dendrite, directed toward the periphery. The latter receives the stimulus, and transmits impulses to the central nervous system where, through a synaptic contact, the two nerve cells are linked; it is therefore called the *receptor neuron,* or the *afferent limb* of the reflex arc. The other neuron, which transmits impulses

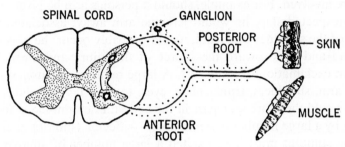

Fig. 12.6   Diagram of a spinal reflex arc with its center in the spinal cord, showing receptor and effector neurons connected by the connector neuron (in the spinal cord).

from the central nervous system to the peripheral organ, muscle, or gland, is called the *effector neuron* or the *efferent limb* of the reflex arc. The region in the central nervous system (brain or spinal cord) where the two neurons form their junction (synapse) is referred to as the *reflex center.* Thus a stimulus applied to the terminal of the receptor neuron sets up an impulse or a volley of impulses which is transmitted to the reflex center; a discharge of impulses then occurs down the effector neuron to the peripheral organ or *effector* (e.g., muscle or gland).

For the sake of simplicity in illustrating the general principles of the reflex arc, one composed of only two neurons has been described, but it is unlikely that more than a very few such simple reflex arcs [1] exist in higher animals. One nerve cell, at least, is, as a rule, interposed between the receptor and effector neurons. This is called the *connector, internuncial,* or *intercalated* neuron. In the great majority of reflex arcs in the central nervous system of mammals, not one but a chain of such connector neurons is present.

[1] One of these is that of the knee jerk (p. 518).

A diagram of a simple reflex arc having its center in the spinal cord is shown in Figure 12.6. It will be noted that the cell body of the receptor neuron is situated, not within the cord itself but just outside—namely, in the ganglion of the posterior root of a spinal nerve. The effector neuron has its cell body in the anterior horn of gray matter (anterior or ventral horn cell, p. 524); its axon leaves the cord in the anterior root of the spinal nerve, and is continued into a peripheral nerve. The connector neuron has its cell body in the posterior (dorsal) horn of spinal gray matter; its axon synapses with the dendrite of the anterior horn cell; its dendrite with the central process (axon) of the receptor neuron.

In most reflex actions of higher animals, a great number of reflex arcs are involved. For example, should a person's arm be given a sharp and unexpected slap, he would jerk the arm away; associated movements of the shoulder and trunk would probably occur; he would turn his head and eyes toward the source of the injury and, most likely, utter an exclamation of some sort. A large number of muscles—those of the arm, shoulders, trunk, neck, eyes, tongue, larynx, and respiration—would therefore take part in the action. Each muscle is supplied in turn by a large number of nerve fibers—effector (motor) neurons—and the stimulus must have excited a large number of afferent nerve endings—receptor neurons—in the skin. If instead of slapping the skin, which stimulates a relatively large area, a stab were made with a pin, the reflex response would probably be the same. A movement involving a large number of muscles would result. Yet, as compared with the slap, the pin must have stimulated much fewer sensory endings. The number of effector (motor) neurons must have been greatly in excess of the sensory endings which had been stimulated. Each receptor neuron must therefore be connected within the central nervous system with a large number of effector neurons. As a matter of fact, *every receptor neuron is potentially in communication with motor neurons throughout the entire spinal cord and brain.* The synapses, normally, offer a certain "resistance" to the passage of impulses which limits the spread of excitation within the central nervous system. In strychnine poisoning or in tetanus, however, synaptic resistance is greatly diminished; a very weak localized stimulus then sets up impulses which spread widely throughout the central nervous system, and may cause forcible convulsive contractions of virtually all the voluntary muscles of the body.

Not only is each afferent fiber in communication with a large number of effector neurons, but, conversely, each of the latter is connected with many afferent fibers. That is to say, stimulation of sensory nerves in widely separated parts of the body may bring about reflex contraction of one and the same group of muscles. An anterior horn cell of the cord is, therefore, a point of convergence of a number of afferent paths, each motor neuron serving as a pathway common to impulses from various sources (see Fig. 12.7). It is therefore called the *final*

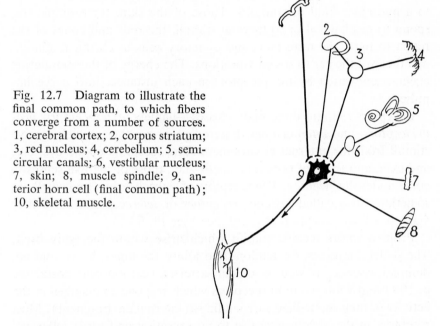

Fig. 12.7   Diagram to illustrate the final common path, to which fibers converge from a number of sources. 1, cerebral cortex; 2, corpus striatum; 3, red nucleus; 4, cerebellum; 5, semicircular canals; 6, vestibular nucleus; 7, skin; 8, muscle spindle; 9, anterior horn cell (final common path); 10, skeletal muscle.

common path. For example, scratching the back of a spinal dog (i.e., one whose spinal cord has been severed in the upper thoracic region some weeks previously) causes rhythmical contractions of the flexor muscles of the hind limb (*scratch reflex*). Painful stimulation of the hind paw also causes contraction of the flexor muscles of the limb, the paw being thus withdrawn from the injurious agent (*flexor reflex*). If one should attempt to elicit both these reflexes at the same time, there must obviously be a conflict between them. They are *antagonistic* and cannot both employ the final common path at the same instant. In such and other instances of two antagonistic reflexes competing for the final common path, the one of less biological importance gives way; it is suppressed. Thus, as compared with a painful stimulus which signals some injury to the animal, the momentary irritation of a flea is of little importance. It is otherwise with reflexes which are *allied* in nature; they can utilize the final common path simultaneously; one reflex tends to strengthen or reinforce the other. For example, stimulation of the toes of the hind paw causes flexion of the corresponding limb. If the opposite forepaw is stimulated simultaneously, the flexion of the hind limb is strengthened.

Receptors. Most types of afferent nerve terminate at the periphery in specialized structures, known as *receptors* or *sense organs*. There are various types of receptor, each being especially adapted to respond to a particular kind of stimulus. Those of the skin, for example, respond to mechanical or to thermal stimuli, the rods and cones of the retina to light, the taste buds and olfactory cells to chemical stimuli, and those of the ear to sound vibrations. The energy of the stimulating agent is converted by the receptor, in each instance, into nerve impulses.

Receptors fall into three main classes—namely, *exteroceptors, proprioceptors,* and *interoceptors.* Exteroceptors are those which receive stimuli from the external environment. The receptors of the eye, ear, and skin, and those of taste and smell—i.e., those of the five senses— come under this heading. The receptors of sight, hearing, and smell are sometimes also called *distance receptors* or *telereceptors,* since they make possible perception at a distance (see Pl. 9A).

Proprioceptors receive stimuli which arise within the body itself. The skeletal muscles, the tendons and joints, the lungs, heart, and abdominal viscera, as well as certain arteries (carotid and aorta, see p. 199) and veins, contain receptors which respond to changes in the activity of their immediate surroundings (internal environment). Most receptors in the viscera give rise to no sensation and serve reflex actions of which we are quite unaware. The proprioceptors situated in the skeletal muscles are stimulated by the contraction or stretching of the muscle fibers; these, called muscle spindles, have been described (p. 483). Of the impulses set up by the stimulation of proprioceptors in muscles, tendons, and joints, some reach consciousness; to such impulses is due our sense of the movement and position of our limbs— *kinesthetic sense.* Many impulses set up by muscular movement end, however, in parts of the central nervous system (e.g., spinal cord and cerebellum) which carry out their activities beneath the level of consciousness. The tonic contractions of skeletal muscle, as well as the smooth and coordinated nature of voluntary movement, are dependent upon impulses, both sensory and nonsensory, arising in the muscle proprioceptors.

The interoceptors are situated in the mucous membrane of the respiratory and alimentary tracts. Though removed from direct influence by the external environment, these receptors, nevertheless, are stimulated by agencies originating in the outside world—namely, air and food.

Conduction over the reflex arc. Reflex conduction differs from conduction over nerve fibers in several particulars. In the first place, the *velocity of transmission of impulses* over the reflex arc is considerably lower than that over the nerve fiber. For example, if a muscle is caused to contract reflexly, the time elapsing between the application of the stimulus to the receptor and the response of the muscle is considerably greater than if the impulses had traveled the same distance over a nerve fiber alone. The difference is due to the synapse, where the impulses are delayed. Second, conduction in the reflex arc is always in *one direction*—to the reflex center in the afferent limb, away from the center in the efferent limb. When a nerve fiber is stimulated, impulses travel in *both directions*. If, for example, a motor nerve fiber is cut just after it leaves the spinal cord, and the central end stimulated, impulses are set up which travel along the efferent fibers to the spinal center. But these impulses, caused by the artificial stimulus, do not reach the afferent neurons; they are blocked at the synapses. The latter thus acts like a valve, permitting impulses to pass in one direction over the reflex arc, but not in the other. (See also p. 521.)

Third, reflex conduction is much more *susceptible to lack of oxygen, fatigue, and to the action of anesthetics.* We have seen that the nerve fiber has a very low rate of metabolism (p. 478), and will continue to respond to stimulation for a considerable time when deprived of oxygen. The metabolism of nerve cells, on the other hand, is high, and the cells very soon lose their irritability when deprived of oxygen. The cells of the cerebral cortex, for example, are permanently injured if their blood supply is cut off for 5 minutes or so. The lower levels of the central nervous system are somewhat less susceptible to lack of oxygen: the cells of the midbrain continue to function for 10 minutes after their blood supply has been arrested; the centers of the medulla oblongata for from 15 to 30 minutes; and those of the spinal cord for from 15 to 35 minutes.

In the presence of oxygen, the nerve fiber continues to respond to stimulation for long periods without showing fatigue, in marked contrast to the reflex arc, which is readily fatigued. In the intact animal, general anesthesia (e.g., by ether or chloroform) quickly abolishes reflex action, whereas little effect is produced upon the excitability of the nerve fiber. Even after an animal has been killed by an anesthetic (death being due to paralysis, by the anesthetic, of vital centers in the brain—e.g., of heart and respiration), the nerves for some time later show little or no alteration in their responses to direct stimulation. Of course, when an anesthetic is applied to an isolated nerve, its excitability is very quickly abolished. Among other characteristic features of reflex action are *summation, after discharge,* and *reciprocal inhibition.*

Summation. It was pointed out on page 476 that the magnitude of the nerve impulse cannot be increased by increasing the rate of stimulation. When a nerve receives stimuli in rapid succession, the impulses do not fuse and produce an impulse of greater magnitude, but always remain separate. Summation, on the other hand, is readily demonstrated in the reflex arc. A single stimulus, for example, applied to an afferent nerve, though it sets up an impulse, rarely causes a reflex response. If, however, two or more stimuli of the same strength as the single one are applied in rapid sequence, a response follows. Each impulse produces a state of some sort in the region of the synapse which is capable of being added to, or summed with, the state produced by previous impulses. The nature of this state produced at the synapses— the *central excitatory state,* as it has been called—is not clearly understood, but evidently it must be raised to a certain threshold value before excitation of the effector neurons can occur.

After discharge. When a motor nerve is stimulated, the response of the muscle ends (i.e., impulses cease to be discharged along the fibers of the nerve) the moment that the stimulus is withdrawn. When, on the other hand, the muscular response is brought about reflexly, the muscle may continue to contract for a short time after the stimulus to the afferent nerve has ceased. This reflex phenomenon is explained upon the basis that the central excitatory state, which has been built up at the synapse, takes an appreciable length of time to be discharged along the effector neuron and, therefore, persists after the stimulus has been withdrawn.

Reciprocal inhibition. Stimulation of a motor nerve results in the contraction of all the muscles supplied by the nerve, irrespective of their actions; muscles having antagonistic actions (e.g., flexors and extensors) contract and oppose one another. No purposeful movement of the part is brought about; the motor nerve does not contain inhibitory fibers. In a reflex action, on the contrary, the muscular response consists of a coordinate movement—flexion of the knee joint, for example (see flexion reflex, below). In such a movement, the flexors of the knee contract while the extensors undergo reciprocal inhibition (relaxation). The mechanism whereby extension or other antagonistic action is inhibited has been much debated, but the inhibitory effect must be developed in the reflex center—that is, at a synapse between the afferent and efferent neurons—for, as just mentioned, the motor nerve itself does not contain inhibitory fibers. We therefore speak of a *central inhibitory state* as well as of a central excitatory state.

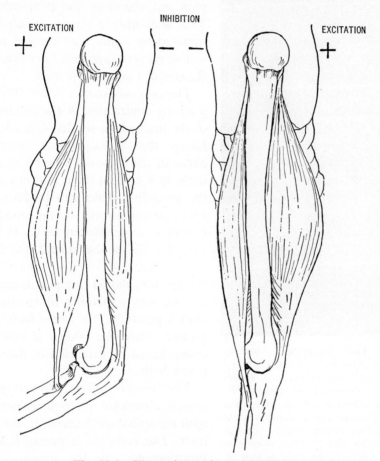

Fig. 12.8   Illustrating reciprocal inhibition.

Reciprocal inhibition is also seen in voluntary movement. For example, in flexing the arm at the elbow, the contraction of the biceps is accompanied by reciprocal inhibition of the triceps. On the other hand, when the elbow is extended, the triceps contracts while the biceps relaxes (Figs. 12.8 and 12.9). Such reciprocal muscular action is, of course, essential for the performance of any purposeful act.

Certain limb reflexes of special interest. *The flexion reflex.* This reflex consists of a strong contraction of the flexor muscles of the limb (together with inhibition of the extensors—reciprocal inhibition) when the afferent nerve of the *same* (*ipsilateral*) limb is stimulated. The limb is flexed at ankle, knee, and hip. The biological significance of this reflex is evident; in the intact animal the limb is withdrawn, automatically, from an agent which causes pain and, therefore, threatens injury. This and other reactions which are initiated by injury, and serve a protective purpose, are called *nociceptive* (L. *noceo,* I injure) *reflexes.*

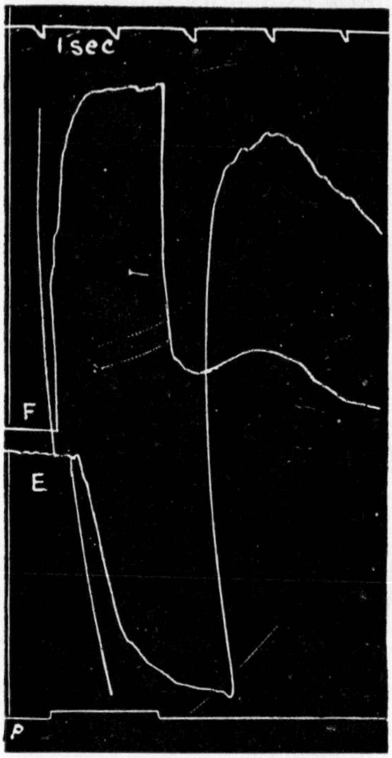

The crossed extensor reflex. This is a strong contraction of the extensors of the limb which results from stimulating the corresponding afferent nerve of the *opposite* (*contralateral*) limb. It is evident then, that this and the preceding reflex can be brought about simultaneously by the stimulation of a single afferent nerve. In the everyday life of the animal, the two reflexes therefore compose a purposeful act, for, should one paw come in contact with something which stimulates it painfully, it is raised from the ground, while the body's support is strengthened by extension of the opposite limb.

Fig. 12.9 Reciprocal innervation. Record from the leg muscles of a decerebrate cat, showing contraction of flexors, F, and inhibition of the extensors, E. The two curves actually were inscribed synchronously but the lever for the extensor muscle is set a little to the right of that of the flexor muscle. (From Sherrington.)

The stretch reflex. Stretching a muscle connected through its nerves with the spinal cord causes it to contract. The response is purely reflex. Proprioceptors in the muscle—the *muscle spindles*—are excited by a stretch stimulus. The impulses thus set up are transmitted to the spinal reflex center, a discharge of impulses then occurring down the effector neurons. A stretching force that lengthens the muscle by a small fraction of an inch is sufficient to elicit this reflex; its importance in maintaining a posture or attitude of the body for a prolonged period will be spoken of presently.

The knee jerk and other tendon (or deep) reflexes. A light tap upon the tendon below the kneecap (patellar tendon), while the knee hangs limply in a semiflexed position, causes a quick contraction of the extensor muscle on the front of the thigh (quadriceps muscle). The leg gives a sharp kick. This is called the *knee jerk* or *patellar reflex;* it is one type of stretch reflex, the tap upon the tendon causing a sudden stretch of the thigh muscle. In the investigation of a person with nervous disease, the knee jerk is tested as a matter of routine. The reflex is *abolished* in any condition which interrupts the reflex arc—namely, disease or injury of the peripheral nerves (efferent or afferent fibers) supplying the quadriceps muscle, or of the reflex centers in the lumbar region of the spinal cord. It is *exaggerated* in disease or injury involving the corticospinal tracts descending from the cerebral cortex to the cells of the anterior horns of the spinal cord (p. 526). Other tendon reflexes of clinical importance are the biceps and triceps jerks (tapping the biceps tendon in front of or the triceps tendon above the elbow) and the ankle jerk (tapping the tendo Achillis—the tendon above the heel). Loss of the biceps and triceps jerks indicates disease or injury of the nerves of the arm or of the motor cells in the thoracic region of the spinal cord; exaggeration of these reflexes is seen in disease involving the fiber tracts connecting the cerebral cortex with the motor cells in the thoracic part of the spinal cord; abolition of the ankle jerk tells of disease or injury involving the nerves to the leg muscles, or of the nerve cells of the lumbosacral part of the spinal cord; exaggeration indicates a lesion of the motor tracts of the cord at his level.

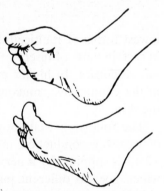

Though they do not come under the present heading, it is convenient to mention here two *cutaneous* or *superficial reflexes* of great clinical importance—namely, the *plantar response* and the *abdominal reflex*. The normal plantar response consists of a downward movement (plantarflexion) of the great toe—i.e., toward the sole, when the skin of the sole is stroked. In certain nervous lesions (e.g., injury to the corticospinal tracts), the great toe instead of being flexed toward the sole moves

Fig. 12.10   Illustrating the normal plantar response, *upper sketch,* and the extensor response (Babinsky), *lower sketch.*

upward (dorsiflexion). This abnormal response is called the *sign of Babinski* (Fig. 12.10).

The abdominal reflex consists in a contraction of the abdominal muscles caused by stroking the overlying skin. It is abolished in lesions of the corticospinal tracts, of the peripheral nerves, or of the reflex centers in the thoracic part of the spinal cord.

The axon reflex. This is not a reflex at all, in the ordinary sense of the term, for nerve cells play no part; that is to say, no reflex center is interposed in the path of the impulses. The reflex depends upon the fact that impulses can pass in either direction along a nerve fiber; in the axon reflex, they travel from some or other receptive surface, along one branch of the fiber (axon), and then down the other branch to an effector—e.g., smooth muscle or gland cell (see Fig. 12.11). In the

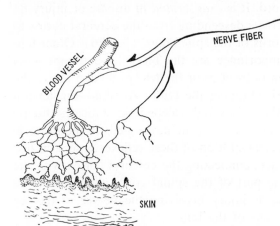

Fig. 12.11   Showing the structural basis of the axon reflex. Note that no nerve cell is involved. The arrows indicate the course taken by the nerve impulse.

lowest forms of multicellular animals, such as mollusks, worms, and in certain parts of insects, these reflexes play a prominent part in nervous responses. In higher animals, they have been studied most often in the conjunctiva, mucous membrane of the intestinal tract, and in the skin.

The following well-known and simple experiment furnishes proof of two-way conduction in nerve. The frog muscle shown in Figure 12.12 is supplied by a nerve which divides into two branches, each of which goes to different parts of the muscle. When the muscle is divided between the two branches, stimulation of one branch causes contraction of both parts of the muscle. Impulses must have passed along the stimulated branch and, turning at the Y formed by the two branches, reached the part of the muscle innervated by the unstimulated branch.

In man cutaneous vasodilatation caused by stimulation of the skin is brought about largely through axon reflexes. One branch of an axon of a sensory nerve ends in the skin, the other in or near the wall of a small blood vessel. Vasodilatation is brought about, apparently, not by the nerve impulse directly, but by a chemical substance which it causes to be liberated from the end of the axon branch. The vascular reactions caused by irritation of the cornea, and the increased vascularity of inflamed tissues, are also largely due to axon reflexes. Such reflexes can be abolished in any part by blocking conduction in the sensory terminals (e.g., in skin or conjunctiva) as by the application of cocaine.

Skeletal muscle tone. During consciousness the voluntary muscles, though not engaged in any movement, are always maintained in a state of slight contraction which is referred to as *tone* or *tonus*. All voluntary

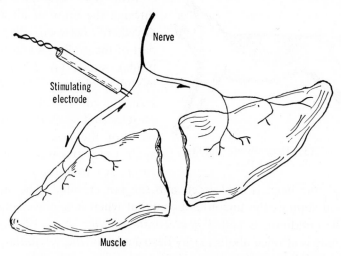

Fig. 12.12   Illustrating two-way conduction in nerve.

muscles show tonus to some extent, but it is seen pre-eminently in those muscles which maintain the posture of the body against the force of gravity—the so-called *antigravity muscles*. These are, chiefly, the extensor muscles of the lower limbs, trunk, and neck. Muscle tonus is entirely reflex in character. The muscles are stretched between their attachments, thus the constant stimulus of stretch applied to the muscle spindles initiates the reflex. Like any other reflex, it is abolished if the reflex arc is interrupted at any point, such as by a lesion of the motor nerve, of the afferent nerve, or of the reflex centers. For example, in injury or degenerative disease of the motor nerves, in locomotor ataxia (which involves the afferent paths in the spinal cord), or in anterior poliomyelitis (commonly known as infantile paralysis, in which the anterior horn cells are attacked), the tone of those muscles implicated by the disease is completely lost.

Higher centers of the brain (their precise location is unknown) exert an inhibitory influence upon muscle tone. Thus, in man a lesion of the corticospinal tracts, which connect the cerebral cortex with the spinal centers, results in an exaggeration of the tonic contraction; this is manifested by the greater resistance offered by the limbs to passive movement (that is, a movement of the patient's limb made by the examiner). The physician, in describing the muscles whose tone is increased in this way, says they are *spastic,* and refers to the hypertonic state itself as *spasticity.* Muscle tone is increased to an extreme degree after complete separation of the lower centers from higher

Fig. 12.13   Decerebrate rigidity. (After Pollock and Davis.)

control. For example, section through the brain of an animal, anywhere between the upper part of the midbrain and the vestibular nuclei (p. 528) in the medulla oblongata results in pronounced rigidity of those muscles that support the body or parts of the body (e.g., head) against gravity (antigravity muscles). All four limbs are stiffly extended, the head is held erect, and the tail elevated. The stiffened limbs will support the unconscious animal when it is placed upon its feet. The condition is called *decerebrate rigidity* (Fig. 12.13). The hypertonus is at once abolished by destruction of the vestibular nuclei or section of the spinal cord, or of the posterior spinal nerve roots, for this latter operation interrupts the afferent limb of the reflex arc.

Destruction of the vestibular nuclei or section of the spinal cord of an animal, whether or not it has been previously decerebrated, also abolishes the normal tone of the muscles. The muscles become completely relaxed (*flaccid*) immediately after this operation. The limbs hang limply like those of an animal immediately after death, and no reflex activity can be elicited. Also, since the vasomotor centers in the medulla oblongata are separated from the spinal centers, there is a profound fall in blood pressure (p. 196). This state, called *spinal shock,* persists for a time which varies with the animal species. Recovery from spinal shock occurs within a few minutes in the frog, but not for several weeks in the dog, and never completely in man.

From these observations it is concluded that the spinal reflex pathways, upon which muscle tone is directly based, must be reinforced by impulses discharged from the vestibular nuclei. The latter, in turn, are under an inhibitory influence from higher centers, especially in the

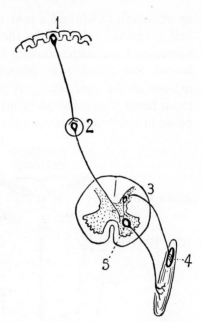

Fig. 12.14 Diagram of the principal factors responsible for muscle tone. 1, cerebral cortex or other higher cerebral region; 2, vestibular nucleus; 3, spinal cord; 4, muscle spindle; 5, anterior horn cell of the spinal cord.

midbrain and cerebellum. The vestibular nuclei, when released by section from the restraint of higher levels, become hyperactive, with consequent exaggeration of tonus and the production of the state known as decerebrate rigidity described on page 522. Though the spinal centers are dependent, normally, upon impulses from the vestibular nuclei for the maintenance of tonus they can, in animals at any rate, act independently when isolated from the higher influence. This is evident from the fact that spinal shock is recovered from after a time (see diagram, Fig. 12.14).

The Spinal Cord

The spinal cord is composed of a central, deeply and irregularly fluted column of gray matter, surrounded by white substance. The latter consists of bundles of nerve fibers (see Fig. 12.15). In a cross section of the spinal cord the gray matter appears as a central mass shaped roughly like the letter H, or the wings of a butterfly. The anterior and broader limbs of the H are called the *anterior* or *ventral horns;* the posterior narrow limbs, the *posterior* or *dorsal horns*. Running through the center of the spinal gray matter is a canal filled with cerebrospinal fluid. This is the *central canal* of the cord; above, in the medulla, it expands to form the floor of the fourth ventricle of the brain. The spinal cord is incompletely divided into two lateral halves by an anterior cleft and a posterior septum. The white matter of each half is marked off again by the anterior and posterior horns of gray matter and the corresponding spinal nerve roots into an *anterior,* a *lateral,* and a *posterior column.* In the thoracic and upper lumbar regions of the cord, the gray matter between the anterior and posterior horns shows a small projection called the *lateral horn;* it is composed of sympathetic nerve cells.

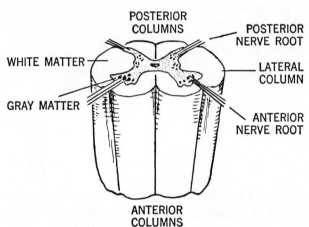

POSTERIOR COLUMNS
POSTERIOR NERVE ROOT
WHITE MATTER
LATERAL COLUMN
GRAY MATTER
ANTERIOR NERVE ROOT
ANTERIOR COLUMNS

Fig. 12.15 A section of the spinal cord showing the central mass of gray matter and the columns of white matter (ascending and descending fiber tracts).

The anterior or ventral horns of gray matter contain large multangular cells. These cells are points of convergence for impulses from various sources—from the periphery of the body along sensory nerves, and from the motor area of the cerebral cortex by the corticospinal tracts (p. 526), as well as from the cerebellum and other parts of the brain. The axons of the anterior horn cells of the cord constitute the only pathway (final common path, p. 513) from the spinal cord to the skeletal muscles; the anterior horn cells, therefore, relay the impulses which bring about voluntary movement, and are also the effector (motor) neurons of the spinal reflex arc. The posterior horns of gray matter contain the cell bodies of connector neurons; afferent impulses, after entering the cord, are relayed by these cells to the anterior horn cells, and to neurons which connect with higher levels of the central nervous system.

The spinal nerve roots. In man there are 31 pairs of spinal nerves. Each nerve of a pair arises from the cord by two roots, an *anterior* or *ventral,* and a *posterior* or *dorsal.* Each root is formed by the fusion of a series of filaments (rootlets) that emerge from the vertical grooves bounding the lateral columns of the cord. The anterior roots are composed of efferent (mostly motor) fibers derived from the cells of the anterior horns of spinal gray matter; other finer fibers are efferents of sympathetic nerve cells in the lateral horns. The posterior roots are composed almost entirely of afferent fibers: sensory fibers from the skin, muscles, viscera, etc., and other afferent fibers which transmit nonsensory impulses—that is, impulses which do not reach consciousness. The cell bodies which give rise to the fibers of a posterior root are situated in a small swelling on the root itself; this is called the *ganglion of the posterior root* (Figs. 12.16 and 12.17). Both dendrite and axon of a ganglion cell arise by a common stem which divides into the respective fibers a short distance from the cell body. One branch (den-

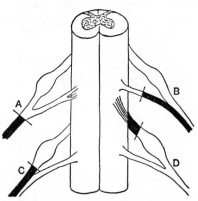

Fig. 12.16   Diagram to illustrate Wallerian degeneration (modified from Halliburton). Section at A causes degeneration of all motor and sensory fibers of the peripheral nerve beyond the point of section (black area). In B, section of the anterior root causes degeneration of the motor fibers since the motor cell bodies lie within the spinal cord; in C, section of the posterior root is followed by degeneration of the sensory fibers of the peripheral nerve because the cell bodies of the sensory fibers lie in the ganglion; in D, section of the posterior root between the ganglion and the cord causes degeneration of the sensory fibers of the spinal stump of the root and of ascending fibers within the cord as far as the next cell station. (See also p. 463.)

drite) of the T-shaped process passes peripherally, the other (axon) carries impulses into the cord where it connects (synapses) with intraspinal neurons or passes without interruption to the medulla oblongata. Certain cranial nerves possess similar ganglia from which their afferent fibers originate (see Fig. 12.32, p. 544). The two roots of a spinal nerve unite within the intervertebral foramen. The trunk so formed divides again almost immediately into a large anterior and a small posterior part, called, respectively, the *anterior* and *posterior primary divisions of the spinal nerves.* Each division receives fibers (motor and sensory) from both spinal nerve roots. The branches of the *anterior primary divisions* fuse with one another, redivide, and continue again in a complicated fashion to form three nerve plexuses— the *cervical, brachial,* and *lumbosacral plexuses*—from which the peripheral nerves to the skin and muscles of the neck and limbs ultimately emerge. Thus, in the formation of the plexuses, the fibers of the original spinal nerve roots become intermingled, the peripheral nerve trunks containing both motor and sensory fibers. The *posterior primary divisions* break up into branches which supply the skin and muscles of the back.

The tracts of the spinal cord. The nerve fibers composing the spinal white matter have various origins and form longitudinal bundles, usually referred to as *tracts* or *fasciculi.* The fibers of some of these tracts arise from higher levels of the nervous system and conduct impulses downward; others arise from lower levels and conduct in an upward direction. They are therefore classed into *ascending* and *descending* groups. Each tract is further given a specific name derived from the origin and destination of its fibers. A cross section of the cord showing the several tracts will be found in Plate 9B.

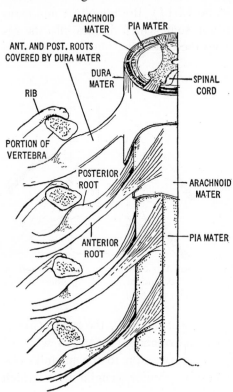

Fig. 12.17   The spinal nerve roots.

The descending tracts. The *corticospinal* or *pyramidal tracts* arise from the large cells of the motor area of the cerebral cortex (p. 532) on each side of the brain. The fibers of each tract synapse with the anterior horn cells of the opposite side of the cord. The tracts descend through the substance of the brain, traversing successively the internal capsule of the cerebrum (p. 539), the midbrain, pons, and medulla oblongata. They form two prominences on the anterior aspect of the medulla oblongata, called the pyramids. At the lower border of the medulla oblongata the greater proportion of the fibers of one side cross to the opposite side of the cord and descend in the lateral column. They constitute, on each side of the cord, the *lateral corticospinal tracts.* The remaining uncrossed fibers—the *anterior corticospinal tracts*—descend in the anterior columns, but these also ultimately cross to the anterior horn cells of the opposite side at various levels of the cord.

The corticospinal tracts transmit impulses which bring about voluntary movements of the limbs and trunk. A lesion involving these tracts in any part of their course, from the motor area of the central cortex to their terminations in the spinal cord, results in weakness or paralysis of the muscles on the opposite side of the body. The fibers conveying impulses to the muscles of the eyes, face, tongue, and throat also rise from the motor area of the cerebral cortex, but they form connections with nerve cells in the motor nuclei of the cranial nerves (third to the twelfth, p. 547). These fibers, though they are strictly analogous to the corticospinal fibers and travel with the latter for a part of their course,

Table 12-1

Effects of lesions of the upper motor neuron	*Effects of lesions of the lower motor neuron*
(1) Paralysis of the spastic type. That is, the paralyzed muscles are hypertonic and offer a greater resistance to passive movements than normally.	The paralyzed muscles are flaccid. They are hypotonic, offering little resistance to passive movement.
(2) The tendon reflexes (knee jerk, etc.) are exaggerated.	The tendon reflexes are absent.
(3) Normal responses to electrical stimulation.	Reaction of degeneration (p. 463).
(4) Little muscular wasting.	Marked wasting of muscles.
(5) Babinski response (p. 519); abdominal reflexes lost (p. 519).	Normal plantar response (i.e., Babinski absent); abdominal reflexes may be lost.

are referred to as the *corticobulbar tracts*. Like the corticospinal tracts, they convey impulses from one side of the brain to the muscles of the opposite side.

Every pathway for the transmission of impulses governing voluntary movements, whether of the limbs and trunk or of the face, eyes, tongue, and throat, consists, therefore, of two neuron links. That neuron which has its cell body in the cerebral cortex is called the *upper motor neuron*. The *lower motor neuron* is the anterior horn cell of the spinal cord or a cell in one or other of the cranial nuclei. The axons of the lower motor neurons form, of course, the peripheral motor nerves (cranial and spinal).

The effects following a lesion of the upper motor neuron differ in certain respects from those resulting from injury or disease of the lower. These differences are summarized in Table 12-1.

The rubrospinal tracts. These descend in the lateral columns of the cord to synapse with the anterior horn cells. They arise from the red nucleus in the midbrain (p. 545). After issuing from the red nucleus, the fibers cross to the opposite side (*decussation of Forel*). Thus the red nucleus of one side is connected with the anterior horn cells of the opposite side of the spinal cord.

The vestibulospinal tracts. These arise from the vestibular nuclei situated in the lower part of the medulla oblongata. The fibers of each tract connect with the anterior horn cells of the opposite side of the spinal cord. These tracts relay impulses transmitted to the vestibular nuclei from the labyrinth (of the internal ear) and cerebellum. They are of essential importance in the maintenance of equilibrium, correlating the tone and movements of the muscles with the position of the head in space.

The chief descending tracts of the brain and cord are represented in the diagram, Plates 10B and 10A.

The ascending tracts. The *fasciculus gracilis* (*tract of Goll*) and *fasciculus cuneatus* (*tract of Burdach*) occupy the posterior column of each half of the cord. They are composed of the axons of cells of the posterior root ganglia (see page 525). The fibers of these tracts transmit impulses of light touch and the sense of position and movement (*kinesthetic sense*) to the nucleus gracilis and nucleus cuneatus in the medulla oblongata; from here the impulses are relayed upward by other neurons to the optic thalamus, and thence to the cerebral cortex. When these tracts are injured, the subject, since he is not informed of the movements and positions of his limbs, has difficulty in executing muscular acts with orderliness and precision; his movements are jerky and poorly controlled. Impaired muscular control of this type is called *ataxia.* The sense of touch is little affected, however, because touch impulses ascend also in the anterior spinothalamic tracts.

The spinocerebellar tracts. These are two in number on each side. One, the *dorsal spinocerebellar tract,* reaches the cerebellum via the inferior cerebellar peduncle (p. 552); the other, the *ventral spinocerebellar tract,* ascends to the midbrain, entering the cerebellum through its superior peduncle. They ascend in the lateral columns of the cord and transmit nonsensory impulses from the muscles to the cerebellum. Injury or disease of these tracts also results in ataxia, because the cerebellum does not receive the impulses that enable it to exercise its function in steadying and strengthening voluntary muscular acts.

The spinothalamic tracts ascend one in the anterior column, the other in the lateral column of each half of the cord. The *anterior spino-*

thalamic tract conducts impulses of light touch from the skin of the opposite side of the body to the thalamus; from the thalamus the impulses are relayed by other fibers to the postcentral gyrus of the cerebral cortex. The *lateral spinothalamic tract* is the pathway for impulses of pain, heat, and cold from the opposite side of the body (see Pl. 10B).

The sensory pathways in the brain are described on page 547.

The Brain or Encephalon

The brain is that part of the nervous system enclosed by the skull. It consists of the *cerebrum, midbrain, pons, medulla oblongata,* and *cerebellum* (see Fig. 12.18).

The cerebrum. The cerebrum is divided incompletely by a longitudinal fissure (the *superior longitudinal fissure*) into two halves called the *cerebral hemispheres.* These are the large ovoid masses lying in contact with the vault and walls of the skull. The hemispheres constitute by far the largest part of the human brain, and of the brains of

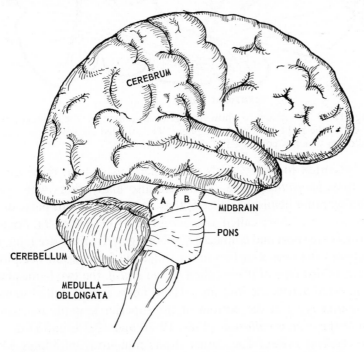

Fig. 12.18   Plan in outline of the brain as seen from the right side. The parts are represented as separated from one another considerably more than is natural so as to show their connections. A, tegmentum; B, peduncle.

apes and monkeys, but are less prominent structures in the brains of lower vertebrates. The most highly developed functions of the nervous system—memory, intelligence, moral sense, etc.—and the centers for sight, hearing, smell, taste, general body sensations, and the voluntary control of bodily movements are seated in the cerebral hemispheres.

The hemispheres are composed of a covering of gray matter, called the *cerebral cortex,* and a central mass of white matter. The latter is formed of tracts of nerve fibers ascending to the cortex and descending

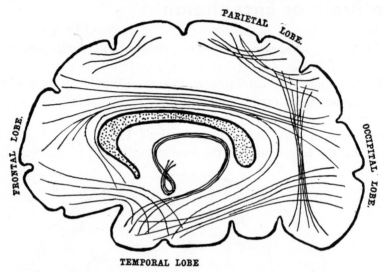

Fig. 12.19   Diagram to show the general course of the association fibers of the right cerebral hemisphere. The stippled area is the corpus callosum which is composed of commissural fibers.

from the cortex to lower levels of the nervous system; these are re-ferred to as *projection fibers.* There are also many fibers which arise and end within a hemisphere itself; they connect different parts of the cerebral cortex and are called *association fibers* (Fig. 12.19). Some of these tracts are short and connect neighboring gyri; others are long, and run between the cortex of two lobes (e.g., the frontal and occipital). Through a third type of fiber, called *commissural,* the two hemispheres are connected across the mid-line. These fibers form a felted mass of white matter lying at the bottom of the superior longitudinal fissure, known as the *corpus callosum* (Figs. 12.20 and 12.25, p. 537).

The cerebral cortex. The cortex shows numerous infoldings which give the surface of the hemispheres an appearance not unlike the sur-face of the kernel of a walnut. These folds are called *convolutions* or *gyri;* the depression or furrow between two convolutions is called a *sulcus,* or if especially deep and long, a *fissure.* By such reduplications of the cerebral surface, the total cortical area is greatly increased. About a third of the gray matter occupies the surface of the convolutions; the remainder lines the sulci and fissures.

On the basis of the characters of their constituent cells, several well-defined layers can be distinguished in the gray matter of the cerebral cortex. The respective cell layers, however, do not show uniform char-

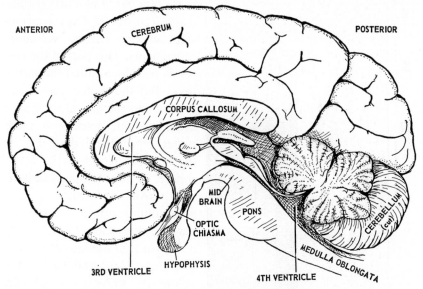

Fig. 12.20   Vertical section through the brain passing between the cerebral hemispheres.

acters throughout all cortical regions. On the contrary, certain layers exhibit special characteristics in certain areas—e.g., the motor area in the frontal lobe and the visual area of the occipital lobe. Upon such characteristics depend, undoubtedly, the special functions of the different parts of the cortex (Fig. 12.21).

Localization of function in the cerebral cortex. For convenience of description, each cerebral hemisphere is marked off into four parts called lobes. The *frontal lobe* is that part in front of the deep cleft (*fissure of Rolando* or the *central sulcus*) which runs obliquely downward and slightly forward from the upper border of the hemisphere (Fig. 12.22). The *parietal lobe* lies behind the fissure of Rolando; the *temporal lobe* lies below the well-marked horizontal fissure—*fissure of Sylvius*—on the lateral aspect of the hemisphere. The *occipital lobe* forms the posterior pole of the hemisphere lying behind the parietal and temporal lobes.

A band of cortex running downwards and forwards, in front of and parallel to the fissure of Rolando, contains giant pyramidal nerve cells (Betz cells). The axons of these cells descend through the brain—internal capsule, midbrain, pons, and medulla—to connect with the motor cranial nuclei and the anterior horn cells of the spinal cord. These fibers constitute the corticobulbar and corticospinal tracts (p. 526). They transmit impulses governing voluntary movements. This part of the cortex is therefore called the *motor area*. But the motor area is not confined to the lateral surface of the cerebrum. It turns over the upper border and descends on the medical aspect of the hemisphere. Commencing about halfway down the medial surface, and running upward to the upper border and then turning downward on the lateral surface (see Figs. 12.22 and 12.23) the voluntary movements of the various parts of the body are represented in the following order: toes, ankle (up medial surface), knee (at upper border), hip, trunk, shoulder, elbow, wrist, hand, face (down lateral surface). The disproportionately large areas for the hand and face shown in the figure are

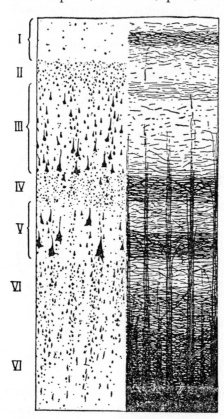

Fig. 12.21 The microscopical structure of the cerebral cortex. The numerals refer to the different layers. The cellular structure of each layer is shown on the left, the fiber structure on the right. (After Economo.)

meant to indicate the relatively large cortical areas representing these parts that carry out the most complicated movements and, therefore, involve the greatest numbers of neurons.

It has been mentioned elsewhere that the corticospinal fibers ultimately cross to the opposite side of the spinal cord. It follows that the muscles of one side of the body are controlled by the motor area of the opposite side of the brain. Injury to the motor area of one hemisphere, or of the corticospinal fibers in their course through the brain above the level of their crossing, especially in the *internal capsule* (p. 539), therefore, results in paralysis of the muscles on the opposite side of the body.

The areas of the motor cortex have been explored and mapped out when exposed in man during intracranial operations. Electrical stimulation of circumscribed areas elicits motor responses from groups of muscles or, if the stimulus is sufficiently localized, of individual muscles on the opposite side of the body.

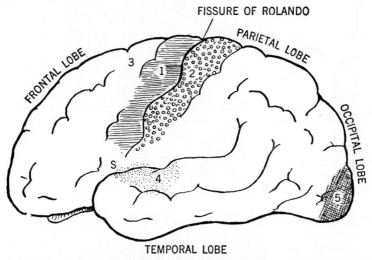

Fig. 12.22   Diagram illustrating the localization of function in the cerebral cortex. 1, motor area; 2, sensory (somesthetic) area; 3, premotor area; 4, auditory area; 5, part of visual area concerned with visual association; S, fissure of Sylvius.

Situated in front of the motor area is the so-called *premotor area.* The functions of this cortical area have not been fully elucidated, but it appears to exert a controlling influence over the motor area itself, probably synthesizing the more localized movements represented in the latter area into more complex acts. Movements of small groups of muscles or even of a single muscle can be elicited by stimulation of the motor area; but excitation of the premotor area causes broader and more or less purposeful well-coordinated movements. The premotor area is also connected by descending fibers with the *corpus striatum* (p. 539) and, through the *frontopontine tract,* with the gray matter of the pons. Through the former connection, it is in indirect communication with the red nucleus, cerebellum, and spinal centers; through the frontopontine fibers, a connection is also established between the premotor area and the cerebellum.

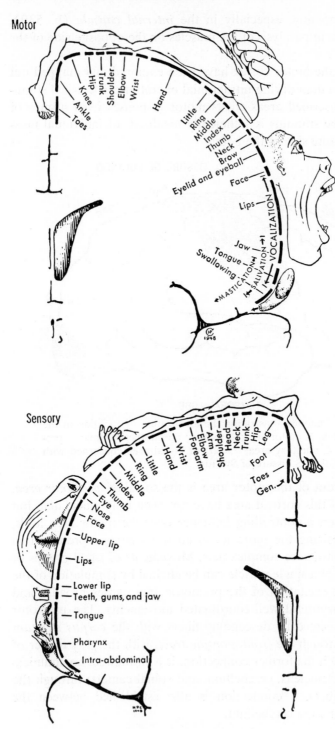

Fig. 12.23 Vertical sections through the frontal lobe of the cerebrum at the fissure of Rolando (central sulcus) showing the motor (above) and sensory representations. The disproportionate sizes of parts of the manikin are meant to indicate the relative extent of the corresponding cortical areas. (After Penfield and Rasmussen.)

Concerning the functions of the remaining and greater part of the frontal cortex—that is, of the part not occupied by but lying in front of the motor and premotor areas—little is definitely known; this region is therefore spoken of as a "silent" area. It is sometimes the site of a tumor, and the surgeon in order to eradicate the growth is often forced to sacrifice a large part of the brain tissue. The frontal lobe of one side, except for the motor and premotor areas, has been excised in a number of instances, but such operations are followed by little or no functional defect. Even after the removal of both frontal lobes in front of the premotor areas, there is remarkably little mental disability. It has been thought that the frontal lobe was the seat of intelligence; the greater development of this part of the human brain, as compared with the brains of lower animals, has supported such an idea. However, in the light of the results just cited and of experiments upon animals, our views on the importance of this part of the brain must be revised. There is apparently no special region or center for intelligence. It depends upon the cortex as a whole; upon the degree of development of the various cortical sensory areas, and the richness of the association paths through which these areas are interconnected. The frontal cortex is simply a region of high associative ability, and as such contributes its share to the general intellectual capacity of the individual.

The parietal lobe. The area of cortex lying behind the fissure of Rolando is sensory in function. It is called the *somesthetic area.* Here sensations of touch, warmth, and coolness, and of muscular movements (kinesthetic sensations), are perceived and interpreted (see also p. 528). But pain does not appear to be represented in the cerebral cortex. Impulses giving rise to this sensation end in the optic thalamus. The sensory representation of the various parts of the body show definite localization, following the same order as that already described for the motor area (see Fig. 12.23); those sensory regions—especially the hands, lips, and tongue—upon which we depend most for our impressions of the world around us have the largest cortical representation. *Taste* is recorded at the lower end of this area.

Like the motor area, the somesthetic area has been mapped out by point to point electrical stimulation, through an operative opening in the skull bone. The patients were conscious and able to describe the sensations aroused.

The temporal lobe. The cortex bordering the fissure of Sylvius, together with that buried in the fissure itself, is the region for the perception of sound. Here the fibers of the *auditory radiation* (p. 621) terminate; it is therefore called the *acoustic area* or the center for hearing.

The acoustic area of each side of the brain receives impulses from both ears. Its unilateral destruction, therefore, does not cause deafness in either ear, though some dullness of hearing in both ears may result. The temporal cortex adjacent to the acoustic area is associative in function, being concerned with the interpretation of sounds—that is, with understanding the meaning and significance of the various kinds of sound (e.g., words, music, etc.) and with the association of a particular sound with visual, tactile, or other sensations. It is therefore called the *psychoauditory area.*

The temporal lobe is thought to be the seat of memory, a region of the cortex from which auditory, visual, and other impressions stored in other regions (e.g., psychoauditory or psychovisual area) can be recalled to consciousness. This belief is based largely upon the fact that a tumor of the temporal lobe or an epileptic seizure commencing in this region of the cortex is not uncommonly associated with or preceded by reminiscences when scenes long past are brought vividly to mind.

The occipital lobe. The cortical area for vision—the *visual area*— is situated chiefly on the inner aspect of the occipital lobe, but it also extends around the posterior extremity of the lobe to a small part of its lateral surface. Impulses from the right halves of the two retinas are transmitted to the visual area of the right hemisphere, impulses from the left halves of the retinas to the left visual area (see Pl. 13A). Destruction of the visual cortex on one side of the brain, therefore, causes blindness in the corresponding halves of the retinas only (see p. 586). The remainder of the posterior part of this lobe is associative in function; upon its activity depend the recognition and interpretation of visual impressions, and the integration of these with other sensations. It is called the *psychovisual area.*

Fig. 12.24   The electroencephalogram recorded from the occipital region of the skull. Eyes closed up to O in tracing, when they were opened to a broken view; kept open to C, when again closed. Note almost complete disappearance of the waves from O to C.

Electrical activity of the brain, the electroencephalogram. It was discovered in 1929, by Berger, a German physician, that rhythmical changes in electric potential—electric currents of low potential—were occurring almost continuously in the cerebral cortex, and could be recorded in man by means of pad electrodes applied to the scalp (see Fig. 12.24). They can also be picked up by needle electrodes in contact with the skull bone. Such a record, obtained by a highly sensitive electric device (amplifier and oscillograph), and a photographic apparatus, is called an *electroencephalogram;* the recording instrument is known as the *electroencephalograph.* Two types of wave are to be

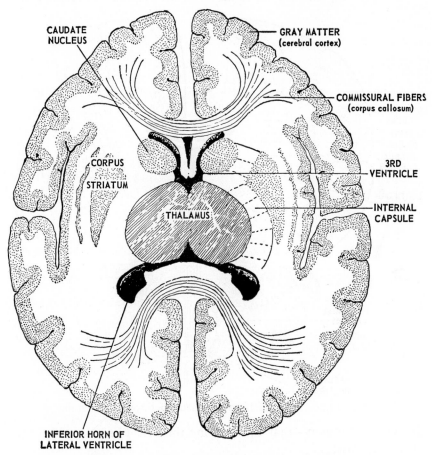

CAUDATE
NUCLEUS

GRAY MATTER
(cerebral cortex)

COMMISSURAL FIBERS
(corpus callosum)

CORPUS

STRIATUM

3RD
VENTRICLE

THALAMUS

INTERNAL
CAPSULE

INFERIOR HORN OF
LATERAL VENTRICLE

Fig. 12.25   Horizontal section through the brain.

seen in the record of a normal person in the waking state but with his eyes closed; they are designated, respectively, the *alpha* and *beta* waves. ·The alpha waves have a frequency of about 10 per second and a voltage of around 50 microvolts.[2] They persist when the eyes are open and the visual field is uniform, as when the subject looks at a blank wall or other surface without pattern. They disappear when the view is broken up by a pattern, such as one composed of several objects, or contain-

_____

[2] A *microvolt* is one millionth of a volt; a *millivolt* is one thousandth of a volt.

ing contrasting areas of light and shade, etc. The beta waves are of higher frequency (25 to 50 per second) and of smaller amplitude—that is, of lower voltage, namely from 5 to 10 microvolts. The beta waves are recorded best from the skull overlying the motor area of the cerebral cortex, whereas the alpha waves are seen best in records from

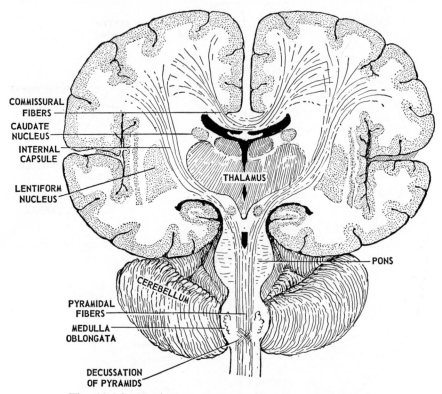

COMMISSURAL FIBERS

CAUDATE NUCLEUS

INTERNAL CAPSULE

LENTIFORM NUCLEUS

THALAMUS

PONS

CEREBELLUM

PYRAMIDAL FIBERS

MEDULLA OBLONGATA

DECUSSATION OF PYRAMIDS

Fig. 12.26   Vertical transverse section through the brain.

the occipital region—that is, overlying the visual area in which they apparently arise.

A third type of wave, called the *delta* wave, is rarely obtained in the electroencephalogram of a normal person while he is awake, but appears during sleep. These waves have a very low frequency (1 to 5 per second) and, very often, a relatively high voltage (up to 200 microvolts).

The electroencephalogram is not affected by dividing the brain below the cerebrum (through the midbrain). The electric currents are not due, therefore, to afferent impulses ascending to the cerebrum from lower levels, but appear to be a manifestation of an inherent electrical activity of the nerve cells of the cerebrum itself.

Departures from the normal configuration of the electroencephalogram are seen in several abnormal conditions of the brain, notably,
epilepsy and cerebral tumors. A study of such records is often of considerable value in diagnosis.

The optic thalamus, corpus striatum, and internal capsule. The *optic
thalamus* is a large mass of gray matter buried in each cerebral hemisphere just above the midbrain. The third ventricle separates the optic
thalami of the two sides (Figs. 12.25 and 12.26). In sections of the
brain a streak of white matter known as the *internal capsule* (Figs.
12.25 and 12.26) is to be seen on the outer side of the thalamus and
separating it from the corpus striatum. The internal capsule is composed of bundles of ascending and descending nerve fibers (e.g., corticospinal and sensory tracts). It is a bottle-neck pass which all fibers
must traverse in order to reach lower levels of the nervous system, and
through which all sensory fibers destined for the cortex must ascend.
An injury to the internal capsule, therefore, causes extensive damage
to the conducting pathways; paralysis and often sensory loss on the
opposite side of the body result. Paralysis confined to one side of the
body is called *hemiplegia.* It most commonly follows rupture of a blood
vessel supplying the internal capsule, with consequent interruption of
the motor and sensory paths. The immediate effect of hemorrhage into
the internal capsule is loss of consciousness and paralysis of all four
limbs. This condition, called *cerebral apoplexy* or in popular parlance
"a stroke," lasts for a variable time; the subject may die without re-
gaining consciousness. If he survives, the paralysis on one side disappears as consciousness is regained, but loss of power in the muscles
of the face and limbs on the side of the body opposite to that of the
hemorrhage persists. The tone of the affected muscles is increased
(spasticity), the tendon reflexes are exaggerated, and the normal plantar reflex is replaced by the Babinski response (p. 519). In other
words, the signs are those of an upper motor neuron lesion (p. 527).

The optic thalamus and corpus striatum are intimately connected by
nerve fibers, and both these gray masses are connected, as well, with
the cerebral cortex, and with the spinal cord, cerebellum, and other
parts of the nervous system. All sensory paths conveying impulses of
pain, temperature, touch, and muscle sense enter the thalamus. The
sensations of pain, of rough contact, and extremes of temperature—
heat above 45° C and cold below 25° C—are appreciated in the thalamus itself. The thalamus is, therefore, an organ of crude consciousness.
The finer sensations—i.e., light touch, moderate changes in temperature (warmth and coolness), and muscle sense—are perceived by the

somesthetic region of the parietal cortex. The impulses subserving these sensations are relayed to the parietal cortex by fibers which arise in the thalamus and ascend in the internal capsule. The cortex of the parietal lobe brings a discriminating and critical ability to bear upon the impulses which it receives, being capable of judging the lesser gradations in stimulus intensity, and of detecting minor qualitative differences in sensation. The thalamus possesses no such discriminating capability. The somesthetic area of the cortex is believed also to send impulses to the thalamus which restrain its activity. When released

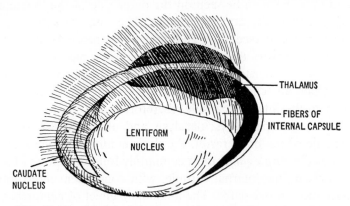

Fig. 12.27   Model of the internal capsule, thalamus, and corpus striatum.

from cortical restraint, the thalamus reacts in an "all-or-none" manner —a diffuse, ill-defined but intensely unpleasant sensation being aroused by ordinarily mildly painful stimuli, or by moderate changes in temperature. Such sensory abnormalities occur in disease of this part of the brain.

The thalamus is not a simple relay station, for it integrates the impulses before passing them on to the cortex.

The *corpus striatum* (striate body) is a large gray mass bent upon itself in such a way that in a horizontal section of the brain it appears as two separate gray masses—the *caudate nucleus* [3] and the *lentiform nucleus* (Figs. 12.25, 12.26, and 12.27). The latter consists of two parts: the outer and larger part is called the *putamen;* and the inner part, the *globus pallidus.* The lentiform nucleus is separated from the thalamus by the posterior limb of the internal capsule, and from the caudate nucleus by the latter's anterior limb. The striate body has numerous fiber connections with other parts of the nervous system—

[3] The term *nucleus* is used to denote any circumscribed group of nerve cells or isolated mass of gray substance within the central nervous system.

e.g., with the premotor area of the cerebral cortex, the thalamus and the red nucleus, and through the latter with the cerebellum and spinal centers. Of the functions of the corpus striatum little is definitely known. It is concerned in some way with the control of skeletal muscle tone; it probably also exerts a steadying influence upon muscular movements. In disease of the corpus striatum or of its connections,

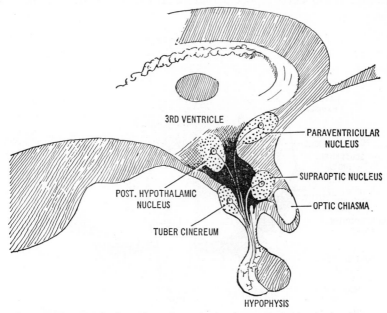

3RD VENTRICLE

PARAVENTRICULAR NUCLEUS

SUPRAOPTIC NUCLEUS

POST. HYPOTHALAMIC NUCLEUS

OPTIC CHIASMA

TUBER CINEREUM

HYPOPHYSIS

Fig. 12.28   Vertical section through the base of the brain in the region of the hypothalamus.

marked rigidity of the muscles—flexors and extensors—is seen. The resistance offered by a limb to passive movements has suggested a comparison with that of a lead pipe ("lead pipe" rigidity). Tremor or jerkiness of the limbs, upon attempting a voluntary movement, is also a common manifestation of disease of the corpus striatum. Both these signs—rigidity and tremor—are seen in *paralysis agitans,* the name given to one form of disease of the striate body.

The hypothalamus. This is the region at the base of the brain lying behind the optic chiasma (p. 586) and beneath the floor of the third ventricle. It contains several groups of nerve cells—the *hypothalamic nuclei*—which constitute centers controlling the sympathetic and parasympathetic functions. Axons from three groups of nerve cells—the *supraoptic, paraventricular,* and *tuberal nuclei*—form a bundle of nerve fibers known as the *hypothalamico-hypophyseal tract.* This tract enters the neural lobe of the hypophysis (pituitary body). It governs the liberation of the hormones of this part of the pituitary (Fig. 12.28). Injury or stimulation of the hypothalamus affects one or more of the fundamental processes of the body—e.g., vasomotor control, temperature regulation, fat, carbohydrate, and water metabolism, interference with the development of the sex functions, as well as gastrointestinal motility. It has been reported that electrical stimulation of the hypo-

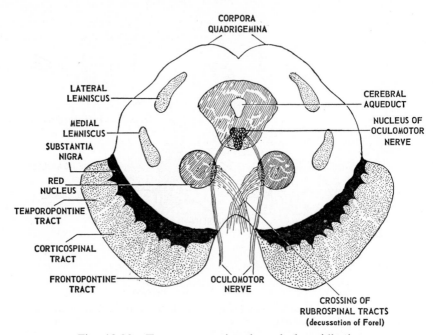

Fig. 12.29   Transverse section through the midbrain.

thalamus in animals induces a sleeplike state. It also appears to be a center from which the reactions expressing the primitive emotions are controlled. For when, in an experimental animal, all restraint of the higher centers of the brain is withdrawn by removal of the entire cerebral cortex, the reactions of an enraged fighting animal are exhibited. Thus, a cat, which before the operation was a placid friendly animal, spits and bares its claws when approached; its fur bristles and its tail becomes bushy, as when a normal cat is attacked by a dog. This state of the decorticated animal has been appropriately termed "sham rage." When, on the other hand, a tract of fibers connecting the frontal lobe of the cerebrum with the hypothalamus is severed, a naturally wild and unfriendly animal becomes docile and affectionate. This latter observation has been put to practical advantage in the treatment of certain mental states in man. Section of this connecting nerve tract is often followed by improvement of the mental condition.

The midbrain or mesencephalon. The midbrain is the short, narrow, pillarlike portion of the brain, lying immediately below the optic thalami. It is traversed by a narrow canal called the *cerebral aqueduct;*

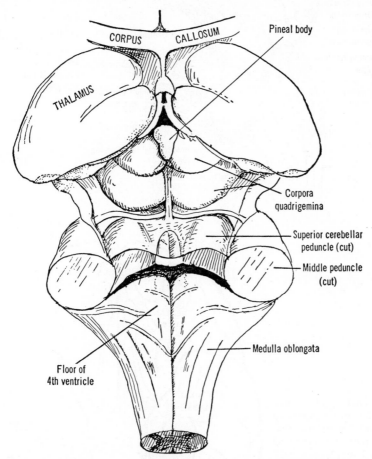

CORPUS CALLOSUM

Pineal body

THALAMUS

Corpora quadrigemina

Superior cerebellar peduncle (cut)

Middle peduncle (cut)

Medulla oblongata

Floor of 4th ventricle

Fig. 12.30   The thalami and brain stem from behind.

this communicates above with the third ventricle of the brain and below with the fourth ventricle. The greater part of the midbrain lies in front of the cerebral aqueduct, and consists of the two *cerebral peduncles* (Figs. 12.29 and 12.31). Anteriorly the latter are separated by a cleft, and appear as two stout columns which emerge from the pons below, and plunge into the substance of the cerebrum above. Each column, which is termed the *base* of the peduncle, transmits the *corticospinal, frontopontine,* and *temporopontine tracts* of the corresponding

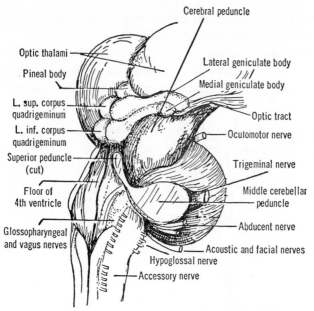

Cerebral peduncle

Optic thalami

Pineal body

Lateral geniculate body

Medial geniculate body

L. sup. corpus quadrigeminum

L. inf. corpus quadrigeminum

Optic tract

Oculomotor nerve

Superior peduncle (cut)

Trigeminal nerve

Floor of 4th ventricle

Middle cerebellar peduncle

Glossopharyngeal and vagus nerves

Abducent nerve

Acoustic and facial nerves

Hypoglossal nerve

Accessory nerve

Fig. 12.31 The midbrain looking from behind and from the right; cerebellum removed.

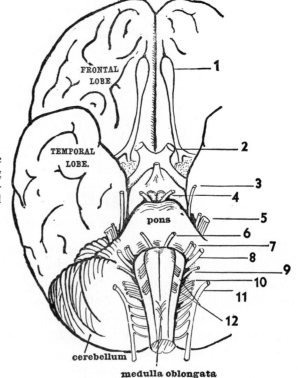

FRONTAL LOBE

TEMPORAL LOBE.

pons

cerebellum

medulla oblongata

1
2
3
4
5
6
7
8
9
10
11
12

Fig. 12.32 The base of the brain showing the origins of the cranial nerves, numbered from 1 to 12.

side of the brain. Posteriorly the peduncles are fused into a single structure called the *tegmentum* (L. *tego,* I cover) which contains, on each
side of the mid-line, an ovoid mass of gray matter—the *red nucleus*—
and two smaller gray masses, the *nuclei of the oculomotor* and *trochlear nerves*. This part of the mesencephalon also transmits two bundles
of sensory fibers—the *lateral* and *medial lemnisci*. The former is the
pathway for auditory impulses, the latter for impulses of touch, pain,
muscle sense, etc. (Fig. 12.29).

The part of the midbrain lying posterior to the cerebral aqueduct
is called the *tectum* (L. *tectum,* roof, from *tego,* I cover). It consists
of two pairs of rounded eminences called, respectively, the *superior*
and *inferior colliculi* (or *corpora quadrigemina*) (Figs. 12.30 and
12.31). The superior colliculus receives impulses from the retina and
is connected with the spinal centers through a tract of descending fibers—the *tectospinal tract*. It is a center for visual reflexes—e.g.,
movements of the head and eyes in response to retinal stimuli. The inferior colliculus receives auditory impulses, and serves as an auditory
reflex center—e.g., the "pricking up" of an animal's ears in response
to sound.

A small oval eminence is seen on the outer side of each colliculus.
These are called, respectively, the *medial* and *lateral geniculate bodies*.
The former, which is connected by a strand of fibers (called the *inferior brachium*) with the inferior colliculus, receives the bulk of the
fibers comprising the auditory pathway (the lateral lemniscus; see also
p. 621). The lateral geniculate body receives most of the fibers of the
optic tract (p. 587) and is connected by a band of fibers—the *superior
brachium*—with the superior colliculus (see Fig. 12.32).

The *red nucleus* (*nucleus ruber*) is connected by fiber tracts with
the cerebral cortex, corpus striatum, thalamus, cerebellum, and spinal
cord. Its functions are imperfectly understood, but it appears to be an
integral part of the nervous mechanism controlling the execution of
skilled muscular movements. The fibers which descend to the spinal
centers are called the *rubrospinal tracts*. Upon issuing from the lower
part of the red nucleus, these fibers cross with the fibers of the opposite
side. This crossing is called the *decussation of Forel*.

The pons (pons Varolii). This part of the brain stem lies below or
(in quadrupeds) behind the midbrain and above or in front of the
medulla oblongata. It transmits the corticobulbar, corticospinal, and
rubrospinal tracts, and the medial and lateral lemnisci. It contains the
sensory nucleus of the trigeminal nerve and the nuclei of the facial
and abducent nerves. It is in communication with the cerebellum

through the middle cerebellar peduncle, and with the cerebrum through the frontopontine and temporopontine tracts. The fibers of these tracts synapse with nerve cells in the substance of the pons called the *pontine nuclei.* The axons of cells composing these nuclei relay impulses to the cerebellum.

The medulla oblongata. The medulla oblongata is the continuation upward of the spinal cord. It is somewhat conical in shape, broadening as it ascends, until at its junction with the pons its circumference is nearly double that of its lower end. A canal, continuous with the central canal of the spinal cord, runs through the center of the lower half of the medulla, but in the upper half the posterior wall of the canal opens out to form a lozenge-shaped space called the fourth ventricle. The floor of the fourth ventricle is composed of gray matter; this represents the prolongation upward of the anterior horns of the cord which, through the opening up of the central canal, have become spread out. Upon the anterior aspect of the medulla are two vertical columns called the *pyramids,* formed by the corticospinal (pyramidal) tracts. At the junction of the medulla with the spinal cord, the pyramid of each side divides into a smaller and a larger part. The latter crosses (decussates) with that of the opposite side and descends in the lateral column of the cord. The smaller division descends uncrossed in the anterior column of the cord (see p. 526). The medial fillets (see below) cross (*sensory decussation*) a little above the decussation of the pyramids (*motor decussation*) and ascend behind the latter. The nuclei of the eighth, ninth, tenth, eleventh, and twelfth cranial nerves are situated in the medulla; it also contains the nucleus gracilis and the nucleus cuneatus, and the so-called vital centers—cardiac, vasomotor, and respiratory. The medulla oblongata is connected through the inferior cerebellar peduncle with the cerebellum (p. 553).

Summary of sensory pathways in the brain. As mentioned, on page 528, impulses reaching the nuclei gracilis and cuneatus along the fibers of the posterior columns are relayed upward by secondary neurons. The axons of the latter, after leaving the nuclei and crossing to the opposite side (*sensory decussation*), ascend through the medulla, pons, and midbrain forming a tract known as the *medial fillet* or *lemniscus.* The medial fillet is joined by the anterior and lateral spinothalamic tracts, as well as by fibers carrying impulses from the face (*trigeminal lemniscus*). These four sets of sensory fibers lead to the optic thalamus. From here all sensations except pain and extremes of temperature (see p. 539) are relayed by other neurons to the postcentral (somesthetic) area of the cerebral cortex (p. 535).

The cranial nerves. The nerves arising from the brain are twelve in number on each side. They are designated by numbers in the order of their origin, from before backward. Roman numerals I to XII are usually employed in referring to them, or the words *first, second, third,* and so on (see Fig. 12.32). Each nerve also receives a name descriptive of its function or distribution. The numbers and the corresponding names of the cranial nerves are given in Table 12-2.

Table 12-2

List of the cranial nerves

I. Olfactory	VII. Facial
II. Optic	VIII. Acoustic (or auditory)
III. Oculomotor	IX. Glossopharyngeal
IV. Trochlear	X. Vagus
V. Trigeminal	XI. Accessory
VI. Abducent	XII. Hypoglossal

The olfactory nerves, or nerves of smell, are distributed to the olfactory mucous membrane covering the roof of the nose. They will be described in the section on the sense of smell (p. 641).

The optic nerve, or nerve of sight, is composed of the axons of the ganglion cells of the retina. The central connections of the fibers of the optic nerve will be described in the section on vision (p. 587).

The oculomotor nerve arises from a group of nerve cells—the *nucleus of the oculomotor nerve*—situated in the gray matter of the floor of the cerebral aqueduct (p. 543). The fibers course forward through the midbrain, emerging from the inner aspect of the cerebral peduncle. The oculomotor nerve supplies all the eye muscles with the exception of the superior oblique and external rectus, which are innervated, respectively, by the trochlear and abducent nerves. It also conveys parasympathetic fibers to the constrictor muscle of the iris, and to the ciliary muscle.

The trochlear nerve has its nucleus in the floor of the cerebral aqueduct, a little behind the oculomotor nucleus. It emerges from the brain at the lateral border of the pons. The trochlear nerve supplies the superior oblique muscle of the eyeball.

The trigeminal nerve contains both sensory and motor fibers. Its *motor* fibers are the axons of a group of cells situated in the upper part of the pons. This collection of gray matter is called the *motor nucleus* of the trigeminal. The *sensory* fibers originate in the *trigeminal (semilunar) ganglion,* which lies upon the floor of the skull and is homologous with the posterior root ganglia of the spinal nerves. Like those composing the ganglia of the posterior spinal nerve roots, the cells of the trigeminal ganglion are unipolar—i.e., each gives off a single process that divides into two. One branch passes centrally, the other peripherally. The central fibers form a short trunk—the sensory root of the trigeminal nerve—which enters the brain in close association with the motor root. Within the brain, the fibers of the sensory root divide into ascending and descending groups. The former end in a collection of gray matter—the *superior sensory nucleus of the trigeminal*—situated in the pons close to the motor nucleus. These fibers convey the discriminative qualities of sensation—namely, light touch, localization, kinesthetic sense, etc.—from the face. The descending fibers terminate in the *spinal nucleus of the trigeminal nerve*—an elongated mass of gray substance, extending from the lower part of the pons to the upper part of the spinal cord. The fibers entering the spinal nucleus transmit impulses of the crude forms of sensation from the face— namely, pain and extremes of temperature.

The peripheral processes of the cells of the trigeminal ganglion form three trunks called the first, second, and third divisions of the trigeminal nerve or the *ophthalmic, maxillary,* and *mandibular nerves,* respectively. The first two divisions (ophthalmic and maxillary nerves) are composed entirely of sensory fibers, but the third division (mandibular nerve) is united with the motor root of the nerve. The first division, or ophthalmic nerve, supplies the skin of the forehead and anterior part of the scalp, the structures within the eye socket (orbit), and the skin of the side of the nose and upper lid. The second division, or maxillary nerve, is distributed to a part of the dura mater, certain structures within the orbit, the lower eyelid, the upper lip, and to the upper teeth. The third division, or mandibular nerve, contains both sensory and motor fibers; it sends sensory fibers to the lower teeth and the lower lip, to the skin of the side and lower part of the face, and to the mucous membrane over the anterior two thirds of the tongue and the floor of the mouth. Its motor fibers supply the muscles of mastication (see Fig. 12.33).

The trigeminal nerve may be the seat of a most severe and stubborn form of neuralgia. All three branches may be involved, or the pain may be confined to the area of distribution of one branch. Surgical division of the sensory root of the nerve, or of one or other branch, may be required in order to relieve the pain.

The abducent nerve. The abducent nucleus is situated in the lower part of the pons beneath the floor of the fourth ventricle. The nerve emerges from the anterior aspect of the brain in the groove lying between the pons and the upper end of the pyramid of the medulla oblongata. It supplies the external rectus muscle of the eyeball.

The facial nerve has a large motor and a small sensory root. The fibers forming the *motor* root arise from the *motor nucleus,* which lies in the lower part of the pons. This root also transmits *secretory* and *vasodilator* (parasympathetic) fibers to the submaxillary and sublingual glands; these fibers arise from a separate group of nerve cells— the *superior salivatory* (or *salivary*) *nucleus*—lying in close proximity to the motor nucleus. The motor root of the nerve leaves the anterior aspect of the brain at the lower border of the pons. The fibers of the *sensory* root (also called the *nervus intermedius*) are the axons of cells situated in the *facial (geniculate) ganglion* which lies within a canal in the temporal bone. The sensory root enters the brain in close association with the motor root. The peripheral processes of the ganglion cells are distributed to the anterior two thirds of the tongue (see Fig. 13.61, p. 640). They transmit impulses of taste to a nucleus in the medulla oblongata named the *tractus solitarius.* From the latter the

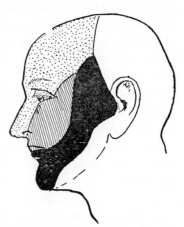

Fig. 12.33   Distribution   of the trigeminal nerve in the face. Ophthalmic division, *stippled;* maxillary   division,   *hatched;* mandibular division, *black.*

impulses are relayed to the thalamus and thence by tertiary neurons to the center for taste in the cerebral cortex (p. 535). Both taste and parasympathetic fibers (secretory and vasodilator) leave the facial trunk in its *chorda tympani* branch.

The motor fibers of the facial nerve form a stout trunk which leaves the cranial cavity through a small opening in the floor of the skull. The nerve curves forward below the ear in the substance of the parotid gland to reach the face, where it breaks up into numerous branches. These supply the muscles of the face, lips, eyelids, forehead, and anterior part of the scalp.

The acoustic or *auditory nerve* is entirely sensory in function. It consists of two distinct sets of fibers, the *cochlear* and *vestibular nerves.* The courses of these nerves and their central connections are described on pages 621 and 632, respectively.

The glossopharyngeal nerve contains *motor, sensory, secretory,* and *vasodilator* fibers. The motor fibers issue from the upper part of the *nucleus ambiguus* situated in the medulla oblongata, and are distributed to a single muscle (the stylopharyngeus). The sensory fibers conduct impulses of taste from the posterior third of the tongue to the lower part of the tractus solitarius. The taste impulses are relayed to the optic thalamus, and thence to the cerebral center for taste in the lower part of the somesthetic area. Sensory fibers are also distributed to the mucous membranes of the pharynx, tonsil, and palate; they convey impulses of ordinary sensation, touch, temperature, etc. The secretory and vasodilator (parasympathetic) fibers leave the glossopharyngeal nerve in its *tympanic branch* and are distributed to the parotid gland. The secretory and vasodilator fibers have their origins in the *inferior salivatory* (*salivary*) *nucleus,* which lies below the superior *salivatory* (*salivary*) *nucleus* (p. 296). The glossopharyngeal nerve also supplies a sensory filament—the sinus nerve, page 199—to the carotid sinus.

The vagus nerve contains *motor, sensory, secretory,* and *vasodilator* fibers. The motor fibers are of two types—voluntary and autonomic. The fibers to voluntary muscle originate in the lower part of the nucleus ambiguus (see accessory nerve, p. 551). These fibers are, actually, derived from the cranial root of the accessory (ninth cranial) nerve; they enter the vagus nerve and supply the cricothyroid muscle of the larynx and the inferior constrictor muscle of the pharynx. The autonomic motor fibers are distributed to the muscle of the bronchi, heart, esophagus, stomach, gall bladder, pancreas, small intestine, and first third or so of the large intestine. The fibers going to the heart are inhibitory in function (p. 187). The involuntary motor fibers, the secretory fibers (to the gastric glands and pancreas), the cardiac inhibitory fibers, and the vasodilator fibers belong to the parasympathetic division of the autonomic system. They arise from the *dorsal nucleus of the vagus.* This nucleus is a mixed one, for it is also a terminal for sensory fibers. Some of the latter connect with motor autonomic neurons within the dorsal nucleus, which thus functions as a reflex center.

The vagus nerve emerges from the lateral aspect of the medulla oblongata as a series of rootlets which soon join to form a stout trunk. This leaves the skull through the jugular foramen, and passes down the neck in close relation to the internal and common carotid arteries. Two ganglia are situated upon the vagus trunk, the upper one lies within the jugular foramen at the base of the skull; the other just below the point where the nerve issues from the skull. The sensory fibers of the vagus have their origin within these ganglia.

The accessory nerve is entirely motor in function, and consists of a *cranial* and a *spinal* root. The cranial fibers arise from a nucleus lying below, and continuous with the lower end of the nucleus ambiguus. They leave the side of the medulla oblongata as four or five delicate strands which, after uniting, pass from the skull through the jugular foramen. The spinal fibers are the axons of anterior horn cells situated in the upper five cervical segments of the spinal cord. This part of the nerve enters the cranial cavity through the foramen magnum and re-enters the neck through the jugular foramen. Within the latter fora-

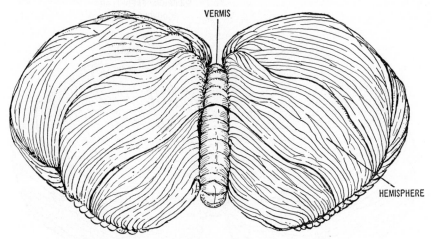

Fig. 12.34   The superior aspect of the cerebellum.

men, it joins the cranial part, but becomes separate again almost immediately.

Most of the muscles of the pharynx, larynx, and soft palate are supplied by the cranial part of the accessory nerve. The fibers pass into the pharyngeal and laryngeal branches of the vagus, through which they are distributed to voluntary muscles in these structures (cricothyroid and pharyngeal constrictors). The spinal part sends fibers to certain muscles of the neck and shoulder (sternomastoid and trapezius).

The hypoglossal nerve is distributed entirely to the muscles (intrinsic and extrinsic) of the tongue. Its fibers arise from the hypoglossal nucleus in the medulla oblongata, and appear as a series of rootlets in the groove situated on the anterolateral aspect of the pyramid. The rootlets leave the skull through the hypoglossal canal and unite just below the base of the skull. The trunk so formed curves forward in the upper part of the neck to reach the cavity of the mouth.

The cerebellum. The cerebellum is situated behind the brain stem (midbrain, pons, and medulla), and beneath the posterior portions of the cerebral hemispheres (Fig. 12.18, p. 529). It is composed of two lateral masses, the *cerebellar hemispheres* (Figs. 12.34 and 12.35) and a central elongated wormlike structure, called the *vermis* (L. *worm*). The white matter of the cerebellum forms a central branching framework within the substance of each hemisphere and in the center of the vermis. The gray matter covering the terminal stems of this structure constitutes the cerebellar cortex. The cortex of the hemispheres is thus constructed of a number of leaves flattened against one

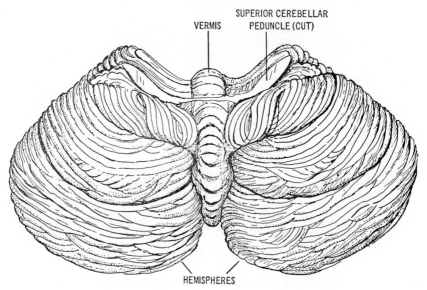

Fig. 12.35   The inferior aspect of the cerebellum.

another with only their edges appearing on the surface. The cerebellar cortex is composed of several layers of cells, but unlike the cerebral cortex it is of uniform cellular structure—i.e., the cells at all depths are of similar type. Large cells with flask-shaped bodies and extensive dendritic arborizations—the *cells of Purkinje*—are peculiar to the cerebellar cortex (Figs. 12.36 and 12.1, p. 507). Three masses of gray matter—the *cerebellar nuclei*—are to be found in the depth of the cerebellum. The largest of these is known as the *dentate nucleus*. The nerve fibers streaming to and from the cortex and entering or leaving the cerebellar nuclei constitute the white matter of the cerebellum.

Each half of the cerebellum is connected with the rest of the central nervous system through three compact bundles of nerve fibers, called the *cerebellar peduncles*. The *superior* cerebellar peduncle (or *brachium conjunctivum*) plunges into the midbrain and transmits impulses from the cerebellum to the red nucleus and thalamus and, through the latter, to the motor area of the cerebral cortex (see Figs. 12.37 and 12.38). It also transmits, in the reverse direction, the ventral spinocerebellar tract which conveys impulses to the cerebellum from the spinal cord (p. 528). The impulses that leave the cerebellum by its superior peduncle originate in the cerebellar cortex. They pass first to one or other of the cerebellar nuclei, from which they are relayed by secondary neurons. The dentate nucleus contributes most of the fibers to the superior peduncle. The other two cerebellar nuclei are

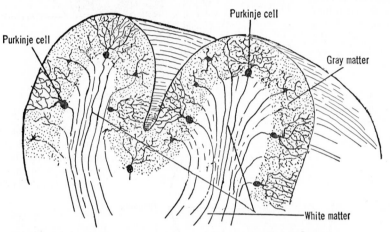

Fig. 12.36   A section through the cerebellar cortex and adjacent part of the white matter.

called, respectively, the *nucleus emboliformis* and the *nucleus fastigii*. The latter receives impulses from the organ of equilibrium in the internal ear via the vestibular nuclei of the medulla oblongata.

The *middle* peduncle (or *brachium pontis*) transmits impulses from the pons *to* the cerebellum; its fibers arise from the pontine nuclei which, as stated elsewhere, receive impulses from the frontal and temporal regions of the cerebral cortex (frontopontine and temporopontine tracts). No fibers leave the cerebellum by this peduncle.

The *inferior* peduncle (or *restiform body*) connects the cerebellum with the lower part of the medulla oblongata. It is composed, mainly, of fibers of the dorsal (direct) spinocerebellar tract and of fibers arising in the vestibular nuclei in the medulla oblongata (*vestibulocerebellar tract*). Thus, through the inferior cerebellar peduncle, the cerebellum receives proprioceptive impulses from the labyrinth (p. 630) and the skeletal muscles. The inferior peduncle also transmits impulses *from* the cerebellum to the vestibular nuclei (*cerebellovestibular tract*).

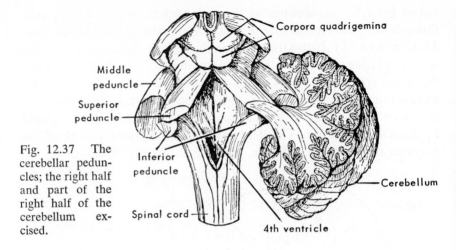

Fig. 12.37 The cerebellar peduncles; the right half and part of the right half of the cerebellum excised.

Corpora quadrigemina

Middle peduncle

Superior peduncle

Inferior peduncle

Spinal cord

4th ventricle

Cerebellum

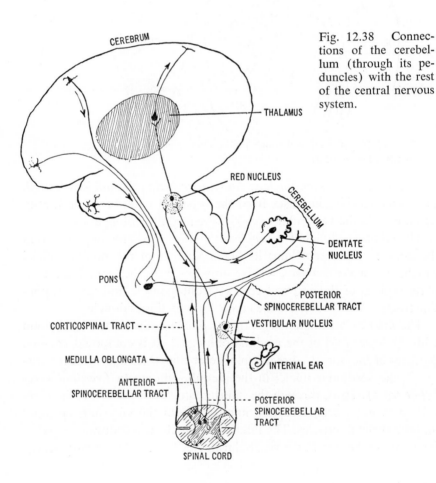

Fig. 12.38 Connections of the cerebellum (through its peduncles) with the rest of the central nervous system.

CEREBRUM

THALAMUS

RED NUCLEUS

CEREBELLUM

DENTATE NUCLEUS

PONS

POSTERIOR SPINOCEREBELLAR TRACT

CORTICOSPINAL TRACT

VESTIBULAR NUCLEUS

MEDULLA OBLONGATA

INTERNAL EAR

ANTERIOR SPINOCEREBELLAR TRACT

POSTERIOR SPINOCEREBELLAR TRACT

SPINAL CORD

The *functions* of the cerebellum are concerned with voluntary movements, yet they play no part apparently in initiating such movements. An animal deprived of its cerebellum shows no actual paralysis, but its movements are shaky, jerky, and poorly controlled. In man, injury or disease of the cerebellum causes the same lack of muscular control; movements are not executed smoothly and evenly, and with the nicety of direction and force characteristic of normal muscular action. For example, the subject of cerebellar deficiency, if asked to touch his nose with his finger, moves the arm jerkily and fails to hit the mark. The gait is staggering in character; the muscles are hypotonic, and the limbs show a coarse tremor upon attempting any movement. *Ataxia* is the term applied in general to disorders of voluntary muscular control; those resulting from disease of the cerebellum are therefore grouped under the designation *cerebellar ataxia*.

As a result of numerous experiments upon animals and of studies of cerebellar deficiency in man (gunshot wounds or disease), it is now generally believed that the chief function of the cerebellum is to blend or *synergize* the actions of the different muscles engaged in a given movement. Through cerebellar activity, the contractions of the individual muscles, or groups of muscles, are so timed and graded in force that their combined action results in a smooth and effective movement. The anatomical basis for such function has been outlined above. Its superior peduncles connect the cerebellum with the motor area of the cerebral cortex on the one hand and, on the other hand, through the red nucleus and the rubrospinal tracts, with the anterior horn cells of the spinal cord. Through the spinocerebellar tracts, on the other hand, the cerebellum is kept constantly "informed" of the position of the limbs and movements of the muscles. Through the vestibulocerebellar tracts, it receives impulses from the labyrinth acquainting it with movements of the head in space.

The impulses reaching the cerebellum give rise to no sensation; the cerebellum carries on its activities entirely beneath the level of consciousness.

The Membranes (Meninges) of the Brain and Spinal Cord

The central nervous system is enclosed within three concentric membranous sheaths. The outermost of these is relatively thick and tough and is therefore called the *dura mater* (L. hard mother). The innermost is very delicate, and is applied closely to the surfaces of the brain and spinal cord. It is known as the *pia mater* (L. tender mother). The membrane between these two has been named the *arachnoid mater,* or simply, the *arachnoid* (Fig. 12.39). Its name is derived from

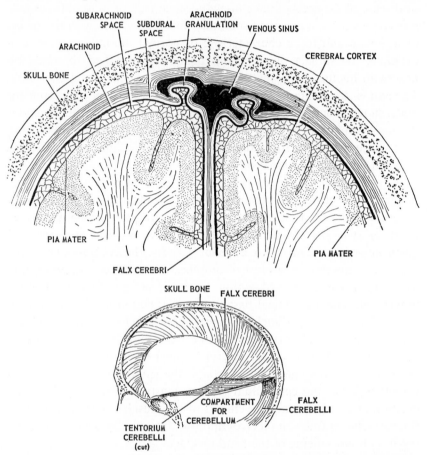

Fig. 12.39 The membranes (meninges) of the brain. *Upper drawing,* a vertical transverse section, label of dura mater omitted. *Lower drawing,* a vertical longitudinal section to show the partitions (septa) of the dura mater.

the meshwork of filaments that connect it with the underlying pia mater, and which somewhat resembles a spider's web (Gk. *arachnē,* a spider).

The dura mater consists of two layers, the outer of which serves as a lining (periosteum) for the skull bone, the inner one as a protective covering for the neural structures; it carries the larger blood vessels. The dura mater gives off a sickle-shaped process, called the *falx cerebri,* which descends vertically between the two hemispheres; a horizontal sheet, the *tentorium cerebelli,* which projects forward between the cerebrum and the cerebellum; and a short vertical crescentic spur, the *falx cerebelli,* that extends forward in the notch between the posterior poles of the cerebellar hemispheres. The narrow interval between the dura mater and the arachnoid is called the *subdural space.* The arachnoid, a much thinner membrane than the dura mater, forms a loose investment for the central nervous system. With one exception —namely, the deep fissure between the hemispheres—it does not dip into the fissures and sulci, and other depressions in the contours of the brain, but bridges over them. The pia mater, on the contrary, adheres to the underlying nervous tissue, following all its irregularities faithfully, even into the depths of the fissures.

The subarachnoid space and the ventricular system. The interval between the arachnoid and the pia mater which, as mentioned above, is interlaced by a delicate network, is known as the *subarachnoid space.* It is filled with a thin limpid liquid called the *cerebrospinal fluid.* This fluid is similar in composition to plasma or lymph, but its dissolved constituents (sodium chloride and bicarbonate excepted) are in lower concentration. Its composition is given below. It will be observed that the protein concentration is extremely low, whereas that of sodium chloride is higher than in plasma (see Table 12-3, and pages 57 and 58).

Table 12-3

**Composition of cerebrospinal fluid
in milligrams per 00 cc**

Protein	15–55
Glucose	50–80
Calcium	4–6
Potassium	12–17
Sodium chloride	720–750
Bicarbonate	
(Volumes percent CO_2)	40–60
Inorganic phosphate	1.25–2.0

Very few cells are to be found in the cerebrospinal fluid, and they are of the lymphocyte variety. The cerebrospinal fluid is under pressure. In the cisterna magna, in the lying down position, it is around 90 mm of water, but falls to zero or a little below when the subject stands. In the lower part of the spinal subarachnoid space (lumbar region), the cerebrospinal fluid pressure in the lying-down position is about the same as that in the cisterna magna, but rises to between 500

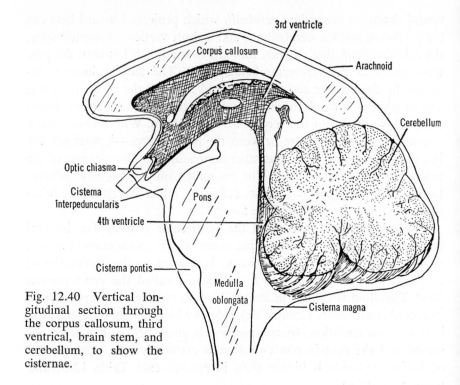

Fig. 12.40 Vertical longitudinal section through the corpus callosum, third ventrical, brain stem, and cerebellum, to show the cisternae.

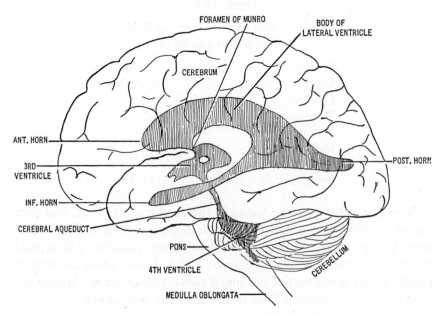

Fig. 12.41 Diagram of the ventricles of the brain.

and 600 mm of water in the standing position. This is about the hydro-static pressure of a column of fluid extending from the cranial cavity to the lumbar region. Coughing, sneezing, blowing, straining at stool, or lifting weights raises the pressure in the veins of the thorax. The augmented pressure is transmitted through the veins of the neck, and thence to the cerebrospinal fluid. The volume of fluid is kept constant at about 130 cc (in man) by the nicely balanced processes of forma-tion (secretion by the choroid plexus) and reabsorption through the arachnoid granulations (see below). There is no communication be-tween the subarachnoid space and the subdural space; the latter, like the pleural and peritoneal cavities, is a potential space only, a thin layer of lymph lying between the two membranes.

The cerebrospinal fluid serves a protective function, serving to shel-ter the delicate nervous structures from mechanical shocks that may be applied to its bony encasement. It gives buoyancy to the brain and spinal cord; the weight of the brain in its normal situation is only about one thirtieth of its weight after removal from the cranium.

Since the pia mater clings to the surface of the brain, dipping into all the fissures and sulci and follow-ing closely all the contours of the cerebrum, brain stem, and cerebel-lum, whereas the arachnoid forms a relatively loose investment, there are certain regions—such as at the junction of the pons with the me-dulla, and of the latter with the cerebellum—where the subarach-noid space is widened. In such re-gions, there are relatively large col-lections of cerebrospinal fluid. These are called *cisternae* (L. a cis-tern or reservoir). The principal cisternae are shown in Fig. 12.40.

Hollow spaces filled with cere-brospinal fluid are to be found

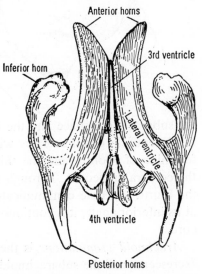

Fig. 12.42   Cast of the ventricular system of the brain. (Redrawn after Retzius.)

within the brain itself. They are called *ventricles,* and are four in num-ber. The largest are the *lateral ventricles,* one in each cerebral hemi-sphere (Figs. 12.41 and 12.42). The *third ventricle* is a much smaller space situated between the optic thalami. The *fourth ventricle* lies be-tween the cerebellum behind and the pons and upper half of the medulla oblongata in front. The posterior aspect of the latter two parts of the brain stem really form its anterior wall which, however, is usually referred to as its "floor." The superior cerebellar peduncles and parts of the cerebellum enter into the formation of its posterior wall or roof. Highly vascular fringes of pia mater project into each of the four ventricular cavities. They are covered with epithelium which secretes the cerebrospinal fluid and are known as the *choroid plexuses*. All the ventricles of the brain communicate with one another, as well as with

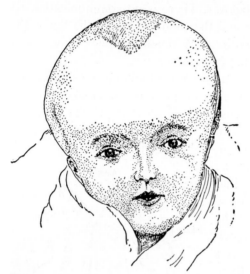

Fig. 12.43 Internal hydrocephalus in a young child. (Drawn from a photograph after Purves Stewart.) The shaded area at the dome of the head represents the part of the skull (anterior fontanelle) which, owing to the wide separation of the bones, is covered by scalp and membrane only. In a normal child of the same age, this fontanelle should be completely, or very nearly, closed, and even at birth it is no more than about 1 inch in its transverse diameter.

the subarachnoid space and the central canal of the spinal cord. The third ventricle communicates with the lateral ventricles through the foramina of Monro, and the third ventricle with the fourth through the cerebral aqueduct. Through an aperture in a recess on each side, the fourth ventricle communicates with the subarachnoid space and, at its inferior angle, it is continuous with the central canal of the spinal cord.

Arachnoid granulations is the name that has been given to small excrescences of the subarachnoid mesh which, carrying a covering of dura mater before them, project into the venous sinuses of the brain. (Fig. 12.39). They filter fluid from the subarachnoid space into the blood stream. A smaller amount of fluid passes into the capillaries of the pia mater. Thus, by this process of reabsorption, the cerebrospinal fluid is maintained at constant volume. Any block, such as in the cerebral aqueduct or at the foramina of Munro (which may occur as a congenital defect, or from disease in infancy or, though less commonly, in later life) will upset the balance between secretion and reabsorption.

Fluid will continue to be formed by the choroid plexuses on one side of the block, but reabsorption of the secreted fluid by the arachnoid granulations will be prevented. Damming back of fluid results, and the part of the ventricular system involved (this includes the third ventricle and usually the lateral ventricles) becomes greatly dilated. As a consequence of the increased fluid pressure, the brain substance becomes thinned and the skull bones separated. There is usually mental deterioration. This condition is known as *internal hydrocephalus* (Fig. 12.43).

External hydrocephalus may be caused by a blockage at some point in the subarachnoid space, as may result from meningitis, tumor, etc. The cerebrospinal fluid is then increased in any part of the subarachnoid space cut off from the arachnoid granulations. Cisternae, so isolated, are enlarged and the ventricular system may be expanded. There is a pronounced rise in intracranial pressure. But this type of hydrocephalus may occur though no blockage exists, and may then be due to an increase in the *production* of cerebrospinal fluid by the choroid plexuses (as in meningitis) or to an elevated pressure in the venous sinuses of the brain.

The withdrawal of cerebrospinal fluid [4] from the subarachnoid space in the lumbar region through a specially designed wide-bore needle introduced between the fourth and fifth lumbar vertebrae (lumbar puncture) is today a common and invaluable procedure in the diagnosis of meningitis, brain abscess, tumor, etc. Lumbar puncture is also employed for the introduction of a spinal anesthetic or of a curative drug. The chief abnormalities in the cerebrospinal fluid that are of diagnostic importance in neurological disease are a cloudy appearance, an increase in the protein content (ten times or more), and a rise in the number of leucocytes.

The Autonomic Nervous System

The *autonomic* (Gk. *autos,* self + *nomos,* law, i.e., self governing) or *involuntary* nervous system governs those functions which are carried out automatically, and which under ordinary circumstances do not obtrude upon consciousness. These functions include the control of the rate of the heart, the movements of the gastrointestinal tract, the caliber of the small blood vessels, the contraction or inhibition of smooth muscle in various other structures (e.g., skin, urinary bladder, gall

---

[4] A sample of cerebrospinal fluid may also be obtained in a comparable manner from the cisterna magna (*cisternal puncture*) or from a lateral ventricle.

bladder, and bronchi) and the secretion of the sweat glands and of various digestive glands.

The efferent nerves of the autonomic nervous system arise from groups of cells situated at different levels of the central nervous system, from the midbrain to the sacral region of the spinal cord. The fibers, after issuing from the brain or cord, make connections with nerve cells situated either in a ganglion or in the innervated organ itself (muscle or gland). Thus, every autonomic pathway consists of two neurons. The axon, whose cell body lies within the central nervous system, is called the *preganglionic fiber;* that of the outlying (ganglionic) nerve cell, the *postganglionic fiber* (see Pl. 12A).

The autonomic nervous system is divided upon an anatomical as well as upon a physiological basis into two parts, called the *parasympathetic* and *sympathetic* divisions (see Pl. 11).

The parasympathetic division. The parasympathetic division is subdivided into a *cranial* and a *sacral* part or *outflow*. The preganglionic fibers of the cranial outflow arise from groups of cells situated in the midbrain, pons, and medulla oblongata. The midbrain fibers originate in the oculomotor nucleus and connect with cells in the ciliary ganglion; postganglionic fibers are distributed to the iris, and transmit impulses which constrict the pupil. The cells in the pons are in close association with the nucleus of the facial nerve; the preganglionic fibers are conveyed in the chorda tympani branch of the facial nerve to ganglion cells situated in, or in close relation to, the submaxillary and sublingual (salivary) glands. From here the impulses are transmitted by postganglionic fibers to the gland cells. The fibers in the chorda tympani nerve are vasodilator as well as secretory in function.

In the medulla, the cells that give rise to the parasympathetic fibers are situated in the glossopharyngeal and vagus nuclei. The former enter the glossopharyngeal nerve and pass to the otic ganglion; from here gostpanglionic fibers conveying vasodilator and secretory impulses are relayed to the parotid gland.

The vagus nerve is composed in the main of parasympathetic fibers; these have a very wide distribution—to the heart, bronchioles, esophagus, stomach, small intestine, and first third of the large intestine, and to the pancreas, liver, gall bladder, and bile ducts. The preganglionic fibers of the vagus may, therefore, be 2 feet or more in length, whereas the postganglionic fibers are very short. The latter form a rich plexus— *Auerbach's plexus*—in the walls of the gastrointestinal tract, bronchioles, and biliary ducts. Groups of (ganglionic) nerve cells are scattered throughout the plexus of fibers.

The cells of the *sacral outflow* are situated in the second, third, and fourth sacral segments of the spinal cord. The fibers leave the cord by the anterior spinal nerve roots. Separating again from the other anterior root fibers, they combine to form the *pelvic nerve*. This nerve supplies *motor* fibers to the distal two thirds of the large bowel and to the wall of the urinary bladder, and *vasodilator* fibers to the penis and clitoris. It also contains *inhibitory* fibers to the internal anal sphincter and to the internal sphincter of the bladder. The postganglionic fibers of the sacral outflow arise from small ganglia situated in close proximity to, or in the walls of, the innervated organ.

The sympathetic division. The preganglionic fibers of the sympathetic nerves are the axons of cells in the lateral gray horns of the spinal cord (p. 524), from the first thoracic to the second or third lumbar segments, inclusive. The sympathetic is, therefore, commonly referred to as the *thoracicolumbar outflow* of the autonomic nervous system. The preganglionic fibers leave the cord by the anterior roots of the corresponding spinal nerves. The ganglia of the sympathetic are in two main groups, the *vertebral* and the *prevertebral*. The vertebral ganglia are situated on either side of the vertebral column (Pl. 12A). They appear as a series of 22 or 23 swellings on each side, connected together to form a long, beaded cord. This extends from the base of the skull to the coccyx, and is called the *gangliated cord of the sympathetic*. At their lower limits the two cords come together and end in a single (unpaired) ganglion called the *ganglion impar*.

The prevertebral ganglia are larger than the vertebral; they lie in front of the spinal column and in close relation to the aorta and its branches.

The sympathetic fibers destined for the supply of the limbs (blood vessels, sweat glands, and smooth muscle of the skin) soon separate from the anterior nerve roots and enter the vertebral ganglia. These fibers (*preganglionic*) are seen issuing as slender glistening strands, one from each anterior spinal nerve root from the first thoracic to the second or third lumbar segment. They are called the *white rami communicantes*. The fibers of which each of these strands is composed enter the vertebral ganglion corresponding to the segment of the spinal cord from which they arise; here synapses are usually made, by at least a small proportion of the fibers, with nerve cells (Pl. 12A). But the fibers of the white rami communicantes do not necessarily terminate around nerve cells in the ganglion which they first enter; they may pass up or down the gangliated cord to synapse with ganglion cells at a higher or lower level. The axons of the cells in the ganglia (*post-*

ganglionic fibers) leave the ganglia as short yellowish-pink filaments, known as the *gray rami communicantes,* which join the spinal nerves. The sympathetic fibers are thus distributed to the periphery with the ordinary motor and sensory fibers. All the spinal nerves receive post-ganglionic fibers, though the anterior roots of only a proportion of the spinal nerves (first thoracic to second or third lumbar) give rise to white rami (preganglionic fibers). That is to say, the spinal nerves above the first thoracic segment or below the third lumbar have gray rami but no white rami. The sympathetic fibers above or below these levels must travel up or down the gangliated cord to the appropriate vertebral ganglion and then pass as gray rami to the spinal nerves (see Pl. 12A).

The sympathetic fibers to the viscera and blood vessels of the abdomen do not connect with the vertebral chain of ganglia, but pass to the prevertebral ganglia—*celiac, superior mesenteric,* etc. The postganglionic fibers form plexuses around the branches of the abdominal aorta, from which the vessels and viscera receive their sympathetic supply. The fibers passing from the spinal cord to the prevertebral ganglia are collected on each side into three well-defined strands called the *greater, lesser,* and *least splanchnic nerves.*

Functions of the autonomic nervous system. The *sympathetic* division exerts a regulating influence on a great number of structures. Through the cardiac accelerator nerves, it increases the rate of the heart; through the splanchnic nerves, it inhibits the movements of the intestinal tract, maintains the tone of the arterioles of the abdomen, hastens the formation of glucose from glycogen by the liver, and causes the liberation of adrenaline from the adrenal medulla. Through the part of the sympathetic in the neck—the *cervical sympathetic*—impulses are conveyed to the pupil (causing dilatation), to the salivary glands, and to the blood vessels of the head and neck. Sympathetic impulses cause relaxation of the wall of the urinary bladder, but contraction of the internal sphincter of this organ. Sympathetic fibers in the cutaneous nerves transmit motor impulses to the smooth muscle of the skin and secretory impulses to the sweat glands.

Many structures—such as the iris, heart, intestines, urinary bladder, salivary glands, and pancreas—receive fibers from both divisions of the autonomic nervous system. The actions of the two upon a given organ are antagonistic and balanced one against the other, the activity shown by the organ at any moment being the resultant of the two opposing influences. The parasympathetic fibers (vagus) to the heart, for example, are inhibitory, the sympathetic excitatory. On the other hand,

Table 12-4

Organ	Parasympathetic effects*	Origin of sympathetic postganglionic fibers	Sympathetic effects
Heart	Inhibition	Superior middle and inferior cervical ganglia	Acceleration
Vessels:			
Cutaneous		Various vertebral ganglia	Constriction
Muscular		Various vertebral ganglia	Dilatation
Coronary	Constriction	Cervical ganglia	Dilatation
Salivary glands	Dilatation	Superior cervical ganglion	Constriction
Pulmonary	Constriction	Thoracic vertebral ganglia	Constriction and dilatation
Cerebral	Dilatation	Superior cervical ganglion	Constriction
Abdominal and pelvic viscera	Dilatation	Prevertebral ganglia	Constriction
External genitalia	Dilatation	Prevertebral ganglia	Constriction
Eye:			
Iris	Constriction	Superior cervical ganglion	Dilatation
Ciliary muscle	Contraction	Superior cervical ganglion	Relaxation
Smooth muscle of orbit and upper lid		Superior cervical ganglion	Contraction
Bronchi	Constriction	Thoracic ganglia	Dilatation
Glands:			
Sweat		Vertebral ganglia	Secretion
Salivary	Secretion	Superior cervical ganglion	Secretion
Gastric	Secretion	Celiac ganglion	Inhibition Secretion of mucus
Pancreas			
Acini	Secretion	Celiac ganglion	
Islets	Secretion	Celiac ganglion	
Liver		Celiac ganglion	Glycogenolysis
Adrenal medulla		No postganglionic fibers	Secretion
Smooth muscle:			
Of skin		Vertebral ganglia	Contraction
Of stomach wall	Contraction or inhibition	Celiac ganglion	Contraction or inhibition
Of small intestine	Increased tone and motility	Celiac and superior mesenteric ganglia	Inhibition
Of large intestine	Increased tone and motility	Inferior mesenteric and hypogastric ganglia	Inhibition
Of bladder wall (detrusor muscle)	Contraction	Inferior mesenteric and hypogastric ganglia	Inhibition
Of trigone and sphincter	Inhibition	Inferior mesenteric and hypogastric ganglia	Contraction
Of uterus, pregnant	Nil	Inferior mesenteric and hypogastric ganglia	Contraction
Of uterus, nonpregnant	Nil	Inferior mesenteric and hypogastric ganglia	Inhibition

* With certain exceptions, (e.g., those supplying the sublingual and parotid glands and the sphincter pupillae), the postganglionic fibers of the parasympathetic arise from cells situated in, or in close proximity to, the innervated organ itself.

motor fibers (*excitatory*) to the wall of the intestine are derived from the parasympathetic, the *inhibitors* from the sympathetic. The walls of the urinary bladder and intestine receive their motor innervation from the parasympathetic (vagus and pelvic nerves), whereas the sympathetic is inhibitory. The internal sphincters of the bladder and anus are innervated in a reverse manner; they are excited by the sympathetic and inhibited by the parasympathetic.

A summary of the actions of the parasympathetic and sympathetic fibers upon a number of structures is given in Table 12-4.

The sympathetic and the hormone of the adrenal medulla are closely similar in their actions. The two, acting in conjunction, constitute what is referred to as the *sympathoadrenal system* and play an important role in the regulation of the internal environment of the body—i.e., the composition and temperature of the fluids bathing the cells of the tissues. Thus, through its effect upon the blood vessels, sweat glands, and smooth muscle of the skin, the sympathetic controls heat loss; through its action upon the blood vessels, it also varies the distribution of water between the vascular system and the tissues. Through an action upon the liver, either through sympathetic nerve impulses or the liberation of adrenaline, the sugar of the blood is raised. The sympathoadrenal system through its various activities increases the body's efficiency in times of stress. Many manifestations of an animal when in danger, or when its powers are being taxed to the utmost, are those of sympathetic stimulation—e.g., dilated pupils, rapid heart action, contraction of the spleen, and the erection of hair or ruffling of feathers (due to contraction of cutaneous smooth muscle; see also p. 423).

The sympathoadrenal system, highly important though it is, can nevertheless be dispensed with. It is not essential to life nor even to well-being, provided the animal is not exposed to some environmental hazard. Animals from which the entire sympathetic and the medulla of both adrenals have been excised live in perfect health in the sheltered surroundings of the laboratory. They cannot, however, withstand cold and are less well equipped than is a normal animal to meet an emergency which demands the marshalling of its resources, either to defend itself or to fly from the threatened danger.

The transmission of autonomic effects by chemical substances. Research of recent years has disclosed the amazing fact that many sympathetic and parasympathetic effects are not brought about directly by the nerve impulses themselves, but by chemical substances which the impulses cause to be liberated at the nerve endings. In treating of the control of the heart, it has been mentioned that, when the vagus is stimulated, *acetylcholine* is liberated, and is the direct cause of the inhibitory effect upon the heart muscle. Similarly, *adrenaline* (p. 420), is liberated at the terminals of the cardiac accelerators, and from certain other nerves of the sympathetic system (see pp. 188 and 425). These facts, which have led to a revolutionary change in our ideas of peripheral nervous action, have been supplemented within the last few years by a number of observations of great interest and importance.

It has been shown, for example, that acetylcholine is liberated at the terminals of such parasympathetic nerves as those going to the iris (in the oculomotor nerve), to the salivary glands (in the chorda tympani), to the stomach and intestines (in the vagus), and to the bladder (in the pelvic), as well as from certain sympathetic nerves—e.g., from those to the sweat glands and from those that cause dilatation of the vessels of the skeletal muscles.

Acetylcholine liberation also plays a part, though its precise mode of action is not altogether clear, in the transmission of nervous effects across sympathetic and parasympathetic synapses—that is, from preganglionic fibers to the ganglionic cell. Still more extraordinary is the discovery that acetylcholine liberation in the region of the motor endplate is an essential event in the contraction of skeletal muscle.

Following the suggestion of Sir Henry Dale, the English physiologist, it is now customary to speak of those fibers that liberate an adrenalinelike substance (see sympathin) as *adrenergic,* and those that liberate acetylcholine as *cholinergic.* All preganglionic fibers (sympathetic or parasympathetic), all postganglionic parasympathetic fibers, and certain postganglionic sympathetic fibers (e.g., to sweat glands), as well as the fibers of voluntary motor nerves are cholinergic (see Pl. 12C).

Conditioned Reflexes

The type of reflex (*unconditioned reflex*) that has been considered (pp. 297 and 510) is carried out entirely through centers situated in the spinal cord or lower (subcortical) levels of the brain. Unconditioned reflexes are inborn; they are not dependent upon past experience, education, or training. In *conditioned reflexes,* on the other hand, the activity of the cerebral cortex plays an essential role. Conditioned reflexes were first demonstrated and studied by Pavlov, the Russian physiologist, and most of the knowledge that we possess of this type of response is the outcome of his investigations. An understanding of

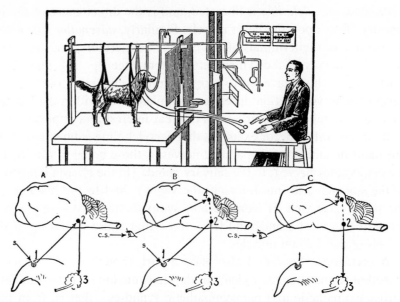

Fig. 12.44   *Upper drawing*, showing arrangement for carrying out a conditioned reflex experiment. The opening of the parotid duct has been transplanted to the skin of the cheek so that the saliva, as it is secreted, may be collected and measured. The animal is separated from the experimenter by a partition in order that extraneous types of stimulation (e.g., movements or sounds made by the experimenter) shall not arouse the animal's interest and thereby interfere with the conditioning process. (From Pavlov, *Lectures on Conditioned Reflexes,* International Publishers, N.Y.) *Below,* diagram to illustrate the theory of the mechanism underlying conditioned reflexes. 1, taste buds; 2, salivary center; 3, salivary gland; 4, occipital (visual) cortex; S, unconditioned stimulus; C.S., conditioned stimulus. In A, the animal is fed and a stimulus thus applied to the taste buds. In B, a conditioned visual stimulus (e.g., a flash of light) is applied at the same time as the unconditioned stimulus. A pathway from the occipital cortex to the salivary center is thus established. In C, the conditioned stimulus is applied alone. Impulses pass from the visual cortex to the salivary center and evoke salivary secretion.

the conditioned response can best be gained by giving a few examples of the results of Professor Pavlov's experiments.

When a newborn puppy is given milk to drink, there is a secretion of saliva, due to the stimulation of the taste buds in the mouth. The reflex arc in this instance is constituted of the nerves of taste, the salivary centers in the medulla, and the secretory fibers (chorda tympani or glossopharyngeal) to the salivary glands. This is a simple or unconditioned reflex. It is an inherent response, and quite independent of previous experience gained through any of the organs of special sense. Now, as the puppy grows older, it associates the appearance or smell of the milk, or both, with its taste and the pleasure of gratifying the appetite. The mere sight or smell of the milk will then elicit a secretion of saliva; such a response is called a *conditioned reflex*. Pathways have become established in the brain between the cortical center for sight or for smell and the salivary center. In other words, the visual and olfactory stimuli—*conditioned stimuli*—set up impulses which, impinging upon the salivary centers, are capable alone (i.e., without stimulating the nerves of taste or other nerves in the mouth) of exciting them (see diagram, Fig. 12.44). If, on the other hand, a puppy which has never tasted meat is offered some (but is not allowed to taste it), there is no secretion of saliva. The association paths between the higher centers of the brain and the secretory centers have not been developed. Conditioned reflexes become established not only with respect to feeding, and the secretion of saliva, but in many other similar ways in the everyday life of the growing animal. Such processes are essentially psychic in character and dependent upon experience. They, therefore, form the basis of training, and are of the greatest biological importance. The animal, through the conditioning process, reacts appropriately to the various stimuli—beneficial or injurious—in the environment.

The Pavlov school has shown that conditioned responses can be developed experimentally to an extraordinary degree. For example, if an animal is fed a number of times, during or shortly after the ringing of a bell, a secretion of saliva occurs merely upon ringing the bell. The contact of food with the taste buds constitutes the *unconditioned stimulus;* the sound of the bell, the *conditioned stimulus*. The flash of a light, the sound of a buzzer, horn, or ticking metronome, a particular odor, a touch upon the skin, or the passive movement of a limb into a certain position, and many other types of stimuli may serve for the establishment of the conditioned response—that is, may act as conditioned stimuli.

Inhibition of conditioned reflexes. There are two main kinds of inhibition affecting conditioned reflexes: *external* and *internal. External inhibition* is that which causes an established conditioned response to be suppressed when the animal is distracted by something which he sees or hears, or by any event extraneous to the experiment itself. *Internal inhibition* is the failure of a conditioned reflex to be elicited after it has been repeated a number of times without the application of the original unconditioned stimulus. For example, if a salivary conditioned response is evoked several times without giving the animal food, it becomes weaker and weaker with each repetition and finally fails completely. The response is said to have been *extinguished*. In order to maintain the conditioned response at full strength, the unconditioned stimulus must be employed after every few repetitions. This reapplication of the unconditioned stimulus is called *reinforcement*.

Another type of internal inhibition known as *conditioned inhibition* is best explained by an example. Let us say that a salivary conditioned reflex has been firmly established to the sound of a tuning fork; another stimulus—e.g., a flash of light—is then combined with it, but whenever the two are in combination reinforcement (feeding) is omitted. Then the single stimulus—namely, the sound of the tuning fork—if regularly reinforced, causes salivary secretion but, if combined with the flash of light, does not. Thus the latter stimulus has an inhibitory effect upon the original conditioned response.

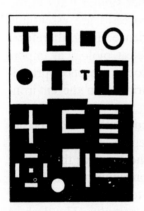

Fig. 12.45   Examples of different figures which were successfully differentiated in experiments upon a dog. The letter T, shown in the upper left-hand corner of the figure, served for the positive stimulus, the other black figures and the white letter T were differentiated from the positive stimulus. In another dog, the white cross was the positive stimulus from which the other white figures were differentiated. (From Pavlov, *Conditioned Reflexes*, Oxford University Press.)

The conditioning process can be so developed that stimuli closely similar in character can be *differentiated* (as indicated by the secretion of saliva) with astonishing precision. A dog in which a conditioned salivary reflex has been established to a sound of a certain pitch will not respond to a sound of the same quality and intensity, but varying in pitch from the original by only two or three double vibrations per second.

Differentiation of *visual stimuli* can also be developed to a phenomenal degree. Figures of various shapes—a cross, square, or circle—are readily differentiated (see Fig. 12.45). A circle can be differentiated by the dog from an ellipse, whose diameters have a ratio no greater than 9 to 10. That is, if a salivary conditioned reflex has been established to a circular object, such as a white cardboard disc, it alone evokes a response. A disc precisely the same in all respects except that it is not quite circular but has diameters in the ratio of 9 to 10 will not cause a secretion of saliva. Olfactory, tactile, and proprioceptive stimuli can likewise be differentiated with remarkable precision.

It is evident that conditioned reflexes afford a valuable means for studying perception in animals. It has been established, for example, that the dog possesses the ability of discriminating between slight variations in the intensity, quality, and pitch of a musical note; between various odors; and by sight between objects of different sizes and shapes, and between lights of different intensities. Colors, on the contrary, cannot be differentiated, nor can a colored object be distinguished from a colorless one of the same size and shape. It is concluded, therefore, that the dog is totally color blind, its surroundings being perceived only in white, gray, and black.

The Physiology of Sleep

During sleep most of the functions of the body are carried on at the lowest levels possible in health. Heat production is from 10 to 15 percent below the so-called basal level. The mechanisms regulating the body temperature are less sensitive than in the waking state and are depressed by from 0.5 to 1.0 degree Fahrenheit; the rate of the heart is reduced in frequency by from 10 to 30 beats per minute, and a decline in blood pressure of about 20 mm occurs in quiet, restful sleep. The urine volume is considerably reduced, but its concentration in solids is increased. The cutaneous vessels are usually dilated and the secretion of sweat is stimulated. The tone of all the skeletal muscles is lessened, the deep tendon reflexes are depressed or abolished, and there may be a Babinski (extensor) response of the great toe (p. 519). The eyes are usually rolled upward and the pupils constricted. Gastric motility and secretion have a tendency to be greater during sleep than in the waking state.

Seriously detrimental effects may be exerted upon the nervous system by lack of sleep. Experiments upon human subjects in which wakefulness was enforced for long periods caused profound psychological changes. In one series of experiments, the volunteers went without sleep for periods of a duration up to 112 hours. Loss of memory, irritability, hallucinations, and even schizophrenic manifestations were observed within from 30 to 60 hours of sleeplessness.

The required hours of sleep; depth of sleep. The amount of sleep required at different ages is given in the table below. Adults vary greatly in the hours of sleep which they find necessary to "knit up the ravelled sleeve of care."

	Hours
New born	18–20
Growing children	10–12
Adults	6– 9
Aged persons	5– 7

The depth of ordinary restful sleep fluctuates throughout the sleeping period. In most adults, sleep deepens through the first hour, after which it lightens rather sharply, and then more gradually until morning, or until the usual time of wakening. In growing children, however, sleep deepens a second time for a little while in the eighth or ninth hour. In these observations the depth of sleep was judged by the amount of movement of the subjects.

Theories of sleep. Many theories have been advanced to explain the temporary loss of consciousness which we know as sleep. Their very multiplicity emphasizes the difficulty of finding a satisfactory explanation of the physiological processes underlying the phenomenon. Probably the oldest theory is that sleep is induced by a reduction in the blood supply to the brain, or at least to the conscious centers. This is the so-called *ischemic theory*. Even the ancient Greek physicians had an idea that the carotid artery was in some way concerned with the onset of sleep. The name itself expresses this belief (Gk. *karotides,* carotid arteries, from *karoō,* put to sleep). In modern times the drowsiness after a meal (the blood being diverted presumably from the brain to the digestive organs) was pointed to in support of the ischemic theory.

Some have favored a chemical theory, in one form or another. Chemicals, such as lactic acid, acetylcholine, bromide, or a specific "fatigue toxin," were supposed to accumulate during the waking hours which acted like a drug upon the nerve cells of the higher centers of the brain. But no sound evidence can be cited in confirmation of this theory. It would carry us too far afield to discuss the various theories, nor would it be of much profit to do so. But three theories will be briefly reviewed.

The first of these places a sleep center in the hypothalamus (p. 541). A state, at least closely resembling sleep, has been induced in animals by the electric stimulation of this region of the brain. It is also true that many of the bodily changes in sleep are manifestations of activity of hypothalamic nuclei (especially of parasympathetic centers), such as constriction of the pupil, cutaneous vasodilatation, reduced frequency of the heart beat, increased gastric tone and secretion, etc.

The second theory to be outlined is that which has as its chief basis the reduction in the discharge of the afferent impulses from the periphery to the conscious centers. During waking hours, these centers are being continually "bombarded" by impulses from the organs of special sense, as well as from the skeletal muscles (impulses of kinesthetic sense) and semicircular canals. The centers are being constantly "alerted." But when the sum of these impulses is reduced to a minimum, consciousness becomes dulled and sleep is induced. That muscular relaxation, and freedom from visual, auditory, and cutaneous stimulation are conducive to sleep needs no emphasis. We require a dark and quiet room, a soft bed, and an even, comfortable temperature in order to sleep. But the reduction in the flow of afferent impulses to the brain can be no more than a contributory factor in the onset of sleep, for the presence of all the desirable conditions mentioned will not always bring sleep. On the other hand, sleep may supervene in the face of the most adverse conditions, in a bright light and noisy surroundings, and even on hard ground.

Pavlov, as a result of his study of conditioned reflexes in dogs, proposed a theory of sleep based upon cortical inhibition (p. 569) caused by the repeated elicitation of a conditioned response without reinforcement. The conditioned inhibition thus established in one area of the cerebral cortex may spread to associated areas and finally involve the entire cortex. Such widespread cortical inhibition is sleep, according to Pavlov. It may be induced by various types of conditioned stimulation, if repeatedly applied without reinforcement. It is a familiar experience that a monotonous sound, an unchanging view, a boring lecture, or any recurring event for which our interest flags, is conducive to drowsiness. Counting sheep, the least exciting of animals, is a well-known device resorted to by those suffering from insomnia. Pavlov described some experiments in which the animal subject would fall into a sleeplike state standing in its harness and even while it was being stimulated. All attempts to elicit the conditioned response failed. On later occasions, it would fall asleep when merely brought into the room where the previous experiments had been conducted. The well-known surroundings had themselves acted as conditioned inhibitory stimuli. There is little doubt but that the familiar appointments of our bedroom (we know very well that it is more difficult to go to sleep in a strange room), the preparation for bed, the feel of the bedcoverings, and even the time of retiring, act in a similar way upon ourselves. Having been associated innumerable times with sleep, they act as inhibitory conditioned stimuli, and induce in the cerebral cortex an inhibitory influence which gradually diffuses over broad areas.

All three of the theories which have been briefly sketched have in them each a degree of truth, but no one alone is entirely satisfactory.

CHAPTER 13

The Special Senses

The Physiology of Vision

General description of the eye. The adult human eye is shaped like a globe and has an approximate diameter of 1 inch (24 mm running anteroposteriorly and transversely, and 23.5 mm vertically). It is actually made up of the segments of two spheres. The anterior part is transparent and is called the *cornea*. It forms about one sixth of the globe and is a segment of a smaller sphere than is that of the posterior five sixths (see Fig. 13.1). The posterior wall of the globe is lined by a light-sensitive tissue called the *retina*. A cylindrical bundle of nerve fibers—the *optic nerve*—passes from the posterior pole of the globe to the brain. The eye, except for the anterior fifth or so of its circumference, is enclosed in a bony case—the eye socket or *orbital cavity*—but a thick layer of aerolar tissue is interposed between the eyeball and the bone, which serves as a cushion to buffer it against external violence. The eyeball is also protected from injury by the eyelids which, as we know, close reflexly, in an instant, to prevent dust or other particles from coming into contact with its surface. The exposed part of the eyeball is covered by a delicate membrane called the *conjunctiva* which is continued forward on to the inner surfaces of the lids. When the lids open and close, the opposed conjunctival surfaces slide over one another. The surfaces are lubricated by a thin film of tears secreted by the *lacrimal gland,* which lies under the shelter of the bone forming the upper and outer part of the wall of the eye socket. The tears, after flowing over the surface of the eye, are drained from its inner angle into the nose by two small tubes—the *lacrimal ducts* (see Fig. 13.2). If it were not for the continual washing and lubrication of the eyeball by the tears, the delicate protective membrane would soon become dry and inflamed; ulceration of the corneal surface would result. The tears also contain a material known as *lysozyme* which destroys bacteria.

The coats of the eyeball. The wall of the eye is composed of three layers or coats—an *outer,* a *middle,* and an *inner* (see Fig. 13.1).

The *outermost layer* or *sclerotic coat* is fibrous in character; it preserves the form of the eyeball and protects the more delicate vascular

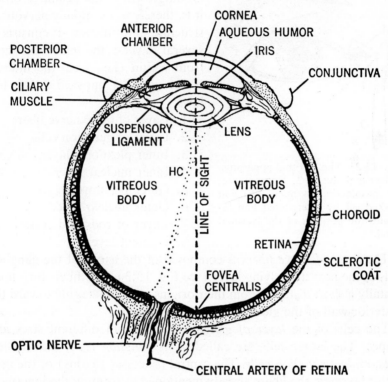

Fig. 13.1   Horizontal section through the eyeball. The dotted lines, HC, mark a narrow canal in the vitreous body (hyaloid canal) which, in the embryo, lodged the hyaloid artery.

and nervous coats within. The sclerotic is transparent in front, where it forms the cornea. It also composes that opaque exposed part of the eyeball surrounding the cornea, and commonly called the *white of the eye.*

The *middle layer* or *vascular coat,* contains the main arteries and veins of the eyeball. It completely surrounds the globe, except for a small circular opening in front called the *pupil.* The vascular coat consists of the *choroid, ciliary body* (p. 591), and *iris* (p. 607) which is the annular colored band surrounding the pupil. The choroid comprises the posterior five sixths or so of the vascular coat.

The *innermost layer, retina,* or *nervous coat* contains the receptors for sight—that is, those elements highly specialized to respond to stimulation by light, and to convert luminous energy into nerve impulses. The retina is developed as an outgrowth of the primitive brain; it is, therefore, essentially nervous in structure and function. It consists of several layers; the chief of these from within (i.e., from the interior of the eyeball) outward are as follows:

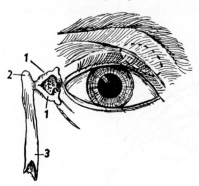

Fig. 13.2   The lacrimal apparatus. 1, lacrimal ducts; 2, lacrimal sac; 3, nasolacrimal duct. Region marked off by interrupted line indicates the position of the lacrimal gland.

1. Layer of optic nerve fibers
2. Layer of ganglion cells
3. Inner plexiform layer
4. Inner nuclear layer
5. Outer plexiform layer
6. Outer nuclear layer
7. Layer of rods and cones
8. Pigment layer

The *layer of nerve fibers* is composed of the axons of the ganglion cells of the next underlying layer (see Fig. 13.3). The fibers turn horizontally a short distance from their origins and, converging toward the posterior wall of the globe, form the *optic nerve.*

The cells of the *layer of ganglion cells* are of different sizes and shapes. The larger cells are called *giant ganglion cells,* the smallest ones, *midget ganglion cells.* The central processes (axons) of the cells of this layer are the fibers already mentioned as forming the innermost layer and the optic nerve. Their dendrites pass outwards and form synapses with cells of the inner nuclear layer.

The *inner nuclear layer* contains relatively small, oval, and flattened cells whose central processes synapse in the inner plexiform layer with the peripheral branching processes (dendrites) of the ganglion cells. Their peripheral (outward running) processes synapse in the outer plexiform layer with the fibers of the rods and cones. The *outer nuclear layer* is composed mainly of the fibers and nuclei of the rods and cones. The *plexiform layers* are composed of fibers of the cells in the nuclear layers (or ganglionic layer) on either side, where, as just mentioned, synapses are formed.

The *rods* and *cones* (Fig. 12.3) are the receptors of sight. They are

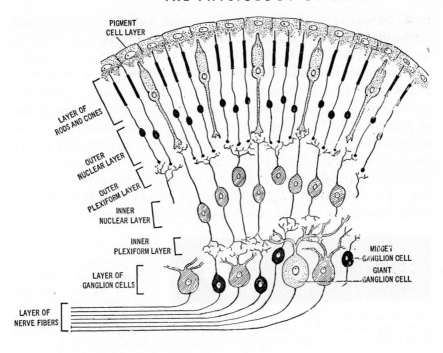

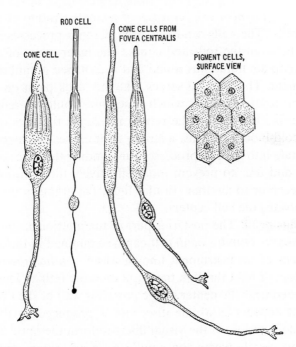

Fig. 13.3   The layers of the retina, *upper drawing; below,* larger drawings of the rods and cones and the pigment cells, surface view.

modified nerve cells. When light strikes them, impulses are set up and transmitted to the nerve cells of the inner nuclear layer, and thence to the ganglion cells, and by the axons of the latter (which constitute the optic nerve) to the visual area of the cerebral cortex (see p. 536). It is evident from their position that light, in order to reach the rods and cones, must penetrate all layers of the retina except the outermost one of pigment cells. It should also be mentioned that, though the visual receptors are stimulated most effectively by light, they respond also to mechanical stimuli. A blow, or even light pressure upon the eyeball, will cause a visual sensation in the form of a flash, circle, or star of light. The sensations of light produced by pressure or other stimulus applied to the eye with the lids closed are called *phosphenes*.

Fig. 13.4 The blind spot. Close the right eye, hold the figure about 6 inches in front of the left eye and look steadily at the white disc. Move the book slowly toward the eye until the cross disappears. When this occurs the image of the cross has fallen upon the entrance of the optic nerve from which rods and cones are absent; it is, therefore, insensitive to light.

The *layer of pigment cells* consists of a single stratum of hexagonal epithelial cells. The cells send out protoplasmic processes which are insinuated between the rods and cones. The inner zones of the bodies of the cells contain numerous round and rod-shaped granules of a dark brown pigment. The pigment serves, like the black paint on the inside of a camera, to absorb light which otherwise would be reflected and diffused causing blurring of the retinal image. In the eyes of the frog and other cold-blooded forms, a strong light causes the pigment granules to migrate into the cell processes surrounding the bases of the rods and cones, and thus to prevent more effectively the diffusion of light from one receptor to another. In dim light, the granules become concentrated toward the cell centers.

The fundus oculi. The posterior part of the interior of the eyeball is called the *fundus* (*fundus oculi*). It can be examined in the living subject by means of an instrument known as an *ophthalmoscope* which throws a beam of light through the pupil onto the retina. The *optic papilla* is situated near the center of the posterior wall of the eyeball (see Pl. 12B). It appears as a pale disc, and is produced by the convergence, as into a vortex, of the visual fibers to form the optic nerve. The retinal blood vessels pierce the papilla near its center, and cross its face to reach the retina. The papilla is composed entirely of nerve fibers, the rods and cones and other retinal layers being absent. It is, therefore, insensitive to light—that is, an object is invisible if its image falls upon this small area. The optic papilla is, for this reason, called the *blind spot* of the retina. The reader is referred to Figure 13.4 for a demonstration of the blind spot in his own eye.

The macula lutea. The macula lutea (yellow spot) is a small yellowish area of the retina situated a little to the outer side of the optic papilla (see Pl. 12B). The color of this area is due to the presence of a yellow pigment. In the center of the yellow spot is a minute depressed area known as the *fovea centralis* (Fig. 13.5). All the layers of the

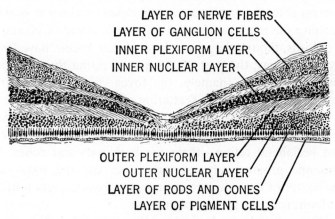

LAYER OF NERVE FIBERS
LAYER OF GANGLION CELLS
INNER PLEXIFORM LAYER
INNER NUCLEAR LAYER

OUTER PLEXIFORM LAYER
OUTER NUCLEAR LAYER
LAYER OF RODS AND CONES
LAYER OF PIGMENT CELLS

Fig. 13.5   Microscopical appearance of the fovea centralis, the region of most acute vision; it contains cones but, in man, no rods.

retina, except the rod and cone and pigment layers, are extremely thin in this area; it is only about $\frac{1}{2}$ mm in diameter ($\frac{1}{50}$ inch). The fovea is the region of most acute vision; when we look at an object, the eyes are directed so that an image of the object falls upon the fovea of each eye. Vision in the rest of the retina (called the peripheral or extrafoveal retina) is much less sensitive, and enables us to gain only a dim, ill-defined impression of our surroundings. The reader can demonstrate this fact for himself if he looks straight ahead and tries to define objects on either side or above and below his line of vision.

The crystalline lens and iris (Fig. 13.1) and the muscles of the eyeball will be described when the functions of these structures are being considered.

The duplicity theory of vision. According to this theory, which is now universally accepted, the rods and cones have different thresholds of excitation and also show differences in function. Vision in bright light (*photopic* or *daylight vision*) and the perception of color are functions of the cones. The rods, on the other hand, having a much lower threshold than the cones, make it possible to see in dim light (*scotopic* or *twilight vision*). That is to say, the rods respond to light of much lower intensity than is required to excite the cones. But the rods do not give rise to any color sensation; this is a sensation entirely dependent upon the cones. Rod vision is in black, white, or a mixture of the two, namely, gray.[1] Thus it is that at twilight the color of the landscape fades, or seems to be brushed over with a gray wash. The cones, though having a higher threshold to light stimulation than the rods, are capable of much more acute vision, making it possible for us to perceive the more precise form and finer detail of objects. Some species of birds, though they possess very acute vision, have few or no rods in their retinas; the part of the human retina that is capable of the most acute vision—namely, the fovea centralis—contains only cones, or, at the most, only a scattering of rods. When we look at an object, the eyes are so turned that the image falls upon this small central area of the retina. Surrounding this rod-free region—the extra-foveal or peripheral retina—there are both rods and cones, but the cones become progressively less numerous and the rods more so, from the center of the retina to its more peripheral parts until, at the extreme limit, rods are present alone.

The retinas of night birds, such as the owl, and certain mammals, such as the rat, contain only rods.

The greater sensitivity of the peripheral part of the retina (rods) in dim light as compared with the foveal region (cones) is sometimes demonstrated in an interesting way when on a dark but starry night we may see a small star out of the "corner of the eye" (i.e., when its image falls on the extrafoveal part of the retina) which disappears when our eyes are turned directly toward where it was seen; its image has now fallen on the fovea which in the prevailing light is blind.

If a subject is seated in a dark room and a colored object is placed before him which, even after his eyes have become accustomed to the dark, he cannot see, and the object is then very gradually illuminated, he sees it without color. As the illumination is further increased, and the threshold of the cones is reached, the object is seen in finer detail

---

[1] It is thought that the rods, though they possess no power of color discrimination, do, nevertheless, give a uniform blue tint to a dimly lighted scene. The blue cast given to our surroundings in the moonlight, in which rods alone are functioning, gives support to this belief.

and in color. The interval between the threshold of the rods and that of the cones—that is, the interval from when the object is first seen to the perception of its color—is called the *colorless* or *achromatic interval*. The rods, like the chemical on a photographic film, are almost insensitive to deep red.[2] The achromatic interval for this color is, therefore, very short. That is to say, in a dim light a deep red object appears nearly or quite black, for black is a sensation caused by complete absence of retinal stimulation. That is the reason that at twilight in the garden the red flowers lose their color, appearing as dark blotches, whereas yellow and blue flowers, though they appear without color, stand out as light patches against the background.

The Purkinje phenomenon. The evidence for the duplicity theory of retinal function is overwhelming. The Purkinje effect, for example, clearly shows that two types of visual receptor are present in the human retina. The Purkinje phenomenon is the shift of the brightest part of the spectrum with changes in the intensity of illumination. If the spectrum (the series of colored lights from red to violet, as in the rainbow, into which white light is split by a prism) is viewed at high illumination, its brightest part is in the yellow, but, when the light intensity is reduced to that of twilight, its colors fade. The brightest part is now in the green; it has shifted to the right. The cones are stimulated maximally by pure yellow light, the rods by light green.

Dark and light adaptation. It is a familiar experience that we are for a time quite blind after passing into a dark room from a bright one. After a short time we begin to see dimly the objects around us, and it almost seems that a faint light is gradually illuminating them. The effect, however, is due entirely to changes occurring in the eye which, it is said, becomes *dark adapted*. The process is called *dark adaptation*.

---

[2] There may be some confusion here in the reader's mind with regard to the statement that deep red light does not stimulate the rods, or does so very slightly. This color, when the illumination is below the threshold of the cones though above that of the rods, does not cause a sensation of light at all, whereas green, blue, and other colored objects appear as varying shades of gray, at low light intensities. In other words, an object, which in bright light appears dark red, causes, when viewed in dim light, little or no photochemical reaction; therefore, it appears black, which is the negative "sensation" resulting from the absence of all retinal stimulation. This fact was made good use of during the late war. It was, of course, of the utmost importance that in air raids at night over enemy territory, the vision of the crew should be at maximum efficiency. Their eyes must be fully dark adapted. But it would be most irksome for the crew to be kept in the dark for an hour or so before they took off on their mission. They were therefore confined in a room illuminated by red light, where they were able to amuse themselves playing cards, or even reading. The breakdown of rhodopsin in this light was negligible; night vision was therefore maintained at maximum efficiency. See visual purple, p. 582.

Seeing with dark-adapted eyes is called *scotopic vision* or *rod vision*. Dark adaptation is due to,

(1) Increased sensitivity of the rods as a result of the regeneration of the light-sensitive substance *visual purple* (see below), and

(2) Dilatation of the pupil which permits more light to enter the eye.

We also have experienced the dazzling effect of a bright light after our eyes have been accustomed to the dark. But after a time we can look at the bright objects around us without discomfort. The eyes have now become *light adapted;* the processes bringing this about are referred to as *light adaptation*. Vision in the light-adapted eye is termed *photopic* and, since it is due to the cones, may also be called *cone vision*. The events which take place in the eye are the opposite of those occurring in scotopic or rod vision—namely,

(1) Bleaching of visual purple and reduced sensitivity of the rods, and

(2) Contraction of the pupil.

Visual purple or rhodopsin. The outer segments of the rods contain a rose-colored pigment which has been named, though somewhat inaccurately, *visual purple*. It also goes by the name of *rhodopsin* (Gk. *rhōdon,* a rose + *ops,* the eye). This substance is of protein nature, with a molecular weight around 300,000. A pigment of the carotene group (p. 385) is linked to the protein. This complex compound (protein + pigment) is bleached by light rays, the pigment being split from the protein and converted to vitamin A. These products are colorless. An intermediate step in this photochemical change is the formation of an orange-yellow pigment called *retinene*. Thus,

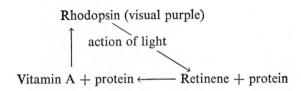

In the dark, rhodopsin is resynthesized from vitamin A and protein.

A photochemical substance—violet colored—is also believed to be present in the cones, but much less is known about it. It has been named *iodopsin* (Gk. *iodes,* violetlike).

The bleaching of rhodopsin by light can be demonstrated in a rabbit's eye which has been recently excised in a darkroom. When the eye is directed toward some brightly illuminated object, such as a window against the sky, the outlines of the window frame can be made out upon the retina, when the eye is opened and examined in a dim light. Where the light fell upon the retina, the visual purple was bleached, but was left unchanged where the bars of the window cast their shadow (Fig. 13.6). The excised eye can thus be made to behave as a camera, the visual purple acting like the chemical in the coating on the film. The crude picture so formed is called an *optogram*.

It is evident then that the initiation of impulses in the nervous elements of the retina is dependent primarily upon a photochemical process. Defective vision in dim light (twilight)—an abnormality known as *night blindness* or *nyctalopia*—is a manifestation of vitamin A deficiency or is due occasionally to a congenital lack of visual purple (see also p. 386).

Fig. 13.6   An optogram. The circular area with radiating vessels is the optic disc (blind spot).

The sensitivity of the retina. The retina of the dark-adapted eye is capable of responding to an almost infinitesimal amount of radiant energy (i.e., light with wavelengths between 4000 and about 8000 millimicrons). It is some 3000 times more sensitive than a rapid photographic film. A single rod, it has been calculated, will give a response when the smallest possible quantity of light (green) energy falls upon it. Dr. Pirenne has estimated that the energy liberated when a pin drops to the ground from a height of 1 inch, if converted to light energy, would be sufficient to give a faint visual sensation to every man who had ever lived! The rods are not equally sensitive to light of all wavelengths; they are most sensitive to light-green rays (wavelength around 5000 millimicrons). The cones show their greatest sensitivity for yellow. Sensitivity for both types of receptor is much less for the longer (red) and shorter (violet) light waves. It has already been mentioned that the rods are almost insensitive to deep red.

Those who have had even a very limited experience in photography know that, with respect to the scene that we propose to photograph, two factors must be taken into account—namely, (1) the *time* of exposure (i.e., the interval between the opening and the closure of the shutter during which the light enters the camera) and (2) the size of the opening or "stop" of the diaphragm. It is entirely a question of the quantity of light to which the sensitive film is exposed. So it is, within limits, with the retina; a light stimulus of a certain intensity and duration that is just capable of causing a visual sensation becomes ineffective if either its duration or its intensity is reduced. Or a light stimu-lus which is just beneath the threshold becomes effective if its duration or its intensity is increased. A similar relationship holds between the size of the retinal area that is stimulated and the intensity of the light. That is to say, a larger object dimly illuminated will be seen, whereas a smaller one even though somewhat more brightly illumi-nated may be invisible. If the intensity of the smaller object is increased so that the total quantity of light energy is equal to that falling upon the retina from the larger body, it then arouses a visual sensation.

The reciprocal relationship between duration and light intensity

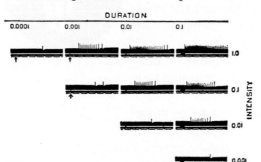

Fig. 13.7 Showing the re-ciprocal relationship between the intensity and duration of a visual stimulus. Records are from a single isolated fi-ber of the optic nerve. (Aft-er Hartline and Graham.)

has been beautifully shown by Dr. Hartline and his associates. A flash of light of varying duration and intensity was thrown into the eye of the king crab, and the impulse frequency recorded from a *single* optic nerve fiber (see p. 475). It will be observed in Figure 13.7 that the frequency of the impulses (intensity of response) is the same when the product of the duration and the intensity of the stimulus (dura-tion $\times$ intensity) are equal, though one or other factor was varied.

Visual acuity. The ability of the eye to determine the precise shape and detail of any object, or to recognize the separateness of two small objects placed close together, is referred to as the visual acuity. It is exhibited in the highest degree by the fovea centralis which, in the hu-man retina, is composed entirely of cones. It is seriously reduced by refractive errors (myopia, etc., p. 611). As a test for visual acuity in the diagnosis of refractive defects of the eyes and to aid in their cor-rection by means of glasses, the oculist most usually employs *Snellens test type* (Fig. 13.8). These consist of heavy block letters printed in black upon a white ground. The letters are of graded sizes, arranged in nine horizontal rows, the largest letters in the top row, the smallest in the lowermost.

The subject is seated 6 meters (approximately 20 feet) from the letters and asked to read the rows of type down to the smallest which it is possible for him to distinguish. The visual acuity is expressed as a fraction, the numerator of which is the distance in meters at which the subject can read a given line of letters, and the denominator is the distance at which a person with normal average vision can read the same line. For example, a person with normal vision can read the seventh line at 6 meters; if the examinee can read this line, his vision is $\frac{6}{6}$, or normal. If, on the other hand, he can read only the third row which can be read by a person with normal vision at 24 meters, then his vision is only $\frac{6}{24}$, or $\frac{1}{4}$ normal.

The examiner, in testing for defective vision in this manner, fits removable lenses (*trial lenses*) before the subject's eyes while he reads. By using trial lenses of different kinds and power, and noting the improvement or lack of it in the patient's sight each time, the examiner is able to determine the type and degree of the refractive error that exists (pp. 610–11). He then prescribes the appropriate convex, concave, or other form of spectacle lens required to correct the defect.

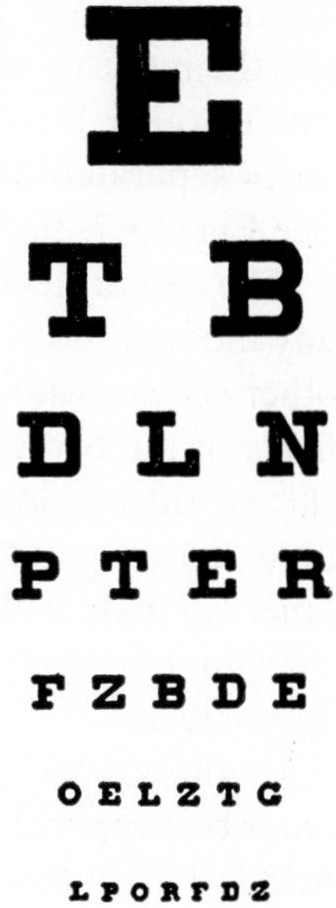

E

T B

D L N

P T E R

F Z B D E

O E L Z T C

L P O R F D Z

Fig. 13.8   Snellen's test type.

Optical action currents: The electroretinogram. When the retina is stimulated by a beam of light thrown into the eye, action currents are set up which can be recorded by a galvanometer. The current is led off to the galvanometer by means of electrodes, one placed upon the cornea of the eye in its usual forward-looking position, and the other on any moist surface of the body. A record of such changes in electrical potential is shown in Figure 13.9. It is called the *electroretinogram*. Four waves are to be seen; they are designated *a, b, c,* and *d*. The wave *a* is a negative wave—i.e., below the base line; the others are positive. The waves *a, b,* and *c* are inscribed when the light is flashed into the eye; *d* occurs when the light is cut off.

Action currents can also be demonstrated in the optic nerve when the retina is stimulated by light. A discharge of impulses then occurs which increases in frequency with the intensity of the illumination, but no change occurs in the amplitude of the waves, no matter how intense the light

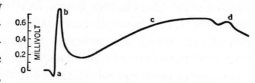

Fig. 13.9   The electroretinogram. Waves a, b, and c occur when a light is flashed into the eye; d occurs when the light is turned off.

stimulus may be. The relationship between frequency of the impulses and the intensity of the stimulus, which we have seen to be a characteristic of other kinds of nerve, has been demonstrated in a single nerve fibers separated by dissection from the other fibers of the optic nerve (see Fig. 13.7, p. 584).

The visual fields. The part of the outside world seen by one eye at any moment is called the *visual field* of that eye. In man, the ape, and other species whose eyes are placed in the front of the head, the visual fields of the two eyes overlap. In other words, a large part of the outside world within the range of vision is seen by both eyes at the same time. This type of vision is called *binocular*. In the rabbit, horse, and other animals with eyes placed laterally in the head, the visual fields overlap to a very small extent; in these, vision is almost entirely *monocular*.

In those species possessing binocular vision, light rays from the *outer* or *temporal* half and from the *inner* or *nasal* half of either visual field fall upon the *nasal* half and *temporal* half, respectively, of the corresponding retina (see Pl. 13A). Now, the optic nerves come together a short distance behind the eyeballs to form the *optic chiasma*. Here, the fibers which have originated in the nasal half of one retina cross with those coming from the nasal half of the other—that is, fibers from the nasal half of the right retina cross to the left side of the brain, those from the nasal half of the left retina to the right side of the brain. Fibers from the temporal halves of the retinas continue uncrossed. Thus, the visual pathway, on each side, from the optic chiasma to the cortex of the occipital lobe (visual center) transmits impulses from the nasal half of one retina and the temporal half of the other. Owing to this peculiar course taken by the visual fibers, the loss of sight following injury or disease of one optic nerve differs from that resulting from a lesion of the fibers anywhere between the chiasma and the occipital cortex, or of the visual center itself. If the function of one retina or of one optic nerve is destroyed, complete blindness of the corresponding eye results, but the sight of the other eye is unaffected. Interruption of the fibers in their course from the chiasma to the visual area (optic tract), or a lesion of the visual area itself, causes blindness in one half of each retina. For example, if the injury involves the left optic tract or left visual cortex, blindness of the *nasal* (left) half of the right retina and of the *temporal* (left) half of the left retina (opposite halves of the visual field) results. Blindness in one half of each eye is called *hemianopia* (half blindness). The *nasal* half of one retina and the *temporal* half of the other are called *homonomous* halves. The type of blindness just described is therefore called *homonomous hemianopia.* Rarer types of hemianopia result from bilateral involvement of the temporal fibers alone at the chiasma, or of the nasal fibers alone; these types are given the qualifying terms of *binasal* and *bitemporal,* respectively (the designations binasal and bitemporal refer to the visual fields, not to the retinas).

The shape and extent of the visual fields in man can be mapped out by means of an instrument known as a *perimeter,* which is shown in

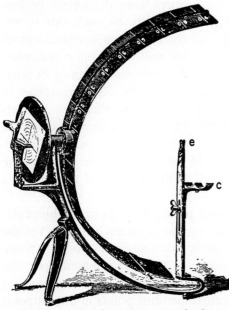

Fig. 13.10   The perimeter. This is an instrument used for mapping the visual fields. It consists of a metal band curved in a large arc of a circle near the center of which is a rest for the subject's chin. The metal arc carries a small object which can be moved to or away from the center. The arc itself can be rotated into any position (meridian); it is rotated into different meridians in succession and, at each new position, the test object is moved slowly from a peripheral point beyond the subject's field of vision toward the center. The examinee indicates the moment that he sees the object ("out of the corner of his eye" as it were). The points in each meridian so determined are marked upon the chart shown on the instrument and in detail in Figure 13.11; c, chin rest; e, position of subject's eye.

Figure 13.10. A chart or "map" of the visual field of one eye is given in Figure 13.11. The instrument is often of great value in the diagnosis of diseases of the retina or of the visual pathways.

From the optic chiasma, the visual fibers—that is, the axons of the ganglion cells from the nasal half of one retina and the temporal half of the other—proceed on each side of the brain to a collection of nerve cells in the midbrain. These latter form on each side a small eminence known as the *lateral geniculate body.* The optic fibers from the chiasma to the lateral geniculate body are known as the *optic tract.* The fibers of the latter terminate by forming synapses with the cells of the lateral geniculate bodies, which are, therefore, *primary visual centers.* In lower animals, but not in man, visual perception is possible to a variable degree through these centers alone—that is, after the occipital

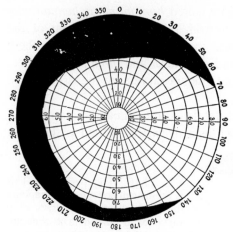

Fig. 13.11   Chart of the normal visual field of the right eye. Note the restriction of the visual field on three sides, caused by the nose, brow, and cheek.

cortex has been destroyed. The axons of the cells of the lateral geniculate bodies relay the visual impulses through the internal capsule (p. 539) to the highest *visual center* situated in the cortex of the occipital lobe of the cerebrum. The nerve fibers from the lateral geniculate body on each side to the corresponding occipital cortex are called the *optic radiation*. A nerve impulse set up by stimulating the visual receptors in the retina, therefore, travels over three neurons to reach the cortex of the occipital lobe.

The first of these has its cell body in the inner nuclear layer of the retina; the second is the ganglion cell of the retina; and the third is a nerve cell in the midbrain (Fig. 13.12).

Identical or corresponding retinal points. Objects in the binocular field of vision must, obviously, cast an image on each retina. Yet the two retinal images do not cause a double sensation; we do not see things in duplicate. The explanation for this fact is based upon the theory of *identical* or *corresponding retinal points*. Points in the nasal half of one retina are paired with corresponding points in the temporal half of the other. The ocular muscles direct the axes of the eyes so that an image falls upon each of these corresponding points. As mentioned above, the optic fibers from the homonomous halves of the retinas proceed to one side of the brain, the *left* halves (nasal of right eye and temporal of left) to the *left* visual area, the *right* halves (nasal of left eye and temporal of right) to the *right* visual area. The two images are fused in consciousness into a single sensation. If, for any reason, the eyes are not directed in such a way that the two images fall on corresponding retinal points, double vision—*diplopia*—results. Diplopia as a permanent condition occurs most commonly as a result of paralysis or weakness of the ocular muscles. It is seen as a temporary state in alcoholic intoxication, being then due to imperfect control and, in consequence, to unbalanced action of the muscles of the two eyes. One can cause double vision in oneself by simply pressing upon the outer side of one eye, and thus displacing the eyeball slightly from its

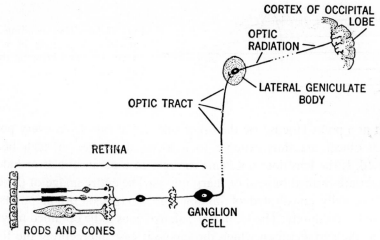

Fig. 13.12 Diagram of the visual pathway.

normal position. Two images are also seen if an object, such as a pencil, is held about 3 inches in front of the root of the nose, or if the pencil is held at arm's length, and the eyes then directed to look at a point some distance beyond it. In the first instance mentioned, it is not possible to converge the eyes sufficiently to bring the two images on to corresponding points on the retinas; in the second instance, images of the near object fall upon noncorresponding points of the retina, because the convergence of the eyes when looking at distant objects is less than that required for near vision.

Elementary optical principles. A ray of light passing from one transparent medium, such as air, into another, such as water, is bent. That is the reason that an upright object, such as a log standing in water, gives the illusion of being broken where the air and water meet. This bending or deflection of the rays of light is called *refraction*. Similarly, light rays passing through a glass prism (Figs. 13.13 and 13.14) are bent toward its *base*. A glass lens having both its surfaces convex, such as the crystalline lens, acts, in respect to the refraction of light, as though it were composed of two prisms placed base to base. Therefore, the rays of light reflected from any object must, after passing through such a lens,

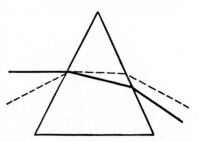

Fig. 13.13 Showing the bending of light rays by a prism. Parallel rays, *continuous lines;* diverging rays, *interrupted lines.*

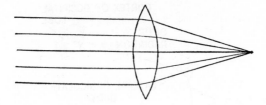

Fig. 13.14 The bending of parallel rays of light by a biconvex lens and bringing them into focus.

meet at a point (focus) on the other side. Light rays from every point in an object are thus brought to a focus, an image of each being formed. If the lens does not bring the rays to a point, circles or haloes of light are formed instead of sharp points. The entire image of the object normally constituted of innumerable images of bright points is blurred accordingly. The failure of a sharp focus to be obtained may be due to the surface upon which the image is cast intercepting the light rays, either before they have come to their meeting point or after they have met and crossed, as shown in Figure 13.15.

Light rays coming from infinity, or for practical purposes from any distance over 20 feet, are parallel, whereas those reflected from a near object are divergent—that is, they radiate from every point in the object (see Fig. 13.16). In order, then, to bend the rays from a near object so that they will meet—i.e., be focused—at the same distance behind the lens as will parallel rays, the lens must be able to bend the rays more acutely in the former instance than in the latter; in other words, its refracting power must be greater. The refracting power of a convex lens increases with the degree of its convexity.

A concave or a biconcave lens (i.e., one with two concave surfaces) acts like two prisms placed apex to apex (Fig. 13.17) and, since the rays are bent toward the bases of the prisms, such a lens diverges or spreads the rays of light.

A line drawn horizontally through the center of a lens is called its

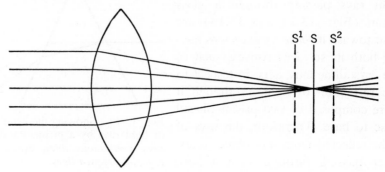

Fig. 13.15   Showing rays focused at S and intercepted at S¹ and S².

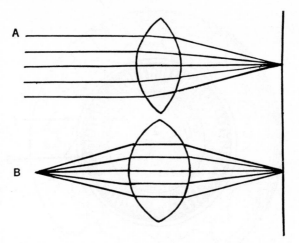

Fig. 13.16   Showing parallel rays of light (A) from a distant object being brought to a focus by a biconvex lens, and diverging rays (B) from a near object being focused at the same distance behind the lens. In the latter instance, however, the lens bends the rays more strongly. This it is able to do because it is more convex.

principal axis, and any line drawn *diagonally* through the center is called a *secondary axis.* Rays of light passing through the principal axis or any secondary axis are not refracted.

The crystalline lens. The crystalline lens is a transparent biconvex disc, about ⅓ inch in diameter, situated within the globe of the eye immediately behind the iris. It is enclosed in a thin membrane called the capsule. The central part of the lens lies a little distance behind the pupil. It is suspended in this position by a delicate annular ligament—the *suspensory ligament*—which blends with the lens capsule, and is attached circumferentially to the interior of the globe through the *ciliary body.* The latter also connects the iris with the choroid, and consists of involuntary muscle fibers and a number of processes—the *ciliary processes.* The latter—about 70 in number—are arranged in the form of a circle to which the suspensory ligament is attached (see Fig. 13.18). The iris and ciliary body divide the part of the eyeball *in front* of the lens into an anterior and a posterior chamber (Fig. 13.1, p. 575). Both chambers are filled with a clear limpid fluid called the *aqueous humor;* a gelatinous transparent substance called the *vitreous body* fills that part of the eyeball lying *behind* the lens.

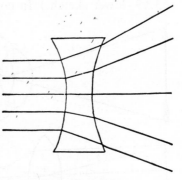

Fig. 13.17   Parallel rays of light being diverged by a biconcave lens.

Though the healthy crystalline lens is perfectly transparent, in the condition known as *cataract* (p. 615) it becomes semitransparent or opaque, causing blindness in the affected eye.

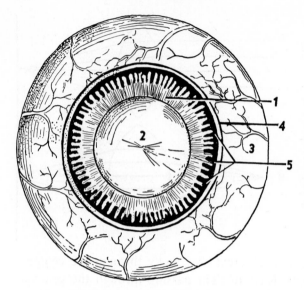

Fig. 13.18 The eyeball from in front, cornea and iris removed. 1, suspensory ligament; 2, lens; 3, choroid; 4, iris, cut edge; 5, ciliary processes (black). (Redrawn and modified from Schultze.)

The refraction of light rays by the eye—the formation of an image upon the retina. There is a very close resemblance between the eye and a camera. In both, the rays of light are refracted (bent) and brought to a focus upon a light-sensitive surface—the photographic film and the retina, respectively. The refracting medium in the camera is, of course, the lens. In the eye, light rays are not only refracted by the crystalline lens, but by the cornea as well and, to a slight degree, by the aqueous humor and vitreous body. The image of an object falls upon the photographic film in an inverted position and reversed from side to side; the retinal image is similarly inverted and transposed. Yet, we do not see objects upside down, because experience has taught us to interpret the retinal messages in accordance with reality. (See Fig. 13.19, lower sketch.) In consciousness, the image is again inverted,

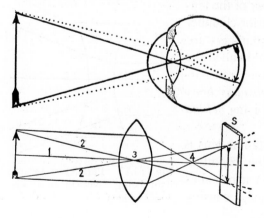

Fig. 13.19 *Upper drawing,* the formation of an inverted image upon the retina. *Below,* diagram showing the formation of an image by a convex lens. 1, principal axis; 2, secondary axes; 3, optical center of lens; 4, principal focus; S, screen. Note that rays passing through the principal and secondary axes are not refracted.

and reversed from side to side, so that it appears to us in its true position. We have come to know by experience (i.e., previous information received through other senses, especially of touch and hearing) that stimulation of the upper or the lower part of the retina, or of one side, is caused by light reflected from an object situated, respectively, in the lower, upper, or other side of the visual field. We are scarcely conscious even that the retina has been stimulated in the way that we feel and localize a touch upon the skin. We "see" the object at a distance and in a position the reverse of that which the image of the object occupies upon the retina. In a word, the object's image is *projected* in consciousness to its true position in space—i.e., in the visual field.

In Figure 13.19 (upper sketch) are shown the paths taken by rays of light coming from an object (represented by the large arrow) placed a little in front of a biconvex lens. The diverging rays are refracted by the lens, and brought to a focus on the screen S, which may be taken to represent the retina. Rays from each point on the object are brought to a point upon the screen, but in a reversed position, those from the upper part of the object being directed to the lower part of the screen and vice versa (only rays emitted from points at the head and tail of the arrow are shown). Similarly, those from the lateral halves of the object pass to opposite sides of the screen. Thus, a small and inverted image of the object is formed. One should note (Fig. 13.16) that the periphery of a lens refracts more strongly than parts more centrally placed, and that rays of light passing through either the *principal* axis or the *secondary* axes are not refracted. In the lower sketch in Figure 13.19, the formation of an image upon the retina is illustrated.

The retinal image can be observed in the excised eye of an albino rabbit. When the eye is directed toward a lighted candle and viewed from behind, an inverted image of the flame is seen shining through the unpigmented wall of the globe. This observation was first made by Christopher Scheiner in 1619. It is worth remembering that the image formed upon the retina is minute; the image of the smallest visible object is little more than $\frac{1}{10,000}$ inch (0.0025 mm) in diameter.

Accommodation of the eye. We have seen that rays of light coming from a distant object are approximately parallel; those from a near object are divergent. Therefore, with a convex lens of a given refracting power, rays from a near object cannot be focused at as short a distance behind the lens as can those coming from a distance (see Fig. 13.16, p. 591), which means that near and far objects cannot be focused upon the retina at the same moment. In order to turn the eyes from a far scene and focus them on a near one, either a stronger lens (that is, one with a greater convexity) must be used, or the distance between the screen and the lens must be increased.

The latter means is employed in photography. In order to take a photograph of a view less than 12 feet or so from the camera, the lens must be moved forward so as to increase the distance between it and the film. Though the eyes of certain species of fish have a mechanism for accommodating the eye to near vision based upon this principle, in man and the higher animals the first-mentioned method is adopted; the

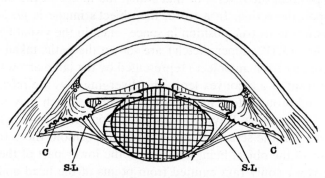

Fig. 13.20   Illustrating the mechanism of accommodation of the eye for near vision. The horizontally shaded lens and the unshaded iris show the position of the parts when at rest; the vertically shaded lens and iris show the position during accommodation for a near point. C, ciliary muscle; S.L., suspensory ligament. (Redrawn from Landolt.)

crystalline lens can alter its refracting power in order that either a far or a near object can be distinctly seen. When the eyes are directed to a distant view, the crystalline lens is least convex; being flatter, its re-fracting power is at the minimum. But when the observed object is within about 20 feet from the eyes, the convexity of the lens increases in order to bring the divergent rays from the near object to a sharp focus upon the retina. These together with the other adjustments made by the eyes in order to see either near or far objects clearly are termed *ocular accommodation*.

The far and near points of the eyes. The farthest point from the eyes at which objects can be focused upon the retina and, therefore, seen distinctly is called the *far point* of vision (*punctum remotum*). The far point is at infinity, for the visibility of a distant object is limited only by its size, the clearness of the atmosphere, and the curvature of the earth; for practical purposes it is taken as any distance beyond 20 feet; at this distance the lens is, as just mentioned, at its least curvature. The shortest distance from the eyes at which an object can be seen clearly is called the *near point* (*punctum proximum*); it lengthens from infancy to old age, in accordance with the gradual diminution in the elasticity of the lens, being between 7 and 9 cm for the former age and 40 cm for the latter (see Presbyopia, p. 610). For the normal eye of the young adult, the near point is about midway between these two extremes—namely, 25 cm, approximately. At any distance between the eyes and the near point an object forms a blurred image upon the retina because the lens is unable to increase its refracting power (convexity) any further. The reader can verify this for himself by bringing the tip of a pencil close to his eyes.

The mechanism of accommodation. The increase in the convexity of the lens and, therefore, in its refracting power are brought about by

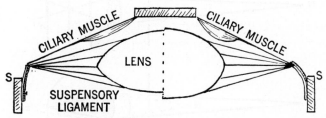

Fig. 13.21   Illustration by means of a mechanical model of the manner in which the lens becomes more convex when the eye accommodates for near vision, right half of figure. The springs, S and S, represent the elastic choroid, and the radiating lines the suspensory ligament.

the inherent tendency of the lens to assume a more convex shape when the restraint offered by the suspensory ligament is released (see Figs. 13.20 and 13.21). The suspensory ligament (which, as already stated, extends outward from the capsule of the lens to be attached to the ciliary processes, and through these and the ciliary muscle to the inner coat of the eye) is taut when the eyes look into the distance. The tension thus exerted upon the lens reduces its curvature. When the eye accommodates for near vision, the ciliary muscle contracts and draws the choroid forward; the ciliary processes are brought closer to the lens—i.e., they form a smaller circle. The suspensory ligament is slackened thereby, and the tension on the lens diminished. The lens by virtue of its inherent elasticity bulges forward (Figs. 13.20 and 13.21). The convexity of the central part of the anterior surface is increased to a much greater extent than the more peripheral part of the lens. Little change in the curvature of the posterior surface occurs.

Scheiner's experiment. That the crystalline lens alters its refractive power when the eyes are turned from a distant scene to look at an object nearer to the eyes was first deduced by Christopher Scheiner (1579–1650), a German priest and scientist, from the following experiment.

A card is pierced by two pinholes about 2 mm apart horizontally (Fig. 13.22); a needle, *N*, is held in front of the card, *C*, while a convex lens placed behind it throws a clear image of the needle on the screen, *S*, at *n* (*upper cut*, Fig. 13.22). If the screen is moved forward (*S'*), it intercepts the rays from the needle before they have come to a focus; two blurred images are formed at *n'* and *n'*. If the screen is

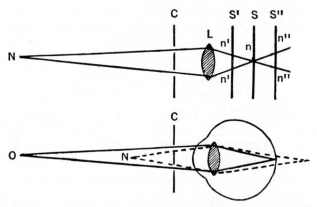

Fig. 13.22　C, perforated card; L, lens. (Explanation in the text.)

moved to a position behind the original one (*S''*), it is now in the path of the rays after they have crossed at the focus *n;* two blurred images are formed at *n''*, *n''*. But if we had a series of lenses graded in refracting power, the image of the needle could be focused on the screen placed at varying distances.

The *lower cut* of Figure 13.22 depicts the pierced card held at a distance of about 5 inches in front of one eye. The other eye is closed. The pinholes should be separated by a horizontal distance a little less than the diameter of the pupil. When the subject looks at an object, *O*, at some distance beyond the needle, *N*, two blurred images of the needle are cast upon the retina (dotted lines), because the rays, as at *n'* and *n'* above, have not been refracted sufficiently. If the subject now looks directly at the needle, the two images fuse into a single clear one. Since we know that in the latter instance the retina cannot have moved back to the point of focus, it must be concluded that the crystalline lens has increased its refracting power.

Purkinje-Sanson images. The change in the form of the lens during accommodation for near vision can be demonstrated by another simple experiment. If one looks into another's eye in a dark room while a lighted candle is held a little in front and to its outer side, one sees three reflected images of the flame (Fig. 13.23). Of these, one is bright and upright; it shines from the surface of the cornea which acts as a convex mirror. A larger but dim upright image is formed by the anterior convex surface of the lens. The third image is inverted, bright and smaller than the others; it is formed by the posterior surface of the lens which acts as a concave mirror. If the positions of the images are noted while the subject gazes at a distant point, and he then

A   **B**

Fig. 13.23 Purkinje-Sanson images. A, during far vision; B, during accommodation for near vision. (Redrawn and modified from Williams.)

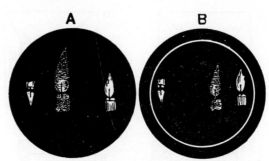

accommodates for near vision, the image reflected from the anterior surface of the lens will be observed to become smaller, and to move toward that reflected from the cornea which, of course, does not alter in size or position. As a rule, no change can be observed in the reflection from the posterior surface of the lens. The change in the position and size of the image on the anterior surface during accommodation can only mean that this surface becomes more convex.

The other adjustments for near vision are *convergence of the eyes,* which is necessary in order to bring the retinal images on to corresponding points (p. 588), and *constriction of the pupil.* The narrowing of the pupil permits light to pass only through the more central part of the lens which, as just mentioned, is increased in its convexity to the greatest degree during accommodation.

The appreciation of distance and depth—stereoscopic vision (Gk. *stereos,* solid + *skopeo,* I view). Our visual judgment of solidity—that is, our recognition that an object has depth as well as height and width—is due largely to the fact that the two retinal images are slightly dissimilar. If the reader will look at some object in front of him, first closing one eye and then the other, he will find that the view seen by the right eye is slightly different from that seen by the left. The right eye is able to see more of the right side of the object, the left eye more of the left side (Fig. 13.24). The two slightly dissimilar images are fused in the brain, yet the composite image has, hidden within it, something of each separate one; upon this the stereoscopic effect largely depends. The fusion of the dissimilar images by the brain, and the impression of depth and solidity produced thereby, lies in a field of psychology of which little is known.

The instrument known as a stereoscope produces an illusion of solidity by making use of the principle of simultaneous stimulation of corresponding retinal points by slightly dissimilar images. A photo-

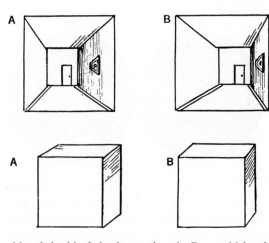

Fig. 13.24 Showing two views of the interior of a long room or corridor (*upper figure*). View A shows more of the right-hand wall than does view B. The former, A, would be seen by the left eye of a person looking into such a room, and B by his right eye. The fusion of the two similar but not identical images gives a visual sensation of depth. In the *lower* figures two views of a block are shown. A, in which more of the right side of the block is shown than in B, would be the view seen by the right eye; B would be the image of the block formed by the left eye. Fusing of the images in the two eyes is an important factor in our perception of the solidity, or three-dimensional nature, of such an object.

If the reader will place one edge of a card about 5 inches wide vertically between the two sets of figures, with the opposite edge of the card touching his nose, and then gaze steadily, with accommodation relaxed, until the figures of each pair fuse into one, a visual sensation of depth (upper pair of figures) and of solidity (lower pair) will be experienced.

graph taken with an ordinary camera appears flat because identical images are formed upon the retinas. A stereoscopic photograph, on the other hand, is taken by a camera provided with two lenses which are set, like the eyes, a short distance apart. Thus, two slightly dissimilar views are taken, which, when looked at through the stereoscope, are projected by means of prisms, one to each eye, so as to fall on corresponding retinal points.

Stereoscopic perception cannot, however, be explained entirely upon the basis of dissimilar retinal images, for the sensation of depth (or distance) is not abolished when one eye is closed; other factors are concerned. These are:

1. *The apparent size of various objects in our field of vision.* We know from experience the approximate size of the objects which we see, but the image which an object casts upon the fovea diminishes as its distance increases. For example, a church steeple at a distance casts an image upon the retina no larger, perhaps smaller, than does a pencil held a few inches from the eyes. We know the relative sizes of the two objects and, therefore, infer that the steeple must be far away and the pencil near.

2. *The apparent change in color of an object with distance.* The atmosphere is not perfectly transparent or equally so for all wavelengths. Tree-clad hills, which we know to be green, appear blue in the distance; the colors of many other objects appear to fade with distance, their detail and outline being dimmed by haze.

3. *The blocking out of parts of a distant view by objects between it and the eyes* gives a sensation of depth.

4. *Mathematical perspective.* Straight lines running into the distance which are actually parallel (or objects along imaginary straight lines) are convergent in the retinal image. When we look down a railway track, for example, the rails appear to converge toward some point beyond the horizon. This arrangement of lines in the image formed upon the retina we have come to associate with distance. Perspective is an elementary principle in drawing, used to create an illusion of depth or distance. The artist draws objects along imaginary lines which run toward a point in the background of his picture.

5. *Parallax.* When one moves in any direction, near objects appear to move in the opposite direction, those in the background in the same direction as ourselves. This apparent movement of near objects in relation to ones farther away is called parallax; it is also produced by a movement of the head or eyes, even though the body remains stationary. Now, involuntary movements of the eyes are continually taking place with the production of parallax; this is believed to be one of the most important factors in giving us a sense of depth.

6. *The distribution of light and shade over the surface of an object and the shadow which it casts upon its surroundings* are also important elements in the production of the stereoscopic effect.

Color vision. White light is in reality a combination of colored lights —red, orange, yellow, green, blue, and violet—which can be separated by means of a glass prism. The series of colored lights so produced is called the (*visible*) *spectrum* (see Pl. 13B). The wavelengths of the lights of the visible spectrum run from 8000 millimicrons for dark red to around 3000 for violet. Rays somewhat longer than the red are called infrared or heat waves; those shorter than the violet are called ultraviolet; neither, of course, gives a sensation of light. The prism refracts the long red rays less than it does the orange, the orange less than the yellow, the yellow less than the green and, so on, in the order of diminishing wavelengths. A beam of white light is thus split into its constituent colors. The separated colors can be recombined to produce white. But, in order to obtain a sensation of white light, it is not necessary to employ all the prismatic colors; not only white, but all colors can be produced from three—namely, *red, green,* and *violet.* These are called the *primary colors.* If we were to set up three lanterns, one of which emitted red light, another green, and a third violet, we could, by blending one, two, or all three of them upon a screen, produce white or any colored light we chose. For example, the three colors in nearly equal proportions would produce white; green and violet would give blue; red and green and a very little violet would give yellow or orange.

Several theories of color vision have been proposed. According to Young's theory, which is very widely accepted, three kinds of cones exist in the retina, each type containing a substance sensitive to light of a different color. One kind is stimulated by red rays, one by green, and another by violet; white light falling upon the retina stimulates all three nearly equally. When a yellow color is seen, the sensation is due to the stimulation of equal numbers of the red and green, and a very few of the violet elements; if violet and green sensitive cones are stimulated, a sensation of blue results; and when the red, green, or violet type of receptor is excited exclusively, we see red, green, or violet, respectively. See Plate 14A.

The qualities of color. There are three qualities of color—*hue, saturation or intensity,* and *tone or brilliance.* Hue is determined entirely by the wavelength of the light, thus red differs from green or blue because its wavelength is greater. Saturation or intensity, also called purity, depends upon the proportion of white mixed with the color— pink has a lower saturation than red. Tone or brilliance, also referred to as value by artists, varies with the proportion of black mixed with the color. A vivid scarlet pigment, for example, can be reduced to a deep cherry by the addition of black.

Retinal areas sensitive to color. The extreme peripheral part of the retina devoid of cones is insensitive to color. It gives impressions of white, black, and gray only. Color perception is confined to the more central retinal regions where cones are present exclusively, as in the fovea centralis, and in the extrafoveal regions where these receptors are mingled more or less plentifully among the rods. Nor is sensitivity to the different colors uniformly distributed over the retina. The area sensitive to blue is the largest, that sensitive to red is next in order of size; then comes the margin of a much smaller area sensitive to yellow. This latter area is little larger than the area sensitive to green which is the least extensive of all. The four areas may be compared to four transparent saucers, respectively colored and graded in size, placed one inside the other. Light passing through the small green saucer must pass through all the others as well; the area of the retina which it represents is, therefore, sensitive to all four colors. Light transmitted through the outer part of the yellow saucer will also pass through the red and blue, but not through the green saucer; the corresponding area is, therefore, sensitive to yellow, red, and blue, but not to green. The outer part of the red area is sensitive to red and blue; the outer part of the blue saucer transmits only blue light and the rim of the area which it represents is sensitive only to blue.

The color areas of the retina can be mapped out by means of the perimeter shown and described on page 587. Small paper discs colored, respectively, blue, red, yellow, and green are used instead of the white test object employed in mapping the visual fields. Normally, the blue disc will be seen at the greatest distance from the center of the visual field; at a somewhat shorter distance the red disc will appear, then the yellow, and finally the green (see Pl. 14B).

Color blindness. In some persons the retina is totally insensitive to color; to such their surroundings are seen in black and white and various tones of gray. Such a condition, called *achromatism,* is very rare. In the common type of color blindness, the subjects are blind to red or to green. On the basis of the Young-Helmholtz theory of color vision, it may be presumed that one of the three color substances present in the retinas of persons of normal vision is absent from the retinas of the red or green blind, the red substance being lacking in the former abnormality, the green substance in the latter. The subjects of these visual defects match any color with only two primary color sensations, green and violet, or red and violet, instead of the three possessed by persons of normal color vision. Their color vision is therefore called *dichromatic* (Gk. *di,* two + *chroma,* color) instead of *trichromatic* (Gk. *tri,* three) which is the normal. Red blindness is also called *protanopia* (Gk. *protos,* first + *anopia,* blindness) and *deuteranopia* (Gk. *deuteros,* second), which means that the blindness is with respect to the first (red) or to the second (green) primary color. John Dalton

(1766–1844), the celebrated chemist who was red blind and gave the first scientific description of protanopia, wrote, "Crimson has a very grave appearance. Woolen yarn dyed crimson or blue is the same to me."

Anomalous trichromatism or *partial color blindness* is the most common defect of color perception. There is not complete blindness for any color, but the appreciation of red or of green is below the normal. If, for example, a person with such a defect is asked to match a pure yellow light with a combination or mixture of red and green lights, he uses more of the red light than would a normal person to make a perfect match; his perception of red is defective. If he uses more green, his perception of this color is subnormal. The defective perception of red is called *protanomally,* that of green *deuteranomally.* A special instrument called an *anomaloscope* is used for testing these defects. It was devised by Lord Rayleigh, the celebrated English physicist.

Ninety-five percent of the subjects who suffer from some form of defect in color vision are males. Most cases are inherited and the inheritance is of the sex-linked character, being transmitted from generation to generation in a manner similar to that of hemophilia (p. 107).

A color-blind person may be quite unaware of his visual abnormality. Though his color sensations are different from normal persons, he is usually able to make some distinction in his own way between different colors, usually by some slight difference in brightness. Though great care is exercised in testing the color vision of men such as seamen and locomotive drivers, whose occupations require a normal color sense, we rarely hear of an automobile driver disregarding a red traffic light because he thought it was green.

Color vision is tested in several ways, but the oldest and most usual method is by means of colored wool yarns. The subject is shown a number of yarns dyed in colors which are most likely to be confused (*confusion colors*), and is asked to pick from the lot the one that matches best another single yarn dyed a rosepink. If he chooses a violet or a blue yarn, he is red blind. If green, red, and brown yarns are chosen, he is green blind. Anomalous trichromatism is tested, as already described, by means of the anomaloscope.

Contrast effects. It is well known that when black is placed against white or vice versa they "set one another off," the black looks blacker and the white a purer white than if either were placed against a colored ground. It is also true that blue against a yellow ground (or yellow against a blue ground) is more vivid than if placed against any other color. Also green is enhanced by red and red by green. These phenomena are examples of *simultaneous contrast.*

The maximum effect of contrast is obtained when *complementary colors* are paired. Any pair of colors which, when fused as lights, produce white are said to be complementary to one another. Examples of complementary color pairs are the following:

> Red and greenish blue
> Orange and cyan blue
> Yellow and indigo blue [3]
> Violet and greenish yellow
> Purple and green

Not only those listed above, but every color and shade of color has its complementary (Fig. 13.25). There are, consequently, a great number of complementary colors, and the contrast effect is produced

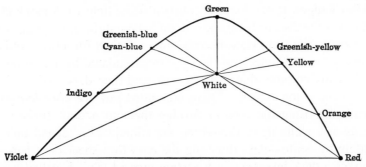

Fig. 13.25   Complementary colors. The colors of the spectrum from violet to red are marked upon the curve (roughly triangular). Other colors would fall upon intermediate points on the curve. The base line of the figure (from violet to red) represents the nonspectral purple. Any two points upon the curve joined by a straight line drawn through the point marked *white* indicate complementary colors. (After Hall.)

when the colors of such a pair are placed side by side. Furthermore, when a color is laid beside one that is not complementary to it, or against white, each color appears to be tinted slightly with the complementary color of the other; or the white becomes tinged with the complementary of the color. For example, blue placed beside green as-

---

[3] A distinction must be drawn here between lights and paints; we know that yellow and blue paints when mixed give green, not white. The color of a paint is due to its reflecting certain wavelengths in white light and absorbing the remainder. Even the bluest paint is not pure blue; it absorbs all light but blue and a little green. These it reflects. A yellow paint is not pure yellow; it reflects a little green with the yellow. When the two paints are mixed, blue light is absorbed by the yellow paint, and yellow light by the blue. The green rays, of which a little is reflected by each separate paint, are doubly reflected when the two are mixed.

sumes a faintly red cast (violet), and yellow against red is tinged faintly green. Again, a lemon or other yellow object, placed in a bright light, casts a shadow which is tinged with blue—the complementary of yellow. The shadow cast by a red object would be tinged with greenish blue, and one cast by a purple object with green. These principles are applied in art. The artist makes a yellow flood of sunshine more brilliant by painting blue into the shadows which, in turn, are given depth and an appearance of reality which they would otherwise lack.

When one stares for a time at a colored surface in a strong light and then directs the gaze to a gray surface the gray appears slightly tinged with the color complementary to the one to which the eyes were first directed, and objects of the complementary color itself are made more vivid. For example, if one looks at a red surface for a time and then at a green one, the latter color is intensified—it appears greener. This phenomenon is called *successive contrast*.

After images. If one looks at a bright white light for a moment and then closes the eyes or turns them upon a dark surface, an image of the light slowly floats into view, becomes more distinct for a time, and then gradually fades. Similarly, if the eyes are stimulated by a colored light or a brightly colored object of any sort, and then darkened, an image of the same color appears. These are called *positive after images*. If, instead of closing the eyes or turning them to a dark surface after looking at a white light, the retinas are stimulated a second time and diffusely by white—e.g., directing the eyes to a sheet of paper—one then sees a dark image against a white ground. This is called a *negative after image*. If the first stimulus was colored, then the after image is in the complementary color. Negative after images of colored objects are the cause of successive contrast described in the last paragraph.

Positive after images are due apparently to the chemicophysical changes in the receptors of the retina, caused by and outlasting the stimulus. Negative after images are thought to be due to a state comparable in certain respects to the refractory period of nerve. Cones which have responded to a stimulus will not for a time respond again. Ordinarily, white light stimulates all three types of cone (p. 600). The negative after image which appears upon applying a circumscribed and then a diffuse white stimulus to the retina is, therefore, a dark patch against a white background. When the object looked at is colored, and the retina is then stimulated by directing the eyes to a white surface, the image is in the complementary color, because only those cones that had not previously been stimulated can respond. For example, if the object looked at is red, the red-sensitive cones are not excited by a subsequent stimulus of white; those sensitive to green and to violet alone respond, giving the complementary of red —namely, a bluish green.

Optical illusions. The brain may be deceived by imitations of certain effects upon which our visual judgments of the size, shape, and distance of objects are based. Visual errors of this nature are called optical illusions or optical deceptions. Some interesting examples are shown in Figures 13.26 to 13.29.

Fig. 13.26   Zollner's lines. The long diagonal lines appear to converge;   actually, they are parallel.

Movements of the eyes and eyelids. The eyeballs are turned in their sockets by small muscles, attached, on the one hand, to the walls of the orbital cavity and, on the other, to the sclerotic coat at a distance of from a third to half an inch behind the circumference of the cornea (Fig. 13.30). There are six muscles for each eye, the four *recti* muscles (*internal, external, superior,* and *inferior*) and the two *obliques* (*superior* and *inferior*). The internal rectus muscle turns the eye inward—i.e., toward the nose; the external rectus turns it outward. The superior rectus turns the eye upward and inward, the inferior rectus downward and inward. The superior oblique rotates the eyeball downward and outward, the inferior oblique upward and outward (see diagram, Fig. 13.31). The eye muscles, especially the obliques, also cause a wheel-like rotatory movement.

The superior oblique muscle is supplied by the trochlear (fourth cranial) nerve, and the external rectus by the abducent (sixth cranial)

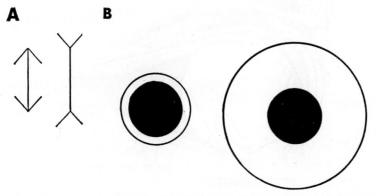

Fig. 13.27   Illusions of size. A, the vertical lines are of the same length; B, the black circles are the same size.

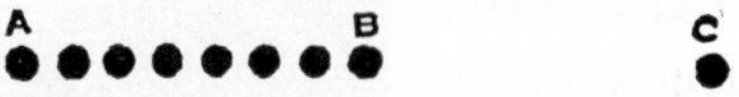

A ● ● ● ● ● ● ●   B   C
                              ●

Fig. 13.28 (*Above*) Illusion of distance. The distance from A to B appears to be greater than that from B to C; they are the same.

Fig. 13.29 (*Right*) Illusion of size. The figure of the man is actually smaller than that of the child, but the effect of distance produced by the converging lines causes it to appear larger.

nerve; all the other ocular muscles are supplied by the oculomotor (third cranial) nerve.

The muscles of the two eyes act in unison. For example, the eyes are turned to one or other side—*conjugate deviation*—by the contraction of the external rectus of one eye and the internal rectus of the other. *Convergence of the eyes*—i.e., turning both eyes inward—is brought about by the contraction of both internal recti. In any movements of the eyes, the muscles which bring about the opposite movement—i.e., the antagonistic muscles—are inhibited. Thus, the principle of reciprocal inhibition (p. 517) applies to the ocular muscles as well as to other muscles of the body.

The visual axis of the eye is represented by a line extending from an

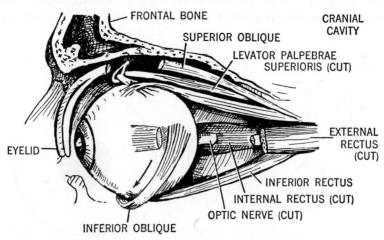

Fig. 13.30 Showing the eyeball in its bony socket (orbital cavity) and the ocular muscles.

object in the visual field, through the cornea, a little to the nasal side of its center of curvature, to the fovea centralis. When the sight is directed to a far view, the axes of the two eyes are parallel. But during accommodation for near vision, when the eyes converge, the axes meet at a point in the object at which we look. This is called the *fixation point*. When (as a result of unbalanced action of the ocular muscles) the visual axes do not bear the normal relationship to one another, they may be converged too acutely ("cross eyes") or not enough, or they may diverge. The condition is known as *strabismus* or *squint*.

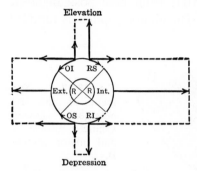

Fig. 13.31   Diagram of the actions of the muscles of one eye. (From Fuchs after Marquez.) OI, inferior oblique; RS, superior rectus; R.ext., external rectus; R.int., internal rectus; OS, superior oblique; RI, inferior rectus. The arrows indicate the direction in which each muscle tends to move the eyeball. It will be noted, however, that the actions of some muscles are antagonized by those of others. For example, the eye is turned outward by the combined actions of the external rectus, inferior oblique, and superior oblique. The upward and rotary movement caused by the inferior oblique is neutralized by the opposing action of the superior oblique.

The eyelid is raised by a muscle attached to the upper bony wall of the eye socket and inserted into the skin and dense connective tissue of the upper lid. It consists of a smooth muscle and a voluntary muscle component. The former is supplied by sympathetic nerve fibers, the latter by a branch of the oculomotor (third cranial) nerve. The muscle is called the *levator palpebrae superioris* (elevator of the upper lid). The lids are closed by a sphincterlike muscle known as the *orbicularis oculi*. The fibers of this muscle are arranged in circles and sweep around the opening between the lids. It is supplied by branches of the facial nerve.

The structure and functions of the iris. The iris is a circular diaphragm or curtain lying behind the cornea, and in front of the lens. The circular opening at its center is called the *pupil*. The iris around its circumference is attached to the ciliary body. It is composed of two sets of smooth muscle fibers. One set of fibers is arranged circularly; this set causes narrowing of the pupil, and is therefore called the *sphincter* or *constrictor pupillae*. The fibers of the other set run radially from the pupillary margin; they dilate the pupil and constitute the *dilator pupillae* muscle (see Fig. 13.32).

The most usual causes of changes in the size of the pupil are variations in the intensity of the illumination and accommodation of the eye for near or far vision (p. 597). Under the former condition, the changes in pupillary diameter are purely reflex. The receptors of the reflex are in the retina. The afferent pathway is over the visual fibers of the midbrain; here, connections are made with the nucleus of the third cranial nerve. The efferent fibers belong to the parasympathetic division of the autonomic nervous system. They issue from the nucleus of the third nerve, and are conveyed in the trunk of this nerve to the ciliary ganglion (see diagram, Pl. 15B); from here postganglionic fibers pass to the constrictor of the iris. The dilator pupillae is supplied

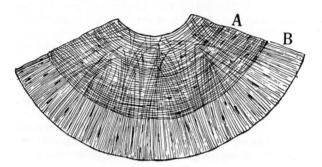

Fig. 13.32   Segment of the iris, enlarged, showing sphincter muscle, A, and dilator muscle, B.

by the sympathetic. The sympathetic fibers descend in the spinal cord where they synapse with cells in the lateral horns of gray matter. They leave the cord in the lower cervical region to enter the gangliated cord of the sympathetic where they connect with cells in the superior cervical ganglion. From these cells, fibers (postganglionic) pass to the dilator muscle of the pupil.

Light falling upon the retina of either eye causes both pupils to constrict, the constrictor pupillae being excited, the dilator pupillae inhibited. The diameter of the pupil at any moment is the resultant of these two opposing actions. Besides changes in the illumination and accommodation of the eye, certain emotional states cause variations in the size of the pupil; anger causes constriction; fear, dilatation; pain causes constriction: The pupil is also constricted during sleep, and during ether or chloroform anesthesia. Drugs such as atropine (the active principle of belladonna) and adrenaline cause dilatation of the pupil; morphine and pilocarpine cause constriction.

Optical defects. *Spherical aberration.* The point of convergence of rays passing through the peripheral parts of an ordinary convex lens is at a shorter distance behind the lens than that of rays transmitted more

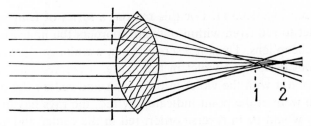

Fig. 13.33 Illustrating spherical aberration. Note that the outer rays come to a focus, 1, in front of the more central rays, 2. The vertical broken lines in front of the lens show how a "stop" of a camera or the iris of the eye cuts off the outer rays.

centrally. The two groups of rays, therefore, cross and cause a blurred image. This is an inherent defect of convex lenses and is called *spherical aberration* (Fig. 13.33). In the making of a high-quality camera lens, special means are employed to correct this defect; the lens is built up of separate pieces of glass of different refractive indices cemented together so that all rays are converged to the same point or focus. Spherical aberration is corrected so some extent in a corresponding fashion in the crystalline lens; the central part of the lens has a greater optical density than the more peripheral and superficial region. The center has, therefore, greater refracting power. Thus all parts of the lens are rendered more uniform in respect to their power of converging the rays of light. The iris, since it covers the outer part of the lens and blocks the peripheral rays, also serves to correct spherical aberration. The diaphragm of a camera serves a similar purpose.

Chromatic aberration. The colors composing white light are refracted to different degrees according to their wavelengths. The long red rays are refracted least; the violet rays most; the other colors of the spectrum are refracted in progressively greater degree from orange

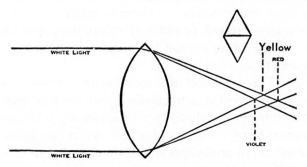

Fig. 13.34 Illustrating chromatic aberration. The small figure shows how a simple convex lens is essentially two prisms placed base to base.

to blue (see Fig. 13.34). For this reason, a series of fringes, colored from violet to red from within outward, borders the image formed by a simple cheap lens. Thus, if a screen (e.g., a white card) were placed at the point designated violet in the figure, a colored halo would be thrown upon it with the violet in the center and red on the outside. If the screen were at the point indicated by red, the rays having crossed, the colors would be in reverse order, red in the center and violet outside. If the black and white circles in Figure 13.35 are observed at a distance of about 1 inch from the eye—nearer the eye than the point of clear vision—the white circles will appear in a faintly bluish tint

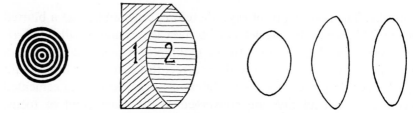

Fig. 13.35   (*Left*) Illustrating chromatic aberration. (See text.)

Fig. 13.36   (*Center*) Diagram showing the structure of an achromatic lens. 1, flint glass; 2, crown glass.

Fig. 13.37   (*Right*) Showing the contour of the crystalline lens at different periods of life. *From left to right,* in infancy, in early adult life, and in old age.

as a result of chromatic aberration, as the defect under discussion is called. It is corrected in camera and microscope lenses by cementing a biconvex lens of crown glass to a concave block of flint glass (see Fig. 13.36). Such a lens is called *achromatic*. The lens of the eye is not corrected for chromatic aberration. A red and a violet object at the same distance from the eye, therefore, cannot both be seen sharply at the same time. If, for example, the eyes are focused upon a violet light, they must accommodate, in order to maintain the focus, when the light is changed to red. In ordinary vision, the colors surrounding the images on the retina are not perceived, largely because we have come to ignore them.

Presbyopia. This is a defect of accommodation which develops after middle age. Distant vision is unimpaired, but the lens, like other tissues, loses its resilience or elasticity with advancing years, and cannot, in consequence, bring the image of a near object into focus upon the retina. The subject of presbyopia is, therefore, unable to read ordinary print without the aid of convex glasses.

The shape of the lens also changes with advancing years, its curvature being flatter, and its refracting power correspondingly less in middle and late adult life than in the young (see Fig. 13.37).

Defects due to abnormalities in the form of the eyeball. The three defects about to be discussed are due to abnormalities in the conformation of the eyeball. The normal or *emmetropic* eye is nearly spherical,

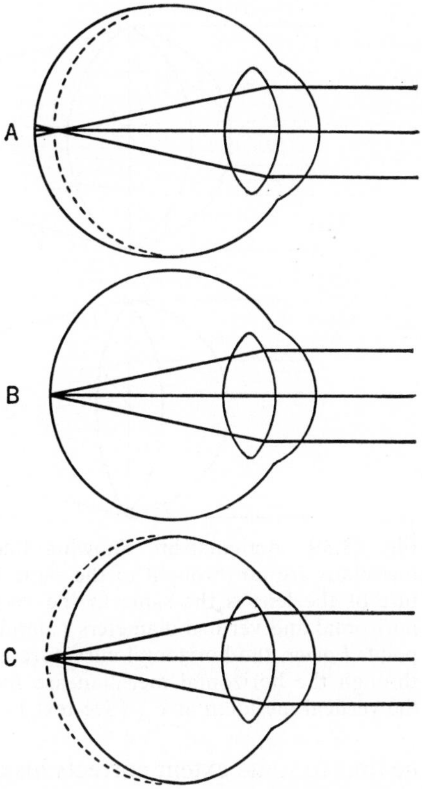

Fig. 13.38   Illustrating myopia, A; emmetropia, B; and hypermetropia, C. Myopia requires a concave lens for its correction; hypermetropia, a convex lens. Note that in the three types of eye, the light rays are focused at the same distance behind the lens; in other words, the defects are due to abnormalities in the length of the eyeball.

the vertical diameter being only about 0.5 mm shorter than the anteroposterior and transverse (see Fig. 13.38 B).

Myopia or shortsightedness. In this defect of the eye, the refracting power of the lens is usually the same as in the normal eye, but the anteroposterior diameter of the globe is abnormally long. The image is therefore brought to a focus a little in front of the retina. In other words, the lens is too strong for the length of the eyeball. The rays after coming to a focus disperse again, and a blurred image is formed upon the retina, just as when the film of a camera is adjusted at too great a distance from the lens. Myopia is corrected by fitting the subject with concave lenses which, by *diverging* the rays before they enter the eye and thus partly offsetting the converging power of the crystalline lens, bring them to a focus upon the retina (Fig. 13.38 A).

When his defect is not fully corrected, the subject of myopia holds any object which he wishes to see clearly very close to his eyes and relaxes his accommodation—that is, accommodates for far vision. The reason is that rays of light from the near object are more divergent;

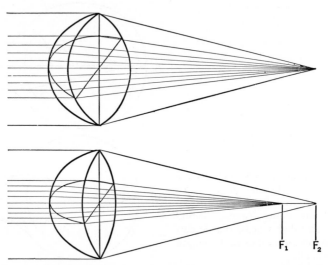

Fig. 13.39 Astigmatism. Showing that light rays passing through different meridians are not brought to the same focus. *Upper cut,* the horizontal curvature of the lens is the same as the vertical; rays of light passing through the horizontal and vertical diameters (meridians) are therefore focused to the same point. *Lower,* the horizontal curvature is greater than the vertical. Rays passing through the horizontal meridian are focused at F_1 and those passing through the vertical meridian at F_2. (See text.)

he thus to some extent corrects his defect. But if he accommodated his eyes for near vision, the curvature of the crystalline lens would be increased and his visual disability accentuated.

Hypermetropia or longsightedness. This defect is due to the anteroposterior diameter of the eyeball being too short. Since the refracting power of the crystalline lens is the same as in the normal eye, the rays cannot be converged acutely enough to form a clear image upon the retina. Hypermetropia is corrected by means of convex lenses which converge the rays before they enter the eye, thus aiding the crystalline lens (Fig. 13.38 C).

Astigmatism. This is probably the commonest of all defects of the eye. In astigmatism, as the name itself implies (Gk. *a, not +*
stigma, a point), rays of light are not brought to sharp points upon

the retina, but form, instead, short lines. The defect is present in all eyes to a certain degree, and it is only when well marked that it can be considered abnormal. The stars, for example, which should appear to us as small dots of light, seem to radiate short lines of light. For the same reason, a light shining through the dark appears to emit radiating beams.

It must be remembered that rays of light pass through all meridians of a lens; in converging to a focus they, therefore, form a cone of light, not simply a flat, pennantlike beam. If, as in the normal eye, all meridians of the lens have approximately the same curvature, then rays in all planes are refracted to almost the same degree and come to a focus together. If the curvatures differ, the rays transmitted through a meridian with the greater curvature will be refracted more strongly and brought to a focus in front of rays passing through other meridians. For example, should the vertical meridian be more curved than the horizontal, then, when the rays passing through the vertical meridian are in focus, those in the horizontal will form, not a point, but a horizontal line (see Fig. 13.39). Such inequalities of curvature in the meridians of the cornea or, less commonly, of the crystalline lens, are the cause of astigmatism. The greater curvature may be in either

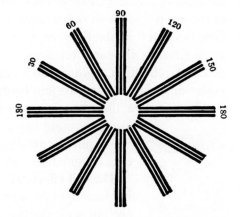

Fig. 13.40   Chart used in testing for astigmatism. In the astigmatic eye, the image of the lines in one or more meridians is blurred (not in focus).

a vertical, horizontal, or a diagonal meridian. When the subject of astigmatism looks at a card on which is printed a figure like the dial of a clock (Fig. 13.40), the vertical lines may be clearly seen, while the horizontal are blurred, or vice versa. Again, the diagonal lines may be out of focus while the horizontal and vertical ones are clearly defined.

Astigmatism is corrected by the use of spectacle lenses, convex in the meridian corresponding to that of the cornea (or crystalline lens) having the lesser curvature. Thus, if the curvature of the cornea is greater in the vertical meridian, the subject is fitted with a cylindrical lens having its convexity in the horizontal meridian.

Opacities in the vitreous body. Minute opacities or semiopaque bodies are present in the vitreous body of the best of eyes. Though they cause no inconvenience and we are usually unaware of them, they can be demonstrated by anyone in his own eyes. They appear when the eyes are closed and one concentrates his attention as he gazes against closed lids, or, without closing the eyes, looks at a clear sky or some blank surface. They are called *muscae volitantes* (L. flying flies). They are seen to move either upward or downward when the eyes are moved, but when one attempts to focus upon them they appear to fly away. The visual sensations are caused by the shadows cast upon the retina by epithelial cells or other debris—e.g., embryonic remnants in the vitreous body.

Contact lenses. These are thin bowl-shaped shells of glass made to fit over the cornea; they are used in some cases of refractive errors, especially those due to an abnormal shape of the cornea, to astigmatism, or to absence of the crystalline lens. The contact lens is made in the form of the normal cornea and before being applied to the surface of the eye is filled with saline solution which, when the lens is in position, lies as a thin film between it and the cornea. Now, the saline is of approximately the same refractive power as the cornea and, for purposes of refraction, cornea and saline are, therefore, one. Thus the posterior surface of the glass lens being in the form of a normal cornea, molds, as it were, the patient's cornea into normal shape. The lens may

Fig. 13.41 Drawing of contact lens.

also be ground like any other lens so as to render it of the required curvature to correct a refractive error—e.g., astigmatism, myopia, etc. (Fig. 13.41).

The evil effects of bad lighting upon the eyes. Reading in a light of such low illumination that the letters are not seen sharply and read easily, too fine a print, or lack of contrast between the letters and the paper, cause eyestrain. Our telephone directories seem to suffer from both of the two last-mentioned defects. The ciliary muscle contracts to its maximum in order to increase the convexity of the lens, and some persons even press upon the cornea with the lids in an effort to bulge it forward—that is, to make it more convex and increase its refractive power. Headache results.

Glare is also a common cause of eyestrain. There are three kinds of glare—*veiling, dazzling,* and *blinding.* Veiling glare is that which is created by a bright light which is uniformly diffused over the scene and reduces the contrast in the image of light and shade. Dazzling glare is caused by a light shining into the eyes at an angle of about 45 degrees. It does not enter into the formation of the retinal image and is scattered by the refracting media of the eye. Blinding glare is light, also not part of the retinal image, which enters the pupil more directly, as when one looks into a very bright light.

The best light for reading is one of from 10 to 20 foot-candles,[4] falling upon a dull-surfaced paper, and not causing glare in any of the ways listed above. There should also be a generally diffused and indirect illumination of the room.

Blindness, partial or complete. Any loss of transparency of the refracting media of the eye—cornea, aqueous humor, lens, or vitreous body—reduces visual acuity. The parts of the eye most commonly affected in this way are the cornea and the crystalline lens. Destruction, by injury or disease, of the corneal surface is replaced by a scar, which is translucent or opaque, and, if so situated that light rays are prevented from entering the pupil in beams which can be focused, blindness of the affected eye results, in so far as recognizing objects is concerned (though light and shade may be appreciated).

Cataract. Cloudiness or opacity of the crystalline lens results in a corresponding limitation of vision. Lack of transparency of the lens is called *cataract.* It is a defect usually occurring in persons past middle age. The changes in the transparency of the lens in the usual form of cataract are due to a degenerative process involving the lens proteins which starts near the center of the lens and spreads toward the surface. During this time, the cataract is said to be *immature.* It is *mature* when the process has extended to involve the superficial layers of the lens. The cure of cataract may be postponed until the mature stage has been reached. The surgeon then resorts to *"needling."* Needling consists of piercing the anterior chamber of the eyeball, making an opening in the lens capsule, and breaking up the degenerated and softened material. This permits the entrance of aqueous humor and the gradual absorption of the lens substance. Then light rays can again reach the retina. The operation for "needling" or *discission* for cataract goes back to ancient times, but today extraction of the lens in its entirety is the most usual operation. After destruction or removal of the lens, strongly convex glasses are prescribed to compensate for the loss of its refracting power.

---

⁴ A foot-candle is a measure of illumination; it is the light given out by a standard candle to 1 square foot of surface 1 foot distant from it.

The cause of the ordinary type of the condition, which is known as *senile cataract,* is thought to be due to the prolonged action of sunlight or other sources of ultraviolet rays upon the lens proteins. It is much more common in India, Egypt, and other tropical and sunny regions than in temperate zones.

Other types of cataract which may occur in earlier life are associated with certain metabolic diseases, especially diabetes. Another type, which occurs in glass blowers, is probably due to heat (infrared) rays.

Total blindness, in which not even a bright light can be perceived, may result from injury or disease of the retinas, of the optic nerves, of the optic tracts, or of the visual areas situated in the cortex of the occipital lobes of the cerebrum. If one retina is affected, or one optic nerve, blindness of the corresponding eye alone results. If the optic tract (i.e., the visual nerve fibers between the optic chiasma and the occipital cortex) or the visual area of the cortex of one side is injured or diseased, partial blindness results in both eyes. Complete blindness results only if the retinas, optic nerves, optic tracts, or visual areas of both sides are involved (see also p. 588).

The pressure within the eyeball; intraocular fluid. The pressure within the eyeball is from 20 to 25 mm Hg during life, but falls to about 10 mm shortly after death. The higher pressure is due to the pressure in the capillaries in the wall of the globe. The lower pressure of 10 mm which persists for a time after death is due to the pressure of the aqueous humor and the fluid in the vitreous body.

The intraocular fluids are not secreted, apparently, but are formed by the passage of fluid by dialysis (p. 18) from the blood across the membranes on the surface of the ciliary body and the posterior aspect of the iris. The fluid is reabsorbed, mainly by drainage through canals at the angles of the anterior chamber formed by the iris and cornea (see Fig. 13.1). There is thus a fairly free circulation of fluid—from blood to the interior of the eyeball and back to the blood by reabsorption.

Glaucoma. This is a very serious disease of the eye of which the initial abnormality is an increase in the intraocular pressure. The ocular hypertension leads to pathological changes within the eyeball which, if the tension persists, lead to blindness through pressure upon the delicate retinal structures. One form of the disease follows some other eye disease and is due either to increased production of intraocular fluid, or to blockage of the drainage canals at the angles of the anterior chamber. Another form of the disease is not preceded by any known ocular disease; its cause remains obscure.

The Ear

The structure of the ear. The ear consists of three distinct parts, called the *outer, middle,* and *inner ears,* each of which has a special part of play in the mechanism of hearing.

The *outer ear* consists of an appendage of cartilage and skin situated on the side of the head and known as the *auricle* or *pinna,* together with a short funnel-shaped passage called the *external auditory meatus* (or *canal*). The latter leads into the temporal bone of the skull, and is closed at its inner end by a flexible membrane called the *drum* or *tympanic membrane.* The auricle and auditory canal serve simply to col-

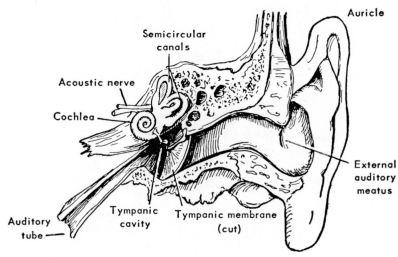

Fig. 13.42   Plan of the ear.

lect and direct the sound waves to the drum membrane; the latter separates the outer from the middle ear (see Fig. 13.42).

The *middle ear, drum,* or *tympanum* is a small chamber within the temporal bone. As just mentioned, the drum membrane is interposed between it and the outer ear. The middle ear contains three miniature bones (the *auditory ossicles*) named individually from their shapes, the *malleus* (hammer), the *incus* (anvil), and the *stapes* (stirrup) (see Fig. 13.43). They stretch across the cavity of the middle ear from the tympanic membrane to the inner wall of this chamber, and are joined to one another by minute joints. The handle of the malleus is attached to the tympanic membrane; its head articulates with the body of the incus. A process of the incus is joined to one end of the stapes; the other end or footplate of the stirruplike bone is fitted into a small

opening in the inner wall of the middle ear, called the *oval window.*
Situated a little lower in the inner wall of the tympanum is the *round
window;* this is closed by a thin membrane.

A narrow canal—the *auditory* or *Eustachian tube*—which connects
the middle ear with the posterior part of the nose, serves for the passage of air between the middle ear and the atmosphere. Thus equality

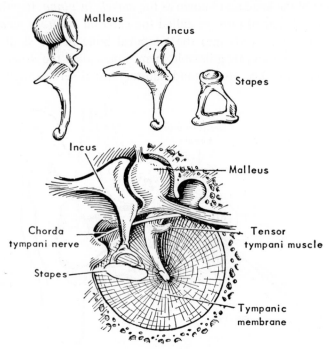

Fig. 13.43   The auditory ossicles.

of air pressures upon the two sides of the drum membrane is maintained.

Two very small muscles are to be found in the middle ear. They
arise from neighboring bone or cartilage and are inserted, one (the
tensor tympani) into the handle of the malleus, the other (the *stape-
dius*) into the stapes. These two muscles contract reflexly and simultaneously when very forcible vibrations strike the eardrum, and by
damping the movements of the ossicles protect the internal ear from
injury.

The *inner ear* or *labyrinth* lies internal to the middle ear; it contains
the organs of hearing and equilibrium. The auditory sense organ is
held within and on the outer wall of a spiral tunnel in the temporal
bone named the *cochlea*—so-called from its resemblance to a snail's

shell (L. *cochlea*, a snail's shell). The spiral canal makes two and
three quarter turns around the central column of spongy bone called
the *modiolus* (Figs. 13.44 and 13.52, p. 631). The larger turns of the
spiral are at the base of the cochlea, the smaller turns at the apex or
cupola. A shelf or ledge of bone which projects from the modiolus and
winds around it like the thread of a screw divides the cochlea incom-

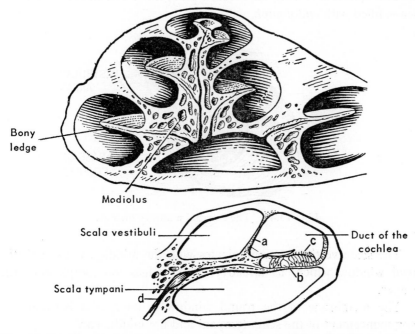

Fig. 13.44   *Upper drawing,* a view of the bony cochlea divided vertically
through the middle; *lower drawing,* enlarged drawing of one turn of the duct of
the cochlea; a vestibular membrane; b, basilar membrane; c, organ of Corti; d,
acoustic nerve.

pletely into two spiral channels. But in the living state, the division of
the cochlea is completed by a membranous septum, called the *basilar
membrane,* which extends from the tip of the bony shelf, mentioned
above, to the outer wall of the cochlea. A second more delicate septum, called the vestibular membrane, proceeds from the upper surface
of the shelf of bone to the outer wall where it is fixed a short distance
above the outer attachment of the basilar membrane. The spiral tube
enclosed between these two membranes is called the *membranous
cochlea* or *duct of the cochlea.*[5] The part of the cochlea lying above

[5] The cochlea is here described as though placed upon its base, but actually it
lies upon its side with its base directed inward toward the cranial cavity and its apex
or cupola pointing outward and forward.

this membranous tube is named the *scala vestibuli,* and the part lying below, the *scala tympani.* The duct of the cochlea is sometimes referred to by its older name, *scala media.* The spiral compartments were given these names from their fancied resemblance to stairways (L. *scala,* a stairway). The scala vestibuli and the scala tympani are filled with a fluid called *perilymph,* which is identical in composition to, and continuous with, the cerebrospinal fluid. The duct of the cochlea is filled with *endolymph.*

Fig. 13.45   The internal auditory meatus.

The scala vestibuli communicates with the middle ear through the oval window which, as already stated, lodges the footplate of the stapes.

The membrane of the round window is interposed between the commencement of the scala tympani and the middle ear.

Resting upon the basilar membrane is a structure consisting of specialized cells of different sizes and shapes, and known as the *spiral organ* or *organ of Corti.* It and the basilar membrane follow a spiral course throughout the entire length of the duct of the cochlea. The specialized cells are the *auditory receptors;* they are elongated elements from the summits of which hairlike processes project. They are therefore called *hair cells.* The tips of the hairs are attached to, or embedded in, a thin elastic membrane—the *tectorial membrane*—which extends outward from near the attachment of the vestibular membrane and, floating in the endolymph, overlies the organ of Corti.

The *internal auditory meatus* is a short, bony canal, about 1 cm long, which runs inward from the internal ear to open into the cranial cavity. It lodges the cochlear and vestibular nerves. The outer end or bottom of the canal (Fig. 13.45) is occupied by the base of the modiolus and a perforated plate of bone. From the former, central fila-

ments of the cochlear nerve enter the meatus (see below); the perforated plate gives passage to the peripheral fibers of the vestibular
nerve (p. 631).

The auditory pathway. The nerve of hearing is known as the *cochlear nerve.* Its fibers are the processes of nerve cells in a small ganglion called the *spiral ganglion of Corti,* which occupies the spiral canal that tunnels through the center of the modiolus. Processes of the
ganglion cells are in two sets—peripheral and central. The former
pass along the spiral ledge of bone to reach the organ of Corti. They
terminate as minute filaments around the bases of the hair cells—the
receptors of hearing. The other processes, which arise from the opposite poles of the ganglion cells, pass centrally with the vestibular nerve

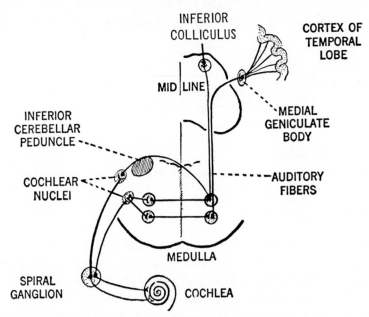

Fig. 13.46   Diagram of the auditory pathway.

in the internal auditory meatus to enter the medulla oblongata; here
they connect with groups of nerve cells (*cochlear nuclei*). Secondary
neurons ascend from here to the midbrain (*medial geniculate bodies*);
from there a third set of neurons passes to the auditory center (see
Fig. 13.46) in the cortex of the temporal lobe of the cerebrum.

Only the auditory part of the labyrinth has been described in the
foregoing paragraphs. The inner ear contains, also, the semicircular
canals and otolithic organs. These, which have no auditory function,
will be described later.

The physiology of hearing. The structure of the auditory apparatus having been sketched, we are in a position to understand the manner in which the energy of sound waves is transmitted to the auditory receptors. The outer and middle ears serve merely to transmit the sound waves to the inner ear in which the receptors are contained. The waves set up in the air by a sounding body strike the ear drum and set it into vibration. In man, the pinna and the somewhat funnel-like shape of the auditory meatus have only a slight effect in concentrating the sound waves upon the drum membrane. In many animals, however, the pinna serves an important function in this regard, being a large funnel-shaped structure which can be turned toward the source of the sound.

The vibrations set up in the tympanic membrane are transmitted across the middle ear by the auditory ossicles. The head of the malleus

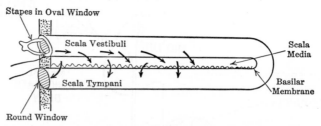

Fig. 13.47   Diagram of the passages of the cochlea straightened out to show the manner in which vibrations are transmitted from the oval to the round window through the scala media. The wavy line represents the organ of Corti.

is connected to the body of the incus in such a way that a movement inward or outward of the tympanic membrane causes a corresponding movement of the handle of the malleus, of the long process of the incus, and of the footplate of the stapes, lodged in the oval window between the middle ear and the scala vestibuli of the cochlea. Thus, movements of the tympanic membrane are transmitted through the ossicles to the inner ear. The series of inward and outward movements of the footplate of the stapes, acting like a plunger in the oval window, sets up corresponding movements in the fluid contents of the scala vestibuli. These movements are transmitted freely through the vestibular membrane to the fluid in the cochlear duct, and through the basilar membrane, in turn, to the scala tympani (Fig. 13.47). Thus, each time the footplate of the stapes is pressed into the oval window, the basilar membrane moves toward the scala tympani and pulls the processes of the hair cells fixed to the tectorial membrane; when the stapes moves outward, the tension on the hair cells is relieved. Thus, by a series of mechanical stimuli, impulses are set up in the terminals of the auditory nerve. The round window, situated between the scala tympani and the middle ear, permits free movements of the contents of the inner ear. Since liquids are incompressible, no movement of the stapes could occur, of course, were there no other part of the bony wall of the cochlea which yielded to pressure.

The auditory ossicles are connected to one another in such a way as to constitute a small lever (see Fig. 13.48). The handle of the mal-

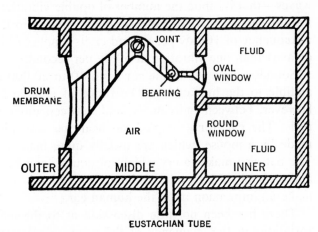

Fig. 13.48 A mechanical model illustrating the transmission of sound waves through the middle ear. The lever represents the chain of auditory ossicles.

leus, attached to the tympani membrane, forms the long arm of the lever; the long process of the incus is the short arm. The long arm is one and a half times the length of the short arm. The movement of the long process of the incus (and of the stapes with which it connects) is, therefore, only two thirds as great as that of the tympanic membrane. We should expect, on the other hand, that the force exerted by the stapes at the oval window would be one and a half times greater than that applied to the handle of the malleus. But, on account of a large proportion of the energy being lost in transmission (due to inertia of the ossicles and friction of the air surrounding them), only about half of the force exerted upon the handle of the malleus reaches the oval window. However, the area of the tympanic membrane is nearly twenty times that of the oval window; this fact alone, were there no loss of energy in transmission, would cause the force concentrated at the oval window to be increased twentyfold over that of the vibrations of the drum membrane. Now, as just mentioned, the force transmitted to the stapes is only one half of that applied to the malleus; the net magnification of the force exerted by the movements of the footplate of the stapes, brought about through the mechanism of the middle ear, is, therefore, about ten.

The appreciation of pitch (discrimination of the frequency of the sound waves). Sound is transmitted from a vibrating body to the ear as a series of alternating condensations and rarefactions of the atmosphere. The disturbance in the air travels as a succession of waves. A complete wave—that is, from the crest or trough of one wave to the corresponding phase of the other—is referred to as a *double vibration* (dv) or a *cycle*. The pitch of a tone depends upon the frequency of the waves—that is, upon the number of double vibrations or cycles reaching the ear per second. For example, a tuning fork which vibrates at a frequency of 100 dv per second emits a note of higher pitch (by an octave) than one vibrating at 50 dv per second.

Sounds ranging in frequency from 40 to 20,000 dv per second are audible to the human ear. The range of audible frequencies varies, however, between individuals, and between different species of animals. The cat, for example, can hear the very high-pitched sounds made by a mouse, which are usually quite inaudible to human ears. The bat also makes a cry which, of course, can be heard by its kind, and probably also by other animals, but which is of a pitch too high to make an impression upon the human ear.

There has been no little discussion as to the mechanism whereby variations in the frequency of the sound waves striking the ear are converted into messages which the brain interprets as differences in pitch. The two classical theories are *the resonance theory of Helmholtz* and *the telephone theory of Rutherford*.

The resonance theory states that the basilar membrane, like the wires of a piano, is a scale of resonators. If the dampers of a piano are raised and a note sung near it, a tone of the same pitch is given out by the instrument. Those wires of the piano alone vibrate which, if struck, would themselves have emitted the same note. This well-known phenomenon is called *sympathetic resonance*. The basilar membrane contains some 24,000 fibers. These so-called *auditory strings* increase progressively in length from the base to the apex of the cochlea. Each fiber, or a group of fibers of a given length, vibrates in unison, it is supposed, with vibrations of a particular frequency transmitted to them from the drum membrane; the short tense fibers at the base of the cochlea vibrate to high notes, and the longer, more lax fibers at the apex to low notes. Of course, only those hair cells overlying the fibers which are set into sympathetic vibration are stimulated.

The resonance theory, therefore, *claims that the analysis of sound is a function of the cochlea, the particular region of the latter from which the nerve impulses are discharged being the sole basis upon which the brain rests its faculty of pitch discrimination.* The resonance theory is supported by a number of facts. (a) When the ears of animals (e.g., guinea pigs and rabbits) are subjected to prolonged stimulation by a loud high- or low-pitched tone, degenerative changes are produced in the basal or the apical portion, respectively, of the organ of Corti. (b) Boiler-makers or others who work among clanging noises sometimes become deaf to high tones (*boiler-maker's disease*); the organ of Corti in the basal turns of the cochlea is found to have degenerated. (c) Destruction of the apical part of the cochlea in animals results in deafness to tones of low frequency; injury to the basal part causes deafness to high tones. (d) The structure of the cochlear duct with its basilar membrane strongly suggests that it acts as a resonator, and recent experimental work has provided direct evidence of such a function.

When the ear is stimulated by a sound, the vibrations of the organ of Corti set up rhythmical changes in electrical potential within the cochlea (*Wever and Bray effect*). When amplified and recorded graphically, these are found to have exactly the same frequency as that of the sound. Indeed, if the electric currents are conducted to a loud speaker the original sound is faithfully reproduced. With low notes, the potential changes are greatest in the apical turns of the cochlea; with high notes, in the basal turns, thus demonstrating clearly the resonating function of the cochlea.

But the electrical effects do not represent nerve impulses originating in the terminals of the cochlear nerve; they are due to movements with consequent pressure changes in the basilar membrane and organ of Corti set up by the sound waves. The mechanical energy (pressure) is transformed to electric energy—a *piezoelectric effect* (Gk. *piezo,* I press).

The telephone or frequency theory. In a telephone system the transmitting instrument converts the sound waves into electrical impulses of the same frequency. Upon reaching the receiver, the electric impulses set up vibrations which reproduce the original sound. The telephone theory of hearing postulates that the basilar membrane does not vibrate selectively in the manner demanded by the resonance theory, but as a whole, in unison with the vibrations transmitted to it from the drum membrane. The frequency of the impulses caused by stimulating the hair cells corresponds with that of the vibrations of the basilar membrane, and, consequently, with that of the sound waves.

The telephone theory *claims, therefore, that the cochlea possesses no power of sound analysis, and that such is purely a function of the brain, the frequency of the impulses received by the auditory center being the basis for the discrimination of pitch.*

The telephone theory as originally proposed is faced with the objection that the maximum frequency at which impulses can be transmitted by a nerve fiber is about 1000 per second, whereas, sounds with frequencies up to 20,000 dv per second are audible. But the auditory nerve consists, of course, of a large number of fibers, and it has been proposed that the impulses are discharged over the separate fibers, not synchronously, but in a scattered volley. That is, some fibers are in their refractory phase (p. 574) while others are conducting. Thus, it is possible for a group of fibers to transmit impulses in "broken step" at frequencies as high as, or even higher than 20,000 per second. Nevertheless, the *volley theory,* as this amplification of the telephone theory is called, does not fit all the facts; it fails to explain the *appreciation* of tones having a vibration frequency higher than about 3000 per second. For example, the action potentials set up by a sound and recorded (p. 469) from the auditory tracts in the brain have exactly the same frequency as that of the sound up to 1000 dv per second. Between 1000 and 2000 dv per second, one impulse occurs for every two sound vibrations, and one for every three between 2000 and 3000 dv per second; but at *higher frequencies* (between 3000 and 20,000 dv per second) there is no relationship.

As a general theory of pitch discrimination, the telephone or frequency theory is unsatisfactory. The resonance or harp theory is now generally accepted. To summarize: The cross fibers or "strings" of the basilar membrane, according to the principle of sympathetic resonance, vibrate at different levels (base to apex) of the cochlea as determined by the frequency of the sound waves reaching the internal ear. Thus, the short tense fibers in the basal turns vibrate in unison or "sympathy" with sound waves of high frequency (high pitched or treble tones); the longer fibers at the apex respond to sound waves of low frequency (low pitched or bass tones). The basilar fibers between these two extremes vibrate to tones of intermediate pitch from treble to bass. The vibrations of the fibers at any particular level of the basilar membrane stimulate the auditory receptors, and thus set up impulses in the nerve terminals in the hair cells at that place alone. The modern resonance theory is, therefore, also spoken of as the *place theory.* Just as we know at once the precise spot on the skin which is stimulated when we feel a touch at that spot, so we are able to discriminate between impulses arising from the different levels of the basilar membrane. But the actual stimulated place in the basilar membrane is not perceived as we perceive the position of a stimulated point on the skin. The different levels of stimulation are interpreted by the brain as differences in pitch. Such localization is possible because each and every level of the cochlea is connected by nerve fibers with a particular group of nerve cells arranged in regular order in the auditory center—

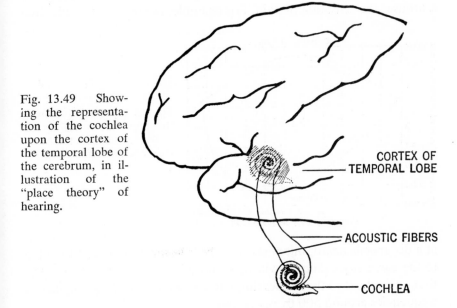

Fig. 13.49   Showing the representation of the cochlea upon the cortex of the temporal lobe of the cerebrum, in illustration of the "place theory" of hearing.

CORTEX OF TEMPORAL LOBE

ACOUSTIC FIBERS

COCHLEA

that is, in the cortex of the temporal lobe of the cerebrum (see Fig. 13.49). In other words, each point upon the basilar membrane is represented by a corresponding point in the cerebral cortex.

Intensity and loudness of sound. The power transmitted through the atmosphere from a sounding body is referred to as the intensity of the sound. Sound intensity is expressed as the quantity of energy, in microwatts, passing per second through an area of 1 square centimeter. The greater the intensity of the sound, the greater, of course, will be the amplitude of the movements of the drum membrane and, generally speaking, the louder will be the sound. But the ear does not possess the same sensitivity at all frequencies. Within the range of from 1000 to 2000 dv per second, the lowest intensity (*intensity threshold*) is required to arouse an auditory sensation, and a sound of any given intensity is loudest. The sensitivity of hearing—i.e., the loudness of a sound of a given intensity—diminishes progressively as the frequency is increased above 2000 dv per second or reduced below 1000 dv per second (see Fig. 13.50). In other words, the *threshold of hearing* is lowest for sounds with frequencies around 2000 dv per second. It will be appreciated from these remarks that intensity and loudness are not synonymous terms. The intensity of sound is an absolute physical value, whereas the loudness of sound is a matter of auditory perception.

As the intensity of the sound increases, other sense organs than those of hearing are stimulated. We *feel* the sound, and, if very intense, it arouses the sensation of pain. For example, the report of a rifle fired

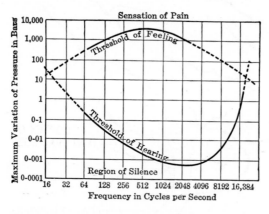

Fig. 13.50 Chart showing the thresholds of hearing and feeling of sound at different frequencies. (After Wegel.)

at a distance is heard, but at short range is felt as well and, if too close to the ear, causes pain. It will be seen that the chart in Figure 13.50 that, in contrast to that of hearing, the *threshold of feeling* is highest at frequencies around 500 dv per second.

Defective hearing, deafness. Deafness is a rather indefinite term, but is usually taken to mean defective hearing of such a degree that ordinary conversation cannot be heard distinctly and without difficulty. It varies greatly in degree from dullness of hearing, the subject being unable to recognize words spoken by another in his usual voice, to complete loss of hearing. As a rule, the hearing defect is not equal for tones of every pitch. In some types of deafness, hearing loss affects, mainly or solely, the higher sound frequencies, in others, the lower frequencies.

Classification of deafness. There are three main types of deafness called, respectively, *transmission deafness, perceptive or nerve deafness,* and *central deafness.* Any condition of the external or middle ear which prevents the sound waves from being transmitted without interference is called transmission deafness. Thus inflammation, with destruction of the structures of the middle ear, plugging of the outer ear with wax, or closure of the auditory tube, will cause some degree of deafness. Fixation of the footplate of the stapes in the oval window by hardened tissue blocks the transmission of the sound waves to the cochlea and is also a frequent cause of deafness. When the auditory tube is blocked, the middle ear becomes a hermetically sealed cavity. The air within it soon becomes absorbed and, as a consequence, the pressure on the inner side of the drum membrane is much less than that of the atmosphere. The membrane is pushed inward against the inner bony wall of the middle ear and, therefore, cannot vibrate freely. Temporary blockage of the auditory tube often occurs with a cold, as a result of swelling of the lining of its mucous membrane. Inequality of pressure on the two sides of the drum membrane is brought about also, in a somewhat different way, in airplane descents. The middle ear is filled with air at the lower pressure of the atmosphere at the high altitude; when the plane reaches the ground, the atmospheric pressure at this level, being much higher, pushes the drum membrane inward. This event is usually guarded against by chewing gum during the descent which, since it stimulates salivary secretion, induces swallowing. Swallowing, in turn, opens the mouths of the auditory tubes in the pharynx and permits air to enter the middle ear from time to time, and thus equal pressures are maintained on the two sides of the drum membrane.

If descent from a high altitude is made too rapidly, and swallowing fails to allow air to enter the auditory tubes, rupture of one or of both eardrums may occur; the higher outside (atmospheric) pressure would be unable to force air upward into the middle ears through the closed pharyngeal ends of the tubes, and thus to equalize the pressures on the inner and outer sides of the tympanic membranes.

In rapid airplane *ascents,* on the other hand, the higher pressure within the middle ear is reduced from time to time by the air forcing open the sphincter muscle around the opening of the auditory tube. In other words, the sphincter can be forced from within but not from without.

Perception deafness is due to disease or injury of the cochlear structures or of the cochlear nerve itself.

Central deafness is caused by a lesion—e.g., a tumor, abscess, or injury of the auditory tracts or of the auditory cortical centers.

Testing defective hearing. Hearing is tested (in a room as nearly silent as possible) by means of a series of tuning forks of graded vibration frequencies held at varying distances from the subject's ear. Or an instrument known as an *audiometer* is used, by means of which tones are produced electrically which can be very precisely varied as to pitch and intensity. The results are plotted on graph paper similar to that shown in Figure 13.51. Such a record is called an *audiogram*. In this instance, hearing is defective only over a limited range of sound frequencies.

The nonauditory part of the labyrinth—the organ of equilibrium. The inner ear contains another organ besides the cochlea, consisting of three *semicircular canals* and two small sacs, called, respectively, the *utricle* and the *saccule*. The semicircular canals and the utricle have no auditory function, being concerned solely with the maintenance of the equilibrium of the body (see Fig. 13.52).

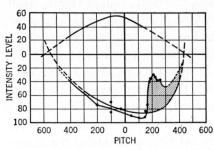

Fig. 13.51 An audiogram. The shaded area indicates the area over which hearing is defective.

The semicircular canals are membranous tubes filled with fluid known as the *endolymph*. They are contained within semicircular tunnels in the temporal bone—the osseous canals—but separated from the bone by *perilymph*. The three canals lie approximately at right angles to one another, one in each of the three dimensions of space. Two canals are vertical, one horizontal. The two vertical canals (superior and posterior) are placed diagonally in relation to the anteroposterior diameter of the skull; the convexity of one is directed outward and backward, of the other outward and forward (see Figs. 13.52 and 13.53), and that of the horizontal (lateral) canal, outward. One end of each canal is dilated into a fusiform swelling called the *ampulla*. A small elevation, called the *crista,* is situated in each of the three ampullae. This is composed of cells with bristlelike processes—the *hair* cells—surmounted by a cap of gelatinous material called the *cupula*. The cristae are the sense organs (proprioceptors) of the canals. Both ends of each canal open into the utricle.

The utricle and saccule are oval membranous sacs measuring (in man) about ⅛ inch in their longest diameters. They are contained within an oval cavity in the bone, called the *vestibule,* situated between the cochlea and the semicircular canals. The utricle, as just mentioned, communicates with the semicircular canals, the saccule connects through a narrow canal with the duct of the cochlea. The utricle and saccule are indirectly connected through a narrow Y-shaped tube

(Fig. 13.52). The entire membranous labyrinth, auditory and non-auditory, thus forms a continuous system of communicating passages and chambers. The utricle and saccule each contains a sense organ called the *macula;* this is a plaque of hair cells covered by a layer of a gelatinous substance. Adherent to the latter are a number of crystals of

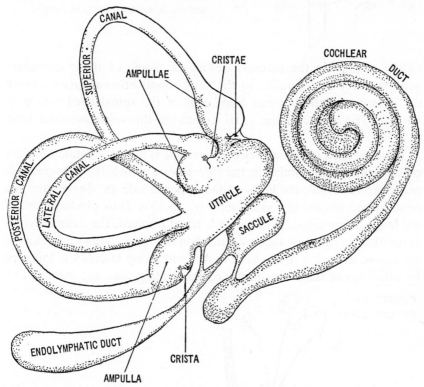

Fig. 13.52   The membranous labyrinth.

carbonate of lime, known as *otoliths* (ear stones) or *otoconia* (ear dust).

The pathway for impulses from the semicircular canals. Impulses from this part of the labyrinth are carried by fibers of the *vestibular nerve*—the other division of the acoustic nerve. Its fibers, like those of the cochlear nerve, are in two sets, peripheral and central, and are processes of cells in the *vestibular (Scarpa's) ganglion* which forms a swelling on the nerve at the bottom of the internal auditory meatus. The peripheral set of fibers ends around the bases of the sensitive hair cells of the semicircular canals, utricle, and saccule. The central processes (fibers) of the ganglion cells connect with groups of cells (*ves-*

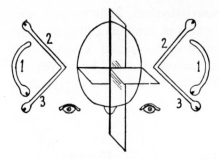

Fig. 13.53 Showing the positions of the semicircular canals in relation to the vertical planes (anteroposterior and transverse) of the skull. 1, horizontal canals; 2, posterior vertical canals; 3, anterior vertical canals.

tibular nuclei) in the medulla oblongata. Some of these secondary neurons carry the impulses to the cerebellum; other neurons convey the impulses to the anterior horn cells of the spinal cord (see Fig. 13.54). The axons of the latter constitute the vestibulospinal tract (p. 528).

The functions of the semicircular canals. If a frog is rotated rapidly on a turntable, the limbs on the side toward which the movement is made are extended; the limbs of the opposite side are flexed, and the head turned toward this side (see Fig. 13.55). Thus displacement of the body is prevented. If the table is tilted forward, the animal avoids being thrown upon its face by extention of its forelimbs; a backward tilt causes extension of the hind limbs; and tilting laterally is followed by extension of the limbs on the corresponding side, accompanied by

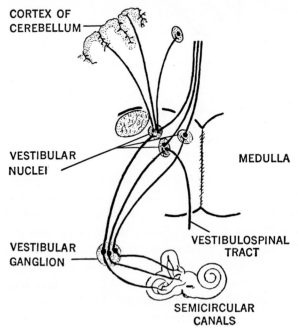

CORTEX OF
CEREBELLUM

VESTIBULAR
NUCLEI

MEDULLA

VESTIBULAR
GANGLION

VESTIBULOSPINAL
TRACT

SEMICIRCULAR
CANALS

Fig. 13.54   The pathway for the transmission of impulses from the semicircular canals. The vestibular ganglion appears as a swelling upon the vestibular nerve as it lies in the internal auditory meatus.

flexion of the opposite pair of limbs.
These reflex reactions, whereby the animal resists being upset from its "normal"
position by some unusual movement, are
the result of stimulation of the end organs
of the semicircular canals. Impulses initiated in the cristae are transmitted to the
vestibular nuclei in the medulla oblongata, and thence relayed to the cerebellum and, by the vestibulospinal tracts, to
the cord. The reactions resulting from rotation in the horizontal plane are due to
stimulation of the horizontal pair of ca-

Fig. 13.55 Position taken
up by a frog during rotation
to the left. (After Ewald.)

nals; those caused by tilting forward or backward, or laterally (i.e.,
by a rotary movement in the plane, approximately, of one or other
pair of vertical canals), are due to stimulation of the cristae of the
corresponding canals. The movement causes a mechanical stimulus to
be applied to the hair cells of the cristae. When the head is rotated
in the plane of one or other pair of canals, the endolymph, owing to
its *inertia,* exerts a momentary pressure which bends the hair cells of
the canal on the side away from which the rotation is made. For the
same reason, the pressure upon the hair cells of the canal of the opposite ear is reduced. The effects upon the two ears, though opposite in
nature, act conjointly in initiating the reflex muscular movement.

Fig. 13.56 Showing en-
dolymph movement dur-
ing and after rotation.
Upper drawing, during
rotation, large arrows indicate the direction of
rotation; small arrows,
the endolymph move-
ment. *Lower drawing,*
after rotation. (After
Best and Taylor, *The
Physiological Basis of
Medical Practice.*)

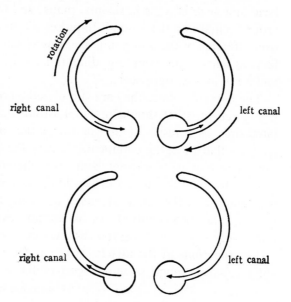

Stimulation of the semicircular canals also causes movements of the eyes. When, for example, a person is rotated rapidly with the head erect—i.e., approximately in the plane of the horizontal canals—the eyes are observed to make a series of rhythmical side to side movements after the rotation has ceased. These to and fro movements, which are termed *nystagmus*, are due to the *momentum* of the endolymph. That is, the endolymph movement continues for an instant after the rotation of the head has ceased, and thus exerts pressure upon the crista of the canal on one side (see Fig. 13.56); the pressure on the hair cells of the canal of the opposite ear is diminished. It is clear that the effects following rotation will be the reverse of those occurring at the commencement of rotation. If the head is bent forward, backward, or onto one shoulder during the rotation, the vertical canals are stimulated. The nystagmus which follows rotation in these positions of the head is not horizontal; the eyes move either up and down (vertical nystagmus) or show a rotary movement (rotary nystagmus), according to which particular pair of vertical canals was in the plane of the rotation.

Other effects follow stimulation of the semicircular canals by a rapid rotary motion. Everyone is familiar with the sensation of dizziness, or *vertigo,* and the staggering gait which result from spinning (stimulation of horizontal canals). A more pronounced disturbance of the equilibrium sense follows stimulation of the vertical canals; this may be demonstrated simply upon oneself by bending over, so as to bring the head and neck into the horizontal plane, and then circling a few times around a mark on the ground. Impulses set up in the canals may travel over efferents of the autonomic nervous system causing such reflex effects as nausea and vomiting, dilatation of the pupil, sweating, pallor, and a fall in blood pressure.

The hair cells, since they are stimulated by rotary motion, are called *rotary receptors.* It should be emphasized that the cristae are stimulated only as a result of the inertia or the momentum of the endolymph—that is, at the commencement or the termination of the rotation. The hair cells are not bent after the rotary movement is well started, for then the inertia of the fluid has been overcome and moves with the wall of the canal. Means of detecting a *continuous* rotary motion have not been evolved, for we are not, except perhaps rarely and under very unusual circumstances, ever exposed to it.[6]

The functions of the utricle. Whereas the receptors of the semicircular canals respond to *movements* of the head, the *position* of the

---

[6] We must, of course, exclude from this statement the rotation of the earth.

head is the factor responsible for excitation of the hair cells of the utricular maculae. The canals are organs of *kinetic* sense, the utricles of *static* sense. Two types of equilibrium reactions—the *righting* and *attitudinal* reflexes—are dependent upon the utricles.

The righting reflexes. When an animal is placed upon its back, it immediately rights itself. The head is first brought into its "normal" position in space by a contraction of the neck muscles, the body follows,

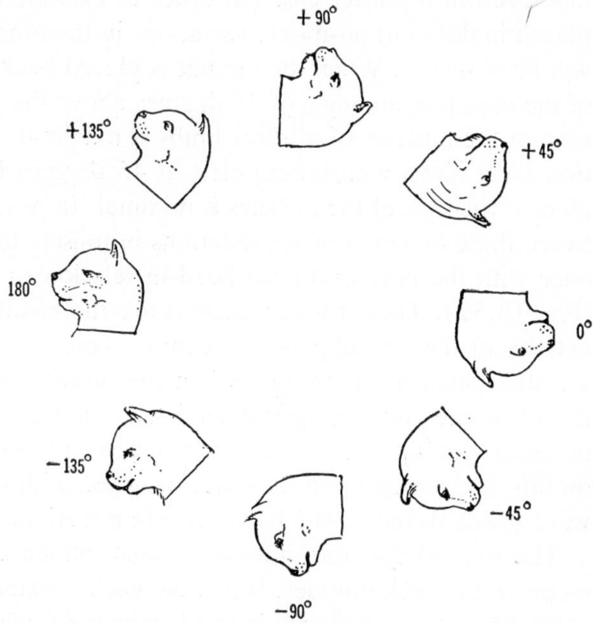

Fig. 13.57 The positions of an animal's head, each marked with the angle which the mouth cleft makes with the horizontal plane. (Drawn from photographs after Magnus.)

being brought into its normal relationship with the head by contractions of the trunk and limb muscles. The movement of the neck muscles, whereby the head is righted, is dependent upon the sense organ of the utricle; it is, therefore, called the *labyrinthine righting reflex;* the center for this reflex is in the midbrain. When the head is in the wrong position, mouth looking upward, the otoliths adhering to the maculae hang downward; the tension which their weight exerts upon the hair cells acts as a stimulus to the sensitive hair cells. The movement of the neck stimulates, in turn, proprioceptors in the neck muscles, through which the reflex righting movements of the trunk and limbs are initiated. These movements of the trunk and limb muscles, caused by stimulation of proprioceptors in the neck muscles, are termed *neck reflexes.* Their center is situated in the upper cervical segments of the spinal cord.

The importance of the righting reflexes in man is evident if one considers how a swimmer, after diving into deep water, orients himself without difficulty and rises to the surface. The other senses (e.g., vision or touch) can give him little or no information of his position in space. He relies upon his utricles to bring his head "right side up." Deaf mutes, whose labyrinths as a whole are not developed, run a grave risk, even though they be good swimmers, if plunged into deep water.

Attitudinal reflexes. When a decerebrate animal, with its neck immobilized in a plaster cast (in order to exclude the neck reflexes) is placed in different positions, variations in the tone of the limb muscles will be observed. When the animal is placed back down with the cleft of the mouth at an angle of 45 degrees above the horizontal plane, the tone of the muscles of all four limbs is maximal; in the opposite position (feet down with mouth cleft at 45 degrees below the horizontal plane), the tone of the muscles is minimal. In positions of the head between these two extremes, gradations in muscle tone result, in accordance with the position of the head in relation to the horizontal plane (Fig. 13.57). These tonus reactions are the result of variations in the activity of the utricular proprioceptors (maculae). The sense organs are stimulated most strongly when the otoliths are hanging from the maculae—i.e., pulling upon the hairs, as when the animal is on its back or on its feet with snout pointing upward (neck extended); when the otoliths are resting upon the maculae—i.e., with snout pointing downward (neck flexed)—the hair cells are not stimulated.

The tone of the limb muscles is also influenced reflexly by movements of the neck muscles. When the neck is extended, the tone of the extensor muscles of the *forelimbs* is increased, while the extensor tone of the *hind limbs* is reduced. Flexion of the neck causes the reverse effects—namely, decreased tone of the forelimb extensors together with increased tone of the extensors of the hind limbs. The neck reflexes are studied best after the vestibular nerves have been severed and the utricular reflexes thus abolished.

Though the attitudinal reflexes are most readily demonstrated in the decerebrate preparation, they constitute an important mechanism controlling the posture of the normal animal. Otolithic and neck reflexes cooperate to facilitate various postural adjustments. When a cat, for example, turns its head to look upward at a piece of food on a shelf, the otolithic organ is stimulated with a consequent tendency for the extensor tone of all four limbs to increase. The neck reflex initiated by the extension of the neck reinforces the otolithic influence on the forelimbs; but the effect of the neck movement upon the hind limbs is the reverse of that of the utricle. The influence of the neck movement upon

Fig. 13.58   Drawings of a normal cat, showing the animal's posture (*above*) when its attention is attracted by an object placed above it. Photograph of the same animal (*below*) when its attention is drawn to an object below it. The difference between the two positions of the forelimbs is very marked, because in them the neck and labyrinthine reflexes reinforce one another; the difference in the position of the hind limbs is not so great, since the two sets of reflexes oppose one another. (Drawn from photographs after Magnus.)

the hind limbs, however, predominates so that the animal assumes a sitting posture with forelimbs extended and hind limbs flexed. On the other hand, when the animal lowers its head to look beneath a cupboard, the otolithic influence reduces the extensor tone in all four limbs; but the neck movement, though it also reduces the extensor tone of the forelimbs and thus acts in conjunction with the labyrinthine effect, antagonizes and predominates over the labyrinthine influence upon the hind limbs. The animal, therefore, assumes an attitude with flexed forelimbs and extended hind limbs—an appropriate posture of the body for that particular position of the head (see Fig. 13.58).

The hair cells of the utricular maculae, since they are stimulated by the weight and consequently the pull of the otoliths, are called *gravity receptors*. Seasickness and other forms of motion sickness are due to the intermittent and erratic stimulation of these receptors by the sudden changes in the positions of the head.

Taste

Smell and taste are chemical senses—that is, the receptors (chemoreceptors) respond to chemical stimuli. In order for a substance to arouse the sensation of taste, it must first be dissolved—either taken in solution or dissolved in the saliva; a solid placed in a perfectly dry mouth cannot be tasted.

The organs and nerves of taste. The anterior two thirds of the upper surface (dorsum) of the tongue is beset with minute projections of the mucous membrane, called *papillae*. The papillae at the edges, tip, and more anterior part of the dorsum of the tongue are very small conical, cylindrical, or mushroom-shaped structures. They give a velvety character to this part of the lingual mucosa. In accordance with their form, they are called *filiform* or *fungiform papillae*. The more posterior

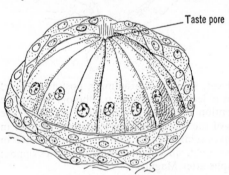

Taste pore

Fig. 13.59   A taste bud.

part of the tongue's surface is rougher owing to the presence of much larger papillae. These are of peculiar construction; each is surrounded by a groove or trench, the whole structure resembling a squat little tower within a moat. They are therefore called *vallate papillae* (L. *vallum,* a rampart) (see Pl. 15A).

Embedded in the covering of the papillae (both large and small types) are groups of slender cells provided with hairlike processes, packed lengthwise into bundles. The cells are the receptors of taste, the bundles which they compose are called *taste buds* (Figs. 13.59 and 13.60). Each cell receives a filament from one of the nerves of taste. The taste bud opens upon the surface of the papilla through a small pore. The ends of the cells converge toward this point, where their processes become massed together.

Substances in solution enter the pores and act as chemical stimuli. A few scattered taste buds are present on the extreme posterior part of the tongue and even in the mucosa of the epiglottis. These later receive fibers from the vagus nerve.

The fundamental sensations of taste are four in number—*sweet, bitter, sour,* and *salty;* two others—namely, *alkaline* and *metallic* tastes—are sometimes included with these. The various other tastes which we experience are due (a) to the blending of some one or other of the fundamental sensations, or (b) to the combination of the latter with sensations caused by the stimulation of the ordinary nerves of the

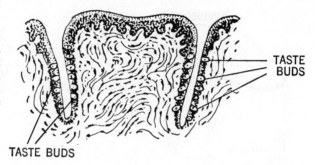

Fig. 13.60 Section of a vallate papilla of the tongue. A taste bud is shown enlarged in Figure 13.59.

TASTE BUDS

TASTE BUDS

mouth. For example, ginger is recognized not only by its actual taste (i.e., by the stimulation of the taste buds), but from the burning sensation which results from excitation of the ordinary sensory nerves of the mouth. Oils are unpleasant to take, largely because of their "feel." Acetic and many other acids, as well as having a sour taste, give rise to an astringent or burning sensation which is confused in consciousness with the sense of taste and blended with it.

Many of the finer flavors are in reality sensations of smell (p. 640), and smell enters largely into the many sensations which we attribute generally to taste. For this reason, when the nose is held or the nasal mucous membrane is inflamed, as by an ordinary cold, the sense of taste is blunted. On the other hand, certain substances which we think we detect by smell are actually recognized by the sense of taste. The sweetish smell of chloroform is an example, the vapor reaching the taste buds in the inspired air.

The four fundamental taste sensations are not aroused with equal intensity over all parts of the surface of the tongue. Each type of taste sensation is served by its own kind of taste bud. Taste receptors sensitive to sweetness and to saltiness are most numerous at the tip and forepart of the tongue, whereas those responding to sourness are found along the edges (Pl. 15A). The taste buds causing a bitter sensation are scattered over the back of the tongue and epiglottis. A bitter-sweet substance (such as sodium salicylate), when first taken into the mouth, tastes sweet, the bitter element being noticeable only after the substance has passed over the posterior part of the tongue. Little or no sensation of taste can be aroused from the central portion of the tongue's surface.

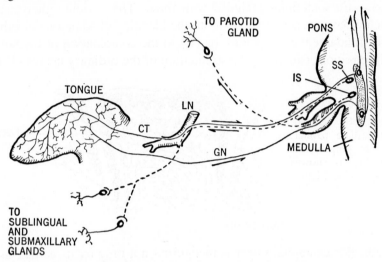

Fig. 13.61   Pathway for the transmission of taste impulses. CT, chorda tympani nerve; GN, glossopharyngeal nerve; IS, superior salivatory nucleus; LN, lingual nerve; SS, superior salivatory nucleus; efferent (secretory fibers), interrupted lines; afferent (taste) fibers, continuous lines.

The sense of taste is much less sensitive than the sense of smell. Sweetness, for example, is detected in a dilution of 1 part in 200, saltiness (common salt) 1 part in 400, sourness (hydrochloric acid) 1 part in 130,000, and bitterness (quinine) 1 part in 2,000,000.

The chief *nerves of taste* are the *chorda tympani* branch of the facial nerve, and the *glossopharyngeal* nerve. The chorda tympani supplies taste fibers to the anterior two thirds of the tongue, the glossopharyngeal to the posterior third (Fig. 13.61). The fibers of the chorda tympani nerve are conveyed to the tongue in the trunk of the lingual nerve (a branch of the mandibular division of the trigeminal nerve). The center for taste lies at the lower end of the somesthetic area of the cerebral cortex.

Smell

Smell is very closely allied to taste and has been aptly described as "taste from a distance." In many animals the sense of smell is almost incredibly acute, a large proportion of the brain being concerned with this sense. In such species the sense of smell is of paramount importance, warning the animal of the approach of its enemies, and guiding it in the quest for food. Even in man, in whom the sense of smell is comparatively rudimentary, certain substances, such as mercaptan, can be detected in a dilution of 1 part in 30 billion or more parts of air.

An odorous material continually emits particles of molecular size which are carried in the air to the olfactory receptors. Substances which pass readily into the gaseous state such as turpentine, gasoline, and the

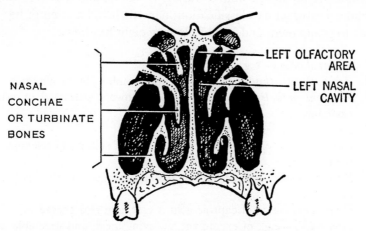

NASAL
CONCHAE
OR TURBINATE
BONES

LEFT OLFACTORY
AREA

LEFT NASAL
CAVITY

Fig. 13.62   Vertical transverse section through the nasal cavities to show position of the olfactory area.

essential oils have, in general, strong odors; whereas nonvolatile materials—e.g., the heavy metals—are relatively inodorous. A substance in order to be smelled must reach the nose in gaseous form.

The mucous membrane on each side of the nose is raised into three ridges by three spurs of bone (the *superior, middle,* and *inferior turbinates* or *conchae*) which spring from the outer nasal wall. The interior of the nose is thus divided incompletely on each side into four compartments or regions placed one above the other (see Fig. 13.62 and Fig. 6.3, p. 227). The lower three of these serve as air passages; they communicate with the outside through the nostrils and behind with the pharynx. The uppermost compartment is a narrow cleft lying immediately beneath the anterior part of the floor of the skull. The olfactory receptors are embedded in a small patch of mucous membrane situated on each wall of this narrow space, which is a blind pocket from which the main air currents are excluded. Air containing the odorous particles must therefore be carried to the olfactory mucous membrane either by diffusion or by convection currents set up when the inspired air meets the warmer air within the nose. When, for example, we wish to smell some particular scent, we make a quick short inspiration or "sniff." This sharp indrawing of the cooler outside air creates ascending (convection) currents which convey the scent to the sensitive area. The material does not act directly upon the olfactory receptors, but is first dissolved in the layer of fluid covering the mucous membrane—a fact which emphasizes the similarity between the senses of taste and smell.

There are an almost infinite variety of odors, and it is very difficult to make a satisfactory classification; nevertheless, an attempt has been made to group them under the following eight headings:

1. *Ethereal odors*—e.g., of fruits
2. *Aromatic* or *resinous odors*—e.g., of camphor, bitter almonds
3. *Fragrant* or *balsamic odors*—e.g., of flowers, extracted or artificial perfumes
4. *Ambrosial odors*—e.g., of musk
5. *Garlic odors*—e.g., of garlic, onions, and of sulfur and selenium compounds
6. *Burning odors*—e.g., of burning feathers, tobacco, roasted coffee, and meats
7. *Goat odors*—e.g., of caproic acid, sweat, and ripe cheese
8. *Foul odors*—e.g., of excrement, decaying meat, and vegetable matter

It is not possible to correlate the chemical nature of substances with the odors which they emit, for materials quite different in their chemical constitution may have similar odors, while others closely similar chemically may have quite different smells. Certain sensations which we usually class as olfactory, such as those aroused by pungent and acrid substances, are in fact due to the stimulation of the common nerves of the nasal mucous membrane.

√The olfactory epithelium is composed of spindle-shaped nerve cells distributed evenly among other elongated cells which are purely supporting in function. Both types of cell lie perpendicular to the epithelial surface (see Fig. 13.63). The nerve cells, or *olfactory receptors,* give rise to two types of process—an axon and a modified dendrite. The axons spring from the deep aspects of the cells and, combining in groups, form a number of slender bundles called the *fila olfactoria.* The dendrites are thick cylindrical processes; they penetrate, individually, to the surface through small gaps between the free ends of the supporting cells; except for these gaps, the supporting cells are joined together to form a continuous covering. Each dendrite, after emerging from between the supporting cells, divides into a tuft of some six or eight straight filaments which project a short distance beyond the epithelial surface. The fila olfactoria pass up through perforations in the floor of the skull and enter the olfactory bulb (Fig. 12.32), the *primary olfactory center*. Here, the axons of the olfactory receptors syn-

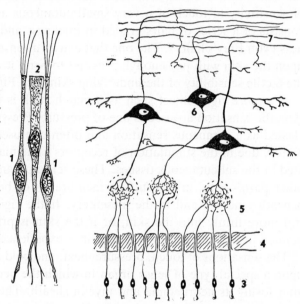

Fig. 13.63   Connections of the olfactory fibers in the olfactory bulb. *Left,* 1, receptors in olfactory mucous membrane; 2, supporting cells. *Right,* 3, olfactory receptors; 4, olfactory nerves entering the cranial cavity through perforations in the bone; 5, connections with mitral cells; 6, mitral cells.

apse with other neurons (mitral cells) which convey the impulses to the cortical center for smell situated in the hippocampal gyrus.

The olfactory receptors adapt rapidly—that is, they soon cease to respond to some particular stimulus. It is common experience that an odor, though strong when first smelled, becomes imperceptible after a short time. This phenomenon of adaptation—a property which the olfactory sense organs exhibit in common with several other types of receptors—should not be confused with fatigue. That it is not simply a matter of fatigue of the olfactory mechanism is evident from the fact that, when some particular odor is no longer smelled, another odor is readily perceived. Some persons are unable to smell certain odors at all, though there is no general impairment of the olfactory sense. Hydrocyanic gas, for example, a powerful poison used in the extermination of vermin, has a strong odor of bitter almonds, but is quite inodorous to a few people.

Cutaneous Sensations

The sensations which can be aroused by stimulating the skin are five in number—namely, *touch, pressure, pain, heat,* and *cold.* Touch may be defined as the sensation elicited by lightly brushing the skin with a wisp of cotton wool, or by pressing a stiff hair vertically upon the skin until it bends. The latter method is used to test the degree of sensitivity to touch of a very small cutaneous area. The apparatus consists of a series of hairs graded in thickness and, therefore, in stiffness (von Frey's hairs). The one that causes a sensation, when pressed upon the skin with just enough pressure to bend it, gives a measure of the tactile sensibility of the underlying skin (see Fig. 13.64).

If a more rigid object such as a match stick is pressed against the skin, the sensation aroused is one of pressure. Pressure, though usually classed as a cutaneous sensation and often confused with touch, is, in reality, due to the stimulation of receptors (Pacinian corpuscles) situated in the subcutaneous tissues. These sense organs are also found in other parts—e.g., in the surface membranes of bones (periosteum), beneath tendons, and in the mesentery. If the rigid object is pressed still more firmly into the skin, or if the skin is pricked with a sharp pointed instrument such as a pin, pain is experienced.

The sensations of touch, pressure, heat, and cold are each dependent upon a special type of sense organ in which the nerve fiber terminates after losing its neurilemma and myelin sheath. The sensation of pain, on the other hand, is transmitted by fibers which terminate as bare axis cylinders. That is, the nerve fiber mediating pain loses its neurilemma and myelin sheath, but does not end in a structure of special design. The receptors of touch, pressure, and temperature each respond to one type of stimulus, but the nerve endings giving rise to pain respond also to any other type of stimulation—mechanical, thermal, electrical, or chemical—provided it is intense enough. Thus the sensation of pain is protective in function, serving to signal a threat of injury to the body. The several types of cutaneous receptor are shown in Figure 13.65.

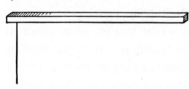

Fig. 13.64 A von Frey hair (or esthesiometer) for measuring the sensitivity of the skin to touch.

The different types of cutaneous sense organ are separated from one another by measurable distances. By applying the appropriate stimulus to points upon the skin, the positions of the receptors can be determined. The small cutaneous areas mapped out in this way are referred to as "spots." Thus, when the sensitivity of the skin to touch is investigated with a von Frey hair, the sensation is elicited only from certain points; these are called touch "spots," while those which respond to heat or cold or to pain are called, respectively, hot, cold, and pain "spots" (see Fig. 13.66). The touch spots are most numerous over the tips of the fingers and in the mucous membrane of the tip of the tongue.

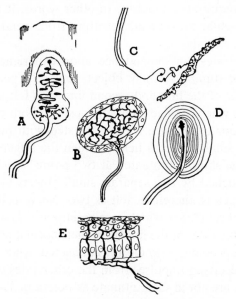

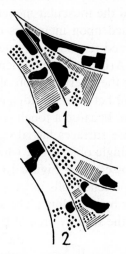

Fig. 13.65 Cutaneous receptors. A, touch (Meissner's corpuscle); B, cold (Krause's end bulb); C, warmth (Ruffini's end organ); D, deep pressure (Pacinian corpuscle); E, pain (bare nerve endings in cornea).

Fig. 13.66 Map of cold spots, 1, and hot spots, 2, within an area on the palm. The sensation in each case was most intense in the black areas, less so in the lined and mildest in the dotted areas. In the blank parts, no definite sensation was aroused. (After Goldscheider.)

In cutaneous regions covered with hair—that is, almost the entire skin surface except the palms of the hands and the soles of the feet—the touch spots lie on the "windward" side of the hairs (the hairs slant in one or other direction like grass bent by a breeze). For this reason, light contact with the hair tips causes a sensation of touch. The hair, when moved, acts as a tiny lever, transmitting the movement to the skin at its base; thus the touch end organ is stimulated. Pain fibers form a rich network in the skin; they also ramify within the hair sockets around the hair roots.

The localization of cutaneous sensations is effected with remarkable accuracy. The localization of touch is tested by bringing a wisp of cotton wool or a von Frey hair in contact with the skin while the subject's eyes are closed, and then asking him to place a finger upon the spot touched. Pain and pressure are also very accurately localized, but the sensations aroused by heat and cold are more diffuse. Cutaneous localization is an acquired faculty, being developed through an association, previously established in the brain, between the point upon the skin and the muscular movement required to touch it. In other words, it is based upon memories of muscular movements resulting from conditioned responses to cutaneous stimuli.

Aristotle's experiment illustrates our dependence upon experience for the interpretation of tactile stimuli. A small object, such as a pea, held between the adjacent sides of the first and second fingers is felt as one, because a touch stimulus when applied simultaneously to both of these surfaces has always in our experience been associated with but a single object. But when the small object is held between the fingers, crossed as in Figure 13.67, the skin is stimulated at two points which experience tells us may be touched by two separate small objects but not by one alone. The single pea is, therefore, felt as two. Nerve cells in the sensory area of the cerebral cortex which receive impulses from

the opposing sides of the fingers in their normal positions are probably very closely connected, whereas those receiving impulses from the other sides of the fingers are not in such intimate association. The dual nature of pain is described on page 475.

Spatial discrimination. This faculty is closely allied to the foregoing; it is the recognition of the separateness of two simultaneous stimuli. For example, if the points of a pair of compasses an inch apart are applied to the skin of the forearm, a single sensation is felt. If the distance between the compass points is increased to one and a half inches or more, and applied as before, two distinct

Fig. 13.67 Aristotle's experiment.

sensations are experienced. Two-point discrimination is a faculty of essential importance. In acquiring information, through the sense of touch, of the size, texture, and shape of various objects, it is indispensable. This faculty varies considerably in different regions, being most highly developed in the coverings of the more mobile parts of the body—that is, parts such as the fingers, lips, and tip of the tongue, which have received the most practice in investigating the immediate environment.

In Table 13-1 several different regions are compared with regard to the minimal distance at which two simultaneous stimuli must be separated in order to arouse a double sensation.

Table 13-1

Different regions compared as to the minimal distance by which two stimuli must be separated in order to arouse a double sensation

Region	Minimal distance in millimeters
Tip of tongue	1.1
Palm side of finger tip	2.3
Red part of lips	4.4
Tip of nose	6.6
Palm of hand	11.3
Heel	22.0
Back of hand	31.6
Forearm	39.6
Middle of back, upper arm and thigh	67.0

CHAPTER 14

The Physiology of Reproduction[1]

The cells that have been set apart from the general body mass for the perpetuation of the race are called the *sex cells, germ cells,* or *gametes* (Gk. *gametēs,* a husband, *gametē,* a wife). The organs that contain them, and in which they are fully or incompletely developed, are known as the *gonads.*

The Female Reproductive Organs

The gonads of the female are called *ovaries,* and the cells that they produce are known as *ova* or *egg cells;* the latter receive different and more specific names at progressive stages of their development (see p. 661). The human ovaries are two bodies about the size and shape of olives, though somewhat flattened from front to back (3 cm long, 1.5 cm broad, and 10 mm thick). They lie one on each side of the pelvis. The ova are developed from columnar epithelial cells—the *germinal epithelium*—covering the surface of the ovary. Columns of these cells penetrate deeply into the connective tissue or *stroma* of the ovary. Small groups of cells separate off from the columns and become arranged with a large one in the center and others in a single layer around it. These structures are found in great numbers in the fetal ovary and in the ovaries of children. They are called *primary, primitive,* or *primordial Graafian follicles* (Fig. 14.1). The central somewhat larger cell is a *primordial ovum* or *oöcyte.* In the sexually mature female—that is, from the time of puberty to the menopause—

---

[1] The sex hormones are dealt with in Chapter 10.

some of the primitive follicles, under the influence of the follicle-stimulating hormone (FSH) of the hypophysis, become, from time to time, mature. Two more layers of cells derived from the ovarian stroma develop around the original one encircling the ovum. The outer of these is fibrous and known as the *theca externa;* the inner layer, called the *theca interna* is more vascular and cellular in character. The cells of the original layer surrounding the primitive ovum multiply to form a mass several strata deep. This cell mass is soon separated into two parts by the collection of fluid—*the liquor folliculi*—near its center.

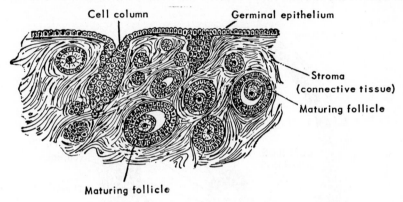

Fig. 14.1   A section of the ovary.

A heaped-up hillock of cells remains at one side of the follicle in which the ovum lies embedded, though separated from the surrounding cells by a clear, rather thick membrane called the *zona pellucida.* The heaped-up mass of cells just mentioned is known as the *discus proligerus* (L. *proles,* offspring + *gero,* I bear) or the *cumulus oöphorus* (L. *cumulus,* a heap + *oophorus,* egg-bearing). A single row of regularly arranged cells immediately encircling the zona pellucida is named the *corona radiata.* The other mass of cells, separated off by the liquor folliculi, is pressed against the wall of follicle which they line. They constitute the *membrana* or *zona granulosa.* As the follicle matures or ripens, it becomes distended by the accumulation of liquor folliculi and moves outward again to the surface of the ovary. It projects from the ovarian surface as a small cystlike oval swelling which eventually bursts and discharges the ovum. In women the discharge of an ovum, or *ovulation,* as it is termed, occurs at regular intervals of about 28 days (see p. 447). The cavity of the ruptured follicle becomes filled with a clot of blood which is soon replaced by a mass of cells filled with a yellow fatlike material called *lutein.* The cells are derived from the membrana granulosa and theca interna of the follicle. The yellow mass filling the follicle is called the *corpus luteum* (yellow body); it elaborates a hormone named *progestin;* when referring to it in pure crystalline form, it is called *progesterone* (Chap. 10).

The ovum itself, when discharged from the ovary, is immature. Maturation occurs during its progress along the *uterine* or *Fallopian tube.* The uterine tubes (called *oviducts* in animals) are two ducts, one on either side, possessing a trumpet-shaped extremity with a fringed rim which lies in close relation to the ovary (Fig. 14.3). This expanded upper end of the uterine tube receives the ovum, which is then conveyed

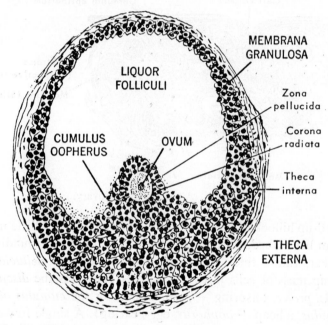

Fig. 14.2   Drawing of a Graafian follicle approaching maturity.

along the duct by the movement of the cilia in its mucosa, as well as by peristaltic contractions of its wall. The uterine tubes open below into the upper part of the *uterus* (womb). Conjugation of the ovum with the male germ cell (spermatazoon), or *fertilization* of the ovum, as this event is usually termed, is thought to take place in the uterine tube. In birds, the oviducts transmit the fertilized ovum to the exterior, but in the human body, and in the bodies of most other mammals, it is delivered into the uterus.

The *uterus* is a hollow pear-shaped organ though somewhat flattened from front to back. Its walls are formed of smooth muscle and lined by mucous membrane; the latter is called the *endometrium*. The small narrower end, the neck or *cervix* of the uterus, is directed downward, opening by its mouth or *os* into the upper end of the *vagina*. The latter is a narrow sheathlike canal of muscle and mucous membrane which

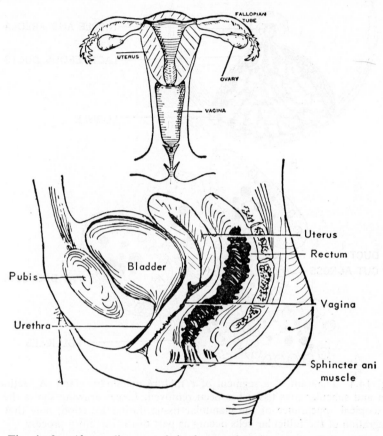

Fig. 14.3   *Above,* diagram of the human female organs of reproduction. *Below,* a section through the female pelvis to show the relations of the reproductive organs to neighboring parts. The bladder is distended.

receives the male copulatory organ or *penis*. The fertilized ovum, upon reaching the cavity of the uterus, establishes connections with the uterine mucosa and develops into the fetus (p. 669). The reactions of the endometrium will be described in greater detail later.

The growth of the uterus in the virgin state and during pregnancy. The virgin uterus reaches its full development at puberty as a result of the maturation of the Graafian follicles and the liberation of the follicular hormone, estradiol. At this time it weighs only 50 grams or less, but

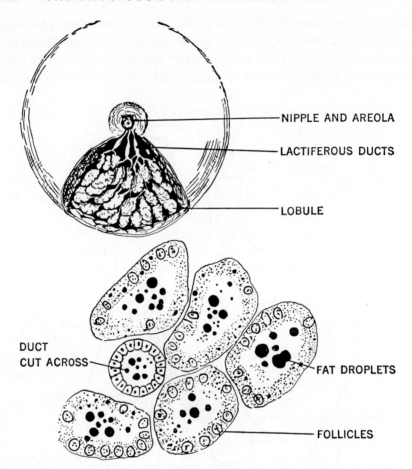

NIPPLE AND AREOLA

LACTIFEROUS DUCTS

LOBULE

DUCT
CUT ACROSS

FAT DROPLETS

FOLLICLES

Fig. 14.4   Diagram of a segment of a mature mammary gland. A section of skin and subcutaneous tissue has been removed. *Lower* drawing shows the microscopical appearance of the glandular tissue during secretion; note that disintegration of the follicular cells occurs as part of the secretory process.

during pregnancy it shows phenomenal growth, reaching a weight exclusive of its contents of some 1000 grams—a twenty-fold increase. Almost immediately after fertilization of the ovum, before it has become attached to the endometrium, and even while it is still in the uterine tube, the uterine muscle shows very active hyperplasia, a great increase in the number of fibers occurring through mitosis. Under microscopic examination, thousands of mitotic figures are to be seen in a small sample of the uterine muscle. But this hyperplastic phase soon comes to an end. The growth of the uterus from this time on is confined entirely to thickening and lengthening of the muscle fibers. The increase in the *number* of fibers (mitosis) is due mainly to the action of progestin. The enlargement of the individual fibers, and the consequent great increase in the size of the uterus, is the result of the distension caused by the progressive increase in bulk of the fetus, a stretch stimulus being thus applied to the uterine muscle. The effect of this stretch stimulus upon uterine growth is modified after a somewhat complicated fashion by both estradiol and progestin. The growth of the uterine muscle ceases toward the end of the sixth month of pregnancy. But the fetus shows rapid growth from this time on, accompanied by a commensurate distension of the uterus. The stretch stimulus applied to the muscle fibers, though it elicits no growth response, induces other effects which lead eventually to the termination of pregnancy (p. 674).

The structure and development of the mammary glands. The composition of milk. The mammary glands of women, commonly known as the breasts, are composed of a mass of cells arranged to form follicles or alveoli which are drained by a branching system of ducts. The mammary tissue, capable of secreting milk under appropriate stimulation, is separated by means of partitions or septa of connective tissue into some twenty lobes in each breast (Fig. 14.4). Each lobe is divided again into a number of lobules. The breast is surmounted at its center by a small conical eminence composed of erectile tissue and covered by darkly pigmented skin; it is known as the *nipple,* and is surrounded by a circular area of similarly pigmented skin called the *areola.* The whole mass of glandular tissue is embedded and covered by a variable, but often a very abundant, amount of fatty (adipose) tissue. In the active gland, the milk is secreted into the cavities of the follicles and drained away by the duct system. The milk is carried from each lobe by a single duct (*lactiferous duct*) to the nipple, from the apex of which it reaches the exterior through a tiny pore.

The development of the mammary glands to the adult size and form commences at puberty. Their enlargement at this time is one of the chief secondary sex characteristics of the mammalian female. Before the age of puberty, the gland of the female shows little difference from that of the male either in the amount or in the histological appearance of the mammary tissue. In both sexes at this time, as well as in the adult male, the glands consist mainly of conective tissue with a limited number of rudimentary collapsed follicles and a few scattered sparsely branched ducts. With the onset of puberty, signs of cellular activity (hyperplasia) appear in the female gland. The duct system becomes more extensively branched, though the follicles remain rudimentary.

Not unless pregnancy supervenes do the latter become fully developed and capable, under ordinary circumstances, of secreting milk. There are, therefore, two periods in the growth of the mammary glands, the first at puberty and confined to the *duct system*. This is brought about by the action of the follicular hormone (estradiol, p. 450). The very active growth of the *follicles* which is characteristic of the pregnant state, is caused by progestin. Due to the high concentration of estradiol in the blood during pregnancy, the duct system also receives further stimulation at this time. Though milk is formed within the gland toward the end of pregnancy, none appears externally, as a rule, until the child or the young animal has been born. The mechanism underlying the *secretion* of milk (lactation) has been described on page 454.

Milk provides all the materials necessary for the growth of the infant up to the age of about 6 months. Human milk contains about 6.7 percent of *sugar* (lactose or milk sugar), 1.5 percent *protein* (mainly lactalbumin and cassein), and about 4 percent of *fat*. Its main mineral is calcium (approximately 1 gram per quart of cow's milk). But it also contains adequate amounts of phosphorus, sodium, potassium, and magnesium. The chief difference between human and cow's milk is the higher concentration of protein (3.5 percent) in the latter. Both kinds of milk are poor in iron; it is for this reason that the infant after the age of about 6 months is likely to become anemic if fed upon milk alone. The baby comes into the world with a good supply of iron, but the stores of this mineral (derived from the hemoglobin freed by the disintegration of the excess of erythrocytes during the few days after birth) become exhausted after the first half year or so. The milk of healthy mothers usually contains the required amounts of vitamins A, B, and C, but tends to be low in vitamin D. This is also often true of cow's milk, and for this reason the diet of a child after 6 months of age—a time when rickets may develop—should be supplemented with some preparation of vitamin D, especially in the winter months.

The various constituents of the milk are derived from the blood flowing through the gland. In a secreting gland the fat can be seen as microscopic globules within the cells of the alveoli. As the globules collect and coalesce, the cells swell, and finally *bursting*, they discharge their load of fat into the center of the alveolus (Fig. 14.4). This type of secretion, known as *apocrine*, is less common than that in which the cells extrude their product—saliva, for example—and remain intact.

The menstrual cycle is described on page 447, the actions of the ovarian hormones on page 449, and of the gonadotrophic hormones of the anterior lobe of the pituitary on page 452.

The Male Reproductive Organs

The testes. These are the gonads or sex organs of the male and, therefore, correspond to the ovaries of the female. They are two ovoid bodies which, in such animals as fish, frogs, reptiles, and birds, lie within the abdominal cavity. Even in the mammalian fetus they occupy the position. Shortly before, or soon after birth, the testes of mammals descend and, leaving the abdomen, become enclosed in a small cutaneous pouch, suspended from the pubic and perineal regions, and called the *scrotum*. In the human fetus the testes enter the scrotum two months before birth.

The interior of the testis is a compact mass of narrow and very tortuous tubules—the *convoluted seminiferous tubules*. Fibrous partitions divide the testicular substance into a great number of wedge-shaped lobes, each of which consists of from one to three convoluted tubules. The tubules of neighboring lobes unite to form a series of larger straight ducts which, after a short course, unite in a plexiform manner. The plexus—known as the *rete testis*—leads again into a number of ducts, small and straight at first, but which, after a short course, become enlarged and tortuous (Fig. 14.5), and ultimately unite into a single large convoluted duct. This is called the *epididymis;* it is applied to the posterior aspect of the testis, its upper part or *head* being considerably larger

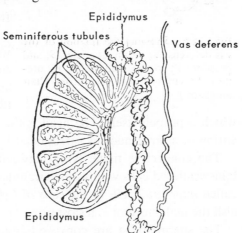

Epididymus

Seminiferous tubules

Vas deferens

Epididymus

Fig. 14.5   Diagram showing the structure of the interior of the testis.

than the lower part or *tail*. From the tail, a straight tube—the *vas deferens*—ascends along the posterior border of the testis to enter the abdomen, wherein it joins the duct of the *seminal vesicle* of the corresponding side (Fig. 14.6).

The seminal vesicles are two coiled tubes with sacculated walls, situated between the lower part of the bladder and the rectum. The *ejaculatory ducts* are short tubes formed one on each side by the union of the duct of the seminal vesicle with the vas deferens; they open into the urethra (the canal of the penis) near the outlet from the bladder.

The seminiferous tubules are lined by several layers of cells. Those of the outermost layer—that is, the layer lying upon the basement membrane—are of two basic types, (a) *spermatogenic* cells and (b) *columnar cells*. The former give rise through a series of divisions (p. 660) to the mature male sex cells (spermatozoa). The columnar cells are supporting cells and are named the *cells of Sertoli;* they extend inward (i.e., toward the center of the tubule) through all the other layers. The inner cell layers forming the wall of the tubule consist of spermatogenic cells showing various stages in the maturation process, those most advanced in development lying nearer the lumen of the tubule. The cells, as they mature into free-swimming spermatozoa, become detached from the tubule wall (Fig. 14.7). The spermatozoon is about 0.1 mm long; it has an oval flattened head and a long tail-like process (Fig. 14.8) by

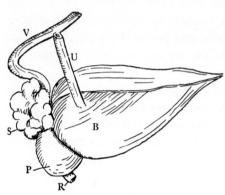

Fig. 14.6   Showing the relation of the vas deferens, V; seminal vesicles, S; and prostate, P; to the bladder, B. R, urethra; U, ureter. (Redrawn from Cunningham.)

which it propels itself. The head is the essential part of the cell, consisting of a large nucleus surrounded by a narrow rim of protoplasm.

The connective tissue lying between the convoluted tubules contains scattered cells with yellow granules in their cytoplasm. These are called *interstitial cells* or the *cells of Leydig.* They are believed to furnish the male hormone, testosterone (p. 452).

The spermatozoa are conveyed from the convoluted seminiferous tubules along the complex system of canals, just described, to the epididymis. The spermatozoa show no spontaneous movements in the convoluted tubules, but become actively motile in the epididymis. As coitus nears completion and the climax or orgasm of the act occurs, contractions of the epididymus and vasa deferentia propel the spermatozoa through the ejaculatory ducts into the urethra. At the same time the seminal vesicles contract and expel a viscous secretion. The *semen,* which this fluid with its suspension of spermatozoa is now called, is ejected from the urethra with considerable force by the contractions of the urethral muscle and of striated muscle in the perineum. The ejection of the semen and the movements which bring it about constitute the *act of ejaculation.* It is a reflex act of which sensory nerves in the penis are its afferent limb, and sympathetic nerves its efferent limb. A thin secretion from the prostate gland and secretions of small urethral glands are added to the semen in the urethra. The secretion of the seminal vesicles appears to be essential for maintaining the life and motility of the spermatozoa, but the prostatic secretion and the secretions of the urethral glands are not of importance in this respect; they probably serve mainly as a lubricant.

The spermatozoa, deposited in the upper part of the vagina during coitus, propel themselves upward by lashing movements of their tails

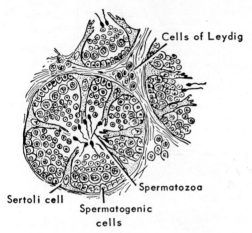

Fig. 14.7   Cross section of seminiferous tubule showing spermatogenesis (semidiagrammatic).

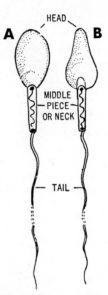

Fig. 14.8   A   human spermatozoon. A, front view; B, profile view.

at the rate of about 6 inches per hour and, passing through the uterus, enter the uterine tube where fertilization normally occurs. It is probable that contractions of the uterus during coitus may draw the semen into the uterine cavity.

The head of the spermatozoon penetrates the ovum; in a short time its tail disappears and the changes described on page 663 follow. The semen contains an enzyme (hyaluronidase, p. 51) which effects the removal of the mass of cells (discus proligerus, p. 649) in which the ovum is embedded, thus facilitating its penetration.

The life of the spermatozoon after it has been deposited in the vagina is from four to five days. The ovum, on the other hand, if unfertilized, survives for only about seven hours; after this, it starts to degenerate.

Nature, in her provisions for the conveyance of the ova to their destination, has taken a rather hazardous chance. Whereas the spermatozoa follow a completely closed course from the testes to their exit from the penis, the trumpet-shaped end of the uterine tube and the surface of the ovary are not structurally continuous. Sometimes the ovum fails to enter the tube, but escapes into the pelvic or abdominal cavity where it may meet a sper-

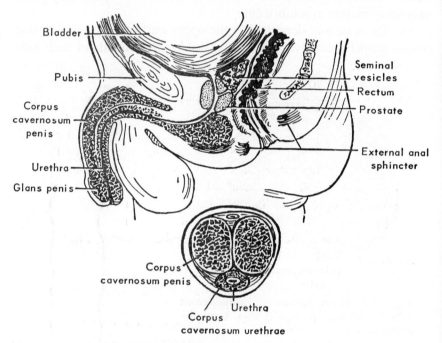

Fig. 14.9   *Upper drawing,* a section through the male pelvis to show the relationship of the reproductive organs. *Below,* a cross section of the penis. The bladder has been artificially distended.

matozoon. Or, after the ovum has entered the tube and been penetrated normally by a spermatozoon, it may be prevented from continuing its journey to the uterine cavity. Or again, the ovum and the spermatozoon may meet upon the surface of the ovary. In the event of one of these serious mishaps occurring, pregnancy takes place in the general abdominal cavity, on or within the ovary, or in one or other uterine tube. This is called *extrauterine pregnancy* or *ectopic gestation,* or, more specifically, *abdominal,*[2] *tubal,* or *ovarian pregnancy* according to the site. The embryo may develop to maturity in the abnormal situation, but more usually severe hemorrhage within the abdominal cavity occurs with death of the embryo and grave danger to the mother.

[2] Pregnancy occurring *primarily* in the abdomen is rare. Abdominal pregnancies are usually secondary to rupture of a tube in which the pregnancy originally occurred. Ovarian pregnancy is also very rare.

The penis. The copulatory organ of the male, the *penis,* is composed of *erectile* tissue arranged as three longitudinal columns bound together by fibrous tissue, and covered with skin. Two of the columnar masses, called the *corpora cavernosa penis,* lie side by side on the upper or anterior aspect of the organ. The third, called the *corpus cavernosum urethrae* or *corpus spongiosum penis,* lies beneath the other two and is canalized by the urethra. The urinary bladder is evacuated through the urethra which also transmits the semen during coitus. The extremity of the corpus cavernosum urethrae is expanded into a pyramidal structure called the *glans penis,* which is molded over the ends of the corpora cavernosa penis (Fig. 14.9).

Erectile tissue possesses a spongelike structure, showing a meshwork of wide blood spaces (cavernous spaces). These are fed by capillaries and arterioles and drained by small veins. Smooth muscle fibers run in the walls of the blood spaces and surround their venous outlets. To this construction of erectile tissue is due its peculiar property, namely, the ability to alter in volume and consistency. Erection of the penis is brought about in the following way. The arterioles feeding the blood spaces dilate, and the muscle fibers in the walls of the latter relax. The muscle guarding the venous outlets contracts, thus tending to impede the outflow of blood. The spaces of the erectile tissue are expanded as the blood under high pressure is driven through them. The organ, thus becoming turgid with blood, is rendered tense, hard, and erect.

The nerve fibers governing this mechanism are derived from the pelvic (parasympathetic) nerves. The sympathetic sends fibers which exert the reverse effect (contraction of the smooth muscle of the arterioles and in the walls of the blood spaces, accompanied by relaxation of that surrounding the venous outlets) with consequent relaxation of the penis.

The erectile organ of the female corresponding to the penis is called the *clitoris.* It is situated above and just outside the entrance to the vagina. Erectile tissue is also present beneath the mucosa of the vagina just within the vaginal orifice.

The prostate. This is a body about the size of a chestnut and somewhat conical in shape. Its base is directed upward and lies in contact with the lowest part of the bladder. It embraces the first $1\frac{1}{2}$ inches of the urethra. The ejaculatory ducts pierce its upper and posterior part (see Fig. 14.9). The prostate is composed of muscular and glandular tissues. It secretes a thin fluid into the urethra.

Prostatic enlargement, with consequent interference with the passage of urine, not uncommonly occurs in men past middle age. There has been much speculation as to the cause of enlargement of the prostate, but so far the problem has not been solved. Some hormonal imbalance is thought to be the fundamental cause.

The Processes of Reproduction

Maturation of the sex cells. The sex cells in the course of their development to their mature form—spermatozoa or ova—pass through a series of divisions which will now be described.

The maturation of the male gametes—spermatogenesis. The youngest male gametes produced by the multiplication of the primary sex

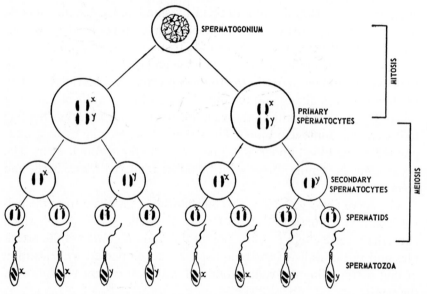

Fig. 14.10   Spermatogenesis. The black bodies represent the chromosomes; X and Y are the sex chromosomes (see p. 665). Only one autosome is shown in the spermatozoa; in man the total number of chromosomes is 46.

cells (*primordial germ* cells) are called *spermatogonia.* They are large plump cells lying adjacent to the basement membrane of the seminiferous tubules.

The spermatogonia multiply by mitosis (p. 25) through several generations. The cells produced in the final mitotic division pass into a growth period. The large cells that result are called *primary spermatocytes* (Fig. 14.10). At the end of the growth period, the latter again divide, but the division with respect to the arrangement of the chromosomes is fundamentally different from that occurring in the mitotic process. The chromosomes come into apposition in pairs but *do not,* as in mitosis, *split lengthwise.* As a result of the mere contact, or synapsis, of the chromosomes and their failure to divide, the *diploid* [3] number is maintained and not temporarily doubled, as in mitosis. When, therefore, the cell divides and two daughter cells, now called *secondary spermatocytes,* are formed, each new cell receives only half the number (*haploid number*) of chromosomes characteristic of the body cells of the species. This type of cell multiplication is called *re-*

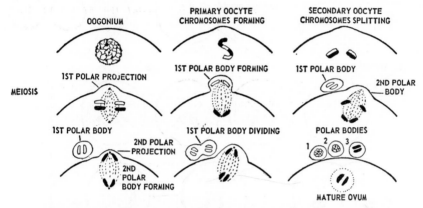

Fig. 14.11   Oögenesis. Oval bodies represent the chromosomes.

duction division or *meiosis,* and is peculiar to sex cells, occurring in no other type of cell. The secondary spermatocytes, having received their haploid quota of chromosomes, now divide by mitosis. The small cells so produced are called *spermatids* which, owing to the splitting of the chromosomes, also receive the reduced number of chromosomes. The spermatids, without further division, are gradually transformed into mature spermatozoa.

Maturation of the female gametes—oögenesis. The maturation of the primitive ovum or *oögonium* follows essentially the same course as that described for the spermatogonia, but there are certain differences. The earliest stage in the maturation process is, as in spermatogenesis, the production by mitosis of daughter cells with the diploid number of chromosomes.

The cells resulting from the final mitotic divisions enter a period of growth and are transformed into *primary oöcytes* (Fig. 14.11). Production of the latter is the last stage of maturation which occurs in the

[3] See glossary for definitions of diploid and haploid.

ovary [4] (Graafian follicle). After rupture of the follicle and the escape from the ovary of the primary oöcyte, the latter enters the uterine tube (or oviduct). If there met and penetrated by a spermatozoon, it undergoes further ripening, otherwise it degenerates. The resumed maturation consists of the meiotic division of the primary oöcyte and the production of cells containing the haploid number of chromosomes. But, unlike the corresponding stage of spermatogenesis, the division of the

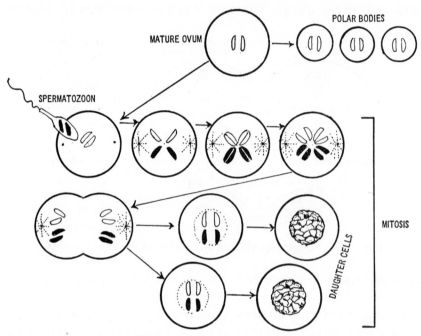

Fig. 14.12   Fertilization of the ovum.

cytoplasm is very unequal; one of the cells—*secondary* oöcyte—is large and functional; the other is diminutive and functionless. It is named the *first polar body* and soon degenerates. The secondary oöcyte divides by mitosis, but again unequally, to produce a *mature ovum* and a *second polar body* which, like the first, is a miniature and functionless cell which degenerates. The first polar body also, as a rule, divides mitotically at this time so that, from each primary oöcyte, one mature egg and three small functionless cells are produced. Each of the four cells contains the haploid number of chromosomes. The ovum is now ready for penetration by the spermatozoon.

[4] According to some authorities, the ova of most vertebrates progress in the ovary to a stage further than that of the primary oöcyte and in the human subject is fully matured in the ovary.

Conjugation of the egg and sperm cells. The unfertilized ovum appears, in some unknown way, to exert an attractive force upon the spermatozoon which, by means of the lashing movements of its tail, reaches the female gamete. The head of the sperm penetrates the ovum. A change in the boundary wall of the ovum then occurs, which, as a rule, serves to prevent the entrance of other spermatozoa. The tail of the spermatozoon soon disappears, leaving the head containing the nucleus within the cytoplasm of the egg (Fig. 14.12). The result is the formation of a single cell, which has a power for growth not possessed by either ovum or spermatozoon alone. The single cell almost at once commences to divide and redivide. In this way are formed great numbers of cells (see *segmentation,* p. 666), which do not separate from one another but are held together. Gradually, as they multiply and develop in various directions, tissues and organs of different structure and functions appear, until finally a new and complete individual is created almost identical with others of its species. Whether plant or worm, fish, bird, or man, nearly all forms of life other than the very primitive have developed from a single cell resulting from the union of sperm and egg (see *parthogenesis,* p. 664).

The conjugation of the male and female gametes is termed the *fertilization or impregnation of the ovum.* The cell resulting from the union is then spoken of as the *fertilized ovum, oösperm,* or *zygote.*

Changes in the nuclei of the conjoined cells. Almost immediately after the penetration of the ovum by the spermatozoon, the two nuclei move toward each other, come together, and finally fuse near the center of the ovum. Fusion is followed by the complicated changes already described as characteristic of mitosis and which leads to masses of cells being produced. In the process of mitosis, the chromatin of each nucleus is not broken up into sections at random or in any haphazard fashion, but is always divided into precisely the same number of chromosomes characteristic of the body cells or primitive germ cells of the species, but double the number in a mature germ cell. In other words, the original (diploid) number which was reduced during meiosis is restored by the fusion of the nuclei. *The fused nucleus must therefore contain an equal number of maternal and paternal chromosomes.*[5] These are important and fundamental facts in the mechanism of reproduction.

[5] In some insects, such as the fruit fly, the number of chromosomes in the body cells is 8, which are reduced to 4 in the sex cells. In certain species of worms, there are 12 in the body cells and 6 in the ova and sperms. The mouse, the trout, and the lily have 24 in their body cells and 12 in their sex cells. Other forms of animals and plants have each a characteristic number, which may be as low as 4 or as high as 168. There are 23 chromosomes in the gametes of the human race and 46 in the body cells.

Chromatin, of which the chromosomes are composed, is believed to be the essential procreative substance. Through it hereditary characters are transmitted, and upon its existence the perpetuation of the species depends. Yet it has been stated that the total quantity of chromatin contained in all the ova and sperms from which have been created the two-billion-odd persons inhabiting the globe could have been no greater in size than a match head.

Parthenogenesis—virgin birth. In some animal forms, especially certain insects, the females, though themselves produced from a fertilized egg, may for some generations lay eggs which are not fertilized. These spermless eggs, nevertheless, develop into the young of the species. In other words, the young of these generations have a mother but no father.[6] To this mode of reproduction *parthenogenesis*, a term derived from the Greek word *parthenos*, a virgin, is applied. The drones (males) of the honeybee, for instance, are developed from unfertilized eggs of the queen. The female workers of the hive arise from fertilized eggs, which have been laid about the same time as the unfertilized. A frog's egg, though under ordinary circumstances it must receive a spermatozoon before segmentation will ensue, may be induced to develop into a tadpole by artificial means. Pricking the wall of the ovum with a needle will start segmentation, which ultimately results in the production of a fatherless frog.[7]

Twinning. There are two ways in which twins may be conceived: (1) by the fertilization of two separate ova, or (2) by the fertilization of a single ovum. When two ova are fertilized—and this is the commoner way—the offspring, known as *fraternal twins,* may be of the same or of different sexes and usually do not resemble each other more than might any two members of a family. When two individuals are formed from a single zygote, the twins are always of the same sex and are remarkably alike. They are called *identical twins* and are formed by the division of the cell mass within the zygote into two distinct parts, each of which develops into a separate child. Identical twins are contained within the same amniotic cavity and are on very rare occasions joined together, as in the case of the Siamese twins. Most animals produce their litters by the fertilization of several ova, but in some, such as the armadillo—a little mammal possessing a hard covering resembling a coat of mail—only one ovum is fertilized, and

---

[6] The unfertilized egg gives off only one polar body (see p. 661).

[7] As a very rare event parthenogenesis may occur in mammals, and the possibility of its occurrence in the human species has been seriously discussed.

the mass of cells within becomes divided into several smaller groups, each of which develops into a fetus.

The determination of sex. It would be an inestimable boon to animal breeders if the sex of the offspring could be determined by artificial means, or even if it could be predicted. Man's ingenuity in this direction seems, however, to be forever checked. Had human interference been possible in the past, the history of nations, no doubt, would have run a different course. The sex of the newly created organism is fixed unalterably at the moment that the spermatozoon fertilizes the ovum. A pair of chromosomes (*sex chromosomes*) in the nuclei of the immature sex cells determines whether the zygote shall develop into a male or a female. None of the other chromosomes (*autosomes*) exercises this function. In the male, the sex chromosomes are dissimilar, one, called the *Y chromosome* (Fig. 14.10), being usually smaller than the other. The large one is called the *X chromosome*. In the immature female sex cells, the sex chromosomes are identical and like the male X chromosomes. Now when the male sex cells develop into mature spermatozoa and reduction division occurs—i.e., when the pairs separate—half of the sperm cells receive Y chromosomes and half receive X chromosomes. If a spermatozoon possessing a Y chromosome conjugates with the egg, a male (XY) will be produced; if the sperm cell contains only X chromosomes, a female (XX) results. Obviously, it is all a matter of chance what the sex of the offspring will be. When the gonads of the embryo develop, the influence of the testicular or the ovarian hormone encourages development along male and female lines, respectively.

Hermaphroditism. The hormonal influence upon sexual development is sometimes seen in a very striking way in cattle when, as a result of a developmental anomaly in the circulations of twin embryos of opposite sexes, the blood of the two fetuses is permitted to mix. The female embryo then comes under the influence of the male hormone and abnormalities in its generative organs are induced. The uterus remains undeveloped and masculinization of other reproductive structures occurs. The masculinized female is called a *freemartin;* it is sterile. Feminization of the male fetus does not occur.

Some lower animal forms—certain worms, mollusks, crustacea, etc. —like most plants, contain both male and female reproductive tissue in the same body. Sometimes both testes and ovaries are functional, producing spermatozoa and ova; sometimes only the testes *or* ovaries produce sex cells. This combination of the sex organs (gonads) is called *hermaphroditism,* and the individual an *hermaphrodite* (Gk.

god and goddess, *Hermes* and *Aphrodite*). An hermaphrodite may fertilize (p. 663) its own eggs or those of another.

In man, hermaphroditism occurs as a rather rare developmental abnormality. The two types of tissue, testicular or ovarian, may be present as separate organs (testes and ovaries) or fused to form *ovo-testes.* The external sex organs—penis, clitoris, etc.—are indeterminate between male and female as a result of the double hormonal influence. Such a condition is called *true hermaphroditism.* It is of genetic origin. On the other hand, only one type of sex gland, testes *or* ovaries, may exist, though the external genital organs show both male and female features. This is called *pseudohermaphroditism.* It most fre-

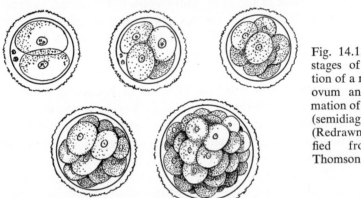

Fig. 14.13 First stages of segmentation of a mammalian ovum and the formation of the morula (semidiagrammatic). (Redrawn and modified from Allen Thomson.)

quently has an endocrine basis. Occasionally certain regions of the body, even an entire half, has male characteristics while other regions or the opposite half are female. Such persons are called *gynandromorphs* (Gk. *gynē,* a woman + *anēr* (*and-*), a man + *morphē,* form). It is often difficult to decide in which sex a pseudohermaphrodite should be placed and, if a child, whether dress, education, training, etc., should be along male or female lines. Recently a means has been discovered whereby the dominant sex can be determined. There is present in the body cells of females, but not in those of males, a dot of chromatin within the nucleus in contact with, or close to, the nuclear membrane. It is called the **sex chromatin.** By excising a small piece of skin and examining it microscopically for the presence or absence of this body, the real sex of the individual can be ascertained.

Segmentation of the fertilized ovum and the development of the embryo. The zygote immediately divides into two. Each daughter-cell again divides, and through a succession of divisions groups of 8, 16, 32, 64, 128 cells, and so on appear. So, by a process of division and redivision, large masses of cells are formed, which ultimately produce a new individual. This process whereby the fertilized ovum undergoes repeated divisions is called *segmentation* or *cleavage*. With each cell division, the chromatin breaks up into chromosomes; and, as described above for mitosis, each chromosome splits into half, and an equal number of halves go to each new nucleus. All the cells resulting from the long series of divisions which occur in the development of the off-spring must therefore contain the same number of chromosomes as

Fig. 14.14   The blastocyst. *On left,* diagram showing the segregation of cells of the morula into an outer and an in-ner group. (After Simon.) *On right,* formation of amni-on, A, and yolk sac, Y. (After Bryce.)

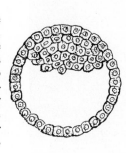
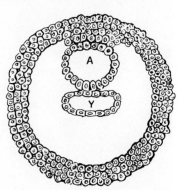

did the original fused nucleus of the fertilized ovum, and each receives chromatin material from both parents.

In the earlier stages of embryonic development of the various mam-malian species, cell multiplication follows a common pattern. At first a rounded, mulberrylike mass of cells is formed, called the *morula* (L. diminutive of *morus,* a mulberry). The morula soon differentiates into an outer and an inner group of cells (Figs. 14.13, 14.14, and 14.15); fluid collects within it. The fertilized ovum at this stage is called the *blastocyst.* The outer group of cells now pressed excentri-cally to form an annular wall is called the *trophoblast* (Gk. *trophē,* nourishment + *blastos,* germ or primitive form) because through its agency the blastocyst receives nutriment from the mother. The tropho-blast later develops numerous fringelike processes which gives the ovum a shaggy appearance. These processes grow larger and branched and are now known as *chorionic villi;* the outer covering of the ovum from which they arise is called the *chorion.* The more centrally situated mass of cells becomes so disposed as to form the walls of two sacs— the *amnion* and the *yolk sac* (see Plates 15C and 16A, and Fig. 14.14). The cells of the area over which the amnion and the yolk sac come into contact multiply to form a plaquelike elevation called the *embryonic shield* or *disc,* from which the body of the embryo is developed. The cavity of the amnion enlarges and comes to enclose the embryo, the sac expanding until it comes into contact with the inner surface of the chorion. The yolk sac shrinks and almost disappears.

When the embryonic shield is no more than 2 mm or so in diameter, its cells become arranged in two layers, separated by a narrow space. The outer of these layers is called the *ectoderm,* and the inner one the

Fig. 14.15   Photograph of an 8-day-old blastocyst of a monkey attached to the mucous membrane of the uterus. The lighter area within is the embryo itself. (After Heuser and Streeter, *Contributions to Embryology,* 479, Carnegie Institute of Washington, 1937.)

entoderm. A little later, a third layer appears in the space between the other two; it is known as the *mesoderm.* From these three *germ layers,* to give them their collective name, all the structures of the body are ultimately formed (Fig. 14.16). The *nervous system,* the *greater part of the eye,* the *salivary glands,* the *skin,* the *epithelial lining of the nose* and *part of the mouth,* and the *dental enamel* originate from the ectoderm. The mesoderm gives rise to the *skeleton* and the *muscles* (both striated and nonstriated), the *heart, blood vessels,* and *blood,* the *lymphatic system,* the *kidneys,* the *urinary bladder* (with the exception of its epithelial lining), and the *connective tissues.* From the entoderm are developed the *epithelial linings of the alimentary* and *respiratory tracts* exclusive of those parts derived from the ectoderm, the *epithe-*

lium lining the urinary bladder, and the *secreting (epithelial) cells of the liver and the pancreas,* and of the *parathyroid* and *thyroid glands.*

The earlier of those changes just described—up to the stage of the blastocyst and the development of the trophoblast—take place in the Fallopian tube while the blastocyst is being propelled toward the uterus by ciliary action and peristaltic movements of the tubal walls. Between the third and the fifth days after fertilization of the ovum the blastocyst enters the cavity of the uterus. Through the destructive effect that the trophoblast exerts upon the uterine mucosa and the reaction set up in the latter, the ovum is enabled to embed itself and, like a parasite, obtain nourishment from the maternal tissue. The activity shown by the uterine mucosa at this time consists of multiplication of the surface epithelium and elongation and hyperplasia of its glands, together with dilatation and twisting of its vessels. A special type of uterine tissue is thus produced called the *decidua* because it is shed after the birth of the offspring (Pl. 16A). These changes in the endometrium commence before the blastocyst reaches the uterus, or after ovulation, even though fertilization has not occurred (see p. 450). They are dependent upon the action of progestin (progesterone).

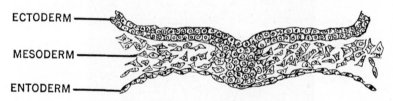

ECTODERM

MESODERM

ENTODERM

Fig. 14.16   The germ layers.

This hormone also diminishes the irritability of the muscle of the uterus; any contractions of the muscle which might occur to disturb the secure implantation of the blastocyst are suppressed. Hyperplasia of the uterine muscle, as mentioned on page 450, also occurs at this time.

In Figure 14.17 a fetus at the age of 8 weeks is shown completely enclosed within the amniotic cavity. Most of the chorion has been cut away. The chorionic villi have disappeared except where the chorion is attached to the uterine wall, in which situation they have increased greatly in size and complexity. They are surrounded by spongy masses of decidual tissue consisting largely of blood spaces; thus the embryonic and the maternal tissues are intimately interlocked. The chorionic villi, which are supplied through a rich vascular system with fetal blood, are bathed by the mother's blood. The structure formed by the union of the maternal (decidua) and embryonic tissues is called the *placenta*. When fully grown, the placenta is a disc-shaped mass which occupies a third or so of the uterine wall (Fig. 14.18). Though the fetal and maternal circulations come into the most intimate association in the placenta, the blood in the two sets of vessels does not mix; the delicate capillary walls of the chorionic villi are interposed. Oxygen,

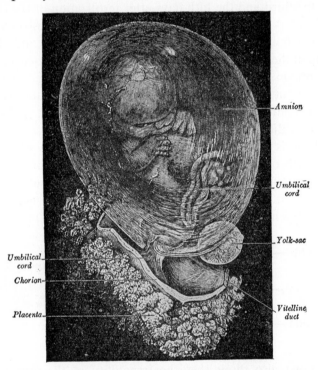

Fig. 14.17   Showing the fetus at age of about 8 weeks enclosed in the amnion, magnified a little over 2 diameters. (After Thomson from Gray's Anatomy.)

food materials, etc., are transferred across the walls of the chorionic vessels from the mother to the fetus, and carbon dioxide and other waste materials from the fetal to the maternal circulation. Thus the placenta serves the respiratory, nutritional, and excretory functions of the fetus.

The law of recapitulation or biogenesis. The vertebrate embryo from the earliest stages of its development tends to recall or *recapitulate* in a more or less vague way the forms of its ancestors from a remote period in its evolutionary history. This is known as the law of recapitulation or biogenesis. For example, the embryo of the human species or of any vertebrate commences its existence as two cells (ovum and sperm) fused into a single one. Some unicellular forms reproduce by a similar preliminary fusion of their bodies. The segmentation of the fertilized ovum with the formation of the morula is identical with that seen in the development of many of the most primitive forms of life.

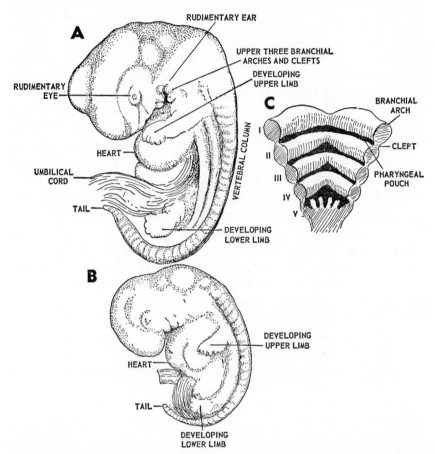

Fig. 14.18   Drawing of a human embryo, A, at the age of 5½ weeks (about 8 mm long), and of a monkey embryo, B, of about the same age. C, enlarged drawing of the five branchial arches and clefts. The inner aspect of the throat region is exposed to show the pharyngeal pouches.

Again, in the early vertebrate embryo, including the human, a series of five arched ridges appear in the entoderm of the primitive pharynx; corresponding elevations are to be seen on the surface (ectoderm) of the neck. The arched ridges have a core of mesoderm, and are known as the *branchial* or *visceral arches;* the depressions or furrows between them on the outer aspect of the neck are called the *branchial clefts;* the furrows (entodermal) in the pharynx between the arches are referred to as the *pharyngeal pouches* (Fig. 14.18). The branchial structures are found in all vertebrate embryos. From them the respiratory apparatus of fish is developed, the tissue between the arches (branchial clefts and pharyngeal pouches) disappearing to leave slits which establish communications between the pharynx and the exterior. In the fish, the arches (with the exception of the most headward one which goes to form the jaw) develop rich capillary plexuses which, with the supporting tissue, constitute the gills. Water taken into the mouth and pharynx is ejected through the slits and, passing swiftly over the gills, gives up oxygen to the blood in the capillary vessels and receives carbon dioxide in return. Obviously a respiratory apparatus of this nature would be quite useless to an air-breathing animal. But the branchial arches of mammalian embryos, which seemingly at first are designed for the development of gills, are devoted to other purposes. They enter into the formation of the lower jaw, the muscles and bones of the face, the structures of the neck, the ear, mouth, pharynx, and the thyroid and laryngeal cartilages. The branchial clefts disappear almost entirely, but the entoderm of the pharyngeal pouches gives rise to the thymus, the parathyroid glands, and part of the thyroid gland.

Other examples to illustrate the law of recapitulation, such as the persistence in the human adult of the useless ear and tail muscles and the outmoded vermiform appendix, may be mentioned. Again, the heart of the early embryo is a simple tubular structure as in fish; but later, it becomes bent upon itself and develops separate chambers. For a short time it closely resembles the heart of an amphibian, such as the frog, possessing a sinus venosus and other features of the cold-blooded heart.

As development proceeds, the human embryo ascends, as it were, the evolutionary ladder, passing rapidly over the lower rungs, more slowly over the higher. For some time it resembles its mammalian kind; not until about 6 weeks after fertilization of the ovum does it show distinctly human characteristics. The human embryo possesses a tail which only commences to disappear in the seventh week.[8]

The fetal circulation. The fetal heart drives the blood which has a low content of oxygen and a high content of carbon dioxide, to the placenta through two vessels—the *umbilical arteries*. The oxygenated blood is returned from the placenta to the fetus by a single vessel—the *umbilical vein* (see Pl. 16A). The umbilical vessels run together, coiled or twisted with one another and covered by a soft jellylike substance,

---

[8] A child is sometimes born with a tail, but it is a developmental anomaly of extreme rarity.

to constitute the *umbilical cord*. This enters the body of the fetus about the middle of the abdomen; its point of entrance is marked in after life by a circular, depressed, and puckered area of skin called the *navel* or *umbilicus*.

The oxygenated blood of the umbilical vein passes, in part, through the liver to enter the *inferior vena cava* of the fetus, but the greater proportion pours directly into the inferior vena cava, wherein it mixes with blood returning from the lower limbs and abdomen. This mixed blood empties into the right auricle; most of it is then directed through an opening in the interauricular septum, called the *foramen ovale,* to the left side of the heart, but a much smaller part passes into the right ventricle. The blood which passes through the foramen ovale, upon reaching the left ventricle, is discharged into the aorta; a part is distributed to various parts of the body; the remainder is carried by the umbilical arteries to the placenta, where it is reoxygenated from the mother's blood.

The blood returned from the upper part of the body (head and neck, upper limbs and thoracic walls) enters the right auricle through the *superior vena cava*. It then passes into the right ventricle (without mixing, apparently, with the stream from the inferior vena cava passing to the left auricle through the foramen ovale). Upon reaching the right ventricle, it is pumped into the pulmonary artery, but only a small proportion is distributed to the lungs—an amount sufficient only for the nourishment of the pulmonary tissue. The greater part is short circuited, through a vessel known as the *ductus arteriosus,* into the aorta. Thus the great bulk of the blood delivered to the right side of the fetal heart is "shunted" to the arterial side by the short cuts provided by the foramen ovale and the ductus arteriosus.

With the first few respirations, the lungs of the newborn child are expanded, and the course of the circulation becomes altered to meet the requirements of an air-breathing organism leading an independent existence. The foramen ovale closes and the channel afforded by the ductus arteriosus becomes obliterated. All the blood reaching the right auricle is now directed through the pulmonary circuit. The umbilical vessels shrink and are converted to solid cords. One or other or both of the circulatory adjustments which direct the blood through the lungs at birth may fail to occur. If the ductus arteriosus remains pervious part of the arterial blood, owing to its higher pressure, is driven from the aorta into the pulmonary artery; also, if the foramen ovale does not close, blood may pass from the left to the right auricle. These abnormalities cause, as a rule, little or no cyanosis. But in other types of circulatory defect, such as a large gap in the interventricular septum combined with narrowing of the pulmonary artery, the subjects —so-called "blue babies"—show intense cyanosis.

If the reader has followed the rather intricate course of the fetal circulation, he will have observed that the fetal tissues are never furnished with fully arterialized blood; the blood is always less saturated with oxygen than the arterial blood after birth. Yet strange to say, the blood returning from the placenta—that is, the blood in the umbilical vein —has a higher oxygen saturation than the maternal blood in the placenta—the only source from which the fetal blood can obtain oxygen. This physiological paradox has been explained by the discovery that the oxygen dissociation curve of fetal hemoglobin is different from that of animals in postnatal life (p. 250). The oxygen dissociation curve of the blood of the fetus is steeper than that of the mother—that is, it lies more to the left. This means that at a given oxygen pressure (tension) the fetal blood absorbs a greater volume of oxygen than can the mother's blood, or than the baby's blood will be able to absorb after birth (see Fig. 14.19). Through such a provision the fetus is more adequately furnished with oxygen than would otherwise be possible.

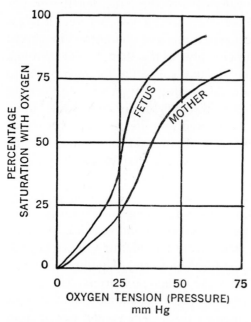

Fig. 14.19 A comparison of the dissociation curves of fetal and maternal hemoglobins.

Pregnancy and parturition. Pregnancy or *gestation* is the term applied to the period in the reproductive cycle occupied by the growth and development of the new organism within the body of the mother —that is, from the fertilization of the ovum (*conception*) to the birth of the young animal (*parturition*). Most of the structural and physiological adaptations of the pregnant state, such as the fertilization and implantation of the ovum, and the enlargement of the uterus and the growth and development of the mammary glands, have been touched upon elsewhere in this chapter. In a book of this scope little more remains to be written.

Pregnancy in the human race has a duration of about 280 days, or from 9 to 9½ months. From the fertilization and implantation of the ovum to the eighth week the product of conception is called the *embryo;* from this time until birth it is referred to as the *fetus.* From about the middle of pregnancy onward, movements of the fetus occur of which the mother is aware; they are referred to as *quickening.* Suck-

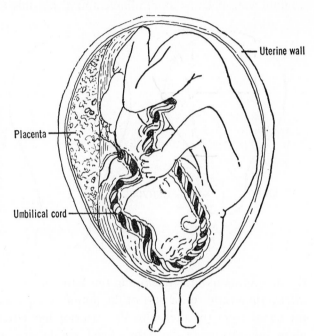

Fig. 14.20. Showing the usual position of the fetus just before birth. The umbilical vein (*black*) carries oxygenated blood from the placenta to the fetus; the two umbilical arteries (*white*) carry reduced blood from the fetus to the placenta.

Uterine wall

Placenta

Umbilical cord

ing and spasmodic movements of the chest resembling those of respiration have been observed in fetal animals. The unborn child lies within the sac formed by the amnion and chorionic membrane, submerged in a fairly large body of fluid (*liquor amnii*) which serves to protect it from sudden jars or injuries from the outside world. This membranous sac fills the uterus, and is considerably larger than the fetus itself which is thus permitted a certain freedom of movement.

Toward the latter part of pregnancy, the unborn child usually takes up a position with its head directed downward and, most frequently, its posterior part (occiput) pointing forward and to the left (Fig. 14.20). It is fitted in this position into the cavity of the pelvis. The descent of the fetus is aided very materially by previous softening of the ligaments and capsules about the pelvic joints which are loosened thereby and rendered more pliable. Indeed, this is a process essential for normal childbirth. The birth of the child is brought about by strong contractions of the uterine muscle, aided in the later stages by voluntary contractions of the abdominal muscles. The contractions of the walls of the uterus, weak at first and of short duration, become stronger and more prolonged in an hour or two; they cause molding of the infant's head and gradual dilatation of the outlet of the uterus with drawing up and disappearance of its neck or cervix; at the same time the vaginal walls become more pliable and distensible (Fig. 14.21). Later,

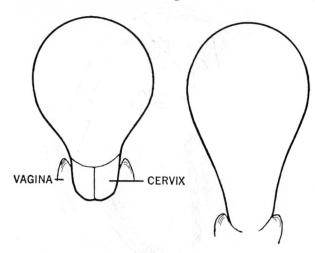

VAGINA   CERVIX

Fig. 14.21 Showing the thinning of the lower segment of the uterus and the dilatation of the outlet during the first stage of labor. *Left,* before the commencement of labor; *right,* toward the end of the first stage.

the membranous sac enveloping the fetus bulges into the vagina, and after a time ruptures, a part of the amniotic fluid then escaping. When the canal from the uterus to the exterior has enlarged sufficiently to allow the passage of the baby's head, the latter is expelled by powerful contractions of the uterus, accompanied usually by contractions of the abdominal muscles. The rest of the child's body follows almost immediately.

For a time the newborn babe still remains attached to the interior of the uterus through the umbilical cord and placenta (Fig. 14.22). The physician ties the cord with tape close to the baby's body and divides it on the mother's side of the tape. Not until 15 or 30 minutes later is the placenta, and the attached sac composed of the chorionic and amniotic membranes expelled. The placenta and membranes are commonly referred to as the *afterbirth. Labor* or *parturition* is the term given to the series of events bringing about the emptying of the uterus and the termination of pregnancy.

A consideration of the factors determining the onset of labor. The termination of pregnancy at the usual time is not due to a single factor, but to several. A sufficient number of these factors are known to enable us to draw in outline a picture of the mechanism leading to the precipitation of labor. The picture must of necessity be incomplete and many details left blank to be filled in when more knowledge has been gained.

It has been stated (p. 653) that the growth of the uterus ceases between the sixth and the seventh months of pregnancy; this is attributed

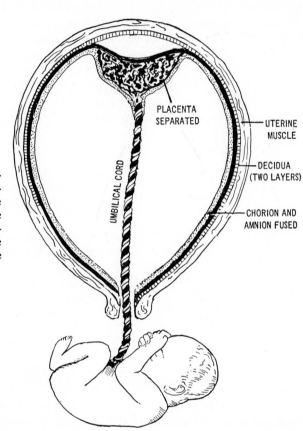

Fig. 14.22 The uterus and child immediately after birth. Note the separation of the placenta and the commencement of the peeling off of the membranes.

PLACENTA SEPARATED

UMBILICAL CORD

UTERINE MUSCLE

DECIDUA (TWO LAYERS)

CHORION AND AMNION FUSED

to the rise, from this time onward, of the concentration in the blood of estradiol which has an inhibitory effect upon the growth response of the uterus to distension. But the fetus is growing rapidly at this time, and the distension of the uterus now takes place in the long axis of the organ. The tension set up in the uterine tissues tends gradually to compress, narrow, and finally obliterate many vessels supplying blood to the placenta. Degenerative changes proceed in the latter, and the nutrition of the fetus suffers; it must be released and take on a new mode of existence if it is to survive. At the same time the output of placental hormones is reduced and the corpus luteum undergoes degeneration. Thus the depressing effect of progestin upon the irritability of the uterine muscle—an effect very necessary in early pregnancy— is withdrawn. The high concentration in the blood of estradiol further increases uterine irritability and thus enhances the tendency of the uterus to contract under slight provocation. Estradiol also raises the sensitivity (lowers the threshold) of the uterus to the action of the oxytocic principle of the posterior lobe of the hypophysis. A further word should be said about this latter principle. Its liberation is appar-

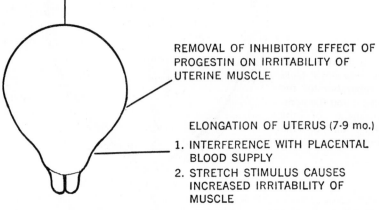

INCREASE IN ESTADIOL CAUSING

1. CESSATION OF UTERINE GROWTH
2. INCREASED IRRITABILITY OF MUSCLE
3. INCREASE SENSITIVITY TO OXYTOCIC PRINCIPLE

REMOVAL OF INHIBITORY EFFECT OF PROGESTIN ON IRRITABILITY OF UTERINE MUSCLE

ELONGATION OF UTERUS (7-9 mo.)

1. INTERFERENCE WITH PLACENTAL BLOOD SUPPLY
2. STRETCH STIMULUS CAUSES INCREASED IRRITABILITY OF MUSCLE

Fig. 14.23   Diagram summarizing the factors leading to the onset of labor.

ently under nervous control, for in animals stimulation of the vagina or uterine cervix causes contractions of the uterus, a response which does not occur if the stalk of the hypophysis, along which nerve fibers reach the posterior lobe, has been first divided. An oxytocic substance is found in the blood and urine of women in labor; though there is a strong suspicion that this substance is derived from the hypophysis, such has not been definitely established. For this reason, it is not possible to estimate accurately the importance of the oxytocic principle of the pituitary body in the mechanism which brings on labor. Furthermore, though labor is sometimes prolonged and difficult in animals after hypophysectomy, in other cases the young are born easily and within the usual time after the pituitary has been removed. It can therefore be said, at any rate, that the pituitary principle is not absolutely essential to the labor mechanism (see Fig. 14.23).

A few facts in the physiology of the fetus and the newborn child. The beating of the fetal heart can be heard in the later part of pregnancy by means of a stethoscope placed on the mother's abdominal wall over the uterus. The heart rate runs from 140 to 200 per minute. In the new born it is around the former figure. The respirations of the new born are from 30 to 35 per minute, as compared with the adult rate of from 18 to 20. The liver as well as the kidneys of the new born are functionally immature. The infant's urine, like that of certain lower orders of animals (e.g., the frog) is hypotonic, indicating that the ability possessed by the adult kidney to concentrate the glomerular filtrate has not yet been acquired (see Chap. 7). The high erythrocyte count with which the baby comes into the world and the difference between the hemoglobin of the fetus and that of the new born or of the adult have been mentioned elsewhere. The destruction of the excess of red cells shortly after birth, combined with the functional immaturity of the liver, accounts for the slight jaundiced tint of the skin sometimes seen in the newborn infant. The intestine of the new born contains a dark brown or black tarry material known as *meconium;* it is quite sterile, and for this reason, the baby, if it does not receive vitamin K from the mother in sufficient amounts before birth, may suffer from hemorrhages which are sometimes fatal (see p. 397). After the first day or so of the infant's life, the danger passes, for by this time bacteria capable of synthesizing the vitamin have reached the intestine in the food, or have been carried from the mouth in the saliva; the hemorrhagic tendency is thus corrected.

Most unconditioned reflexes are well developed at birth. The accommodation reflex of the eye is, however, usually in abeyance; and, since the corticospinal tracts of the brain and spinal cord are not fully developed, the plantar response (p. 519) is of the extensor type (Babinski response).

The puerperium or puerperal period. This is the period following the third or final stage of labor during which the mother is recuperating, and the uterus with the other structures of the birth mechanism are being restored to the nonpregnant state. Immediately following the expulsion of the placenta and fetal membranes (afterbirth), the uterus contracts down to a firm rounded body which can be plainly felt by a hand pressed upon the mother's abdomen. This strong gripping contraction compresses the open mouths of blood vessels and vascular spaces in the uterus, and is essential to prevent excessive bleeding. Intermittent uterine contractions at this time may be distressingly painful ("after pains"). In the days which follow, the uterine muscle shrinks, the redundant tissue being absorbed, and the uterus returns nearly to its virgin size. This process, which is called the *involution of the uterus,* is accompanied by a gradually lessening vaginal discharge consisting chiefly of blood and endometrial debris. The completion of the process of involution, which takes from 6 to 10 weeks, marks the end of the puerperal period.

The secretion of milk becomes well established usually by the end of the first day or so, and if the baby is put to the breast, the act of suckling stimulates contractions of the uterus and encourages its involution.

The two chief dangers of the puerperal period are hemorrhage and infection.

Glossary

Pronunciation. The vowel sound of an accented syllable is indicated by the position of the accent mark; if the vowel is long, the mark immediately follows it; if short, the mark follows the consonant. Thus, in *ab'scess,* the *a* is short, whereas in *adeno'ma* the *o* is long. Vowel sounds in all unaccented syllables unless otherwise indicated are short. Further information on pronunciation is given by the mark - or ᴗ above the vowel letter, or in round brackets following the word.

Plurals are given after the word, separated from it by a dash.

Derivations are within square brackets; the following abbreviations are used: F., *French;* G., *Greek;* Ger., *German;* L., *Latin;* ME., *middle English;* Med., *medieval;* OE., *old English;* fr., *from;* prec., *preceding* (item); foll., following.

Only those words are listed that have not been described adequately in the text, or have been mentioned before they have been fully explained.

A, an [privative, Greek negative, meaning the absence or removal of something, fr. L. *privatio,* deprive]. Used as a prefix (*a* before a vowel and *an* before a consonant), in words derived from the Greek, to indicate negation.

Ab- [L. from]. A prefix meaning away from, off.

Ab'oral [L. *ab.* away from + *os* (*or-*), mouth]. In a direction away from the mouth.

Ab'scess [L. *abscessus,* going away]. A circumscribed area of tissue, usually accompanied by the signs of acute inflammation, and containing pus. *Cold* abscess is one not showing the ordinary signs of inflammation; it is usually tuberculous.

Accessory food factors. Old term for vitamins.

Acidophil, acidophile [*acid* + G. *philos,* fond]. Having an affinity for acid; oxyphil.

Ad [L.]. A prefix meaning *to, toward,* or a suffix indicating in a direction *toward* a part as designated by the main part of the word, such as *caudad* toward the tail, or *cephalad* toward the head.

Adapta'tion. The failure to respond to a stimulus which has been applied repeatedly for some time. Thus, the ticking of a clock is after a time unperceived, and the pressure and rubbing of the clothes against the skin is disregarded. This is a property of receptors, but not of nerve fibers.

Adeno'ma [G. *adēn,* a gland + *ōma,* indicating a tumor]. A tumor of glandular tissue.

Adrenalec'tomy [adrenal + G. *ektomē,* excision]. Removal of the adrenal glands.

681

Adrenolyt'ic [*adreno* (*adrenal*) + G. *lysis* (*lyt-*), solution]. Referring to the action of certain agents which annul the effects of adrenaline.

Adsorp'tion [L. *ad*, to + G. *sorbo*, to suck up]. The attraction and adhesion of minute particles to the surface of a solid.

Ægoph'ony [G. *aix* (*aig*), a goat + *phōnē*, voice]. The sound like a goat bleating heard in auscultation of the chest in certain diseases of the lungs.

Aero'bic [G. *aēr*, air + *bios*, life, manner of living]. Referring to respiration and other processes carried on in the presence of oxygen.

Ag'minated [L. *agmen* (*agmin*), a multitude]. Aggregated, arranged in clusters.

Agno'sia [G. ignorance, fr. *a*, privative + *gnosis*, knowledge]. A condition allied to aphasia due to a cerebral lesion, in which the patient does not know the meaning of the sounds that he hears (*auditory agnosia*), or recognize the nature and use of ordinary things that he sees (*visual agnosia*), though his hearing and sight may be perfect.

Agran'ulocyto'sis [G. *a*, privative + *granulocyte* + *osis*, a state or condition]. A disease, often fatal, characterized by an almost complete absence of granulocytes from the circulation. Since these cells are of such importance in the defense of the body against the inroads of bacteria, severe uncontrollable infections may result. The disease is often caused by certain synthetic drugs or antibiotics which poison the bone marrow and suppress its function.

Agraph'ia [G. *a*, privative + *grapho*, to write]. A condition allied to aphasia in which the patient cannot express himself in writing, or write from dictation.

Aldos'terone. A steroid hormone obtained from the adrenal cortex which has a more pronounced effect than has desoxycorticosterone upon the metabolism of water and salts (sodium and potassium).

All'ergy [G. *allos*, other + *ergon*, work]. Hypersensitivity to certain agents, e.g., pollen, in hay-fever.

Alve'olus of tooth [L. diminutive of *alveus*, a trough]. A tooth socket.

Amne'sia [G. *a*, privative + *mnēmē*, memory]. Loss of memory due to cerebral lesion.

Am'phi-, ampho- [G. on both sides, around, both]. A prefix in words of Greek origin meaning on both sides, around, surrounding, both.

Amphoter'ic [G. *ampho*, both]. Referring to compounds, such as the amino acids that can act either as an acid or a base, depending upon the *p*H of the medium in which they are dissolved.

Ampul'la [G. a double-handled bottle]. A saclike dilatation of a tube or canal; e.g., a semicircular canal of the inner ear.

Ana- [G. up]. A prefix in words of Greek origin meaning up.

Anabolism [G. *anabole*, a building up, fr. *ana*, up + *bole*, to throw]. The metabolic process es involved in the synthesis of compounds, as in growth.

Anaero'bic [G. *an*, privative + *aerobic*]. Referring to respiration or other process carried on in the absence of oxygen.

An'alogue [fr. G. *ana-logus*, analogous]. An organ, or part, of one species which though differing more or less in structure from that of another species is similar in function; e.g., the hoof of a horse and the fore part of the human foot.

Anastomo'sis [G. to furnish with a mouth (*stoma*)]. The junction between the branches of two nerves or arteries either produced naturally in development, or by surgical operation, or the surgical union of two hollow organs; e.g., intestine to stomach, intestine to intestine, ureter to colon, etc.

An'drogen [G. *anēr* (*and*), a man + root *gen*, to produce]. Any compound that exerts an effect like that of the male hormone, testosterone.

An'eurysm [G. *aneurysma*, an *aneurysm*, fr. *eurys*, wide]. A localized, usually saccular or fusiform, dilatation of an artery with weakening of its wall. *Arteriovenous* aneurysm, communication between a large vein and an artery, with a local dilatation of the former.

Angi'na [L. a sore throat]. Sore throat or severe pain from any cause.

Angina pectoris [L. *pectus* (*pector*), the chest]. Severe, often agonizing, pain in the chest radiating down the left arm, due to disease of the coronary arteries resulting in a deficiency in the oxygen supply to the heart muscle.

An'nular [L. *annulus,* a ring]. Ring-shaped.

Anorex'ia [G. *an,* privative + *orexia,* appetite]. Loss of appetite.

An'te- [L. before]. A prefix in words of Latin derivation meaning before, in front of.

Anteflex'ion [L. *ante,* before, forward + *flexio,* bend]. A bending forward; anteflexion of the *uterus,* bending forward of the uterus, upon itself at the junction of the cervix with the body.

Anteversion [L. *ante,* before, forward + *versio,* to turn]. Falling forward of the uterus as a whole without bending upon itself.

Anti- [G. against]. A prefix meaning against, opposite, antagonistic.

Antiketogenic [L. *anti,* against + *keto* (*-ne*) + root, *gen,* produce]. Indicating an action of certain foods, especially glucose, in antagonizing the tendency to ketogenesis.

Antisep'sis [G. *anti,* against + *sepsis*]. The destruction of bacteria usually by the use of chemicals.

Aphasia [G. *a,* privative + *phasis,* speech]. A speech disorder due, not to any paralysis of the muscles normally involved in speech, but to a lesion of the part of the cerebral cortex concerned with the memory of words or of the motor mechanism of articulation. There are several types: *motor, visual, auditory,* etc. In motor aphasia, due to a lesion of the posterior and inferior part of the frontal lobe, the patient, though he may understand spoken and written words, cannot speak some or any words. In visual aphasia, the ability to recognize printed or written words is lost, and in auditory aphasia the patient does not understand what is said to him.

Ap'o [G. from]. A prefix in words of Greek origin meaning from.

Ap'ocrine [G. *apo,* from + *crino,* I separate]. Indicating a type of secretion in which the gland cells discharge a part of their protoplasm.

Apraxia [G. *a,* privative + *pratto,* to do]. The inability to perform a given act at will or when commanded to do so; this is *motor* apraxia. In *sensory* apraxia, the patient does not comprehend the use of an object; when given a pencil, for example, and asked to use it, he may attempt to brush his teeth with it, or to smoke it like a cigarette.

Arboriza'tion [L. *arbor,* a tree]. Fibers arranged in a pattern like the branchings of a tree.

Archen'teron (k) [G. *archē,* beginning + *enteron,* intestine]. The cavity of the gastrula.

Arrect'or muscles [L. *arrector,* to raise]. Smooth muscles in the skin attached to the shafts of the hairs.

Arthro'dia [G. a gliding joint]. A joint that permits a sliding or gliding movement only.

Arth'us phenom'enon. A localized anaphylactic reaction; when a sensitized rabbit is injected with the antigen, necrosis occurs and a sterile abscess forms at the site of the injection.

Artic'ular [L. *articulo,* articulate]. Relating to a joint.

Articula'tion [prec.]. (1) A joint. (2) Speech.

Asci'tes [L. fr. G. *askos,* a bag]. An abnormal and excessive collection of serous fluid in the peritoneal cavity, as may occur in hepatic, renal, or cardiac disease.

Asep'sis [G. *a*, privative, not + L. *sepsis*, putrefaction]. The state of being free from bacteria, or the method of bringing this about, usually by means of a high temperature.

Ataxia [G. *a*, privative + *taxia*, order, arrangement]. Muscular incoordination.

Atresia [G. *a*, privative + *trēsis*, a hole]. Congenital absence of an opening, e.g., the anus, or pathological closure of a normal orifice.

At'rophy [G. *a*, privative + *trophe*, nourishment]. Reduction in size of any organ or tissue due to shrinkage or wasting of its parenchyma which is largely, or at least in part, replaced by connective tissue.

Aur'icle [diminutive of L. *auris*, ear]. The pinna of the ear or the older term for an atrium of the heart.

Auscultation [L. *ausculto* (*atus*), listen to]. A method of examination in which the examiner listens, usually with a stethoscope, for sounds within the chest or any other part of the body.

Autocoid [G. *autos* (*o*) + *akos*, a remedy]. An active principle secreted by one of the endocrine organs. It may be either a hormone or a chalone.

Aut'o- [G. *autos*, self]. A prefix in words of Greek origin meaning self.

Autotransplanta'tion. The transplantation of an organ or the grafting of a tissue into another part of the same body. The transplanted structure has a good chance of surviving.

Avitamino'sis [G. *a*, privative + *vitamin* + *osis*, a state or condition]. Deficiency of one or other of the several vitamins; thus, one may speak of avitaminosis A, avitaminosis B_1, etc.

Az'ygos [G. *a*, privative + *zygon*, a yoke]. Single, unpaired.

Babin'ski response. Extension of the great toe upon gently stroking the inner side of the sole with the finger or a pencil. It is seen in certain nervous diseases; e.g., interruption of the corticospinal tracts. The normal response to such a stimulus is plantar flexion of the great toe.

Bacteriol'ysin [foll.]. An agent which causes bacteriolysis; some formed in the body act specifically upon the type of bacteria which causes a certain disease.

Bacteriol'ysis [*bacteria* + G. *lysis*, solution]. Destruction of bacteria by breaking up or dissolving the cell.

Bacteriostat'ic [*bacteria* + G. *statikos*, causing to stand]. Referring to agents; e.g., sulphonamide drugs and antibiotics which do not destroy bacteria or do so as a secondary effect, but interfere with some normal and essential process in the bacterial cell, and thus arrest or inhibit their multiplication.

bel [after *Alex. Graham Bell*, inventor of the telephone]. A unit of loudness.

Bi-, bis- [L. twice]. A prefix meaning twice, double.

Bi'ceps [L. *bi*, double + *caput*, head]. Two heads, designation for a muscle or other structure with two origins or heads—e.g., biceps of arm or of the thigh.

Bicip'ital [G. *biceps* (*cipitis*), two-headed]. Relating to any structure with two heads; e.g., the biceps brachii or biceps femoris.

Bicus'pid teeth. Premolar teeth.

Biliver'din [L. *bilis*, bile + Fr. verd (L. *viridis*), green]. A green pigment in bile derived from the oxidation of bilirubin.

Bi'otin [G. *bios*, life]. A factor of the vitamin B complex which neutralizes the effects of a poisonous protein in egg-white, called *avidin*. Animals fed a diet with a high percentage of egg-white, and deprived of biotin, develop a severe skin condition and other symptoms. Biotin deficiency in man apparently does not occur.

Blas′tula. Blastocyst.

Blee′ding time. The interval, measured in minutes, elapsing between the moment that blood appears from a prick of the skin, and when it clots, as determined by dabbing the wound with a scrap of filter paper.

Bohr effect. The action of carbon dioxide in causing a shift to the right of the oxygen dissociation curve of blood; that is, in reducing the affinity of hemoglobin for oxygen.

Bo′lus [L. a throw, a choice morsel]. A masticated mass of food in the mouth ready for swallowing, or in the esophagus or intestine that is moved along the tube by peristalsis.

Bradycar′dia [G. *bradys,* slow + *kardia,* the heart]. Unusually slow action of the heart.

Brain case. The part of the skull that encloses the brain.

Bronchioli′tis (k). Inflammation of the bronchioles.

Bronchi′tis (k). Inflammation of the bronchi.

Cal′cify [L. *calx,* lime + *facio,* make]. To harden a tissue, such as the arterial wall in arteriosclerosis, by the pathological deposition of insoluble salts of calcium, or the incorporation of calcium into cartilage or membrane in the normal formation of bone.

Calc′ulus [L. a pebble]. A stone formed in any organ (usually hollow), such as the gall-bladder, ureter, urinary bladder, salivary duct, etc.

Canalic′ulus [Diminutive of L. *canalis,* a canal]. A minute canal.

Can′thus [G. *kanthus*]. The junction of the eyelids at the outer and inner angles of the eye.

Car′dia [G. *kardia*]. The cardiac orifice.

Caryokinesis. *See* Karyokinesis.

Caryoplasm. *See* Karyoplasm.

Castra′tion [L. *castro* (*-atus*), to deprive of genital organs]. Excision of the gonads, either male or female.

Cat′a, Kat′a [G. *kata,* down]. A prefix in words of Greek origin meaning down, as opposed to *ana,* up.

Catab′olism [G. *cata,* down + *bolē,* throw]. The metabolic processes involved in the breakdown of compounds to simpler ones, *see* Anabolism.

Catal′ysis [G. *cata,* down + *lysis,* solution, dissolution]. The process whereby certain agents (e.g., enzymes), while not entering intimately into a chemical reaction or forming part of the final product, increase the speed of the reaction.

Caud′a equi′na [L. *cauda,* a tail + *equinus,* relating to *equus,* a horse]. The bundle of nerve roots arising from the lower part (lumbar region) of the spinal cord resembling a horse's tail and which descends for some distance in the spinal canal.

Celiac (se′liak) [G. *koilia,* belly]. Relating to the abdomen.

Cellulitis (seluli′tis) [L. *cellula,* a cell + *itis,* meaning inflammation]. Inflammation of connective tissue.

Ceph′alad [G. *kephalē,* head + L. *ad,* to]. In a direction toward the head, or brain.

Cephal′ic [prec.]. Relating to the head, or brain.

Cerebroside (ser′ebrōsīd). A lipid containing the sugar galactose.

Chalone (kalōn) [G. *chalāo,* to relax]. An internal secretion with an inhibitory action; e.g., enterogastrone.

Chem′orecep′tor. A receptor, as in the carotid body, that responds to chemical stimuli.

Cheyne-Stokes respiration (chān-stōks). An abnormal type of breathing occurring in grave disease in which the respirations increase progressively in depth and vigor to a maximum, then diminish again and finally cease (apnea) for a time. The return of the breathing marks the beginning of another cycle.

Chlor'ophyll [G. *chloros*, green + *phyllon*, a leaf]. The green pigment of plant life which functions in photosynthesis; it is allied to hemoglobin.

Choana—ae (ko'an-ah) [G. *choanē*, a funnel]. A funnel-like passage, such as the posterior apertures of the nasal cavities.

Choline (ko'lēn). A factor of the vitamin B complex deficiency which results in fatty liver. Deficiency, however, does not appear to occur in man.

Chorda tympani nerve (kor'da) [L. *chorda*, a chord or string + *tympani*, of the tympanum (fr. G. *tympanon*, a drum)]. A branch of the facial nerve that passes through the tympanum of the ear and supplies the submaxillary gland and the anterior part of the tongue (taste fibers).

Chromaffin (kro'mafin) [*chrom* (-*ic* salts) + L. *affinis* (fr. *ad* + *finis*, boundary, end), meaning attraction]. Having an affinity for the salts of chromic acid; e.g., the cells of the adrenal medulla and of the carotid body which are stained yellowish brown.

Chro'matid. One of the parts resulting from the longitudinal splitting of the chromosomes in the prophase of mitosis.

Chro'moproteins [G. *chroma*, color + *protein*]. Proteins whose molecules contain a pigment group; example, hemoglobin.

Chronaxia, chronaxie (krōn-ak'se-a, krōn-ak'sē) [G. *chronos*, time + *axia*, value]. The length of time, measured in thousandths of seconds, required for an electrical stimulus to act in order to excite a tissue, such as nerve or muscle, when the strength of the stimulus is twice that of the rheobase.

Cicatrix, cicatrices (sik'a-tricks, sik-a-tri'sēz) [L. scar]. A scar.

Cir'cum- [L. around]. A prefix meaning around, surrounding, circular.

Clearance. *See* Plasma clearance.

Coagula'tion time. The time elapsing between the instant that a sample of blood is collected and the appearance of the first signs of clotting. There are a number of methods for determining this, but whatever method is used the conditions are standardized so that all results by that method are strictly comparable. The coagulation time of human blood is normally between 3 and 4 minutes.

Coelom (se'lōm) [G. *koilōma*, a hollow]. The cavity of the embryo formed between the layers of the mesoderm, and from which the pericardial, pleural, and peritoneal cavities are developed. This is the *intra-embryonic coelom;* it communicates with the cavity of the chorion which is called the *extra-embryonic coelom.*

Col'or in'dex. An index employed in distinguishing between different types of anemia that expresses the relative quantity of hemoglobin in each red cell. It is a quotient derived from the following fraction:

$$\frac{\text{Hemoglobin in percent of normal}}{\text{number of red cells per millimeter of blood in percent of normal}}$$

The index is 1.0 in normal blood, above this in hyperchromic anemias, and below in hypochromic anemias.

Com'missure [L. *commissura*, a joining, a seam]. Any band of fibrous, nervous, or other tissue that joins two parts of (usually) similar structure.

Complemen'tal air. The volume of air that can be inspired above that of a normal ordinary inspiration.

Congen'ital [L. *congenitus*, born with]. Relating to any disease, condition, structure, etc., present at birth.

Con'jugated pro'teins [L. *con-jugo* (*-jugatus*), join together]. Any protein containing in its molecule a pigment, carbohydrate, lipid, nucleic acid, or other nonprotein group; e.g., hemoglobin, glycoprotein, nucleoprotein, etc.

Con'tra [L. against]. A prefix meaning against, opposite.

Convec'tion [L. *con-veho* (*-vectus*), carry or bring together]. The change in the positions of particles in a gas (e.g., air) or liquid caused by temperature, the heated particles rising while the cooler particles, being heavier, fall. Thus, convection currents are set up.

Corpus—corpora [L. body]. A body.

Cor'tex [L. bark]. The outer part of a structure that is distinguishable from the more centrally placed tissue—called the *medulla*.

Crepita'tions [L. fr. *crepo*, to rattle]. Fine grating, rattling, or crackling sounds characteristic of certain rales; or the gritty, grinding, or clicking sensation given to an examiner's fingers laid upon a fractured bone. They are caused by the fragments rubbing upon one another and can usually be felt by the patient himself.

Crib'riform [L. *cribrum*, a sieve + *forma*, form]. Perforated, sieve-like.

Crossing over. The interchange of chromatids between the members of a chromosome pair which occurs in the prophase of mitosis.

Cum-, com-, co- [L. with]. A prefix meaning with, combined, joined.

Cūne'iform [L. *cuneus*, a wedge + *forma*, form]. Wedge-shaped.

Cuta'neous [L. *cutis*, skin]. Relating to the skin.

Cy̆st [G. *kystis*, a bladder]. Any sac-like structure.

Cy̆sti'tis [G. *kystis*, bladder + *itis*, meaning inflammation]. Inflammation of the urinary bladder.

Cȳtol'ogy [G. *kytos*, cell (hollow) + *logos*, word, discourse, treatise]. The study of cells, histology.

Cȳtol'ysis [G. *kytos*, cell (a hollow) + *lysis*, breaking up, solution, dissolution]. Disintegration, solution of cells.

Deamina'tion, deaminiza'tion [L. *de*, from + am (fr. ammonia)]. The splitting off of an amino group, as from an amino acid.

Decibel (des'i-bel) [L. *deci* (abbrev. decimus) ten + *bel*]. One tenth of a bel.

Deciduous (de-cid'ū-us) [L. *decido*, to fall down]. Pertaining to anything that falls off or is discarded; e.g., the first set of teeth or the part of the endometrium that is shed with the placenta or during menstruation.

Decussa'tion [L. *decusso*, make in the form of an X]. A crossing as of nerve fibers with their fellows of the opposite side.

Dēhȳdra'tion [L. *de*, from + G. *hydor*, water]. The removal of water from the body or from any structure or substance.

Del'toid. Shaped like the Greek capital letter delta(Δ).

Dĕsquima'tion [L. *de*, from + *squama*, a scale]. The shedding of the superficial layers from the surface of the skin or of any part covered by squamous epithelium.

Deutoplasm, deuteroplasm (du'to-plazm) [G. *deutero*, second + *plasma*, a something formed]. The nutritive yolk of an egg. It is very small in the ova of mammals, but relatively enormous in the eggs of birds. The rest of the yolk, from which the embryo is developed, is called the cytoplasm or the *formative yolk*.

Di-, dis- [L. apart, sundering into two parts, two]. A prefix meaning two or separating into two.

Dia- [G. through]. A prefix meaning through, in different directions, or completely.

Diapede'sis [G. *dia*, through + *pedesis*, a leaping]. The passage of leucocytes through the capillary wall.

Diath'esis [G. an arrangement]. A constitution predisposed to some disease or abnormal state.

Dichotomy [G. *dicha*, in two + *tomē*, a cutting]. A branching into two, hence, *dichotomous* in referring to such a division.

Dicrot'ic pulse [G. *dicrotos*, fr. *di*, two + *crōtos*, a beating, a pulse]. A type of pulse occurring in typhoid fever and certain other conditions associated with low blood pressure and lax arterial walls, in which the dicrotic wave (ordinarily not palpable) can be felt as a distinct tap following the main pulse wave.

Dig'it [L. *digitus*]. A finger or a toe.

Digita'tion [L. *digitus*, a finger or toe]. One of a series of fingerlike projections, especially of a muscle.

Dip'loë [G. feminine of *diplous*, double]. The cancellous layer of bone lying between the two layers of compact bone of the cranium.

Dip'loid [G. *diplous*, double + *eidos*, resembling]. The double number of chromosomes characteristic of the immature sex cells, the zygotes, and the body cells generally; *see* Haploid.

Dist'al [L. *dist* (*ant*) + *al*]. In a position farther from the center or midline of the body, or from the origin of a limb or structure, such as an artery or nerve, thus the elbow is distal to the shoulder.

Dominant [L. fr. *dominus*, a master]. (1) Relating to an hereditary character which appears in the offspring and masks another character called *recessive*, though the gene carrying the latter has also been transmitted. (2) Relating to the cerebral hemisphere which determines right or left "handedness." Thus, the left hemisphere is dominant in right-handed persons and the right hemisphere in those who are left-handed.

Dors'ad [prec.]. In a direction toward the back.

Dor'sal [L. *dorsum*, the back]. Relating to or in a position toward the back.

Drop'sy [G. *hydrops*, an abnormal collection of fluid in a tissue or cavity]. An old term for edema or ascites and still in popular use; any abnormal and excessive collection of fluid in the tissues or a body cavity.

Dȳne [G. *dynamis*, force]. A unit of force, defined as that which acting on a mass of 1 gram for 1 second causes an acceleration of 1 cm. per second.

Dȳs- [G. bad, difficult]. A prefix in words of Greek derivation meaning difficult, bad, abnormal, or distressing.

Dȳsarthr'ia [G. *dys*, bad + *arthrōo*, articulate]. Difficulty in speaking due to weakness or paralysis of the muscles of articulation, or to stuttering or stammering.

Dȳspha'gia [G. *dys*, bad + *phagein*, to eat]. Difficulty in swallowing owing to pain or any other cause.

Ec-, ex- [G. *ektos*, without, out of]. A prefix meaning out of, outside, removal of.

Ectop'ic [G. *ek*, out + *topos*, a place]. Misplaced, not in the normal situation; e.g., *ectopic gestation*, pregnancy occurring in a uterine tube or in the peritoneal cavity.

Edema [G. *oidema*, a swelling]. An abnormal increase in tissue fluid, especially in the subcutaneous tissues, causing a puffy swelling of the part which, when pressed with a finger or thumb, shows a hollow imprint due to the temporary dispersal of the fluid.

Elec'trocor'tin [*electro* (abbrev. electrolyte) + *cortin*]. Aldosterone.

Elec'trophore'sis [*Electro* + G. *phorēsis,* a carrying]. The movement of particles, such as protein molecules, in an electric field to the anode or cathode.

Embolus [G. a wedge or stopper]. A clot, mass of agglulinated cells, a piece of fibrin, etc., carried in the blood stream and blocking a vessel.

Em'bryo [G. *embryon,* fr. *en,* in + *bryo,* be full, to swell]. The developing organism from the fertilization of the ovum to emergence from the egg, as in birds; in man, the product of conception from the second to the eighth week of pregnancy.

Embryol'ogy [G. *embryon* (prec.) + *logos,* treatise, discussion, word]. The study of the development of the embryo and fetus.

Empir'ical [G. *eperikos,* experience]. Not based upon any known scientific fact but purely upon experience.

Empyē'ma [G. *empyema,* suppuration, fr. *en,* in + *pyon,* pus]. Pus in any cavity, but, especially in the pleural cavity.

En [L. in]. A prefix meaning within.

Endem'ic [G. *endemos,* a native, fr. *en,* in + *demos,* the people]. Relating to a disease of which one or more cases are always present in the particular district under consideration.

Endo- [G. *endo,* within]. A prefix meaning in, within.

Endog'enous (j) [G. *endon,* within + root *gen,* beget, produce]. Formed within the body.

En'terogastro'ne [G. *enteron,* intestine + *gaster,* belly]. A principle (chalone) formed in the mucosa of the duodenum which under the influence of fatty materials in the chyme passes into the blood stream and inhibits the secretion of gastric juice and the movements of the stomach.

En'to [G. *entos,* in]. A prefix meaning within.

Ep'i- [G. upon]. A prefix meaning upon, above, on top of, the upper side.

Erg [G. *ergon,* work]. A unit of work, defined as that performed in moving a mass against a force of 1 dyne.

Es'trogen [G. *oistros,* mad desire + root, *gen,* produce]. Any substance that induces effects similar to those of estradiol.

Eu [G. well, good]. A prefix in words of Greek origin meaning good, well, or normal.

Ēvagina'tion [L. *e,* out + *vagina,* a sheath]. The protrusion of the wall or other part of any structure.

Exfōlia'tion [L. *ex,* out + *folium,* a leaf]. The shedding of superficial parts of any structure, especially in layers or sheets; a form of desquamation.

Ex'ocrine [G. *exo,* outside + *krino,* to separate (secrete)]. Relating to an external secretion; e.g., saliva, gastric juice, etc., that is secreted on to the surface of the body or into one of the body cavities.

Exog'enous (j) [G. *exo,* outside, *gen,* produce]. Formed or originating outside the body.

Exophthal'mos [G. *ex,* out + *ophthalmos,* the eye]. Protrusion of the eyeballs beyond their normal positions.

Ex'tero [L. *exterus,* outside]. Same as preceding.

Ex'terofec'tive [L. *exterus,* outside + *facio,* do]. Professor Cannon's term for the cerebrospinal nervous system, as opposed to the interofective (or autonomic) nervous system.

Ex'tra [L. outside]. A prefix meaning on the outside.

Ex'udate [L. *ex,* out + *sudare,* to sweat]. A fluid or semifluid material; e.g., serum or pus, which flows or oozes from any part.

Facet' [F. a very small face]. A small smooth area on a bone (usually for articulation), or other hard structure.

Falciform (făl'si-form) [L. *falx* (*falc-*), a sickle + *forma*, form]. Shaped like a sickle.

Fascia (fash'ia) [L. a band]. A thin sheet of fibrous tissue covering a muscle or other structure or separating one structure from another.

Fecunda'tion (k) [L. *fecundo* (*atus*), make fruitful]. Fertilization.

Fenes'tra [L. a window]. A window; e.g., fenestra ovale of the internal ear.

Fe'tus, foe'tus [L. offspring]. The unborn offspring from the eighth week to the termination of pregnancy.

Fibril'la—ae [L. *fibrilla,* diminutive of fibre, a fiber]. A minute fiber.

Fibril'lation [prec.]. Fine contractions or twitchings of muscle due to independent activity of the separate fibers. Such occurs in degenerating skeletal muscle, in cardiac muscle in electrocution, as a result of poisoning by certain drugs, and just preceding death from almost any cause.

Fil'ament [fr. L. *filum,* a thread]. An extremely fine fiber or thread-like structure.

Fi'lum termina'le [L. terminal thread]. A slender filament that descends from the end of the spinal cord to the termination of the vertebral canal.

Fim'briated [L. *fimbria,* a fringe]. Fringed or like fringe.

Fis'tula—fis'tulae [L. a pipe, tube]. An abnormal passage leading from an abscess cavity, or any hollow organ or part, to the exterior.

Fora'men—foram'ina [L. an aperture]. A small opening or hole in a bone (usually) or other structure.

For'eign pro'tein. A protein not naturally present in the body; e.g., a vegetable protein or one from another species; it acts as an antigen.

Fos'sa [L. a trench or ditch]. A depression, usually in a bone and longitudinal in shape.

Funic'ulus (k) [diminutive of L. *funis,* a cord]. A cord or cord-like structure, such as the umbilical or spermatic cord.

Galvanom'eter [Luigi Galvanni + G. metron, a measure]. An instrument for indicating and measuring a galvanic electric current.

Gang'lion—gang'lia [G. a small subcutaneous tumor]. A circumscribed collection of nerve cells in the brain, on a sensory nerve, or of the autonomic nervous system. (2) A small cystlike swelling on a tendon usually at the wrist.

Gasse'rian gang'lion. Semilunar ganglion, trigeminal ganglion.

Gas'trula [fr. G. *gaster,* belly]. The embryo in the stage of development when it consists of a sac with a double-layered wall; the inner layer is the endoderm, the outer the ectoderm.

Gēne [G. root, gen, beget]. One of the theoretical particles of a chromosome which carries an hereditary character.

Genera'tive [L. *generare,* beget]. Capable of reproduction, of procreation.

Genet'ic [G. *genesis* (*-etic*), generation]. Relating to heredity.

Genet'ics [prec.]. The study of the laws and processes of heredity.

Ge'notype [G. *genos,* birth + *typos,* an imprint]. The genetic constitution (combination of genes) of an organism.

Genus [L. birth, descent]. In the classification of animals or plants, the division next above the species; i.e., below the Family or the Tribe.

Glauco'ma [G. *glaukos,* bluish-green]. Raised pressure within the eyeball due to an excess of fluid, the result in turn of blockage of the drainage system. It is a progressive disease leading to failure of vision.

Gli'a. Neuroglia.

Gliss'on's cap'sule. The capsule of the liver.

Glÿcogen'esis [G. *glykys*, sweet (sugar) + root *gen*, produce]. The formation of glucose from glycogen or of glycogen from glucose.

Glÿcogenol'ysis [G. *glykys*, sweet (sugar) + *lysis*, dissolution]. The breakdown of glycogen to glucose.

Glÿcol'ysis [G. *glykys*, sweet (sugar) + lysis, dissolution]. The breakdown of glucose to lactic acid, or to carbon dioxide and water.

Gly'coneogen'esis, glu'coneogen'esis [G. *glykys*, sweet (sugar) + *nēos*, new genesis, origin]. The formation of glucose from noncarbohydrate material, as from protein or fat.

Gly'coprotein, glu'coprotein [G. *glykys*, sweet (sugar) + protein]. A conjugated protein containing a sugar group; it is present in mucin.

Granula'tion(s) [L. *granulum*, diminutive of *granum*, a grain]. Masses of small grain-like bodies.

Granula'tion tissue [prec.]. The vascular granular tissue that covers a healing open wound and becomes converted to scar tissue.

Hap'loid [G. *haplous*, single]. Refers to the reduced number of chromosomes in the gametes; *see* Diploid.

Heart block. Disease of the atrioventricular bundle, that slows or blocks conduction of the impulse from the atria to the ventricles. In complete blockage, the atria beat at the normal rate (70 per minute), but the ventricles beat at their own rate of about 40 per minute. The arterial pulse is, of course, at the ventricular rate.

He'matin [G. *haima* (*haimat-*), blood]. The pigment (porphyin) of hemoglobin plus iron.

Hemi- [G. half]. A prefix meaning a half.

Hemol'ysis [G. *haima*, blood + *lysis*, a setting free, dissolution]. The liberation of hemoglobin from the red cells.

Hen'le's loop. The U-shaped part of a renal tubule.

Hep'ar [G. the liver].

Hepat'ic [G. *hēpar* (*hepat-*), the liver]. Relating to the liver.

Hetero- [G. *heteros*, other, different]. A prefix in words derived from the Greek, meaning different from, something else.

Heterol'ogous [G. *heteros*, different, other + *logos*, relation]. Indicating a tissue or part derived from another species, or of a tissue or cells in a part not normal to them.

Het'erotran'splant [G. *heteros*, different, other + transplant]. The grafting of a tissue or organ taken from an animal of one species to the body of an animal of another species. Except for certain tissues and under very special circumstances the operation is not permanently successful; i.e., the transplanted tissue dies.

Hia'tus [L. an opening, fr. *hio* (*hiatus*), yawn]. A gap or opening, aperture or fissure.

Histol'ogy [G. *histos*, a web (tissue) + *logos*, treatise, discussion, word]. The microscopic study of tissues.

Hol'ocrine [G. *holos*, all + *krino*, separate (secrete)]. Referring to a type of glandular secretion which consists of the cells of the gland itself.

Ho'mo- [G. *homos*, same]. A prefix in words of Greek derivation meaning of the same kind or class, alike.

Homoge'neous (j) [G. *homos*, same + *genos*, family, kind]. Having uniform structure and composition throughout.

Homog'enous (j) [prec.]. Having the same consistency throughout and usually the same composition.

Homol'ogous [foll.]. Referring to a homologue, having the characters of a homologue.

Hom'ologue [G. *homos,* same + *logos,* relation, treatise, word]. Any organ or part of the body that resembles in structure or origin another organ or part elsewhere in the body; or an organ or part in one species that corresponds in some way with an organ or part in another species, such as the wing of a bird and the arm of a man.

Ho'motransplanta'tion [G. *homos,* same + transplant]. The grafting of tissue or of an organ from one person to another, or from one animal to another of the same species.

Hōst [G. *hospes,* a host]. An organism that harbors and gives sustenance to another (usually pathogenic) organism.

Hu'mor [L. *humor* (or *umor*), a fluid]. (1) One of the body fluids, such as the aqueous humor of the eye which fills the space between the cornea and the lens. (2) A substance, such as a secretogogue (extractive) in the food which is absorbed into the blood and stimulates a digestive secretion. (3) A substance liberated at nerve endings, e.g., acetylcholine, and acting locally. (4) One of the fluids of the body, e.g., blood, phlegm, black bile and yellow upon which the ancient theories of disease were based (humoral doctrine).

Hy'aloid [G. *hyalos,* glass + *eidos,* a resemblance]. Glass-like in appearance.

Hydrocephalus (hī-drō-kef'al-us) [G. *hydor,* water + *kephalē,* head]. Excessive amount of fluid in the ventricles of the brain (*internal hydrocephalus*), or in the subarachnoid space (*external hydrocephalus*).

Hydrol'ysis [G. *hydor,* water + *lysis,* solution, dissolution]. The taking up of water by a compound which then splits into smaller molecules. It is brought about by certain enzymes and by the action of heat and strong chemicals—acids or alkalis.

Hȳdrostat'ic pressure [G. *hydor,* water + *statos,* standing]. The pressure exerted by the weight of water or other liquid.

Hy'per- [G. *hyper,* above, over]. A prefix indicating excess; above the normal.

Hyperpla'sia [G. *hyper,* above + *plasis,* a molding]. Active multiplication of the cells of any tissue.

Hyperpnea [G. *hyper,* above + *pnoia,* the breath]. Exaggerated respirations, with an increase usually of the volume of air breathed per minute.

Hyperton'ic [G. *hyper,* above + *tonus,* tone]. Having a relatively high tone (e.g., muscle) or a high osmotic pressure (e.g., a solution of salt).

Hyper'trophy [G. *hyper,* above + *trophe,* nourishment]. Increase in bulk of a tissue or organ caused by an increase in the individual cells.

Hy'po- [G. *hypo,* under]. A prefix meaning under, beneath, less than normal.

Hypoderm'ic [G. *hypo,* under + *derma,* skin]. Beneath the skin.

Hypoton'ic [G. *hypo,* under + *tonos,* tone]. Having a relatively low tone (e.g., muscle) or a low osmotic pressure (e.g., a solution of salt).

Impreg'nate [L. in (im) + *praegnans,* pregnant]. (1) To introduce particles of one substance into any other substance, to saturate. (2) To fertilize (the penetration of the ovum by the spermatozoon), to fecundate.

Incon'tinence of urine [fr. L. *in,* negative + *contineo,* hold together]. Involuntary passage or dribbling of urine.

Inertia (in-ursh'ĕa) [L. *in,* negative + *iners* (fr. *in,* negative + *ars,* art), sluggishness, unskilled]. In physics, the "resistance" which a body offers to a force tending to move it from a position of rest. *Inertia of the uterus,* sluggishness or absence of contractions of the uterus during labor.

In'guinal [L. *inguen* (*inguinis*), the groin]. Relating to the groin.

Inhibition (in-hib-ish'un) [L. *hibeo* (*hibitus*) keep back, fr. *habeo,* to have]. Depression or arrest of function of any organ; e.g., slowing or stoppage of the heart by stimulation of the vagus nerve, or the lessening of any process.

Inorgan'ic [L. in, not + G. *organikos,* from *organon,* a tool, organ]. Not organic, inanimate; in chemistry, indicating compounds that do not contain carbon.

Inos'culate [L. *in* + *osculum,* diminutive of *os,* mouth]. Anastomose.

Insemina'tion [L. *insemino,* sow or plant, fr. *semen* (*semin-*), seed]. The deposition of semen in the vagina either during coitus or artificially.

In'sula [L. an island]. The small part of the cerebral cortex hidden in the Sylvian fissure. It is disclosed by raising the adjacent overlapping parts of the frontal and parietal lobes.

Integ'ument [L. *integumentum,* a covering]. The skin.

In'ter [L. between]. A prefix in words of Latin origin meaning between.

In'terofect'ive nervous system [L. *inter,* between + *facio,* do]. Professor Cannon's term for the autonomic nervous system.

Interstitial (in'tur-stish'al) [L. *interstitium,* fr. *inter,* between + *sisto,* stand]. Relating to spaces between fibers, cells, etc., especially in the tissues generally, as *interstitial fluid.*

In'tra- [L. within]. A prefix in words of Latin derivation meaning within.

In'tro- [L. into]. A prefix meaning into.

Invag'ina'tion (j) [L. *in,* in + *vagina,* a sheath]. The pushing of one part of a hollow structure inwards towards its center; to ensheath.

Inversion (in-vur'shun) [L. *inverto* (*inversus*), a turning about]. (1) a turning into a reversed position, as inversion of the uterus, in which the interior of the uterus is turned outward and the organ displaced downward. (2) A turning inward, as inversion of the foot. (3) The conversion of a disaccharide to a monosaccharide; e.g., of cane sugar to glucose and fructose.

I'soagglu'tinin [foll.]. An antibody present in the serum of a member of one of the blood groups which agglutinate the red cells of the blood of another group, that is, causing agglutination of cells in blood of the same species.

I'soagglutin'ogen [G. *isos,* same, equal + L. *agglutino,* glue together]. A substance (antigen) associated with the erythrocytes that reacts with an agglutinin (antibody) in the serum of a member of the same species and causes clumping together of the cells; *see* blood groups.

Kar'yokine'sis [G. *karyon,* a nut (*nucleus*) + *kinesis,* movement]. Mitosis.

Kar'yoplasm [G. *karyon,* a nut (*nucleus*) + *plasma,* a thing formed]. The nonchromatin substance of the cell nucleus.

Kata. *See* Cata.

Ker'atin [G. *keras* (*kerat*), horn]. A protein in the outer layers of skin, and in horn, nails, etc.

Kerati'tis [G. *keras* (*kerat*), horn (cornea) + *itis,* meaning inflammation]. Inflammation of the cornea of the eye.

Kētogen'ic [*keto* (*ketone*) + root, *gen,* produce]. Referring to certain foods, especially fats, which tend to cause the production of ketone bodies.

Knee-jerk. A quick extensor movement of the knee, a kick, caused by tapping the ligamentum patellae while the leg is hanging loosely in the flexed position. It is absent in certain nervous diseases and abnormally active in others.

Kup'ffer cells. Large star-shaped shells attached to the walls of the sinusoids of the liver. They belong to the reticulo-endothelial system and are phagocytic.

La'bile [L. *labilis,* unsteady]. Not steady, susceptible to change, as relating to temperament or to a chemical compound.

Lacta'tion [L. *lacto* (*atus*), to suckle (fr. *lac,* milk)]. The secretion of milk.

Lacu'na, -ae [L. diminutive of *lacus,* a hollow or a lake]. A hollow space or gap in any tissue or organ.

Lamel'la, -ae [L. diminutive of *lamina,* a layer or plate]. A thin layer, plate, or stratum.

Lanu'go [L. down, wool]. The very fine hair covering the body of the embryo or the surface of the adult body, except the palms of the hands and the soles of the feet and where the hair is long, as on the scalp.

Larva—larvae [L. a mask]. The wormlike stage of an insect as hatched from the egg, grub, maggot, or caterpillar, or the young of any species that differs essentially from its parents in form.

Larval, Larvate [prec.]. (1) Relating to larvae. (2) Masked, applied to a disease in which the symptoms are not typical or are absent.

Lesion (le'zhŭn) [L. *laedo* (*laessus*), to injure]. Any injury or any structural abnormality in a tissue, organ, or part due to disease; e.g., a tubercle of a lung in tuberculosis, or the pustule of the skin in smallpox.

Leuce'mia, leuke'mia [G. *leukos,* white + *haima,* blood]. A disease of the blood in which the white cells are greatly increased in number, there being many abnormal and primitive forms in the circulation. The disease may be acute or chronic, and according to which type of cell predominates in the blood, lymphocyte, myelocyte, or myeloblast, or monocyte. It is called *lymphatic, myelogenous,* or *monocytic* leukemia.

Leucope'nia [*leuco* (*leucocyte,* fr. G. *leukos,* white + *kytos,* cell) + *penia,* poverty]. A pronounced reduction of leucocytes; scarcity of leucocytes.

Lip'opro'tein [G. *lipos,* fat + *protein*]. A conjugated protein containing a lipid group in its molecule.

Lob'ūle [L. *lobulus,* diminutive of *lobus*]. A small lobe or a subdivision of a lobe.

Lu'men—lu'mina [L. a window, a light]. (1) The cavity of a tubelike structure, such as an artery or the intestine. (2) A unit of light.

Lymphangi'tis [L. *lympha,* clear water + G. *angeion,* a vessel + *itis,* meaning inflammation]. Inflammation of lymph vessels.

Ly'sin [G. *lysis,* disintegration, dissolution]. Any agent that destroys cells by breaking them up or dissolving them. One that destroys blood cells is a *hemolysin;* bacteria, a *bacteriolysin;* and cells in general, a *cytolysin.*

Ly'sis [G. disintegration, dissolution]. Disintegration of any structure, red cells, bacteria, fibrin, etc. Also used as a suffix in words of Greek origin meaning breakdown or disintegration; e.g., *cytolysis.*

Macera'tion [L. *macero* (*atus*), soften by soaking]. Soften or break up by soaking in water or other liquid.

Mac'roscopic (k) [G. *macros,* large + *skopeo,* to view]. Capable of being seen by the naked eye.

Mag'enstras'se [Ger. *magen,* stomach + *strasse,* road]. The part of the interior of the stomach extending along the lesser curvature from the cardia to the region of the pylorus that is first traversed by the food after it has entered the stomach.

Maras'mus [G. *marasmos,* a withering]. A state characterized by dehydration, wasting, and weakness; seen especially in infants as a result of infection, or faulty feeding.

Medul'la [L. fr. medius, middle]. Any very soft structure, or the interior of an organ; e.g., the adrenal medulla, as opposed to the outer part or cortex; marrow, spinal cord, medulla oblongata.

Meibomian gland (mi-bo'me-an). One of the glands at the margin of an eyelid.

Meiosis (mī-o'sis) [G. a lessening]. Reduction division.

Mem'brane [L. a skin or membrane]. A thin sheet of tissue that serves as a lining for various hollow structures (e.g., *mucous membranes*), covers or separates organs (e.g., *fibrous membranes*), or lines such cavities as the thorax and abdomen (e.g., *serous membranes*).

Mende'lian laws. The laws of heredity discovered by Gregor Mendel, an Augustinian monk, of the 19th century, living in Brunn, Austria. Studying inheritance in pea plants he found that characters were transmitted to the offspring as independent factors or genes. When two varieties of plant, each pure for a different character (shortness and tallness) are crossed, their progeny (F_1 generation) will be all tall; but they received a gene for shortness from their short parent as well as a gene for tallness from the tall parent; the character tallness which appears is called *dominant,* the hidden character shortness is termed *recessive.* These hybrid individuals produce three types of gametes, 25 percent of which contain only genes for tallness (dominant), 50 percent genes for both tallness and shortness, and 25 percent genes for shortness (recessive) only. When these are interbred, the offspring (F_2 generation) will be 75 percent tall and 25 percent short, that is, only those which had not received a gene for tallness from either parent will be short.

Mer'ocrine [G. *meros,* a part + *krino,* to separate (secrete)]. A secretion, such as the gastric or pancreatic juice, which is merely a product of the gland cells, and not part of their substance; *see* Holocrine and Apocrine.

Meta- [G. after, between, over, beyond]. A prefix meaning after, over, beyond or indicating a transformation from something else that has gone before.

Metamorphosis [G. *meta,* prec. + *morphē,* form]. A change, usually radical, in form; transformation, as that of the tadpole into the frog.

Metazoon, -a [G. *meta* + *zoon,* animal]. A member of any class of animal above the Protozoa, that is one composed of many cells.

Mic'turate [L. *micturio,* pass urine]. Urinate.

Micturition (micturish'un) [prec.]. Urination.

Min'imal air. The air that remains in the lungs after their removal from the body, and that gives pulmonary tissue its buoyancy.

Mōmen'tum [L. motion]. The quantity of motion, the product of mass and velocity; impetus, the tendency of a moving body to continue in its course.

Mon'ocȳte [G. *monos,* single + *kytos,* a hollow (cell)]. A white blood cell with a single unlobed nucleus. It resembles a large lymphocyte, but its nucleus is more deeply indented, being kidney- or horseshoe-shaped. Monocytes constitute from 2 to 8 percent of the leucocytes. They are elements of the reticuloendothelial system.

Mononu'clear [G. *monos,* single + *nuclear* (nucleus)]. Referring to a cell with but one nucleus.

Morbil'li [L. *morbillus,* diminutive of *morbus,* a disease]. Measles.

Motor end-plate. The structure on the muscle fiber in which the motor nerve terminates.

Multicellular [L. *multi,* many]. Consisting of many cells.

My'eloblast [G. *myelos,* marrow + *blastos,* a germ]. A granulocyte in a very early stage of its development (in the bone marrow).

My'elocyte [G. *myelos,* marrow + *kytos,* hollow (cell)]. A granulocyte in a late stage of its development (in the bone marrow).

Mȳogen'ic [G. *mys*, muscle + root, *gen*, produce]. Originating in muscle or from muscle.

Mȳoneur'al [G. *mys*, muscle + *neuron*, nerve]. Relating to both muscle and nerve. Myoneural *junction;* the connection between a motor nerve ending and the muscle fiber. It has the properties of a synapse.

Navic'ular (k) [L. diminutive of *navis*, a boat]. Shaped like a boat; scaphoid.

Ne'oplasm [G. *neos*, new + *plasma*, something formed]. A new growth, a tumor composed of masses of newly-formed cells.

Neurogen'ic [G. *neuron*, nerve + root *gen*, origin]. Of nervous origin.

Neurohu'moral [G. *neuron*, nerve + *humor*, q.v.]. Relating to the theory that nervous effects are transmitted by chemical substances (humors) liberated at the nerve endings; e.g., acetylcholine.

No'tochord [G. *nōtos*, back + *chordē*, cord]. A flexible bar in the early embryo around which the vertebral column is developed.

Nuclease [*nucleus* + *ase*, meaning an enzyme]. An enzyme that splits nucleic acids.

Nu'cleopro'tein. A conjugated protein containing nucleic acid. It is an essential constituent of chromatin.

Nu'cleus—nu'clei [L. a small nut or kernel]. The body containing chromatin and surrounded by the cytoplasm that is present in nearly all types of cell. (2) A circumscribed mass of gray matter (nerve cells) in the central nervous system. (3) a focus, such as a speck of foreign material, around which other material collects.

Nȳstag'mus [G. *nystagmos*, a nodding]. A rhythmical oscillation of the eyeballs occurring in certain diseases, and normally after rapid rotation of the body. The movements are most commonly from side to side, but may be up and down or rotary.

Ob- [L. against, toward]. A prefix in words of Latin origin meaning against or toward.

Odont'oid [G. *odous* (*odont-*), a tooth + *eidos*, a resemblance]. Shaped like a tooth.

-oid [G. *eidos*, a resemblance]. A suffix in words of Greek derivation meaning a likeness to, resembling.

Oligu'ria [G. *oligos*, few, little + *ourēsis*, urination]. Scanty urine.

-oma. A suffix added to words of Greek derivation to indicate a swelling or tumor of any kind, e.g., carcinoma, sarcoma.

Ontogenesis, ontogeny [G. *on*, being + *genesis*, origin]. The developmental history of an individual as opposed to the history of a race. *See* Phylogeny.

Ontol'ogy [G. *ōn* (*ontos*), being + *logos*, discussion, treatise]. The study of the development of an individual; embryology.

Onychia [G. *onyx* (*onych-*), nail]. Inflammation of the root of a finger- or toe-nail with suppuration and usually shedding of the nail.

O'öcyte [G. *ōon*, an egg + *kytos*, a hollow (cell)]. The primitive ovum in the Graafian follicle.

Op'sonins [G. *opson*, sauce]. Substances in blood that stimulate the leucocytes (neutrophils) to attack bacteria—fancifully speaking, they make the latter more appetizing.

Oral [L. *os* (*oris*), mouth]. Relating to the mouth.

Or'der. A division in the classification of animals or plants between the Class or Subclass (above) and the Family (below).

Organ'ic [G. *organikos,* relating to an organ, from *organon* a tool, organ]. (1) In chemistry, relating to compounds containing carbon. (2) Relating to a disease associated with a structural change in a tissue or organ as opposed to functional. (3) Pertaining to animal or vegetable life, as opposed to the inorganic world.

Or'ganism. Any living thing, animal, or plant.

Orthope'dic [G. *orthos,* straight, right, true + *pais* (*paid*), a child]. Relating to the study and treatment of chronic diseases of bones and joints and the correction of deformities.

Orthostat'ic [G. *orthos,* straight, right, true + *statos,* standing]. Relating to the upright (standing) position.

Os—ora [L. mouth]. A mouth.

Os—ossa [L. a bone]. A bone.

Osteogen'esis [G. *osteon,* bone + *genesis,* production]. Bone formation.

Ovariec'tomy [L. *ovarium,* ovary + G. *ektomē,* excision]. Excision of the ovaries; castration of the female.

Ox'yphil [G. *oxys,* sharp, acid + *philos,* fond]. Acidophil, eosinophil.

Oxytocin (oks-i-to'sin) [G. *oxys,* swift + *tokos,* childbirth]. Pitocin.

Palpa'tion [L. *palpatio,* fr. *palpo,* to touch]. Determining, usually with a finger or the fingers or palm of the hand, by touching.

Para- [G. alongside, near, beside] A prefix meaning beside, on the side of, not quite normal.

Para-aminobenzoic acid. A factor of the vitamin B complex essential for the growth of certain microorganisms. Some sulfonamides exert their antibacterial action by rendering this vitamin unavailable for the infecting bacteria.

Paren'chyma [G. anything poured in beside]. The part of an organ or tissue composed of cells that perform the specific function of the organ or tissue, such as the contractile fibers of muscle or the secreting cells of a gland, as opposed to the nonspecific supporting tissue or stroma of connective tissue.

Paren'teral [G. *para,* beside, contrary to + *enteron,* intestine]. Referring to a route of administering a drug or agent of any kind other than by the gastrointestinal tract, that is, subcutaneously, intravenously, etc.

Path'ogen [G. *pathos,* suffering, disease + root *gen,* produce], Any organism which causes disease, hence, *pathogenic.*

Pectoril'oquy [L. *pectus* (*pector-*), breast, chest + *loquor,* to speak]. In auscultation of the chest, the transmission of the sounds of the patient's voice to the examiner's ear.

Ped'icle [L. a little foot, diminutive of *pes* (*ped-*)]. A stalk.

Pepsin'ogen [*pepsin* + G. root *gen,* produce]. The inactive enzyme secreted by the gastric glands and converted to active pepsin by acid.

Per- [L. through]. A prefix denoting through, around; (in chemistry) the highest compound in a series.

Percussion (pur-kush'un) [L. *percussio,* a beating]. A method of physical examination, especially of the chest, in which the nature of underlying structure is determined from the sound caused by tapping with an instrument or finger.

Per'i- [G. around, beyond, surrounding]. A prefix meaning around, surrounding, exceedingly.

Peri'pheral [G. *peri,* around + *phero,* I carry]. In a position away from the center of the body or of any organ or part; nearer the circumference.

Pe'trous [G. *petra,* a rock]. Hard, like stone.

Phe'notype [G. *phainō,* display + *typos,* model]. The appearance, structure, coloring, and other characteristics of an organism.

Phlebi'tis [G. *phleps* (*phleb-*), a vein + *itis,* meaning inflammation]. Inflammation of a vein.

Phlebot'omy [G. *phleps,* (*phleb-*) a vein + *tomē,* a cutting]. Incision into a vein, as for withdrawing blood.

Pho'bia [G. *phobos,* fear]. An unreasonable fear of some particular thing or condition. For example, *claustrophobia* is a morbid fear of any closed space; *agoraphobia,* fear of open spaces. The term is also used to indicate hypersensitivity to some form of stimulation; e.g., *photophobia,* pain in the eyes and spasm of the lids to a light which normally would cause no discomfort.

Phos'phagen [*phosphorus* (*phōs,* light + *phoros,* bearing) + root, *gen*]. Creatine phosphate, phosphocreatine.

Pho'topho'bia [G. *phōs* (*phōt*) + *phobia*]. Hypersensitivity of the eyes to light.

Pho'tosyn'thesis [G. *phos* (*phot*) + *synthesis*]. The formation of carbohydrate from carbon dioxide and water, and the liberation of oxygen by sunlight acting upon chlorophyll.

Phren'ic [G. *phrēn,* diaphragm]. Relating to the diaphragm.

Phreni'tis [G. *phrēn,* diaphragm, seat of the emotions (an ancient belief) + *itis,* inflammation]. Delirium, inflammation of the brain.

Phylogen'esis, phylog'eny [G. *phylē, phylon,* a tribe + *genesis,* origin]. The development (evolution) of a race of animals or plants; *see* Ontogenesis.

Phy'lum [L. fr. G. *phylon,* a tribe, race]. In the classification of animals or plants, a large division below the Subkingdom and above the Subphylum or the Class.

Pi'siform [L. *pisum,* pea + *forma,* form]. Resembling a pea in shape and size.

Plank'ton [G. *planktos,* wandering]. Minute free-swimming or floating marine organisms either of the animal or vegetable kingdom.

Plant'ar [L. *planta,* the sole of the foot]. Relating to the sole of the foot.

Plas'ma clea'rance. A term for the volume of plasma from which a substance (such as urea) is completely removed by the kidney and excreted in the urine. It is determined by dividing the figure for the total quantity of the substance excreted in the urine per minute by its concentration in the plasma. Thus, $\dfrac{UV}{P}$ = plasma clearance. U is the concentration of the substance (e.g.,urea), V is the volume of the urine secreted per minute, and P is the concentration of the substance in the plasma.

Pleth'ora [G. *plethore,* fullness]. A fullness, an excess, especially of blood; congestion.

Plex'us [L. a braid]. An interlacement or network of nerves (nerve plexus) or of veins (venous plexus).

Pli'ca, -ae circula'ris -es [fr. L. *plica,* a fold + *circularis,* in the form of a small circle]. One of the transversely circular folds of mucous membrane in the small intestine.

Polyu'ria [G. *poly,* many, much + *ouron,* urine]. Excessive secretion of urine.

Post [L. after]. A prefix meaning after, behind.

Prae. *See* Pre.

Pre [L. *prae,* before]. A prefix meaning before, in front of.

Priv'ative [L. *privatio,* to deprive, negation]. The letter *a* used as a prefix in words of Greek origin to indicate negation, not, as *atypical,* not typical.

Pro- [G. before]. A prefix denoting before, forward.

Pro'cess [L. *processus,* an advance or progress]. (1) A physiological or pathological mode of action. (2) In anatomy, a projection from the main part of any structure—e.g., bone, nerve cell (axons and dendrites), etc.

Prolapse (prō-laps') [L. *prolapsis,* a falling]. The descent of an organ from its normal position; e.g., prolapse of the *uterus.*

Proliferation [L. *proles,* offspring + *fero,* to bear]. Multiplication of the cells of any tissue, usually in the sense of excessive.

Protozo'on, -a [G. *protos,* first + *zoon,* an animal]. An animal composed of a single cell; unicellular animal.

Prox'imal [L. *proximum,* next, nearest]. Nearer to the center of the body or to the origin of any structure—e.g., artery, nerve, limb, etc., as opposed to distal.

Pterygoid (ter'ĭgoyd) [G. *pteryx* (*pteryg-*), a wing + *eidos,* a resemblance]. Resembling a wing.

Pto'sis [G. a falling]. A falling down, prolapse of any structure, but especially drooping of one or both eyelids.

Pulse pressure. The pressure of the arterial system in excess of the diastolic pressure. For example, if the diastolic pressure amounts to 80 mm. of mercury and the systolic pressure to 120 mm., the pulse pressure will be 40 mm. of mercury.

Purpura (pur'pū-rah) [L. fr. G. *porphyra,* purple]. A hemorrhagic state in which spontaneous bleeding occurs into the subcutaneous tissues, deeper layers of the skin, into or from the surface of mucous membranes, or into joints and other structures. It is often due to a deficiency of platelets.

Pyogen'ic [G. *pyon,* pus + root *gen,* to produce]. Relating to any agent that causes the formation of pus, especially certain bacteria (e.g., staphylococci).

Pȳram'idal. Shaped like a pyramid.

Pyr'iform [L. *pirium,* a pear + *forma,* form]. Pear-shaped.

Pyrogen'ic [G. *pyr,* fire + root *gen,* to produce]. Heat producing; causing fever.

Quad'riceps [L. *quadri-,* four + *caput,* a head]. Four heads, term applied to the large muscle on the front of the thigh (quadriceps extensor).

Quadrigem'inal [L. *quadri,* four + *geminus,* twin]. Referring to any structure having four similar parts, but especially to the four bodies on the dorsal aspect of the midbrain (quadrigeminal bodies or colliculi).

Quin'sy [ME. corruption of Med. L. *quinancia,* fr. G. *cyanche,* sore throat, dog-throttling dog collar, fr. *kynōn,* dog + *anchein,* to throttle]. Inflammation of the tonsils, with suppuration (suppurative tonsillitis).

Rale (rahl) [Fr. rattle]. A crackling, clicking, bubbling, rubbing, or whistling sound heard upon auscultating the chest in certain diseases of the lungs.

Ra'mus, -i [L. a branch]. A branch, as of an artery or nerve; or a bar-like part of a bone, such as the ramus of the mandible.

Reac'tion [*re* + *action*]. (1) A term indicating the acidic, neutral, or basic nature of any material—e.g., acid reaction, neutral reaction, basic reaction. (2) The response of the body or of any tissue, especially muscle and nerve, to a stimulus. (3) In chemistry, the interaction occurring between two or more chemicals in which an exchange of molecules results in new compounds being formed.

Reces'sive [L. *recedo* (*recessus*), draw back]. An hereditary character that is latent, or masked by another character called *dominant.*

Regurgitation (rēgurj-it-a'shun) [L. *re,* back + *gurgito* (*atus*), flood]. The movement of material in a direction the reverse of normal, as the passage of the stomach contents into the esophagus (usually without vomiting), of duodenal contents into the stomach, or of blood from the aorta during diastole into the left ventricle.

Reis'sner's mem'brane. The membrane of the internal ear that separates the scala vestibuli from the cochlear duct.

Re'nal clea'rance. *See* Plasma clearance.

Retic'ulo-endothe'lial sys'tem [L. *reticulum*, a network + *endothelial*, relating to the endothelial tissues]. A system of cells in or associated with various reticular and endothelial structures, and also present in the general connective tissues; they have diverse functions. There are several types of these cells; some of those in the connective tissues are wandering, others are fixed. Those in the reticulum of the spleen are very large and phagocytic (*macrophages*), and those in the blood sinuses of the liver (*Kupffer cells*) as well as some in the general connective tissues convert hemoglobin into bile pigment. Others are found in the reticulum of the bone marrow. The monocytes of the blood and certain small cells in neuroglia (*microglia*) belong to this system.

Retic'ulum [L. diminutive of *rete*, a net]. A fine network.

Re'tro- [L. back, backwards]. A prefix meaning backwards, behind, posterior to.

Rhe'obase [G. *rheos*, a stream (current) + *basis*, base]. The minimal strength of an electric current that, acting for an indefinite but fairly long time, causes excitation of a tissue; e.g., nerve or muscle.

Rhom'boid [G. *rhombos* + *eidos*, a resemblance]. Resembling a rhombus, which is a figure (exclusive of the square) with four equal and parallel sides.

Santori'ni's duct. An accessory pancreatic duct.

Sciatic foramen (sī-at'īk for-a'men) [corruption of G. *ischiadikos*, fr. *ischion*, the hip]. One of the two foramina, greater and lesser, formed by a ligament closing the gap of the corresponding sciatic notch of the os coxae.

Sciat'ic notch [prec.]. One of the two notches, greater and lesser, of the os coxae. The greater sciatic notch is the large indentation on the posterior border of the ilium below the posterior inferior spine; the lesser sciatic notch is situated on the posterior border of the ischium just above the tuberosity. Both notches are converted into foramina in the living subject by ligaments.

Sciatica (si-at'ika). Inflammation or pain in the sciatic nerve.

Sclero'sis [G. *sklerosis*, hardness]. Induration, hardening of a structure, such as the walls of arteries (arteriosclerosis) due to the deposition of calcium salts or of any tissue, such as nervous or hepatic, by the replacement of its parenchyma by fibrous tissue.

Semi- [L. *semis*, half]. Prefix meaning half, equivalent to Greek *hemi*.

Se'rous [foll.]. (1) Relating to serum. (2) Qualifying certain membranes (*s. membranes*) that are covered by a layer of mesothelium—e.g., peritoneum, pleura, etc.

Se'rum [L. *whey*]. Blood fluid from which the fibrinogen has separated out through clotting of plasma.

Sig'moid [G. *sigma*, letter S + *eidos*, a resemblance]. S-shaped; e.g., the *sigmoid colon* (iliac and pelvic colons) which together form an S-shaped curve.

Spay'ing [G. *spadōn*, a eunuch]. Ovariectomy, castration of a female.

Species (spe'shēz) [L. kind, form, appearance]. In the classification of animals and plants, the division next below the Genus; its members interbreed.

Specific gravity (abbreviated Sp. g.). The weight of any given substance as compared with an equal weight of distilled water. Thus, water as having value 1.000, the specific gravity of urine is 1.002–1.030 (depending upon the concentration); blood, 1.055–1.060; plasma, 1.022–1.26; and cerebrospinal fluid, 1.006–1.08.

Sphyg'mogram [G. *sphygmos*, pulse + *gramma*, a record]. A pulse tracing.

Sphyg'momanom'eter [G. *sphygmos,* pulse + *manos,* pressed (pressure) + *metron,* measure]. An instrument for measuring the blood pressure.

Spi'na bif'ida [L. *spina,* a spine, thorn, the back + *bifida,* cleft into two parts]. A congenital anomaly in which the arches of the vertebrae of a portion of the spinal column are absent or defective so that the spinal membranes protrude, or even the cord itself, and come to lie just beneath the soft tissues of the back. It occurs most commonly in the lumbar region.

Sta'ble, sta'bile [L. *stabilis,* steady]. Firm, steady, not susceptible to change; applied to a chemical compound or to temperament, behavior, mentality, etc.

Stel'late [L. *stella,* a star]. Star-shaped.

Steno'sis [G. *stenos,* narrow]. A narrowing, usually applied to an orifice or tube; e.g., aortic stenosis.

Sten'son's duct. The duct of the parotid gland.

Stokes-Adams disease. Heart block, causing a slow pulse, with arteriosclerosis, the combination of the two conditions making for a low diastolic pressure and consequent interference with the blood supply to the brain. Attacks of syncope and convulsions result.

Sto'ma—stomata [G. *stoma* (*-atis*), a mouth]. Any mouth-like opening.

Stomati'tis [G. *stoma* (*-atis*), a mouth + *itis,* inflammation]. Inflammation of the mouth.

Stri'a [L. *a furrow* or line]. A fine line, linear groove, or elevation.

Stri'ation [*prec.*]. The appearance given by numerous fine lines.

Stro'ma—stromata [G. a bed, mattress]. The framework of any tissue or organ; it is usually composed of connective tissue.

Sty, stye (stī) [fr. OE. *stigan,* to rise]. Inflammation of one of the small glands at the margin of an eyelid; hordeolum.

Sub- [L. below]. A prefix indicating below, less than.

Sul'cus [L. a furrow, a ditch]. A narrow, relatively deep, depression in any structure, but especially in the cerebral cortex.

Su'per-, su'pra- [L. *above,* beyond]. A prefix indicating above, beyond, greater than, on the upper side.

Suppura'tion [L. *suppura* (*-atus*), to form pus (*pur*)]. Pus formation.

Su'ture [L. *sutura,* a seam]. (1) A surgical stitching. (2) One of the joints between the bones of the skull.

Sym'patholyt'ic [*sympatho,* fr. G. *syn,* with + *pathos,* feeling + *lysis* (*lyt-*), freeing from, dissolution]. Referring to the action of certain agents in temporarily paralyzing sympathetic nerve fibers.

Sym'pathomimet'ic [*sympatho* (prec.) + G. *mimikos,* imitating]. Referring to any drug or other agent; e.g., adrenaline that imitates the action of sympathetic nerve fibers.

Syn-, sym- [G. together with]. A prefix meaning with, together, joined; equivalent to Latin *con-.*

Synarthro'sis [G. *syn,* together + *arthrosis,* articulation]. An immovable junction between two bones without an intervening joint.

Syncy'tium [G. *syn,* together, with + *kytos,* a hollow (cell)]. A mass of multi-nucleated protoplasm, such as the cardiac muscle, in which the cells are not distinct and separate units, but are continuous with one another without an intervening cell membrane.

Syndesmo'sis [G. *syndesmos,* ligament, fr. *syn,* together + *deō,* bind]. A synarthrosis in which the opposed bones are held together by fibrous tissue, as at the lower ends of the tibia and fibula.

Syndrome (sin'drōm or sin'drō-mē) [G. *syn,* together + *dromos,* a running]. A group of symptoms which (running) together form the picture of a disease.

Syn′thesis [G. *syn*, together + *thesis*, a putting, an arrangement]. A building up of smaller parts into a larger whole; the putting together of smaller chemical groups to form larger and more complex compounds.

Ta′bes dorsa′lis [L. *tabes*, a wasting away + *dorsalis*, of the back]. A nervous disease affecting the ganglia of the posterior spinal nerve roots and posterior columns of the spinal cord. It is characterized by ataxia, loss of the knee-jerks, severe shooting pains, and often atrophy of the optic nerve. It is usually the result of syphilis.

Tach′ycar′dia (k) [G. *tachys*, rapid + *kardia*, heart]. Rapid action of the heart.

Tach′yphylax′is (k) [G. *tachys*, rapid + *phylaxis*, protection]. Loss of or reduction in sensitivity to any agent; tolerance following repeated use.

Tax′ia, tax′is [G. order, arrangement]. (1) Suffix in words of Greek origin. (2) The word is also used alone, and then means to correct a dislocation or to return a hernia by gentle pressure to its normal position. (3) The tendency for certain organisms to move toward or away from a particular thing or state or to arrange themselves in a position relating to that particular thing or state. The word is then usually used as in (1) above; *electrotaxis, chemotaxis, thermotaxis*, etc.

Te′lophase [G. *telos*, end, fulfillment + *phasis*, appearance]. The final stage of mitosis.

Ther′mola′bile [G. *thermē*, heat + L. *labilis*, perishable]. Susceptible to change or destruction by heat.

Ther′mosta′ble, ther′mosta′bile [G. *thermē*, heat + L. *stabilis*, stable]. Not altered by moderate heat.

Thrombo′sis [G. a curdling]. Clotting of blood within the vascular system.

Throm′bus [G. *thrombos*, a clot, curd]. A clot within a blood vessel.

Thymus [G. *thymos*, an excrescence, sweetbread]. A soft structure occupying the upper part of the mediastinum and lower extremity of the neck. It is relatively large in infants, but shrinks in later childhood, and is a mere vestige in adults. It consists of a reticulum, the spaces of which are packed with lymphocytes. Its outer part is called the cortex, its central part the medulla. Scattered throughout the latter are peculiar bodies, known as *Hassall's corpuscles* and composed of concentric layers of flat epithelial cells surrounding a large round granular cell. Though it has been suggested that the thymus is an endocrine organ, there is no definite evidence that it should be classed as such; its function is obscure.

Thy′rotoxico′sis [*thyro* (*thyroid*) + G. *toxicon*, poison + *osis*, state or condition]. The condition caused by an excess of thyroid hormone—e.g., exophthalmic goiter.

Ti′dal air. The air breathed during ordinary respiration; it amounts to about 500 cc. in man.

Tone [G. *tonos*, tone or a tone]. (1) Continuous action, as said of a nerve (such as the vagus), or of the slight continuous contraction of healthy muscle. (2) The pitch of a sound. (3) A quality of color, depth, brilliance, intensity.

Trans- [L. across, through beyond]. A prefix meaning across, through, beyond.

Traum′a—traumata [G. a wound]. A wound or injury, usually one caused by violence or some mechanical agency.

Tri′be [L. *tribus*]. In the classification of animals and plants, a subdivision of the *Family*, frequently synonymous with *Subfamily*.

Tri′ceps [L. *tri*, three + *caput*, a head]. Applied to any structure, but especially a muscle that has three heads or origins.

Troch′lea (k) [L. a pulley]. A pulley.

Troch'oid joint (k) [G. *trochos,* wheel + *eidos,* a resemblance]. A pivot joint, such as that between the odontoid process of the axis vertebra and the atlas.

Tro'pism [G. *trope,* a turning]. The tendency for certain organisms to turn toward something, as growing sprouts of plants turn toward the light, *phototropism,* and its roots into the ground, *geotropism.*

Tu'bercle [L. fr. *tuberculum,* diminutive of *tuber,* a swelling]. (1) a small circumscribed elevation on a bone. (2) The lesion in tuberculosis.

Tuberos'ity [L. *tuberositas,* an elevation, or swelling]. An elevation on a bone larger than a tubercle.

Tympani'tes [fr. G. *tympanon,* a drum]. Swelling of the abdomen due to gas in the intestine or, rarely, in the peritoneal cavity.

Ul'tra [L. beyond]. A prefix meaning beyond, excessive.

Ul'trafiltra'tion [prec. + filtration]. The separation of salts (crytalloids) from colloids by filtration.

U'vea [L. *uvea,* a grape]. The middle coat of the eyeball, consisting of the choroid, ciliary muscle and iris.

U'veal tract. Uvea.

Va'gusstof'fe [*vagus* + Ger. *stoffe,* substance]. The humor formed at the terminals of the vagus nerve; acetylcholine.

Vallate [L. *vallo (ate),* surround with, fr. *vallum,* a rampart]. Referring to certain structures, e.g., papillae of the tongue, that are surrounded by a circular moatlike depression bounded in turn by a slightly elevated rim.

Vallec'ula [L. diminutive of *vallis,* a valley]. The depression on either side of the tongue, or of the vermis of the cerebellum.

Varicel'la [L. diminutive of *variola*]. Chickenpox.

Vario'la [L. diminutive of *varius,* spotted]. Smallpox.

Văs [L. *vasa* (genitive, plural, *vasorum*), a vessel, dish]. A vessel or tube; e.g., *vas deferens.*

Va'sa vasor'um [prec.]. The small blood vessels supplying the walls of the larger arteries.

Vas'cular [L. *vasculum,* diminutive of *vas,* a vessel]. Referring to any tube or system of tubes containing fluid, but most commonly to the blood vessels or lymphatics.

Va'somo'tor. Referring to changes in the calibers of the blood vessels.

Ven'trad [L. *venter,* belly]. Toward the ventral aspect; opposed to dorsad.

Ven'tral [prec.]. Indicating the front aspect of the human body or the under side of a quadruped; opposed to dorsal.

Vermiform [L. *vermis,* a worm + *forma,* form]. Wormlike; e.g., vermiform appendix.

Ver'nix caseo'sa [L. *vernix,* varnish + *caseus,* cheese]. The fatty substance on the skin of the newborn.

Vestib'ular mem'brane. Reissner's membrane.

Vestib'ular or'gan. The utricle and saccule.

Vi'ral. Relating to viruses.

Vi'rus—viruses [L. poison]. One of a group of infecting agents of uncertain nature, but probably a large and complex nucleoprotein molecule near the border line between the living and the nonliving. Unlike bacteria, they can multiply only within cells. They are much smaller than bacteria being able to pass through a filter with much finer pores than those required to hold back bacteria, hence the term *filtrable viruses.* Though viruses cannot be seen through an ordinary type of microscope, however powerful, the electron microscope reveals minute objects called *elementary bodies* that are probably the viruses themselves.

Viscosity [L. *viscosus,* viscid viscous]. Stickiness, internal friction of a liquid or semiliquid, as measured by the rate at which the material flows along a narrow tube. The value is expressed in relation to the viscosity of water taken as 1.

Viscous [prec.]. Sticky, glutinous.

Vis'cus—viscera [L. an internal part]. Any internal organ, but especially of the thorax, abdomen or pelvis.

Vo'lar [L. *vola,* palm of the hand or sole of the foot]. Relating to the palm of the hand or the sole of the foot, or to any similarly directed part—e.g., the front of the arm or the back of the leg. It is synonymous with ventral and palmar in the former instance, and with dorsal and plantar in the latter.

Whar'ton's duct. The duct of the submaxillary gland.

Whit'low [etymology dubious, perhaps corruption fr. OE. *quick* (*whick*) or *white* + *flaw*]. Inflammation of the soft tissue in the neighborhood of a nail; paronychia.

Wirsung's duct. The pancreatic duct.

Wis'dom tooth. One of the four molar teeth that erupt very late—from the eighteenth to the twenty-third year; it is the third molar on each side of the upper or the lower jaw.

Zoology [G. *zōon,* an animal + *logos,* treatise, discussion]. The study of animals, their classification, structure, and physiology, etc.

Zy'mogen [G. *zyme,* leaven (*enzyme*) + root *gen,* produce]. The substance from which an enzyme is formed; proenzyme.

Appendix

Appendix

Weights and Measures

Linear measures

The unit of the metric system is the meter, which is the one ten-millionth part of the meridian quadrant of the earth. In the nomenclature of the system, multiples of the meter are indicated by prefixes derived from the Greek, as follows:

Meter; decameter, 10 meters; hectometer, 100 meters; kilometer, 1000 meters.

Fractions of the meter are indicated by prefixes derived from the Latin, as follows:

Meter; decimeter, $\frac{1}{10}$ meter; centimeter, $\frac{1}{100}$ meter; millimeter, $\frac{1}{1000}$ meter.

In microscopy, the unit of measure is $\frac{1}{1000}$ of a millimeter, called micron (symbol μ).

Weights

The unit of weight is the gram, or gramme; abbreviation, usually g. or gm. It is practically the weight of one cubic centimeter of distilled water at its maximum density (4°C.). Multiples of this unit are designated by prefixes derived from the Greek numerals, as follows:

Gram; decagram, 10 grams; hectogram, 100 grams; kilogram (abbr. kilo), 1000 grams.

Fractions of the gram are designated by prefixes, derived from the Latin numerals as follows:

Gram; decigram, $\frac{1}{10}$ gram; centigram, $\frac{1}{100}$ gram; milligram, $\frac{1}{1000}$ gram; $\frac{1}{1000}$ milligram (or $\frac{1}{1000000}$ gram) is called a microgram or gamma (symbol γ); $\frac{1}{1000}$ micron or $\frac{1}{1000000}$ millimeter, called the millimicron (symbol $m\mu$), and $\frac{1}{10000}$ micron, called the Ångstrom unit (symbol Å, or abbreviated Å.U.), are used as measures of the wavelengths of light.

Fluid measure; volume; capacity

The unit of volume is the cubic decimeter, called a liter; one liter of water weighs practically 1 kilogram. It is divided into the deciliter, $\frac{1}{10}$ liter (weight 100 grams); centiliter, $\frac{1}{100}$ liter (weight 10 grams); and milliliter, (or cubic centimeter), $\frac{1}{1000}$ liter (weight 1 gram).

APOTHECARY AND AVOIRDUPOIS SYSTEMS

Weights

The apothecary system (or the metric) is used in the United States for measuring drugs and other medicinals. In Britain the avoirdupois system is used for the latter purpose, and, as in the United States, for measuring ordinary commodities.

Apothecaries' Weights (U. S.)

Pound		Ounces		Drachms		Scruples		Grains
1	=	12	=	96	=	288	=	5760
		1	=	8	=	24	=	480
				1	=	3	=	60
						1	=	20

Avoirdupois Weights

Pound		Ounces		Drachms		Grains
1	=	16	=	256	=	7000
		1	=	16	=	437.5
				1	=	27.34375

Fluid measures

United States

Gallon		Quarts		Pints		Fluid Ounces		Fluid Drachms		Minims
1	=	4	=	8	=	128	=	1024	=	61440
		1	=	2	=	32	=	256	=	15360
				1	=	16	=	128	=	7680
						1	=	8	=	480
								1	=	60

British (Imperial)

Gallon		Quarts		Pints		Fluid Ounces		Fluid Drachms		Minims
1	=	4	=	8	=	160	=	1280	=	76800
		1	=	2	=	40	=	320	=	19200
				1	=	20	=	160	=	9600
						1	=	8	=	480
								1	=	60

EQUIVALENTS

Linear measures

One kilometer = ⅝ mile or 3281 feet; 8 kilometers = 5 miles; 1 meter = 39 inches; 1 centimeter = ⅖ inch; 1 millimeter = 1/25 inch or ½ line; 1 micron = 1/25000 inch.

One mile = 1⅗ kilometers; 1 yard = 92 centimeters; 1 foot = 30.5 centimeters; 1 inch = 25 millimeters.

Weights

One kilogram = 2⅕ pounds, or 35⅕ ounces, avoirdupois; 1 gram = 15½ grains.

One pound avoirdupois = 453.6 grams; 1 ounce avoirdupois = 28.4 grams; 1 drachm = 3.89 grams; 1 grain = 0.065 gram.

To convert kilograms to pounds avoirdupois multiply by 1000 and divide by 454; to convert pounds avoirdupois to kilograms, multiply by 454 and divide by 1000.

To convert grams to ounces avoirdupois, multiply by 20 and divide by 567; to convert ounces avoirdupois to grams, multiply by 567 and divide by 20.

Metric equivalents of apothecaries' weights

Grains	Grams	Drachms	Grams
½	0.032395	1	3.88788
1	0.064798	4	15.55152
5	0.323990		
10	0.647980	Ounces	Grams
20	1.295960	1	31.10394
30	1.943940	4	124.41576

Metric equivalents of avoirdupois weights

The equivalents for grams and fractions of a grain are the same as those of apothecaries' weights.

Drachms	Grams	Ounces	Grams
1	1.77182	1	28.34912
4	7.08728	8	226.79296
		16	453.58592

Equivalents of metric in apothecaries' or avoirdupois weights

Grams	Grains
0.1	1.54339
0.5	7.71699
1.0	15.43399
5.0	77.16995
10.0	154.33991

Kilograms	Ounces (Avoirdupois)	Kilograms	Pounds (Avoirdupois)
1	35.27	1	2.2048
5	176.37	5	11.0240
10	352.74	10	22.0480

Fluid Measures

One liter = 1.76 imperial pints or 2.1 U. S. pints; 1 cubic centimeter = 17 minims (British) or 16¼ minims (U. S.).

One imperial gallon = 4.55 liters; 1 U. S. gallon = 3.79 liters; 1 imperial pint = 568 cubic centimeters; 1 U. S. pint = 473 cubic centimeters; 1 fluid ounce (British) = 28.4 cubic centimeters; 1 fluid ounce (U. S.) = 29.5 cubic centimeters; 1 fluid drachm (British) = 3.5 cubic centimeters; 1 fluid drachm (U. S.) = 3.7 cubic centimeters; 1 minim = 0.065 cubic centimeter.

To convert liters to imperial gallons, multiply by 22 and divide by 100; to convert liters to U. S. gallons, multiply by 265 and divide by 1000 (by moving the decimal point three places to the left); to convert imperial gallons to liters, divide by 22 and multiply by 100; to convert U. S. gallons to liters divide by 265 and multiply by 1000.

Metric equivalents of U. S. measures

Minims	Cubic Centimeters	Fluid Drachms	Cubic Centimeters	Fluid Ounces	Cubic Centimeters
1	0.061618	1	3.697086	1	29.576686
5	0.308091	5	18.485431	6	177.460116
10	0.616181			16 (pt.)	473.226976
15	0.924272				

Metric equivalents of British (Imperial) measures

Minims	Cubic Centimeters	Fluid Drachms	Cubic Centimeters	Fluid Ounces	Cubic Centimeters
1	0.059205	1	3.5523	1	28.4184
5	0.296025	5	17.7615	5	142.0920
10	0.592050			10	284.1840
15	0.888075			20 (pt.)	568.3680
20	1.184100				

Equivalents of metric in U. S. measures

Cubic Centimeters	Minims	Liter	Fluid ounces	Pints
0.1	1.62341	1	33.82108	2.11381
0.5	8.11706			
1.0	16.23412			
5.0	81.17061			
10.0	162.34122			

Equivalents of metric in Imperial measures

Cubic Centimeters	Minims		Liters	Fluid ounces	Pints
0.1	1.68911		1	35.19691	1.75984
0.5	8.44556				
1.0	16.89112				
5.0	84.45560				
10.0	168.91123				

MEASURES OF ENERGY

One kilogrammeter is the energy or force expended in raising a weight of 1 kilogram to a height of 1 meter. One foot-pound is the energy or force expended in raising a weight of 1 pound avoirdupois to a height of 1 foot.

One kilogrammeter = 7.24 foot-pounds.

One foot-pound = 0.1381 kilogrammeter.

SYMBOLS

℞	minim.	>	greater than; whence, from which is derived.
℈	scruple.		
ℨ	drachm.	<	less than; from, derived from.
℥	ounce.	∞	infinity.
O	pint.	:	ratio; "is to."
μ	micron.	::	equality between ratios; "as."
μμ	micromicron.	*	birth.
℞	misce, mix.	†	death.
+	plus; excess; acid reaction; positive.	♀	female.
−	minus; deficiency; alkaline reaction; negative.	♂	male.
±	plus or minus; either positive or negative; indefinite.		

COMPARATIVE TEMPERATURE SCALES

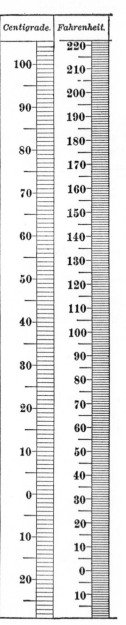

Centigrade.	Fahrenheit.

The zero of the centigrade scale marks the temperature of melting ice (32°F.); the zero of the Fahrenheit scale is an arbitrary point, that of the lowest temperature observed by the deviser of the scale during the winter of 1709, practically the temperature of a mixture of ice and salt; it corresponds to $-17.77°C$. The temperature of boiling water, at sea-level, is marked 100° on the centigrade scale and 212° on the Fahrenheit scale. A degree F. is therefore $\frac{5}{9}$ degree C.

The following are rules for the conversion of the temperature of one scale into that of one of the others:

Above 0°C. or 32°F.

F. to C.: subtract 32, multiply by 5, divide by 9.
C. to F.: multiply by 9, divide by 5, add 32.

Between 0° and 32°F. or −17.77; and 0°C.

F. to C.: subtract from 32, multiply by 5, divide by 9.
C. to F.: multiply by 9, divide by 5, subtract from 32.

A CLASSIFICATION OF THE PROTEINS

CLASS OF PROTEIN	CHARACTERISTICS	EXAMPLES
	A. Simple proteins	
(1) *Albumins*	Soluble in water and coagulable by heat. Present in both animal and plant tissues	*Serum albumin, egg albumin, lactalbumin* and various vegetable albumins such as *leucosin* (in wheat, rye and barley), *legumelin* in lentils, soy-bean, beans and peas and *phaselin* in kidney bean
(2) *Globulins*	Soluble in dilute saline solutions; insoluble in water. Animal globulins are coagulated by heat. Vegetable globulins imperfectly or not coagulated by heat	*Serum globulin, fibrinogen* (and *fibrin*) *vitellin* of egg yolk and vegetable globulins such as *excelsin* (Brazil-nut), *edestin* (hemp), *phaseolin* (kidney bean), *legumin* (peas and lentils) and *tuberin* (potato). A number of other vegetable globulins have been isolated and named
(3) *Glutelins*	Found only in plants. Insoluble in water, saline or alcohol, but soluble in very dilute alkali	*Glutenin* of wheat, *oryzenin* of rice and *glutelin* of maize
(4) *Prolamines* or *Gliadins*	Found in cereals (except rice) soluble in 70–90 per cent alcohol. Insoluble in water. They contain a large proportion of proline and ammonia nitrogen	*Gliadin* of wheat, *hordein* of barley and *zein* of maize
(5) *Albuminoids* or *scleroproteins*	Especially resistant to the usual reagents. They enter into the construction of protective and connective tissues, e.g., skin, tendons, ligaments and bones	*Keratin* of hair, skin, bone, feathers, tortoise shell and egg-shell, *elastin, collagen, ossein* and *gelatin* of tendons, ligaments, bone, etc.
(6) *Histones*	Soluble in water and precipitated by ammonia solution and by alkaloids. They contain a large percentage of diamino acids (p. 625)	*Globin* of hemoglobin, *thymus histone; scombron* and *gadus histone* in spermatozoa of mackerel and cod-fish respectively
(7) *Protamines*	Found in combination with nucleic acid in heads of fish spermatozoa. Constructed predominantly of diamino acids	*Salmine* and *sturine* in spermatozoa of salmon and sturgeon respectively

B. Conjugated proteins. Proteins whose molecule is combined with another non-protein group

CLASS OF PROTEIN	CHARACTERISTICS	EXAMPLES
(1) *Nucleoproteins*	Nucleic acid in combination with a protein belonging usually to the class of histones or protamines. Found in cell nuclei	See ch. 48
(2) *Chromoproteins*	Protein in combination with a pigment (e. g., hematin) containing iron, copper or other metal	Hemoglobin, hemocyanin, etc.
(3) *Glycoproteins*	Proteins other than nucleoproteins in combination with a carbohydrate group	*Mucin* in salivary gastric and intestinal secretions; *ovomucoid* of egg white and *chondromucoid* of cartilage
(4) *Lipoproteins*	Proteins in combination with lipid	Present in plasma, milk, cell nuclei
(5) *Phosphoproteins*	Proteins other than nucleoproteins and lecithoproteins in combination with a phosphorus-containing group	*Caseinogen* (and casein), *vitellin* of egg-yolk

C. Derivatives of proteins—derived proteins. These are produced by the action of acids, alkalis or proteolytic enzymes upon certain of the proteins listed above

CLASS OF PROTEIN	CHARACTERISTICS	EXAMPLES
(a) *Primary derivatives* (1) *Proteans*	Insoluble products formed in the early stage of the action upon proteins of water, dilute acids and enzymes	

CLASSIFICATION OF THE PROTEINS (CONT.)

C. *Derivatives of proteins—derivated proteins.—Continued*		
(2) *Metaproteins*	Formed in a later stage of the action of acid or alkali	*Acid* metaprotein, *alkali* metaprotein
(3) *Coagulated proteins*	Formed by the action of heat or of alcohol upon solutions of proteins	
(b) *Secondary derivatives*		
(1) *Proteoses*	Formed by the action of pepsin or trypsin upon proteins. They are soluble in water from which they are precipitated by saturation with ammonium sulphate. They are incoagulable by heat	*Albumose* from albumen, *globulose* from globulin, *caseose* from casein
(2) *Peptones*	These represent a further stage in action of proteolytic enzymes. They are soluble in water but are not precipitated from an aqueous solution by ammonium sulphate. They are not coagulated by heat	
(3) *Peptides, di-peptides, tripeptides and polypeptides*	Products formed in the final stages of proteolytic digestion	Glycyl-alanine, leucyl-glutamic acid, etc.

A LIST OF THE AMINO ACIDS PRESENT IN MOST COMPLETE PROTEINS

I. ALIPHATIC AMINO-ACIDS

A. *Monoamino-monocarboxylic acids*

Glycine (or glycocoll) $C_2H_5NO_2$, or amino-acetic acid

$$CH_2—NH_2$$
$$|$$
$$COOH$$

Alanine $C_3H_7NO_2$ or α-amino-propionic acid

$$CH_3 \cdot CH—NH_2$$
$$|$$
$$COOH$$

Serine, $C_3H_7NO_3$, or α-amino-β-hydroxy propionic acid

$$CH_2 \cdot CH—NH_2$$
$$|\ \ \ \ |$$
$$OH\ \ COOH$$

Threonine $C_4H_9NO_3$

$$CH_3CH \cdot CH—NH_2$$
$$|\ \ \ \ |$$
$$OH\ \ COOH$$

Valine $C_5H_{11}NO_2$

$$CH_3$$
$$\diagdown$$
$$CH \cdot CH—NH_2$$
$$\diagup\ \ \ \ \ |$$
$$CH_3\ \ \ \ COOH$$

Norleucine $C_6H_{13}NO_2$

$$CH_3 \cdot CH_2 \cdot CH_2 \cdot CH_2 \cdot CH—NH_2$$
$$|$$
$$COOH$$

Leucine, $C_6H_{13}NO_2$,

$$CH_3$$
$$\diagdown$$
$$CH \cdot CH_2 \cdot CH—NH_2$$
$$\diagup\ \ \ \ \ \ \ \ \ |$$
$$CH_3\ \ \ \ \ \ \ COOH$$

Isoleucine, $C_6H_{13}NO_2$,

$$CH_3$$
$$\diagdown$$
$$CH \cdot CH—NH_2$$
$$\diagup\ \ \ \ \ |$$
$$CH_3 \cdot CH_2\ \ \ COOH$$

Sulphur-containing monoamino-monocarboxc acids

Cystine, $C_6H_{12}N_2S_2O_4$,

$$CH_2—S—S—CH_2$$
$$|\ \ \ \ \ \ \ \ \ \ \ |$$
$$CH—NH_2\ \ \ \ CH—NH_2$$
$$|\ \ \ \ \ \ \ \ \ \ \ \ \ |$$
$$COOH\ \ \ \ \ \ COOH$$

AMINO ACIDS PRESENT IN MOST COMPLETE PROTEINS (CONT.)

Methionine, $C_5H_{11}SNO_2$,
thiol-*n*-butyric acid

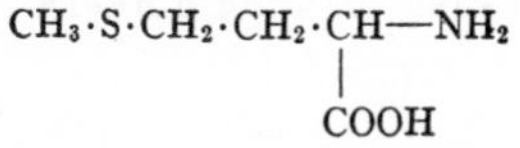

$$CH_3 \cdot S \cdot CH_2 \cdot CH_2 \cdot CH-NH_2$$
$$|$$
$$COOH$$

B. *Monoamino-dicarboxylic acids*

Aspartic acid, $C_4H_7NO_4$,

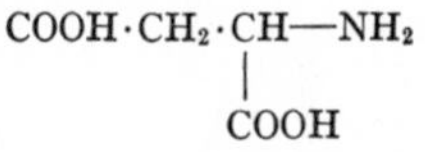

$$COOH \cdot CH_2 \cdot CH-NH_2$$
$$|$$
$$COOH$$

Glutamic acid, $C_5H_9NO_4$, or α-amino-glutaric acid

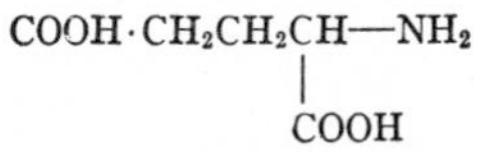

$$COOH \cdot CH_2CH_2CH-NH_2$$
$$|$$
$$COOH$$

Hydroxyglutamic acid, $C_5H_9NO_5$,

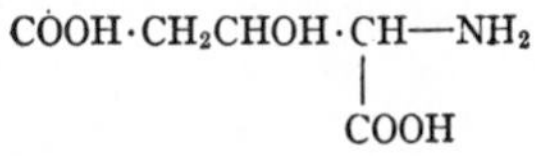

$$COOH \cdot CH_2CHOH \cdot CH-NH_2$$
$$|$$
$$COOH$$

C. *Diamino-monocarboxylic acids*

Arginine, $C_6H_{14}N_4O_2$,

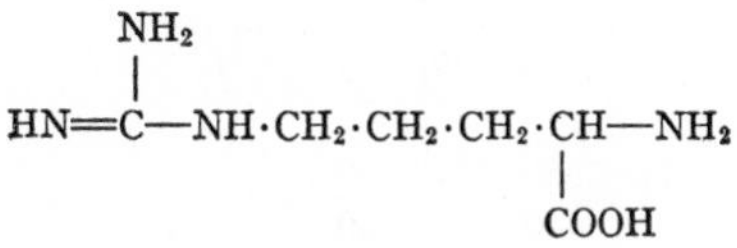

$$NH_2$$
$$|$$
$$HN=C-NH \cdot CH_2 \cdot CH_2 \cdot CH_2 \cdot CH-NH_2$$
$$|$$
$$COOH$$

Lysine, $C_6H_{14}N_2O_2$,

$$NH_2$$
$$|$$
$$CH_2 \cdot CH_2 \cdot CH_2 \cdot CH_2 \cdot CH-NH_2$$
$$|$$
$$COOH$$

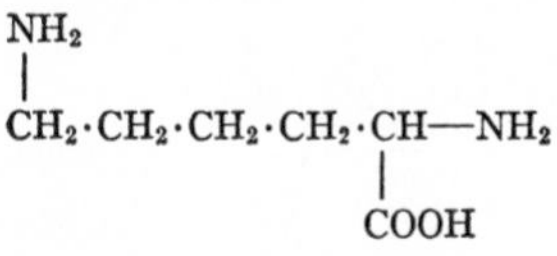

II. Aromatic Amino-Acids

Phenylalanine, $C_9H_{11}NO_2$,

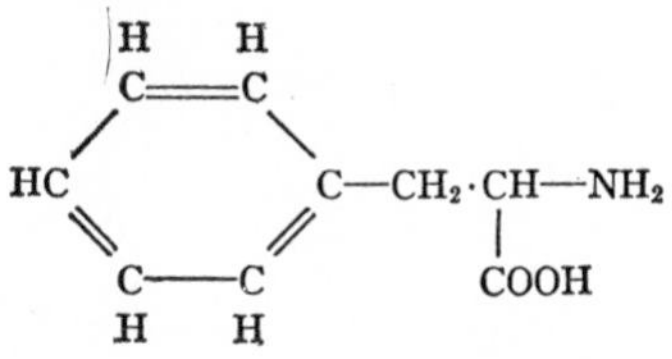

Tyrosine, $C_9H_{11}NO_3$,

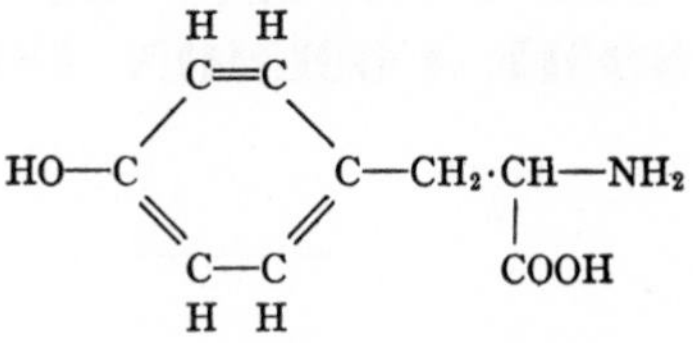

III. Heterocyclic Amino Acids

Tryptophane, $C_{11}H_{12}N_2O_2$,

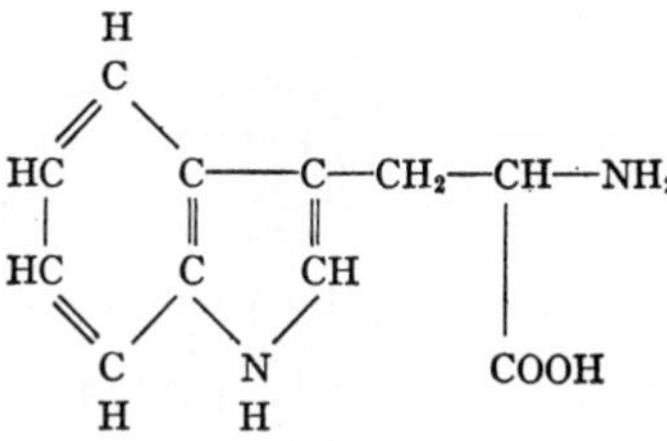

Indole nucleus

Histidine, $C_6H_9N_3O_2$,

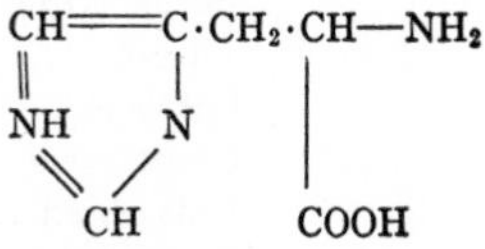

Imidazol ring

Proline, $C_5H_9NO_2$,

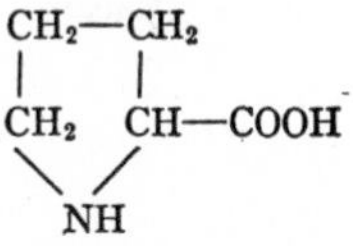

Pyrrole nucleus

Hydroxyproline (oxyproline), $C_5H_9NO_3$,

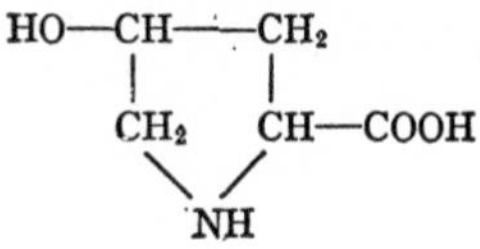

ASH CONTENT OF THE EDIBLE PORTION OF SOME COMMON FOODS

(Modified from Lusk)

	IN 100 GRAMS FRESH SUBSTANCE						
	Iron	Calcium	Magnesium	Sodium	Potassium	Phosphorus	Chlorin
	mg.	mg.	mg.	mg.	mg.	mg.	mg.
Beefsteak, lean..	3.8	8	24	67	35	22	50
Liver (beef)....	8.0	11.0	....	....	....	....	....
Eggs............	3.0	67	9	15	14	16	100
Milk, whole.....	0.2	120	11	51	142	94	120
Cornmeal.......	1.1	....	....	....	..	..	..
Oatmeal........	3.7	93	127	81	380	380	35
Rice, polished...	0.7	8	27	21	68	89	50
Wheat flour.....	1.5	26	30	69	146	86	76
Wheat, entire grain.........	5.2	44	170	106	515	469	88
Beans, lima, dried	7.2	71	187	245	1743	336	25
Beans, string, fresh..........	1.6	....	....	....	....	....	....
Cabbage........	0.9	49	14	20	243	27	13
Corn, sweet.....	0.8	....	....	....	....	....	....
Peas, dried......	5.6	100	145	118	880	397	40
Potatoes........	1.2	11	22	19	440	61	30
Spinach.........	3.8	....	....	....	....	....	....
Turnips.........	0.6	64	169	59	332	51	40
Apples..........	0.3	10	8	15	125	13	4
Raisins..........	3.6	57	9	141	830	126	70

AVERAGE COMPOSITION AND ENERGY VALUES OF EDIBLE PORTIONS OF SOME COMMON FOOD MATERIALS

	PER CENT					ENERGY VALUE	
	Water	Protein N × 6.25	Fat	Carbo-hydrate	Ash	Per kg.	Per pound
	grams	grams	grams	grams	grams	calories	calories
Meat:							
Beef, round steak, medium fat..........	54.8	23.5	20.4	....	1.2	2,860	1,300
Mutton, leg roast......................	50.9	25.0	22.6	....	1.2	3,125	1,420
Pork, ham, luncheon bacon, side........ {	49.2	22.5	21.0	....	5.8	2,870	1,305
	18.8	9.9	67.4	....	4.4	6,665	3,030
Chicken:							
Broilers...............................	74.8	21.5	2.5	....	1.1	1,110	505
Fish, cod, whole..........................	82.6	16.5	0.4	....	1.2	715	325
Herring, whole......................	72.5	19.5	7.1	....	1.5	1,455	660
Salmon, whole......................	64.6	22.0	12.8	....	1.4	2,090	950
Trout, brook, whole.................	77.8	19.2	2.1	....	1.2	980	445
Fats:							
Butter...............................	11.0	1.0	85.0	....	3.0	7,930	3,605
Lard.................................	....	....	100.0	....	....	9,285	4,220
Suet.................................	13.7	4.7	81.8	....	0.3	7,790	3,540
Cheese:							
American, red.........................	28.6	29.6	38.3	....	3.5	4,765	2,165
Milk.......................................	87.0	3.3	4.0	5.0	0.7	715	325
Eggs, hens', boiled......................	73.2	13.2	12.0	....	0.8	1,685	765
Flour, white, wheat......................	11.5	11.4	1.0	75.6	0.5	3,650	1,660
Bread, white.............................	35.6	9.3	1.2	52.7	1.2	2,650	1,205
Fruit:							
Apples...............................	84.6	0.4	0.5	14.2	0.3	640	290
Banana...............................	75.3	1.3	0.6	22.0	0.8	1,010	460
Cherries.............................	80.9	1.0	0.8	16.7	0.6	805	365
Grape fruit...........................	93.6	0.6	0.1	5.7	....	267	120
Oranges..............................	86.9	0.8	0.2	11.6	0.5	528	240
Vegetables:							
Beans, dried...........................	12.6	22.5	1.8	59.6	3.5	3,530	1,605
Cabbage..............................	91.5	1.6	0.3	5.6	1.0	320	145
Lettuce...............................	94.7	1.2	0.3	2.9	0.9	206	90
Potatoes..............................	75.5	2.5	0.1	20.9	1.0	968	440
Sugar, granulated.........................	....	....	....	100.0	....	4,090	1,860
Chocolate..............................	5.9	12.9	48.7	30.3	2.2	6,295	2,860
Cocoa, powder..........................	4.6	21.6	28.9	37.7	7.2	5,105	2,320

RECOMMENDED DIETARY ALLOWANCES *

(Food and Nutrition Board, National Research Council)

	CALORIES	PROTEIN GRAMS	CALCIUM GRAMS	IRON	VITAMIN A‡	THIAMIN (B₁)	RIBO-FLAVIN	NIACIN (NICO-TINIC ACID)	ASCOR-BIC ACID	VITAMIN D
				mg.	I.U.	mg.†	mg.	mg.	mg.†	I.U.
Man (70 Kg.)										
Sedentary...........	2500	—	—	—	—	1.5	2.2	15	—	—·
Moderately active...	3000	70	0.8	12	5000	1.8	2.7	18	75	**
Very active.........	4500	—	—	—	—	2.3	3.3	23	—	—··
Woman (56 Kg.)										
Sedentary...........	2100	—	—	—	—	1.2	1.8	12	—	
Moderately active...	2500	60	0.8	12	5000	1.5	2.2	15	70	**
Very active.........	3000	—	—	—	—	1.8	2.7	18	—	—
Pregnancy (latter										
half).............	2500	85	1.5	15	6000	1.8	2.5	18	100	400 to 800
Lactation..........	3000	100	2.0	15	8000	2.3	3.0	23	150	400 to 800
Children up to 12 years:										
Under 1 year§.......	100/kg.	3 to 4/kg.	1.0	6	1500	0.4	0.6	4	30	400 to 800
1–3 years¶.........	1200	40	1.0	7	2000	0.6	0.9	6	35	**
4–6 years........	1600	50	1.0	8	2500	0.8	1.2	8	50	—
7–9 years..........	2000	60	1.0	10	3500	1.0	1.5	10	60	—
10–12 years........	2500	70	1.2	12	4500	1.2	1.8	12	75	—
Children over 12 years:										
Girls, 13–15 years...	2800	80	1.3	15	5000	1.4	2.0	14	80	**
16–20 years...	2400	75	1.0	15	5000	1.2	1.8	12	80	—
Boys, 13–15 years.....	3200	85	1.4	15	5000	1.6	2.4	16	90	**
16–20 years.....	3800	100	1.4	15	6000	2.0	3.0	20	100	—·

* Tentative goal toward which to aim in planning practical dietaries; can be met by a good diet of natural food. Such a diet will also provide other minerals and vitamins, the requirements for which are less well known.

† 1 mg. thiamin equals 333 I.U.; 1 mg. ascorbic acid equals 20 I.U.

‡ Requirements may be less if provided as vitamin A; greater if provided chiefly as the pro-vitamin carotene.

§ Needs of infants increase from month to month. The amounts given are for approximately 6–8 months. The amounts of protein and calcium needed are less if derived from human milk.

¶ Allowances are based on needs for the middle year in each group (as 2, 5, 8, etc.) and for moderate activity.

** Vitamin D is undoubtedly necessary for older children and adults. When not available from sunshine, it should be provided probably up to the minimum amounts recommended for infants.

Further Recommendations, Adopted 1942:

The requirement for *iodine* is small; probably about 0.002 to 0.004 milligram a day for each kilogram of body-weight. This amounts to about 0.15 to 0.30 milligram daily for the adult. This need is easily met by the regular use of iodized salt; its use is especially important in adolescence and pregnancy.

The requirement for *copper* for adults is in the neighborhood of 1.0 to 2.0 milligrams a day. Infants and children require approximately 0.05 per kilogram of bodyweight. The requirement for copper is approximately one-tenth of that for iron.

The requirement of *vitamin K* is usually satisfied by any good diet. Special consideration needs to be given to newborn infants. Physicians commonly give vitamin K either to the mother before delivery or to the infant immediately after birth.

STANDARD WEIGHT ACCORDING TO HEIGHT AND AGE

Men

Age	5 Ft.	5 Ft. 1 In.	5 Ft. 2 In.	5 Ft. 3 In.	5 Ft. 4 In.	5 Ft. 5 In.	5 Ft. 6 In.	5 Ft. 7 In.	5 Ft. 8 In.	5 Ft. 9 In.	5 Ft. 10 In.	5 Ft. 11 In.	6 Ft.	6 Ft. 1 In.	6 Ft. 2 In.	6 Ft. 3 In.	6 Ft. 4 In.	6 Ft. 5 In.
15	107	109	112	115	118	122	126	130	134	138	142	147	152	157	162	167	172	177
16	109	111	114	117	120	124	128	132	136	140	144	149	154	159	164	169	174	179
17	111	113	116	119	122	126	130	134	138	142	146	151	156	161	166	171	176	181
18	113	115	118	121	124	128	132	136	140	144	148	153	158	163	168	173	178	183
19	115	117	120	123	126	130	134	138	142	146	150	155	160	165	170	175	180	185
	5	1	2	3	4	5	6	7	8	9	10	11	6	1	2	3	4	5
20	117	119	122	125	128	132	136	140	144	148	152	156	161	166	171	176	181	186
21	118	120	123	126	130	134	138	141	145	149	153	157	162	167	172	177	182	187
22	119	121	124	127	131	135	139	142	146	150	154	158	163	168	173	178	183	188
23	120	122	125	128	132	136	140	143	147	151	155	159	164	169	175	180	185	190
24	121	123	126	129	133	137	141	144	148	152	156	160	165	171	177	182	187	192
	5	1	2	3	4	5	6	7	8	9	10	11	6	1	2	3	4	5
25	122	124	126	129	133	137	141	145	149	153	157	162	167	173	179	184	189	194
26	123	125	127	130	134	138	142	146	150	154	158	163	168	174	180	186	191	196
27	124	126	128	131	134	138	142	146	150	154	158	163	169	175	181	187	192	197
28	125	127	129	132	135	139	143	147	151	155	159	164	170	176	182	188	193	198
29	126	128	130	133	136	140	144	148	152	156	160	165	171	177	183	189	194	199
	5	1	2	3	4	5	6	7	8	9	10	11	6	1	2	3	4	5
30	126	128	130	133	136	140	144	148	152	156	161	166	172	178	184	190	196	201
31	127	129	131	134	137	141	145	149	153	157	162	167	173	179	185	191	197	202
32	127	129	131	134	137	141	145	149	154	158	163	168	174	180	186	192	198	203
33	127	129	131	134	137	141	145	149	154	159	164	169	175	181	187	193	199	204
34	128	130	132	135	138	142	146	150	155	160	165	170	176	182	188	194	200	206
	5	1	2	3	4	5	6	7	8	9	10	11	6	1	2	3	4	5
35	128	130	132	135	138	142	146	150	155	160	165	170	176	182	189	195	201	207
36	129	131	133	136	139	143	147	151	156	161	166	171	177	183	190	196	202	208
37	129	131	133	136	140	144	148	152	157	162	167	172	178	184	191	197	203	209
38	130	132	134	137	140	144	148	152	157	162	167	173	179	185	192	198	204	210
39	130	132	134	137	140	144	148	152	157	162	167	173	179	185	192	199	205	211
	5	1	2	3	4	5	6	7	8	9	10	11	6	1	2	3	4	5
40	131	133	135	138	141	145	149	153	158	163	168	174	180	186	193	200	206	212
41	131	133	135	138	141	145	149	153	158	163	168	174	180	186	193	200	207	213
42	132	134	136	139	142	146	150	154	159	164	169	175	181	187	194	201	208	214
43	132	134	136	139	142	146	150	154	159	164	169	175	181	187	194	201	208	214
44	133	135	137	140	143	147	151	155	160	165	170	176	182	188	195	202	209	215
	5	1	2	3	4	5	6	7	8	9	10	11	6	1	2	3	4	5
45	133	135	137	140	143	147	151	155	160	165	170	176	182	188	195	202	209	215
46	134	136	138	141	144	148	152	156	161	166	171	177	183	189	196	203	210	216
47	134	136	138	141	144	148	152	156	161	166	171	177	183	190	197	204	211	217
48	134	136	138	141	144	148	152	156	161	166	171	177	183	190	197	204	211	217
49	134	136	138	141	144	148	152	156	161	166	171	177	183	190	197	204	211	217
	5	1	2	3	4	5	6	7	8	9	10	11	6	1	2	3	4	5
50	134	136	138	141	144	148	152	156	161	166	171	177	183	190	197	204	211	217
51	135	137	139	142	145	149	153	157	162	167	172	178	184	191	198	205	212	218
52	135	137	139	142	145	149	153	157	162	167	172	178	184	191	198	205	212	218
53	135	137	139	142	145	149	153	157	162	167	172	178	184	191	198	205	212	218
54	135	137	139	142	145	149	153	158	163	168	173	178	184	191	198	205	212	219
55 & up	135	137	139	142	145	149	153	158	163	168	173	178	184	191	198	205	212	219

STANDARD WEIGHT ACCORDING TO HEIGHT AND AGE

Women

Age	4 Ft. 8 In.	4 Ft. 9 In.	4 Ft. 10 In.	4 Ft. 11 In.	5 Ft.	5 Ft. 1 In.	5 Ft. 2 In.	5 Ft. 3 In.	5 Ft. 4 In.	5 Ft. 5 In.	5 Ft. 6 In.	5 Ft. 7 In.	5 Ft. 8 In.	5 Ft. 9 In.	5 Ft. 10 In.	5 Ft. 11 In.	6 Ft.
15	101	103	105	106	107	109	112	115	118	122	126	130	134	138	142	147	152
16	102	104	106	108	109	111	114	117	120	124	128	132	136	139	143	148	153
17	103	105	107	109	111	113	116	119	122	125	129	133	137	140	144	149	154
18	104	106	108	110	112	114	117	120	123	126	130	134	138	141	145	150	155
19	105	107	109	111	113	115	118	121	124	127	131	135	139	142	146	151	155
	8	9	10	11	5	1	2	3	4	5	6	7	8	9	10	11	6
20	106	108	110	112	114	116	119	122	125	128	132	136	140	143	147	151	156
21	107	109	111	113	115	117	120	123	126	129	133	137	141	144	148	152	156
22	107	109	111	113	115	117	120	123	126	129	133	137	141	145	149	153	157
23	108	110	112	114	116	118	121	124	127	130	134	138	142	146	150	153	157
24	109	111	113	115	117	119	121	124	127	130	134	138	142	146	150	154	158
	8	9	10	11	5	1	2	3	4	5	6	7	8	9	10	11	6
25	109	111	113	115	117	119	121	124	128	131	135	139	143	147	151	154	158
26	110	112	114	116	118	120	122	125	128	131	135	139	143	147	151	155	159
27	110	112	114	116	118	120	122	125	129	132	136	140	144	148	152	155	159
28	111	113	115	117	119	121	123	126	130	133	137	141	145	149	153	156	160
29	111	113	115	117	119	121	123	126	130	133	137	141	145	149	153	156	160
	8	9	10	11	5	1	2	3	4	5	6	7	8	9	10	11	6
30	112	114	116	118	120	122	124	127	131	134	138	142	146	150	154	157	161
31	113	115	117	119	121	123	125	128	132	135	139	143	147	151	154	157	161
32	113	115	117	119	121	123	125	128	132	136	140	144	148	152	155	158	162
33	114	116	118	120	122	124	126	129	133	137	141	145	149	153	156	159	162
34	115	117	119	121	123	125	127	130	134	138	142	146	150	154	157	160	163
	8	9	10	11	5	1	2	3	4	5	6	7	8	9	10	11	6
35	115	117	119	121	123	125	127	130	134	138	142	146	150	154	157	160	163
36	116	118	120	122	124	126	128	131	135	139	143	147	151	155	158	161	164
37	116	118	120	122	124	126	129	132	136	140	144	148	152	156	159	162	165
38	117	119	121	123	125	127	130	133	137	141	145	149	153	157	160	163	166
39	118	120	122	124	126	128	131	134	138	142	146	150	154	158	161	164	167
	8	9	10	11	5	1	2	3	4	5	6	7	8	9	10	11	6
40	119	121	123	125	127	129	132	135	138	142	146	150	154	158	161	164	167
41	120	122	124	126	128	130	133	136	139	143	147	151	155	159	162	165	168
42	120	122	124	126	128	130	133	136	139	143	147	151	155	159	162	166	169
43	121	123	125	127	129	131	134	137	140	144	148	152	156	160	163	167	170
44	122	124	126	128	130	132	135	138	141	145	149	153	157	161	164	168	171
	8	9	10	11	5	1	2	3	4	5	6	7	8	9	10	11	6
45	122	124	126	128	130	132	135	138	141	145	149	153	157	161	164	168	171
46	123	125	127	129	131	133	136	139	142	146	150	154	158	162	165	169	172
47	123	125	127	129	131	133	136	139	142	146	151	155	159	163	166	170	173
48	124	126	128	130	132	134	137	140	143	147	152	156	160	164	167	171	174
49	124	126	128	130	132	134	137	140	143	147	152	156	161	165	168	172	175
	8	9	10	11	5	1	2	3	4	5	6	7	8	9	10	11	6
50	125	127	129	131	133	135	138	141	144	148	152	156	161	165	169	173	176
51	125	127	129	131	133	135	138	141	144	148	152	157	162	166	170	174	177
52	125	127	129	131	133	135	138	141	144	148	152	157	162	166	170	174	177
53	125	127	129	131	133	135	138	141	144	148	152	157	162	166	170	174	177
54	125	127	129	131	133	135	138	141	144	148	153	158	163	167	171	174	177
55 & up	125	127	129	131	133	135	138	141	144	148	153	158	163	167	171	174	177

Index

Index